MECHANISMS OF ORGANIC AND ENZYMIC REACTIONS

MECHANISMS OF ORGANIC AND ENZYMIC REACTIONS

BY

S. G. WALEY

OXFORD
AT THE CLARENDON PRESS
1962

CHEMISTRY

Oxford University Press, Amen House, London E.C.4

GLASGOW NEW YORK TORONTO MELBOURNE WELLINGTON
BOMBAY CALCUTTA MADRAS KARACHI LAHORE DACCA
CAPE TOWN SALISBURY NAIROBI IBADAN ACCRA
KUALA LUMPUR HONG KONG

PRINTED IN GREAT BRITAIN

Addl.

FOREWORD

As the author mentions in his preface, this book is intended to appeal both to biochemists and chemists, and it is from the viewpoint of the latter that I introduce it. The study of the mechanism of action of enzymes is one of the most interesting and fruitful fields of biochemistry at the present time. This development is long overdue. For many years the study of enzyme-catalysed reactions was still faintly obscured by the last remnant of the tradition of vitalism, which manifested itself in the feeling that enzymic reactions are in some mysterious way different from 'chemical' reactions.

This obscurantist attitude has finally been dispelled. The isolation of crystalline urease by Sumner, with the demonstration that enzymes are proteins and can be purified and characterized as such, was a great stride forward in this direction. The classical work of Warburg then laid the foundations for the understanding in chemical terms of the function of coenzymes, and of the relationship between vitamins and coenzymes. These advances opened the way to a study of enzyme reactions in terms of the chemistry of the coenzymes, but the role of the enzyme protein itself remained quite obscure.

A new level of understanding of enzyme chemistry was achieved when it was shown that the enzyme protein itself may react stoicheio-metrically with a substrate, with the formation of stable bonds. In an investigation of the enzyme sucrose phosphorylase, Barker, Hassid, and Doudoroff obtained evidence of the formation of glucosyl-enzyme intermediate, implicating the enzyme itself as a reactant rather than a 'noble' catalyst. To take another example, several esterases have been thoroughly studied with the aid of organo-phosphorus poisons (such as di-isopropyl phosphorofluoridate) which react specifically with them. This has led not only to a much more satisfactory knowledge of the mechanism of the enzymic hydrolysis of esters, but also has yielded valuable information on the actual sequence of amino acids near the reactive centres of such enzymes.

Parallel to these developments in enzymology, there has been a rapid growth in the knowledge of the mechanism of organic reactions. It has become imperative for the biochemist (and especially the enzymologist) to master at least the fundamentals of this relatively new area of organic chemistry, since the application of this information to biological systems

725

will be of growing importance in the years to come. In the present volume, Dr. Stephen G. Waley presents in non-mathematical terms an up-to-date account of the physical-chemical theory of organic reactions. In addition, he considers the mechanism of certain enzyme-catalysed reactions in the light of such theory. The book is thus admirably designed to bridge the gap between the two fields. For the biochemist who is not a specialist in organic chemistry, or for the organic chemist who is interested in learning about enzymic reactions, this volume should be of special interest and value.

EUGENE P. KENNEDY

Department of Biological Chemistry
Harvard Medical School

PREFACE

MUCH is now known about the detailed course of many organic reactions. Indeed, the results of the studies of organic reactions, taken as a whole, form an impressive and coherent body of knowledge, which gives much insight into the reactivities of organic compounds. An understanding of mechanism has thus become a necessary part of the education of every student of chemistry and of biochemistry. Ordinarily, books on organic reactions do not discuss enzyme-catalysed reactions, interesting though these are. Symposia on the mechanism of enzyme action cannot give the background knowledge necessary to appreciate the remarkable advances made recently. I hope, therefore, that both biochemists and chemists will find it useful to have a book in which the mechanisms of organic reactions, and of enzyme-catalysed reactions, are discussed together. Throughout this book, enzymic reactions are discussed shortly after their non-enzymic counterparts.

The selection of topics in a large and rapidly growing subject is necessarily difficult, but I have tried to describe sufficient examples in enough detail for the reader to be able to master the principles. Practice in applying the ideas of theoretical organic chemistry is necessary; familiarity comes gradually. The treatment has to be fairly detailed, because if one only gives conclusions about mechanisms, with very little discussion of how the conclusions are reached, then the reader makes no real progress towards being able to judge for himself how well based the conclusions are.

The first two chapters are introductory and deal, in outline, with the structure of organic molecules, and with the general nature and classification of organic reactions. Nucleophilic substitutions are the first reactions described, as several important concepts can be introduced here. Olefine formation often competes with nucleophilic substitution, so this reaction, and its reverse, are then described.

The next three chapters form a (loosely connected) group. Carbonyl addition reactions are especially important in biochemistry, as they seem to be the main way in which carbon-carbon bonds are formed *in vivo*. After aldehydes and ketones, the discussion continues with other compounds containing the carbonyl group, such as carboxylic esters and acids, and thence to other esters and acids, such as the phosphoric esters. These chapters have provided examples of substitutions, additions, and eliminations; rearrangements form the fourth main class of reactions and some examples are discussed in the next chapter.

The chemistry of aromatic compounds has always been a corner-stone of theoretical organic chemistry, and many individual aromatic compounds play notable roles in cells; some aromatic substitutions are described in the penultimate chapter. Finally, the importance of macromolecules in biology has led to the inclusion of a chapter describing some polymerizations.

My indebtedness to many is manifest. I have tended to cite books and reviews, and to give the most recent references, as these refer back to earlier papers. I can only hope that this practice will not cause any researcher to feel slighted. I have been most fortunate in the kindness of the following, who have read all or part of the manuscript, and made many helpful comments: Mr. R. P. Bell, F.R.S., Dr. R. O. C. Norman, Dr. A. G. Ogston, F.R.S., and Dr. G. T. Young. I am grateful to Professor Eugene Kennedy for writing the Foreword, to my colleagues at this laboratory for their encouragement, and to Miss Hutchinson for preparation of the typescript.

For permission to reproduce copyright material I am grateful to: Professor T. L. Cottrell, Professor C. A. Coulson, Professor J. Hine, Professor Sir Christopher Ingold, Dr. P. B. D. de la Mare, Dr. V. Massey, Dr. J. H. Ridd, Professor C. P. Smyth, Dr. A. Streitweiser, Dr. L. E. Sutton, Professor K. Wallenfels, Professor C. Walling, and to the Council of the Chemical Society, the editors of the *Biochemical Journal*, the editors of *Chemical Reviews*, and to the Academic Press, Inc., Messrs. Butterworths, J. & A. Churchill, Ltd., Cornell University Press, the Delegates of the Oxford University Press, the McGraw-Hill Book Company, Inc., and John Wiley & Sons, Inc.

S. G. W.

Nuffield Laboratory of Ophthalmology
University of Oxford

CONTENTS

V. ADDITIONS TO ALDEHYDES AND KETONES

ILLUSTRATIONS

Plate I is facing page 12 and Plate II is facing page 16

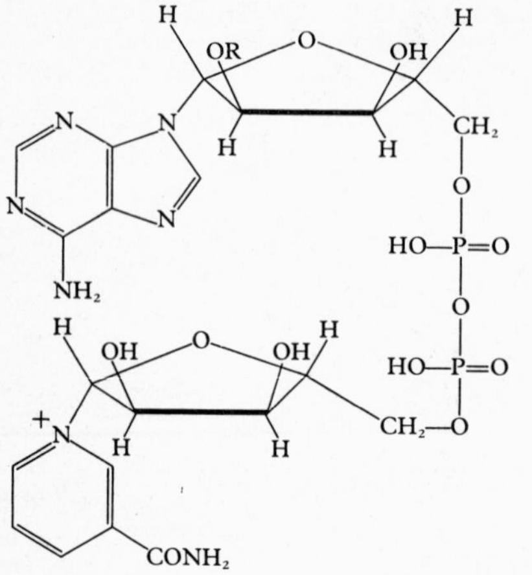

R=H: Diphosphopyridine nucleotide (DPN)
(Coenzyme I)

R=PO_3H_2: Triphosphopyridine nucleotide (TPN)
(Coenzyme II)

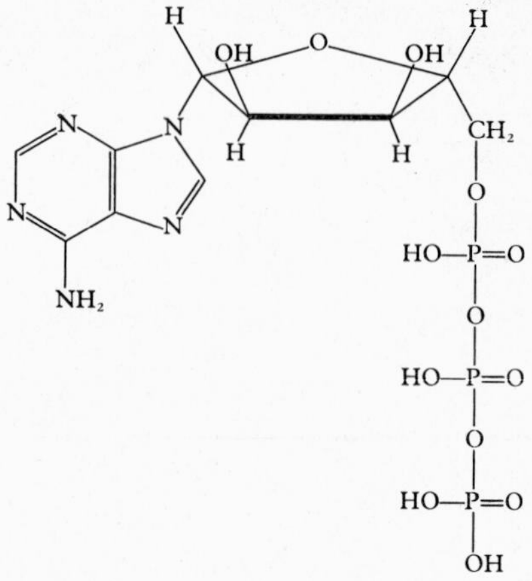

Adenosine triphosphate (ATP)

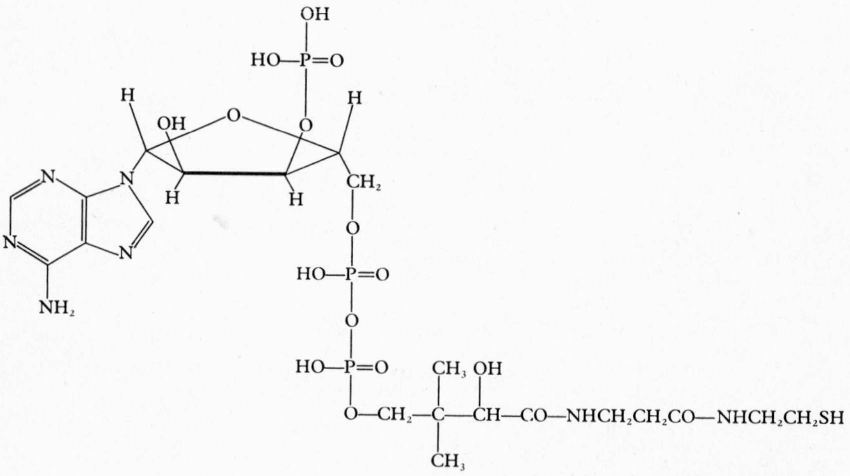

Coenzyme A

I

MOLECULAR STRUCTURE

1. Atoms and molecules

(a) *Introduction*. Accounts of the mechanisms of organic reactions are couched in terms of the relative dispositions of the atomic nuclei and electrons of the reacting species. Such ideas cannot be grasped without some familiarity with modern concepts of molecular structure, so an introduction to these concepts is presented here: the next four sections (§ 1 *b* to § 1 *e*) are of an elementary nature.

(b) *Nuclei and electrons*. Atoms consist of positively charged nuclei and negatively charged electrons. The positively charged nuclei are small; their diameter is of the order of 10^{-12} cm, whereas the diameter of the atom is of the order of 10^{-8} cm, i.e. 1 Å. However, virtually all the mass of an atom is due to the nucleus. Thus the hydrogen atom consists of the nucleus (called the proton), and one electron which is some 2,000 times lighter than the whole atom. The unit of charge that we shall use is the charge on the electron (-1, as the electron is negatively charged). The charge on the proton is $+1$.

The number of electrons in the atom of an element is equal to the atomic number of the element in the Periodic Table. It is the electrons which affect chemical properties, and so the isotopes of a given element (which differ in nuclear mass but have the same number of electrons) have qualitatively the same chemical properties. Thus hydrogen, deuterium, and tritium have nuclei of masses of approximately one, two, and three (in atomic mass units) respectively, but in each case there is one electron in the atom.

(c) *The quantum theory*. We now consider the simplest atom, the hydrogen atom, in rather more detail. As the nucleus is positively charged and the electron is negatively charged there is an attractive force between the two particles. This tends to pull the electron into the nucleus and so, for the atom to be stable, the electron must be supposed to be rotating round the nucleus. But, according to classical ideas, the electron would then emit radiation continuously, gradually lose energy by so doing, and thus move nearer and nearer to the nucleus. This model of the atom, then, cannot account for its stability. A way out of this difficulty was seen by Bohr, who applied the quantum theory to the hydrogen atom.

The quantum theory, put forward by Planck in 1900, was concerned with the radiation emitted by a heated body. The problem was how to account for the way the energy of the heated body is related to the wavelength of the emitted radiation. A familiar example is that a white-hot poker is at a higher temperature than a red-hot one. Planck showed that the experimental results could be explained if the energy of the body could only change by integral multiples of a definite unit of energy. In rather the same way, the second-hand on some clocks jumps from one second-mark to the next, so that time, on these clocks, is measured with a quantum of one second. Planck's idea was applied by Einstein to the relation between the energy of electrons emitted from an irradiated metal plate and the frequency of the radiation used. The value of the quantum of energy (E) is proportional to the frequency (v) of the radiation:

$$E = hv,$$

where h is a constant, called Planck's constant ($h = 6 \cdot 62 \times 10^{-27}$ erg sec).

These ideas were then applied to the hydrogen atom by Bohr, as follows. On the basis of two assumptions he accounted for the stability of the atom, and (quantitatively) for the wavelengths of the lines in the spectrum of the hydrogen atom. The first assumption was that the electron could only move in definite orbits, and when it was moving in these orbits radiation was neither emitted nor absorbed. The second assumption was that when the electron moved from one orbit to another nearer the nucleus, radiation was emitted of frequency v, which was related to the energy difference $(E_1 - E_2)$ between the orbits by the equation

$$E_1 - E_2 = nhv,$$

where n is a whole number. The frequency (v) and wavelength (λ) are related by $v = c/\lambda$, where c is the velocity of light, so that

$$E_1 - E_2 = nhc/\lambda. \qquad [1]$$

When a discharge is passed through a tube containing hydrogen, an electron may acquire enough energy to 'jump' to a relatively distant orbit; as this 'excited' electron drops back to an orbit nearer to the nucleus it emits radiation. Thus the origin of spectral lines on the Bohr model of the hydrogen atom may be depicted as in Fig. 1, in which lines of wavelengths 972·5, 1,026, and 1,216 Å (observed by Lyman) and the electronic transitions responsible for them are shown.

(d) *Energy levels*. By the use of equation [1], the energy differences

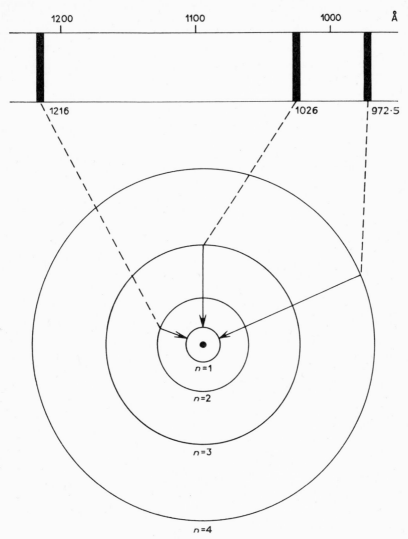

FIG. 1. The origin of spectral lines on the Bohr model of the hydrogen atom. The orbits are shown as circles, and the nucleus is the central dot. The radiation emitted when the electron moves from one orbit to another that is nearer to the nucleus is represented by the spectrum at the top of the figure.

between the orbits are obtained from the wavelength of the radiation emitted. If sufficient energy is absorbed by the hydrogen atom, the electron is effectively removed from the field of force of the nucleus; this is ionization, and this state is taken as the zero in Fig. 2, which shows the energy of the hydrogen atom when the electron is in the various possible orbits. When the electron is in, say, the $n = 2$ orbit, the energy level is given as −78 kcal/mol in Fig. 2; this means that a hydrogen atom with the electron in this ($n = 2$) orbit is more stable than a bare proton and an electron at a distance by 78 kcal/mol. These energy levels are especially important as they apply (approximately) to elements other than hydrogen.

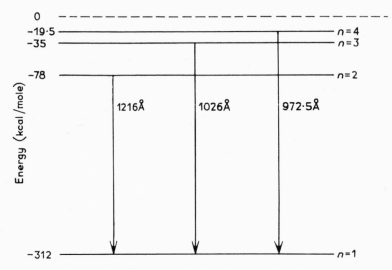

FIG. 2. Some energy levels in the hydrogen atom. The same electronic transitions as in Fig. 1 are also shown here.

(e) *Electronic configuration of atoms.* When the electron is in the orbit nearest to the nucleus, the hydrogen atom is in its state of lowest energy (ground state); this orbit is characterized by the value $n = 1$ in equation [1], and is the lowest energy level (Fig. 2). The energies of successive orbits depend mainly on the value of n, and n is called the *principal quantum number.*

We now consider other atoms, in outline. As in the hydrogen atom, the electrons will be assigned to orbits. We shall be guided by three principles:

(i) The energy levels of the orbits are similar to those shown in Fig. 2.
(ii) An orbit with principal quantum number n can accommodate up to $2n^2$ electrons.
(iii) A completely filled orbit is chemically inert.

The application of these principles to the first three periods of the Periodic Table is shown in Fig. 3. The next element after hydrogen in the Periodic Table is helium. It has two electrons in the most stable, innermost, orbit, the orbit with principal quantum number one. This

Atomic number	Element	Number of electrons in orbit with:		Atomic number	Element	Number of electrons in orbit with:		
		$n = 1$	$n = 2$			$n = 1$	$n = 2$	$n = 3$
1	H	1		11	Na	2	8	1
2	He	2		12	Mg	2	8	2
3	Li	2	1	13	Al	2	8	3
4	Be	2	2	14	Si	2	8	4
5	B	2	3	15	P	2	8	5
6	C	2	4	16	S	2	8	6
7	N	2	5	17	Cl	2	8	7
8	O	2	6	18	A	2	8	8
9	F	2	7					
10	Ne	2	8					

FIG. 3. Arrangements of electrons in the atoms of elements in the first three periods of the Periodic Table.

is as many electrons as this particular orbit can accommodate. In the second period (Fig. 3) the orbit with $n = 1$ is completely filled, and for most chemical purposes may be ignored; the orbit with $n = 2$ is being filled along this period, and the electrons in this outer orbit are called *valency electrons*. Thus carbon has four valency electrons, phosphorus (in the next period) has five. The inert gases (helium, neon, and argon) all have completely filled orbits, and of course are chemically unreactive. These electronic arrangements are based upon the rule that the orbits nearest to the nucleus (i.e. lowest energy levels) are filled first; a few electronic configurations are also shown pictorially in Fig. 4.

We may now consider chemical bonds, i.e. the forces responsible for the existence of molecules. Consider a binary species AB (e.g. HCl). The nuclei of the two atoms are positively charged and repel each other. The electrons are negatively charged, and they, too, repel each other. But the electrons and the nuclei attract each other. In some species (e.g. solid NaCl) the units are found to be the ions and the bonding is called ionic, or electrovalent. A sodium atom loses an electron to give the cation, Na^+, and a chlorine atom gains an electron to give the anion, Cl^-; both these ions have the stable electronic configurations of inert gases. The pair of ions thus results from the transfer of one electron from the electropositive sodium atom to the electronegative chlorine atom. Similarly, two electrons are transferred from the electropositive magnesium atom to the electronegative oxygen atom, to give the ionic magnesium oxide. The transfer of two electrons is, however, the limit, in crystals of the AB type, where A and B are each one atom; thus the bonding in boron nitride is not ionic, i.e. three electrons are not transferred. And the ions C^{4+} and C^{4-} do not exist. Thus the bonds in organic compounds are not (normally) ionic.

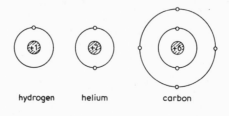

hydrogen   helium   carbon

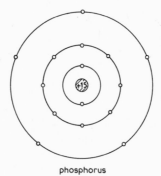

phosphorus

FIG. 4. Electronic configurations of some atoms.

The type of bonding characteristic of organic molecules is called covalent. In 1916 Lewis suggested that this kind of bond was formed by the sharing of a pair of electrons; the nature of the covalent bond is discussed later (§ 1 *j*). If only the valency electrons (those in the outermost orbit) are shown, then the dash of ordinary structural formulae is replaced by a pair of electrons shown as dots in the following examples:

$$
\text{H:H} \qquad \text{:}\overset{..}{\underset{..}{Cl}}\text{:}\overset{..}{\underset{..}{Cl}}\text{:} \qquad \text{H:}\overset{..}{S}\text{:H} \qquad \text{H:}\overset{\text{H}}{\underset{\text{H}}{\overset{..}{C}}}\text{:H} \qquad \text{H:}\overset{\text{H}}{\underset{\text{H}}{\overset{..}{C}}}\text{:}\overset{\text{H}}{\underset{\text{H}}{\overset{..}{C}}}\text{:H}
$$

This is a convenient notation, as it is the outer shell, or valency, electrons which are concerned in chemical reactions. The symbol for the element stands for the screened nucleus (the nucleus and inner shell electrons). Since the atom is neutral, the positive charge on the screened nucleus is equal to the number of valency electrons. Thus, in the formulae given above, the symbol C stands for the nucleus of the carbon atom (charge $+6$) together with the two inner electrons, and so the net charge on the screened nucleus is $+4$. Similarly, the charge represented by the S is $+6$, and by Cl, $+7$. The formulae given also show the unshared electrons (e.g. in Cl_2, and in H_2S), which are often most important in chemical reactions.

Since covalent bonds are formed by sharing valency electrons between two atoms, there is a relationship between the numerical value of the covalency and the number of valency electrons. Thus carbon has four valency electrons, and hydrogen has one valency electron, and one carbon atom can combine with four hydrogen atoms. Nitrogen has five valency electrons, but only eight valency electrons can surround nitrogen (this is discussed again in § 1 j), so nitrogen, when it shares all its five valency electrons with four atoms, provides both of the electrons which form one bond. Trimethylamine oxide (1), for example, may be shown as:

$$\text{H}_3\text{C} \overset{\bullet\text{x}}{\underset{\bullet\text{x}}{\text{:}}} \overset{\overset{\text{CH}_3}{}}{\underset{\text{CH}_3}{\text{N}}} \overset{\bullet\bullet}{\underset{\bullet\bullet}{\text{:}}} \overset{\overset{\text{H}}{}}{\underset{\text{H}}{\text{O}}} \text{:}$$

(here $\text{H} : \text{C} \cdot$ is written as $\text{H}_3\text{C} \cdot$)

(1)

Here the valency electrons of the nitrogen atom are shown as crosses. The nitrogen atom has provided both of the shared electrons which constitute the nitrogen–oxygen bond. However, in the molecule of trimethylamine oxide, the electrons of a shared pair may be considered as divided between the atoms, so that the nitrogen in (1) is surrounded by four of 'its' electrons, and the oxygen similarly by seven electrons. As the symbols N, O in (1) stand for screened nuclei with positive charges of 5 and 6 respectively, the nitrogen atom in (1) has a formal charge of $+1$, and the oxygen atom of -1, and trimethylamine oxide is usually written as (2), or sometimes as (3):

$$(\text{CH}_3)_3\overset{+}{\text{N}}\text{---}\overset{-}{\text{O}} \qquad\qquad (\text{CH}_3)_3\text{N}{\rightarrow}\text{O} \qquad\qquad \begin{matrix}\text{CH}_3 \\ \diagdown \\ \diagup \\ \text{CH}_3\end{matrix}\overset{+}{\text{O}}\text{---}\overset{-}{\text{B}}\begin{matrix}\text{F}\\ \diagup\\ \diagdown\\ \text{F}\end{matrix}\text{F}$$

(2)   (3)   (4)

The charges in (2) are called formal charges because the dipolar character is not so extreme as is implied by the formula. Another example is (4), and here also the formal charges are derived by counting the valency electrons.

We now proceed to a slightly more detailed picture of atoms and molecules. The conclusions so far reached may be briefly summarized as follows:

(i) The number of electrons in the atom of an element is equal to the atomic number of the element in the Periodic Table.

(ii) The electrons in an atom are arranged in orbits. The orbits are characterized by the principal quantum number, n.

(iii) The orbit nearest to the nucleus has $n = 1$, and successive orbits have $n = 2, 3, 4$, and so on.

(iv) Each of these orbits can have no more than $2n^2$ electrons in it.

(v) Atoms in their normal states have the orbits nearest to the nucleus as nearly completely filled as possible.

(vi) Completely filled orbits are chemically inert; the valency electrons are in the outermost orbit (in the first three periods of the Periodic Table).

(vii) Ionic bonds are a consequence of electron transfer; covalent bonds are formed by the sharing of a pair of electrons.

(*f*) *Subdivision of orbits.* So far electronic orbits have been characterized entirely by the value of the principal quantum number, n. It turns out to be necessary to subdivide these orbits in the following way. There is just one orbit with $n = 1$; this is called the 1s orbit. There are two subsidiary orbits when $n = 2$, called the 2s and 2p orbits. There are three subsidiary orbits when $n = 3$, called the 3s, 3p, and 3d orbits. In fact (up to $n = 4$) there are n subsidiary orbits when the principal quantum number is n. (The letters s, p, d used to label these subsidiary orbits are derived from descriptions by spectroscopists of certain bands as 'sharp', 'principal', and 'diffuse'.) Now we know that the 1s orbit can only hold two electrons (this is the only orbit when $n = 1$, and any orbit can hold only $2n^2$ electrons), and the same is true for the 2s and the 3s orbits (and also the 4s and 5s orbits, but we shall not be concerned with these). The subsidiary orbits with $n = 2$ are the 2s and the 2p orbits. Together they can accommodate $2 \cdot 2^2 = 8$ electrons; but of these, the 2s orbit can hold two, so the 2p orbit must be able to hold six. Again the 3p orbit can hold six electrons. And similarly, the 3d orbit can hold ten electrons. In fact the capacity of these subsidiary orbits is characteristic: s, p, or d orbits can hold two, six, or ten electrons, respectively. The value of the principal quantum number determines what subsidiary orbits are available.

(g) *Pauli Exclusion Principle.* It is necessary to ascribe to an electron a spin. The spin can be in one of but two directions, just as the hand of a clock can only be rotated clockwise or anti-clockwise. Thus any two electrons can have parallel (like) or anti-parallel (opposed) spins. We now come to Pauli's Exclusion Principle. This idea has far-reaching implications, and has been described as the cornerstone of chemistry. In the simple form in which it was first put forward, this principle states that *only two electrons in an atom can occupy the same orbit, and these two electrons must have opposed spins.*

Thus when any *s* orbit (which holds but two electrons) is filled, the two electrons in the orbit must have opposed spins. Now a *p* orbit can hold six electrons, so that if only two electrons can follow the same orbit we must further subdivide the *p* orbit. These subdivided *p* orbits are called p_x, p_y, and p_z orbits, and each can hold two electrons.

In the electronic configurations describing the ground states of atoms, the electrons are distributed amongst the orbits so that as many as possible of the orbits with the same energy are occupied. Thus the nitrogen atom has seven electrons; two are in the 1s orbit, two in the 2s orbit, and one in each of the three 2p orbits, i.e. each of the three 2p orbits is occupied by one electron, instead of there being two electrons in one of the 2p orbits, one in another, and none in the third.

The two electrons in one orbit which must have opposed spins are called *paired electrons.* Thus the two electrons in the 1s orbit in the helium atom (in the ground state) are paired electrons; but the electrons in the three different 2p orbits in the nitrogen atom are unpaired electrons (French: *électrons célibataires*). The distinction between paired and unpaired electrons is important in the description of the formation of covalent bonds. Paired electrons are shown as arrows pointing in opposite directions in Fig. 5, which shows the electronic configurations of atoms (in the ground states) of the elements of the first two periods of the Periodic Table.

(h) *Orbitals, and the wave equation.* The Bohr model of the hydrogen atom was the basis for our description of the electronic configuration of other atoms. The ideas derived from the Bohr model must be modified by the concepts derived from the application of wave mechanics to atoms and molecules. The picture of an electron moving on an exactly defined orbit, with an exactly defined velocity, is inconsistent with Heisenberg's Uncertainty Principle, which states that the position and velocity of a particle cannot both be precisely known. Furthermore, electrons have some of the properties of waves. Thus, when a beam of electrons impinges on a very thin piece of metal foil, a diffraction pattern is observed, such as is seen in X-ray powder photographs. Indeed, electrons are used in basically the same sort of way as light waves in the electron microscope. Schrödinger suggested that the hydrogen atom could be represented by an equation of the kind used to describe the motion of waves.

	Element	1s	2s	$2p_x$	$2p_y$	$2p_z$
1	H	↑				
2	He	↑↓				
3	Li	↑↓	↑			
4	Be	↑↓	↑↓			
5	B	↑↓	↑↓	↑		
6	C	↑↓	↑↓	↑	↑	
7	N	↑↓	↑↓	↑	↑	↑
8	O	↑↓	↑↓	↑↓	↑	↑
9	F	↑↓	↑↓	↑↓	↑↓	↑
10	Ne	↑↓	↑↓	↑↓	↑↓	↑↓

(column group heading: Orbit)

FIG. 5. Electronic configurations of atoms.

If this is done, then the wave equation has satisfactory solutions only if the energy has certain fixed values, given by $-W/n^2$, where n is the principal quantum number. The quantization of the energy, then, follows from the mathematical form of the wave equation. The term W was found to have the value 311·93 kcal/mol, in agreement with the experimental value for the normal state of the hydrogen atom (Fig. 2).

The wave equation for the hydrogen atom is written in terms of a variable ψ which has no clearly discernible meaning. However, $\psi^2 dv$ gives the probability of finding the electron within the small volume dv. The solution of the wave equation for the hydrogen atom in the ground state is

$$\psi = \frac{1}{\sqrt{(\pi a^3)}}\, e^{-r/a}, \qquad [2]$$

where r is the distance of the electron from the nucleus, and a is the radius of the orbit of the electron (in the ground state) on the Bohr model. When this value of ψ is substituted into the wave equation, the energy of the hydrogen atom is found to be $-e_0^2/2a$, where e_0 is the charge on the electron; we have already mentioned that this tallies with the experimental value. Equation [2] tells us where to 'expect' the electron. No preferred direction is specified in equation [2], so the probability of finding the electron in a volume dv depends only on the distance (r) between the electron and the nucleus. The electron distribution is thus described as being spherically symmetrical, and the volume dv is $4\pi r^2\,dr$, the volume between two spheres, one of radius r and the other of radius $r+dr$. So the probability (P) of finding the electron in the volume dv at a distance r from the nucleus is now given by

$$P = \psi^2\,dv = (\pi a^3)^{-1}e^{-2r/a}\,.\,4\pi r^2\,dr. \quad [3]$$

Although we can no longer speak of the exact position of the electron, the probability P plotted in Fig. 6 has a maximum value at exactly the radius of the orbit in the Bohr model of the hydrogen atom. The electron is there-fore most likely to be found at a certain distance (a) from the nucleus, and this distance corresponds to the innermost orbit shown in Fig. 1. Thus the value of ψ in equation [2], obtained by solu-tion of the wave equation, replaces the orbit on the Bohr model, and so is called

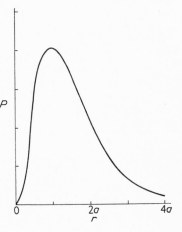

Fig. 6. Probability (P) of finding the electron in a volume dv at distance r (in units of a) from the nucleus. (From Coulson, *Valence*, Clarendon Press, 1952.)

an *orbital*: it tells us all we can know about the electron in the ground state of the hydrogen atom. Henceforward we will talk about orbitals instead of orbits; thus the electron in the ground state of the hydrogen atom is described as being in a $1s$ orbital. Similarly, the configurations shown in Fig. 5 still hold, but we now say that, for example, carbon has two electrons in the $1s$ orbital, two in the $2s$ orbital, and one in each of two $2p$ orbitals.

The stability of the hydrogen atom was the topic which brought us to the Bohr model. The potential energy resulting from electrostatic forces between two charges, one of e_0 (the nucleus) and the other of $-e_0$ (the electron), at a distance r apart is $-e_0^2/r$. The total energy of the hydrogen atom (in the ground state) is $-e_0^2/2a$. So the kinetic energy, when the distance (r) of the electron from the nucleus is a, is $e_0^2/2a$, as the total energy is the sum of the kinetic energy and the potential energy. It is, in fact, general that in atoms and molecules, the mean kinetic energy is $(-\frac{1}{2})$ times the mean potential energy.

(*i*) *Shapes of orbitals*. The shapes of atomic orbitals are important in chemistry. Only two, the s and the p orbitals, will be discussed, as the d and f orbitals do not play such an important part in organic chemistry.

The $1s$ orbital for the electron in the hydrogen atom is spherically symmetrical: this holds also for all other s orbitals in all other atoms. But p orbitals are different: they are directed. This means that the probability of finding a p orbital electron in a volume dv is greater in certain directions than in others. The three p orbitals are in fact directed along axes at right angles to each other; that is why they have been referred to as p_x, p_y, and p_z orbitals. Thus in the nitrogen atom there are three such electrons, one in each of these three orbitals. The most likely state of affairs is that these three electrons will be in regions of space centred round three mutually perpendicular axes.

The shapes of the orbitals can be visualized most easily by pictures representing the electron density. Although there is only one electron in the hydrogen atom, if the different positions of the electron could be observed at different times we should have a picture of the average electron density. Plate I shows such pictures representing the electron density of the hydrogen atom, in the ground state ($1s$), and in excited states ($2s$ and $2p$). The density distribution is spherical in the $1s$ and $2s$ orbitals and directed in the $2p$ orbitals. The latter consist of two portions separated by a plane in which the electron density is zero.

(j) *Covalent bonds.* The simplest molecule which can be observed (although it cannot be isolated) is the hydrogen molecule-ion, H_2^+. This charged molecule consists of two protons and one electron. As two protons would always repel each other, and as H_2^+ exists, the one electron must bind together the two protons. The wave equation for this simple species can be solved, and so the electron density distribution can be determined (Fig. 7). There is a high probability of finding the electron between the protons.

In the hydrogen molecule-ion one electron binds two nuclei; similarly, two electrons may bind three nuclei. But in the majority of molecules we shall be concerned with electron-pair bonds. The statement that these bonds are formed by the sharing of a pair of electrons (§ 1 e) may now be amplified somewhat. We want particularly to know:

(i) what governs the covalency of an element;
(ii) what governs the spatial arrangement of the atoms held together by covalent bonds.

When two negatively charged electrons bind two positively charged nuclei, each electron is being attracted by each nucleus. A bond, in

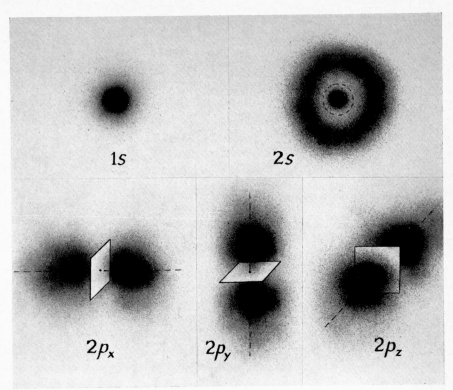

PLATE I. The electronic charge density distribution in the lower states of the hydrogen atom. The interior spherical node in the 2s state is represented by the broken circle. The plane nodes of the 2p states are indicated by the squares (represented as opaque to aid perspective). (From Ingold, *Structure and Mechanism in Organic Chemistry*, Cornell University Press, 1953.)

fact, is formed only if there is a high probability of both bonding electrons being in the region of space between the two nuclei. Now the Pauli Exclusion Principle (§ 1 *g*) applies to electrons in molecules as well as in atoms: the consequence is that electrons of like spin (unpaired

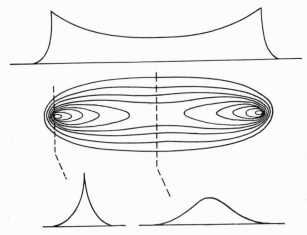

Fig. 7. Electron distribution function of the hydrogen molecule-ion (after Burrau). The upper diagram represents the function along a line through the nuclei, and the centre one the contours of the function over a plane through the nuclei, while the lower diagrams show the function along lines perpendicular to the internuclear line, through a nucleus (left), and through the point mid-way between the nuclei (right). (From Ingold, *Structure and Mechanism in Organic Chemistry*, Cornell University Press, 1953.)

electrons) tend to avoid each other. Electrons with opposed spins are not subject to this tendency. Hence the pair of bonding electrons has to be a pair of electrons with opposed spins. These electrons are also called paired electrons, so that the term refers both to a pair of electrons occupying one orbital of an atom, and to the pair of bonding electrons.

The formation of the hydrogen molecule from two hydrogen atoms may be represented as:

$$H \cdot + \cdot H \rightarrow H : H. \qquad [4]$$

If the two electrons in the two hydrogen atoms have opposed spins, the covalent bond can be forged. If we represent the electron in the 1*s* orbital by a circle, such that there is only a low probability of finding the electron outside the sphere formed by rotation of the circle, then the formation of the hydrogen molecule may be depicted as:

| | | | | | | |
| hydrogen atom | + | hydrogen atom | → | intermediate state | → | hydrogen molecule |

The covalent bond is here pictured as the result of the overlap of the atomic orbitals. The overlap gives some idea of the region in which there is a relatively high probability of finding both of the bonding electrons; the bonding electrons in a molecule are described as being in a bonding molecular orbital. This picture gives a measure of the strength of a bond, as the larger the overlap, the stronger the bond. This mode of description will be used henceforward. In the intermediate state (intermediate between two atoms and one molecule), each electron can, as it were, move out of the orbital it was originally in, and into the orbital surrounding the other nucleus. This extra freedom lowers the kinetic energy of the system, and so may be said to help the system on its way towards the formation of the molecule from the atoms. A third hydrogen atom cannot unite with the hydrogen molecule and form a triatomic molecule; the spin of the electron in the third atom would necessarily be parallel to the spin of one of the other two electrons, and these two electrons would, in this case, avoid each other to such an extent as to render combination of the atoms impossible.

Similarly, the next element, helium, has a filled $1s$ orbital (two paired electrons), and so cannot enter into chemical combination, in its normal state. This also applies to the other inert gases (Fig. 5).

The maximum covalency of the elements in the second period of the Periodic Table is four. The valency electrons can occupy four orbitals, the $2s$ orbital and the three $2p$ orbitals. So there are only four atomic orbitals available for overlapping. However, in the next period, the $3s$, $3p$, and $3d$ orbitals are available, and so the maximum covalency is no longer restricted to four.

(*k*) *Directed valencies.* The representation of the covalent bond as a result of the overlap of atomic orbitals gives us our clue to spatial arrangements of atoms in molecules, or stereochemistry. Thus the oxygen atom has two orbitals containing unpaired electrons; these are the $2p_x$ and $2p_y$ orbitals which are directed at right angles to each other (§ 1 *i*). Each of these $2p$ orbitals can overlap with the $1s$ orbital of a hydrogen atom. So, in water, the angle between the two O—H bonds will be in the neighbourhood of 90°. This argument can be applied to other bonds formed by the overlap of p orbitals.

The bond angle in water is, in fact, about 104°. There are two pairs of electrons which are unshared in the oxygen atom of the water molecule, and, as there is a general tendency for *all* the valency electrons to repel each other, the bond angle is somewhat nearer to the tetrahedral angle ($109\frac{1}{2}°$) than to 90°. The configurations of most simple molecules can be inferred on the basis that all the pairs of valency electrons repel each other, and so take up approximately symmetrical positions with respect to each other.

The conclusions we have reached about the covalent bond may be summarized as follows:

(1) The whereabouts of an electron in an atom is characterized by the orbital, which is a refinement of the orbit described by the electron on the Bohr model.

(2) Each orbital can accommodate one or two electrons.

(3) If there are two electrons in an orbital their spins must be opposed (paired electrons).

(4) In covalent bonds, negatively charged electrons bond positively charged nuclei.

(5) The covalent bond is regarded as resulting from the overlap of orbitals. The larger the overlap, the stronger the bond.

(6) A single bond normally involves two electrons, and two orbitals.

(7) The spins of the bonding electrons must be opposed.

(8) One kind of orbital (s) is not directed; another kind (p) is directed.

(9) Bond angles reflect the directions of the orbitals, so that there is maximum overlapping of the orbitals.

(*l*) *Hybrid orbitals*. The carbon atom, in the ground state, has four valency electrons, two in the $2s$ orbital and one in each of the two $2p$ orbitals (Fig. 5). Now for carbon to be tetravalent, four unshared electrons are necessary. One of the electrons in the $2s$ orbital must therefore be promoted to a $2p$ orbital. Now the carbon atom has four orbitals, each with one unpaired electron, all ready to form covalent bonds. Pauling has shown that these four orbitals will overlap with other orbitals best (i.e. form the strongest bonds) if the four orbitals are mathematically rendered equivalent; these equivalent orbitals (derived from one s and three p orbitals) are called sp^3 hybrid orbitals. They are directed towards the corners of a regular tetrahedron; the nucleus of the carbon atom is at the centre of the tetrahedron. Thus the four tetrahedral bonds of a singly-bound carbon are accounted for.

(*m*) *Multiple bonds*. So far we have not mentioned multiple bonds. The simplest viewpoint is to consider multiple bonds as a result of multiple overlap of orbitals. Thus in ethylene each carbon atom has four orbitals and binds two hydrogen atoms. This leaves two orbitals on each carbon atom, which can overlap with each other (Fig. 8 *a*). Thus we may visualize electron pairs tetrahedrally disposed round the carbon atoms in ethylene, just as they are in ethane, as in the

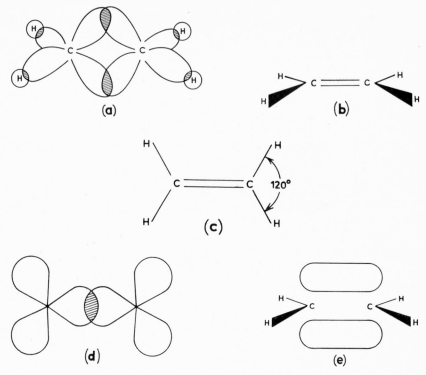

FIG. 8. Views and representations of ethylene.

(*a*) Overlap of the tetrahedral sp^3 orbitals.

(*b*) Conventional formula corresponding to (*a*); the four nuclei lie in a horizontal plane perpendicular to the plane of the paper.

(*c*) View in which the four nuclei lie in the plane of the paper.

(*d*) Overlap of sp^2 hybrid orbitals; the molecule is oriented as in (*c*); the π-orbitals are not shown.

(*e*) π-molecular orbitals; the molecule is oriented as in (*b*).

description of a double bond in terms of two tetrahedra with a shared edge. The 'double overlap' has three consequences:

  (i) All the four atoms lie in one plane.

 (ii) The overlap is greatest with this configuration, and is lessened if one CH_2 group is twisted about the carbon-carbon axis so that it is no longer in the same plane as the other CH_2 group. This twisting is thus opposed by a potential barrier; hence the existence of stable *cis* and *trans* isomers.

(iii) The overlap is less than when the two atomic orbitals are pointing directly towards each other, so that a double bond is less than twice as strong as a single bond.

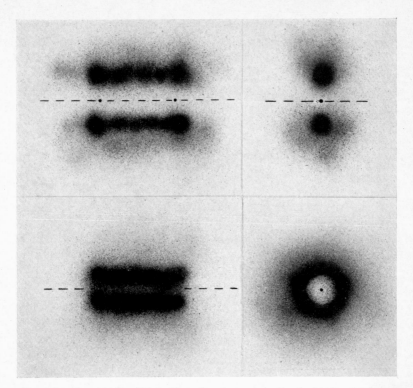

PLATE II. The density distribution of π-electrons in the double bond (above), and in the triple bond (below). A side view and an end view are given in each case. (From Ingold, *Structure and Mechanism in Organic Chemistry*, Cornell University Press, 1953.)

It is often convenient to describe the double bond rather differently; this alternative description also accounts for the bond angle of 120° in ethylene. One s orbital and two p orbitals of carbon may form three sp^2 hybrid orbitals (trigonal hybridization). These three orbitals are directed towards the corners of an equilateral triangle, i.e. the orbitals are coplanar and at an angle of 120° to each other (Fig. 8 d; in this figure the trigonal sp^2 orbitals are in the plane of the paper). There is left one p orbital (containing an unpaired electron) on each carbon atom, directed at right angles to the plane containing the trigonal hybrid orbitals. Bond formation between the carbon atoms then occurs in two ways. The sp^2 hybrid orbitals overlap in the usual endways (co-axial) fashion, but the left-over p orbitals can only overlap sideways. This sideways overlap results in what is called a π-bond (Fig. 8 e); the electrons that form a π-bond are above and below the plane containing the nuclei (see Plate II). The other bond, resulting from the usual endways overlap of the trigonal sp^2 orbitals, is called a σ-bond; it is (in contradistinction to the π-bond) symmetrical about the carbon-carbon axis. The relatively small extent of sideways overlap means that the π-bond is weaker than the σ-bond, and the π-electrons more 'mobile'. The characteristic reactivity of double bonds is associated with these properties. On this view, then, a double bond is regarded as a $(\sigma+\pi)$-bond.

The extension of these ideas to the triple bond in acetylene is straight-forward. Three of the tetrahedral sp^3 orbitals of each carbon atom overlap, and the fourth orbital of each carbon atom overlaps the orbital of a hydrogen atom. The bond angles are 180°, and all four nuclei lie on a straight line:

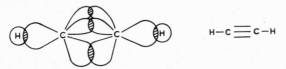

The triple bond can also be regarded as composed of a σ-bond, from the endways overlap of an sp hybrid orbital, and two π-bonds, from the sideways overlap of the two remaining p orbitals on each carbon atom. Thus the triple bond is a $(\sigma+2\pi)$-bond; it has axial symmetry as the orbitals together form a cylindrical sheath round the inter-nuclear axis (Plate II).

These descriptions of the types of bonds between carbon atoms are summarized in Table 1.

TABLE 1. *Types of carbon-carbon bonds*

Example	Ethane	Ethylene	Acetylene
Type of bond	single	double	triple
Atomic orbitals which overlap endways (σ-bonds) .	one, sp^3	one, sp^2	one, sp
Atomic orbitals which overlap sideways (π-bonds) .	none	one, p	two, p
Description in terms of σ- and π-bonds . . .	σ	$\sigma + \pi$	$\sigma + 2\pi$
Bond angles	$109\frac{1}{2}°$	$120°$	$180°$
Is the bond axially symmetrical ?	yes	no	yes

Hitherto, the only type of multiple bonds described have been those between carbon atoms. The carbon-oxygen double bond can be described in the same terms as the carbon-carbon one, although the electron distribution is profoundly modified by the larger charge on the nucleus of the oxygen atom, so that the bonding electrons are drawn towards the oxygen atom. Multiple bonds are much less common beyond the second period of the Periodic Table; this is one of the reasons for the differences in the chemistry of phosphorus and nitrogen compounds, and of sulphur and oxygen compounds. A rough-and-ready explanation of this tendency is that when these larger atoms get sufficiently close for their p orbitals to overlap sideways, the relatively large number of non-bonding electrons repel each other extensively.

(*n*) *Electronegativity.* If unlike atoms are joined by a covalent bond, the atom which tends to attract preferentially the pair of bonding electrons is said to be more electronegative than the other; thus if HCl splits into ions, the ions are H^+ and Cl^-, and not the other way round; chlorine is more electronegative than hydrogen. It is possible to assign numbers to atoms which are, in a general way, measures of this tendency (Table 2);† examples of the use of electronegativity values will be encountered later (see, for example, § 1 *q*).

TABLE 2. *Electronegativity values*

H						
2·1						
Li	Be	B	C	N	O	F
1·0	1·5	2·0	2·5	3·0	3·5	4·0
Na	Mg	Al	Si	P	S	Cl
0·9	1·2	1·5	1·8	2·1	2·5	3·0
						Br
						2·9
						I
						2·5

† Coulson, *Valence*, p. 132, Clarendon Press, Oxford, 1952.

(o) *Mesomerism* (*resonance*). Structural formulae, as ordinarily written, have their limitations. Nowhere is this limitation more evident than in benzene, for which structures (1) and (2) were written by Kekulé.

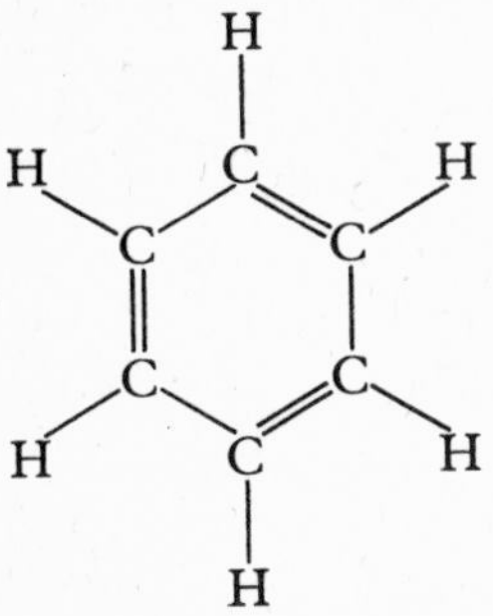

The reactions of benzene are, of course, very different from those of cyclohexene (3), which behaves as a normal olefine. The general way in which the reactions of benzene differ from those of cyclohexene is that benzene reacts so that the original (conjugated) system of alternating single and double bonds is preserved in the product; thus benzene reacts by substitution (e.g. with bromine) and cyclohexene by addition. This tendency of benzene (and other aromatic compounds) towards 'preservation of type' is characteristic and suggests that these compounds are peculiarly stable. This is confirmed by the observation that the hydrogenation of cyclohexene is exothermic (to the extent of about 30 kcal/mol), but the hydrogenation of benzene (one double bond) is endothermic (to the extent of about 6 kcal/mol). In its chemical properties, then, benzene is more stable than would be expected from structures (1) and (2). The physical properties of benzene are not well interpreted by these structures; the molecule is a regular hexagon, i.e. all the carbon-carbon bond lengths are the same. In short, the classical structures (1) and (2), for benzene, are unsatisfactory. So we must try to see why this is so, and then produce some acceptable modification of the classical structures.

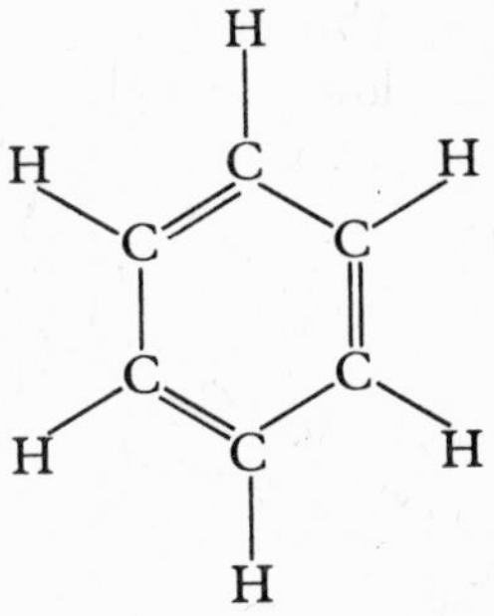

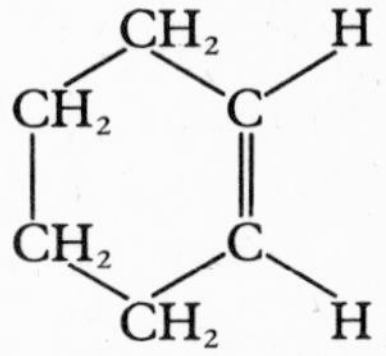

The simplest account of the problems raised by the structure of benzene (and other molecules for which several 'unsatisfactory' classical structures can be written) is given by the theory of resonance, developed especially by Pauling. This theory states that the two classical structures (1) and (2) must be superimposed to represent the molecule of benzene (which is called a resonance hybrid), and that there are theoretical grounds for believing that this conceptual superimposition is always associated with stabilization. We may say that the actual structure is more symmetrical than is indicated by either of the formulae (1) and (2); that this high symmetry is associated with the bonding electrons having more space available for them; and that this lowers the energy of the system. The implications, and the usefulness, of this idea will become apparent as it is developed.

The concept of mesomerism had been advanced (on chemical grounds) by Ingold; the terms mesomerism and resonance are used interchangeably in this context. The relationship between a mesomeric molecule (or resonance hybrid) and the classical formulae (such as (1) and (2)), may be illustrated by analogy. The classical formulae may be regarded as having a similar logical status to the plan and section drawings of a building; when viewing them, the reader makes the imaginative effort to see a real, three-dimensional, object. A more picturesque analogy, due to Wheland, compares a resonance hybrid with a mule, derived indeed from a donkey and a horse, but with characteristics quite of its own; certainly a mule is not a horse part of the time and a donkey the rest of the time, and similarly the benzene molecule does not have structure (1) part of the time and structure (2) the rest of the time.

The particular features present in the benzene molecule can be seen on the basis of the $(\sigma+\pi)$ description of the double bond. The bonds are formed by the endways overlap of the sp^2 (trigonal) hybrid orbitals (Fig. 9 a); the important point here is that the bond angle in a regular hexagon is 120°, just right for a large overlap of the sp^2 orbitals which are also at 120°. Hence a particularly strong bond can be formed from the sp^2 orbitals. Thus, although five- and seven-membered rings may show aromatic properties, the most stable aromatic systems contain six-membered rings. Each carbon atom has one p orbital left (Fig. 9 b), and these coalesce sideways to form π-bonds. In the two pictures on the middle and right of Fig. 9 b, if there is a π-bond between carbon atom number C-1 and C-2 in one formula, then there is a π-bond between C-2 and C-3 in the other. So an electron moving in the field of force of C-1 and C-2 in one formula, may be moving in the field of force of C-2 and C-3 in the other. Thus we may produce a modified picture (Fig. 10) which shows the extended path of the six π-electrons above and below the plane that contains the atoms.

The idea that the aromatic properties of benzene could be ascribed to the presence of six especially mobile electrons had been inferred (on chemical grounds) by Robinson, who described these electrons as the aromatic sextet.

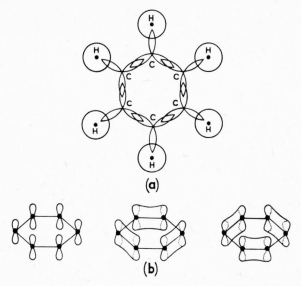

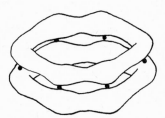

FIG. 9. (*a*) Overlap of sp^2 orbitals, to give σ-bonds; (*b*) the *p* orbitals, and their overlap, to form π orbitals in the classical structures for benzene. (From Coulson, *Valence*, Clarendon Press, 1952.)

FIG. 10. The orbitals containing the six π-electrons in benzene. (From Hine, *Physical Organic Chemistry*, McGraw-Hill, 1956.)

We conclude then that resonance (or mesomerism) is, like the covalent bond itself, a concept rather than a physical phenomenon. The questions (*a*) when does resonance occur? and (*b*) what difference does it make when it does? are tantamount to (*a*) when are ordinary structural formulae particularly misleading? and (*b*) how should we adjust them (or at least what mental reservations should we make) so that they are less misleading?

(*p*) *Conditions for mesomerism. When two (or more) formulae show all the atomic nuclei in very nearly the same positions, the molecule is mesomeric.*

Another condition (which is less important as it only applies to free radicals) is that the number of unpaired electrons must be the same in the several formulae. The mesomerism will, however, only be important if the formulae depict structures of comparable stability; moreover, symmetrical mesomerism, as in benzene, is especially important.

Often it is easy to say when mesomerism occurs, but sometimes care is needed; in general, we shall take the view that when it is difficult to decide whether mesomerism occurs, classical formulae are as good a guide as we can reasonably expect them to be, and so no adjustments are needed. As we are concerned mainly with reactivity, we shall use the notion of resonance whenever it seems helpful in interpreting the course of a reaction. There are two reasons why this leads to a more lavish use of the notion than would be justifiable if we were mainly concerned with structural features (such as bond lengths). The first reason is that fairly small energy differences (of a few kilocalories/mol) have a large effect on the rates of reactions, and the second is that the unstable compounds which are frequently intermediates in organic reactions are especially often not well represented by a single formula.

Mesomeric structures can be expressed by the 'partial valency' symbol, introduced by Thiele some sixty years ago, e.g. (1) for benzene:

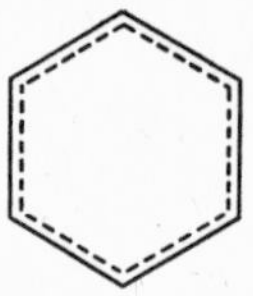

(1) 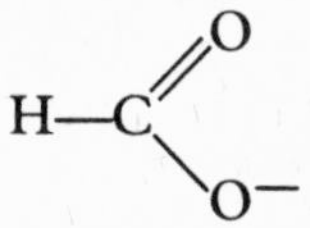   (2) 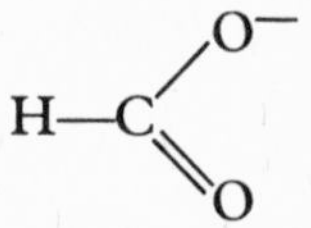   (3)

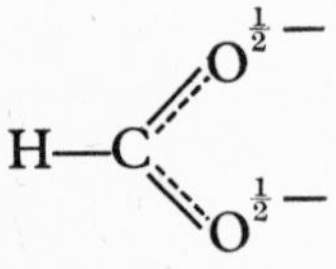

(4)

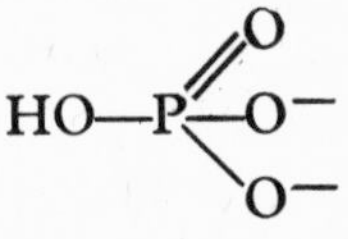

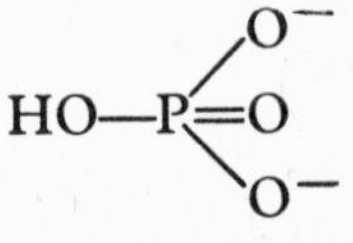

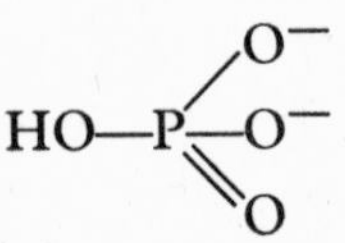

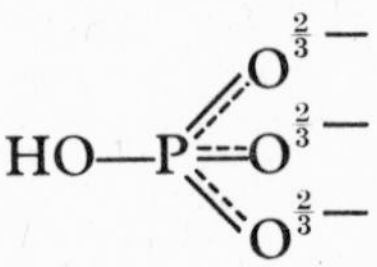

Two other examples are the formate ion (4), mesomeric between (2) and (3), and the hydrogen phosphate ion. Here the unshared pairs of electrons on the oxygen atoms are playing a part; although they are not shown in ordinary formulae their presence must not be forgotten. The common feature in these examples is that the mesomeric structure differs from the classical formulae by representing the electrons as distributed over more bonds. This is, in fact, perfectly general, and the term delocalization is sometimes used to describe this effect.

(*q*) *Further examples of mesomerism.* Three examples of reactive intermediates, typical of the types which will be encountered in later chapters, may be given. The allyl carbonium ion is mesomeric between (1) and (2), and may be represented as (3):

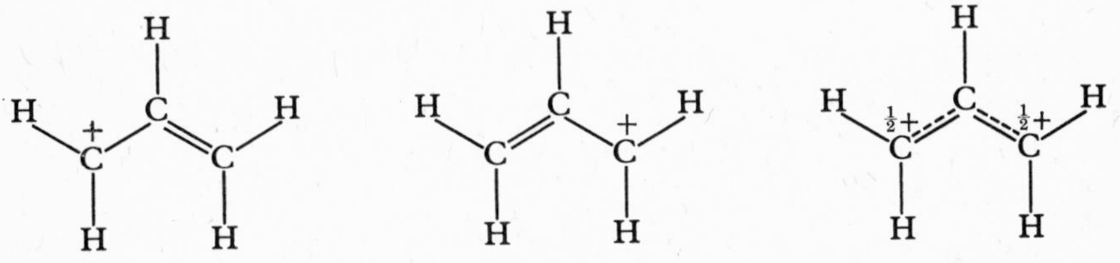

(1)   (2)   (3)

The carbanion from acetone is usually regarded as mesomeric between (4) and (5), and may be represented as (6):

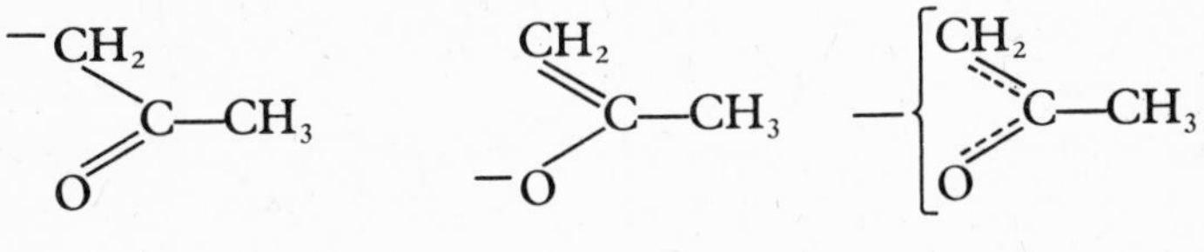

(4)   (5)   (6)

The symmetry of the allyl carbonium ion results in each terminal carbon atom having an equal, fractional, positive charge; but in the carbanion, as oxygen is more electronegative than carbon (Table 2), the oxygen atom will have a larger fraction of the negative charge than the carbon. Indeed, it seems adequate to represent the anion simply as the enolate (5).

The triphenylmethyl (free) radical, in which the unpaired electron is shown as a dot, is mesomeric between (7) and nine other formulae, of which (8) is one (note that the unpaired electron cannot be assigned to a *meta*-position in the benzene rings in any formula with thirty carbon-carbon bonds):

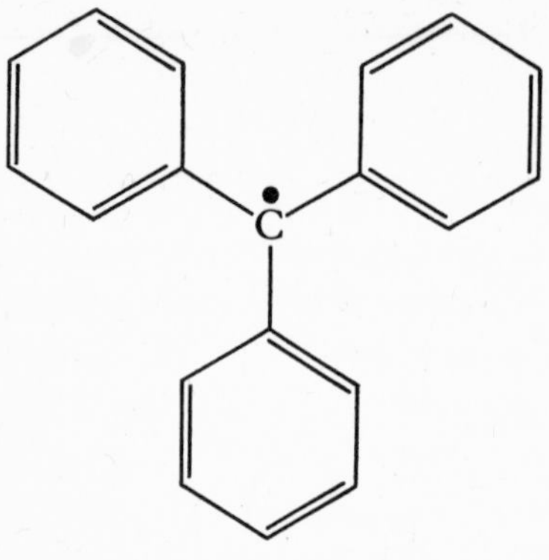

(7)

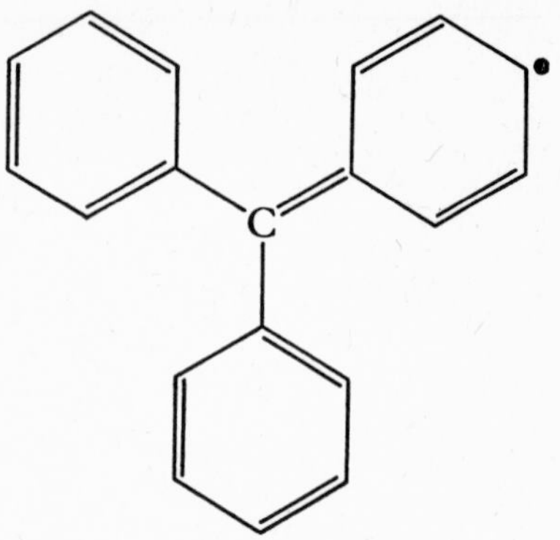

(8)

The application of the idea of mesomerism can also be illustrated by the properties of compounds containing a carbonyl group. As oxygen is more electronegative than carbon there will be a partial positive charge on the carbon atom ($>\overset{\delta+}{C}=\overset{\delta-}{O}$); the reactivity of aldehydes and ketones is associated with this charge, and if the magnitude of the charge at this point is lessened, the carbonyl group reactivity is decreased. The following compounds form a series

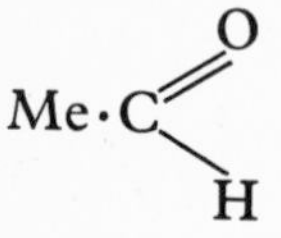

acetaldehyde 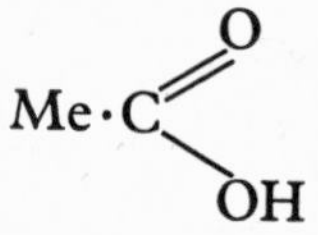   acetic acid 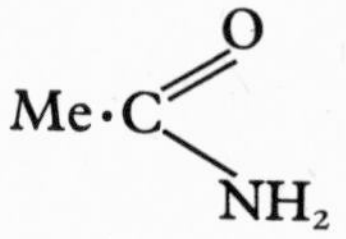   acetamide 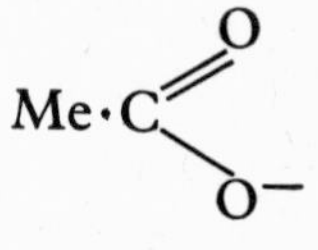   acetate ion

in which the tendency of the substituents (H, OH, NH_2, and O^-) to donate electrons increases. The H has none to offer, but the other substituents have unshared pairs of electrons, and the other three molecules are mesomeric, e.g. formulae (9) and (10) for acetic acid.

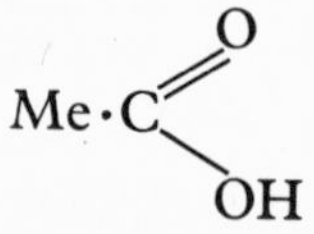

(9) 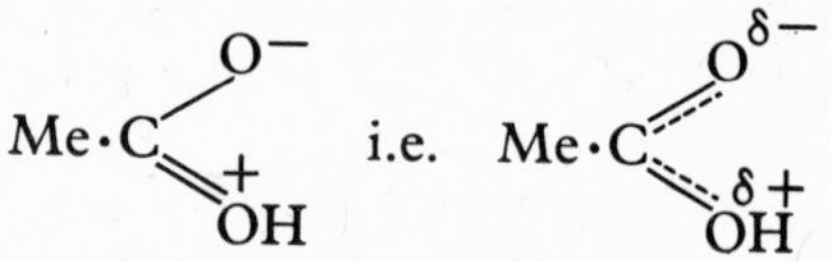   (10)

The extent of mesomerism is greater in acetamide than in acetic acid. Nitrogen is less electronegative than oxygen, and so less reluctant to be saddled with a positive charge.

The carbonyl group in acetic acid is less reactive than the carbonyl group in acetone, as the partial positive charge which would otherwise be on the carbon atom is relayed to the oxygen atom in acetic acid. This may be said to be the effect of the OH on the CO in acetic acid; but interactions are reciprocal. It is obvious that the effect of the CO in acetic acid is to make the OH group acidic. Now mesomerism in the acetate ion will be similar to that in the formate ion, shown above. The negative charge in the ion is spread, or dispersed. This is energetically favourable, while the separation of opposite charges in the mesomerism of acetic acid (10) is not. Therefore the ion is preferentially stabilized by mesomerism, which may be regarded as an acid-strengthening tendency. Of course, this is only tantamount to showing how structural formulae can be modified to account for the fact that a carboxylic acid is a stronger acid than alcohol (by a factor of roughly 10^{10}), although both contain the OH group.

Similar ideas can account for the facts that phenol is more strongly acidic than an aliphatic alcohol, and aniline more weakly basic than an aliphatic amine (by factors of roughly 10^6 in both cases). In both examples an unshared pair of electrons on the substituent affects the distribution of electrons in the benzene ring. Phenol is mesomeric between formulae of the type (11) and of the type (12), and the phenolate ion between (13) and (14):

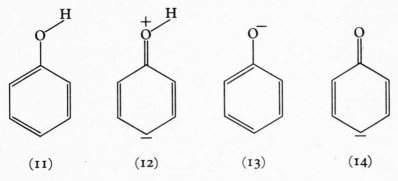

(11)   (12)   (13)   (14)

The argument used to account for the acidity of acetic acid can be applied here too. The formulae shown are sufficient to illustrate the argument, but two Kekulé formulae can be written for phenol, and there are three dipolar formulae, two with the charge on *ortho*-positions, as well as the one (12) with the charge on the *para*-position.

Aniline is mesomeric between (15) and (16), but such mesomerism is no longer possible in the anilinium ion (17) (which has not got an unshared pair of electrons on the nitrogen atom), so that aniline is a weaker base than would be expected by comparison with aliphatic amines.

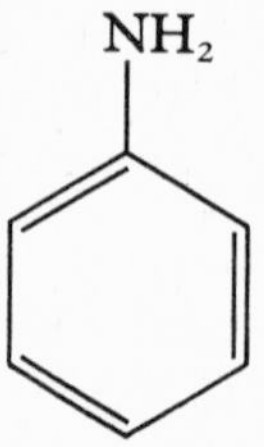

(15) 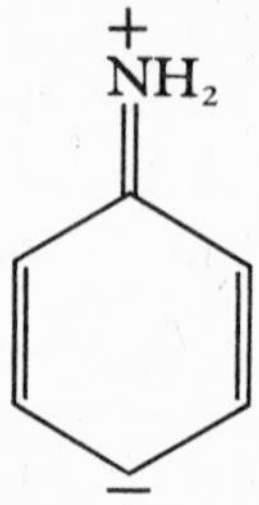   (16) 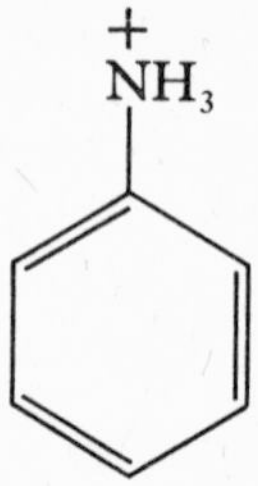   (17)

Mesomerism has important stereochemical consequences, or, to put it another way, mesomerism demands certain steric conditions. This is a large and important topic, but only one example can be mentioned here. Glycylglycine can be represented as mesomeric between (18) and (19):

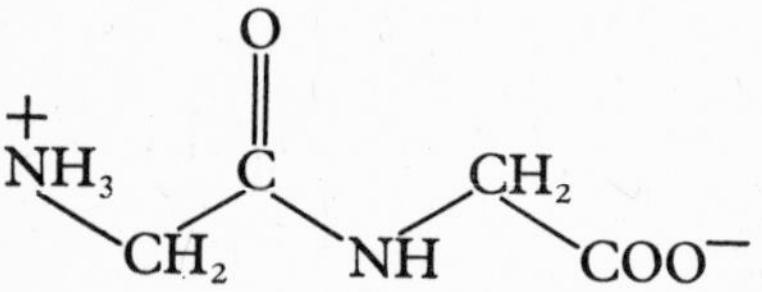

(18) 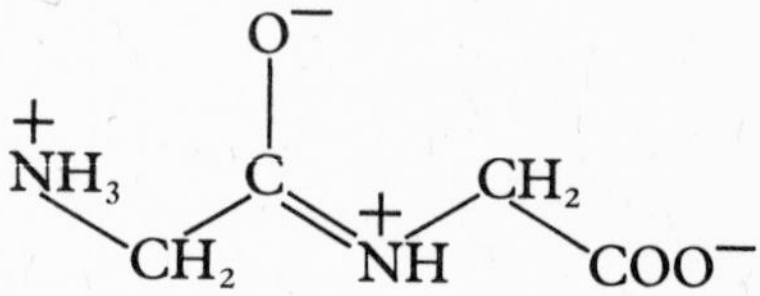   (19)

This mesomerism can be held to account for the observations that the carbon, nitrogen, and oxygen atoms of the moiety

$$\cdots CH_2 \cdot CO \cdot NH \cdot CH_2 \cdots$$

all lie in one plane. This planar arrangement around the peptide bond is an important factor in deciding the probable shape of protein molecules.

Summary

    (i) Certain molecules are not well represented by classical structural formulae.

    (ii) Experimental evidence shows that the electrons are less localized than is implied by the classical formulae.

    (iii) Theoretical evidence shows that the delocalization of electrons (resonance, mesomerism) is, in general, energetically favourable.

    (iv) A molecule can only be described as mesomeric between several classical structures of comparable stability if the positions of the atomic nuclei are in very nearly the same position in the classical structures.

(r) *Hyperconjugation.* As hyperconjugation is commonly encountered in discussions of the structure and reactivity of organic compounds, the meaning of the term is explained in this section. The status and usefulness of hyperconjugation, however, is a controversial subject.†

There is considerable evidence that the tertiary butyl carbonium ion (1) is more stable than the methyl carbonium ion (2). Now the positive charge in (1) will attract electrons from the methyl group, and in (2)

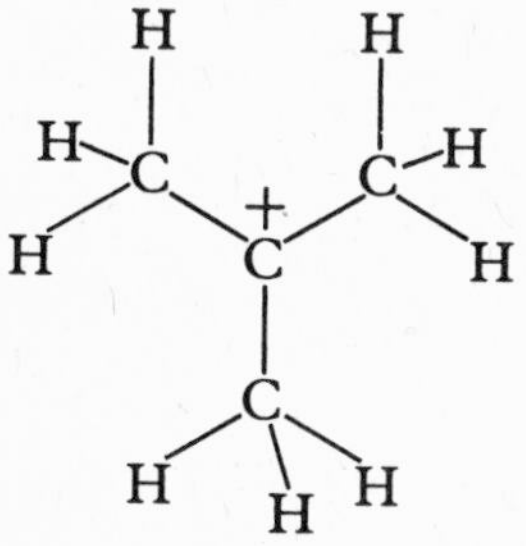

(1) 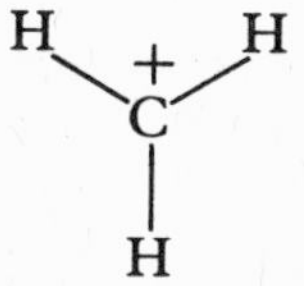   (2) 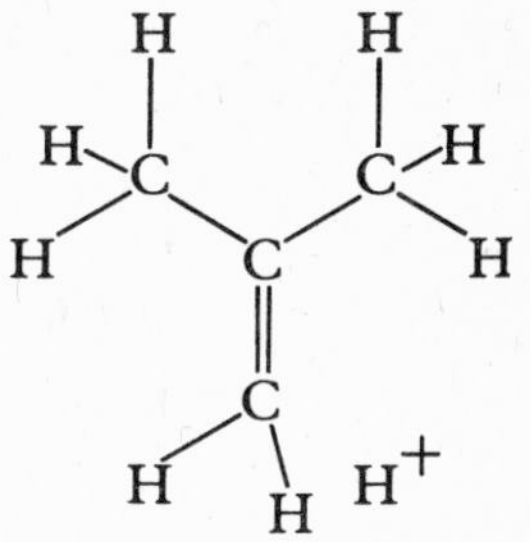   (3)

from the bond to the hydrogen atoms. The positive charge will thus be delocalized in both (1) and (2). The extent of delocalization is much greater in (1) than in (2) because there are more electrons to be affected, and because a methyl group is electron-repelling relative to a hydrogen atom (§ 2 a). Now all the valency electrons in (1) take part in bond formation, so that if we want to modify our structural formula to take account of the delocalization of the charge, we are driven to write formulae of the type of (3). There are obviously nine formulae of this type; these formulae are meant to indicate that in the tertiary butyl carbonium ion a fraction of the charge is distributed over the nine hydrogen atoms. Formulae of this type, with 'severed bonds', are the distinguishing feature of hyperconjugation. The idea of hyperconjugation, as applied to this example, is that it is profitable to consider the tertiary butyl carbonium ion as mesomeric between (1) and the nine formulae of the type of (3); as the ion is mesomeric, each C—H bond is only fractionally weakened. The same idea can be applied to the analogous free radical (4).

† Dewar and Schmeising, *Tetrahedron*, 1959, **5**, 166; Mulliken, ibid., p. 253; Muller and Mulliken, *J. Amer. Chem. Soc.* 1958, **80**, 3489.

(4)   (5)   (6)

The total number of bonds in (1) and (3) is the same. However, in propene, hyperconjugation entails mesomerism between (5) and (6), and (6) has one bond fewer than (5), and in fact propene is adequately represented by the classical formula (5).

2. Physical properties

(a) *Dipole moments.*† One of the most informative physical properties of a molecule is the dipole moment. To explain this property let us consider HCl. The table of electronegativity values shows that the chlorine is more electronegative than the hydrogen, so the shared electrons forming the bond will be somewhat nearer the nucleus of the chlorine atom than they are to the nucleus of the hydrogen atom. The extreme case is an ionic bond, H^+Cl^-. Here the positive charge is centred on the hydrogen and the negative charge on the chlorine atom. In an electric field a molecule of HCl will twist so that the more electronegative chlorine is towards the positive side of the field (Fig. 11); the

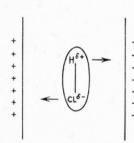

FIG. 11. Tendency of HCl molecule to twist in an electric field.

twist, as measured by the turning moment in a field of unit strength, is called the dipole moment. The interatomic distance in HCl is 1·27 Å (1 Å $= 10^{-8}$ cm), and the charge on an electron is $4·8 \times 10^{-10}$ electrostatic units, so the dipole moment for the transfer of an electron through this distance is $1·27 . 10^{-8} \times 4·8 . 10^{-10} = 6·1$ D where D stands for Debye units, the moment resulting from the movement of unit charge for unit distance. The observed dipole moment of HCl is about 1 D, and so the H—Cl bond could be described as having 1/6·1, or 16 per cent., ionic character.

† Sutton, in *Determination of Organic Structures by Physical Methods*, edited by Braude and Nachod, Academic Press, 1955.

Dipole moments are particularly useful because they are a sensitive measure of fractional charge separation in a molecule, which is an important factor in governing reactivity.

An important application of dipole moments is the support they give to the concept of mesomerism. Thus the dye (1) has a dipole moment of 17·7 D; this remarkably high value shows that the molecule is mesomeric between (1) and dipolar structures such as (2).†

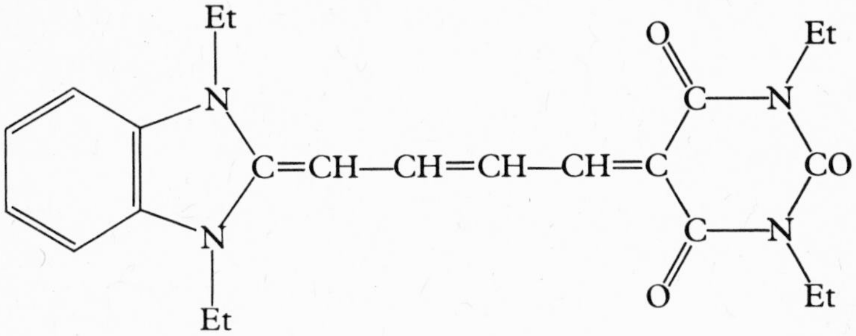

(1)

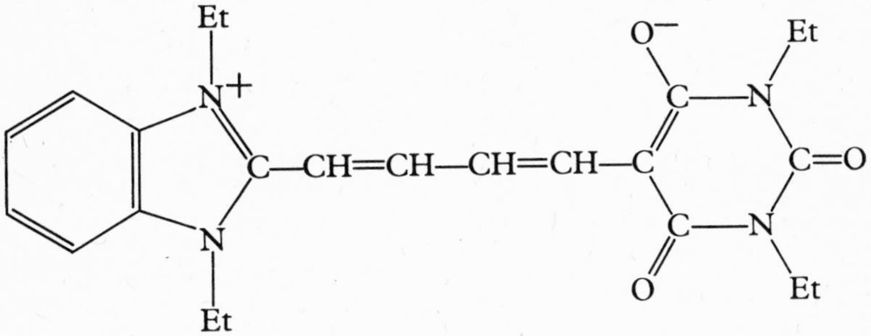

(2)

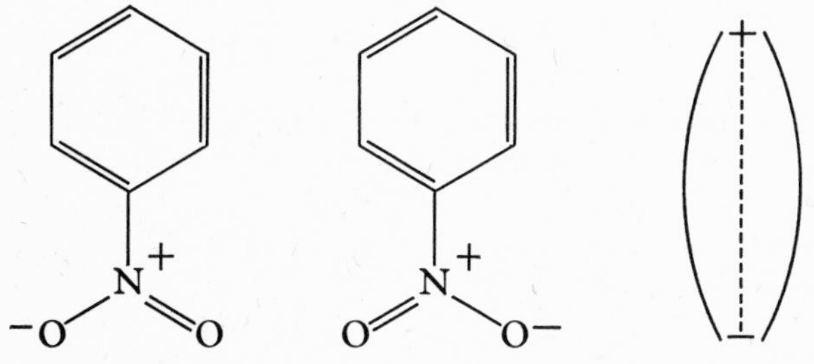

(3) 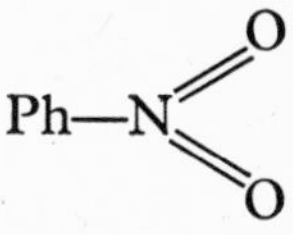   (4)

† Kushner and Smythe, *J. Amer. Chem. Soc.* 1949, **71**, 1401.

The structure of aromatic compounds has been investigated by measurements of dipole moments. We shall first consider the direction of the dipole in nitrobenzene (3). This is easily answered: the oxygen atoms share a negative charge, and so are at the negative end of the dipole. The maximum covalency of nitrogen is four (§ 1 *j*), so that nitro groups cannot have the alternative structure (4); there must be a dipolar, or dative bond (3) (as in trimethylamine oxide, § 1 *e*), and this bond gives away the direction of the dipole. The dipole moment of chlorobenzene will also be in the same direction, as chlorine is more electronegative than carbon. Now if both the chlorine atom and the nitro group are at opposite ends of a benzene ring, they should 'compete', and the moment of *p*-nitrochlorobenzene should be nearer the difference of the moments of nitrobenzene and chlorobenzene than it is to their sum. The values given below show that this is correct.

	Cl		Me	Me	Me
		Cl			
	NO$_2$	Cl	NO$_2$	NO$_2$	Cl
dipole moment (D)	4	1·6	2·6	0·4	4·5	1·9

In the formulae given, the positive end of the dipole is at the top. In the monosubstituted derivatives there is, of course, a hydrogen atom at the *para*-position. So, relative to hydrogen, the nitro group and the chloro group are electron-attracting, and the methyl group is electron-repelling. These conclusions apply to aromatic compounds.

Now, by comparing the dipole moments of aliphatic and aromatic compounds we may gauge how the aromatic ring and the attached group interact. Values of the (vector) differences between the dipole moments of aromatic compounds and the corresponding aliphatic ones (e.g. chlorobenzene and tertiary butyl chloride) are listed in Table 3; these differences are called mesomeric moments. A positive mesomeric moment signifies that a group X is less electron-attracting in Ph.X than it is in Me$_3$C.X.

Most of the groups (e.g. NH$_2$, OH) which have positive mesomeric moments have atoms with unshared pairs of electrons. Aniline and phenol were represented above (§ 1 *q*) as mesomeric, and the dipolar formulae account for the positive mesomeric moments. Similar formulae

TABLE 3

Group	Mesomeric moment	Group	Mesomeric moment
NMe_2	1·66	Cl	0·41
NH_2	1·02	CH_3	0·35
OMe	0·8	$CHCl_2$	0
OH	0·6	CCl_3	−0·5
$(CH_3)_3C$	0·53	$COCH_3$	−0·46
I	0·5	CN	−0·45
SH	0·44	NO_2	−0·76

Values from Sutton, loc. cit.

can be written for the halides. Another mode of description is to say that there is some overlap between the unshared pairs of p electrons in the chlorine atom of chlorobenzene and the electrons of the benzene ring; in this interaction, the chlorine atom, with its completely filled p orbitals, must release electrons rather than gain them.

Most of the groups which have negative mesomeric moments have double bonds. Acetophenone, for example, can be represented as mesomeric between (5), (6), (7), and (8), and so the negative mesomeric moment can be accounted for.

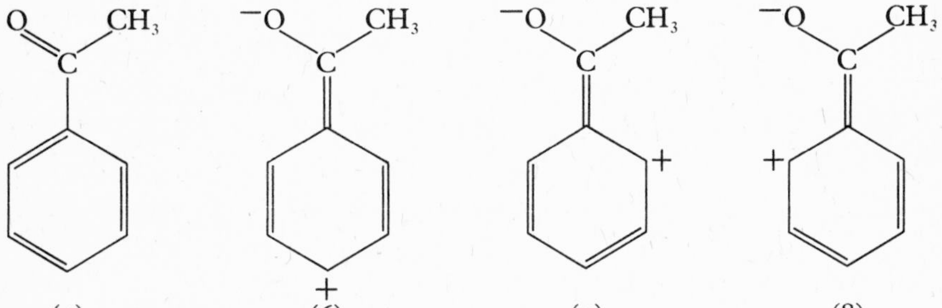

(5)   (6)   (7)   (8)

The fractional charge separation, which is what formulae (6) to (8) are meant to convey, is important in chemical reactions. Some forty years ago Robinson, and Ingold, had formulated electronic theories to account for why some substituents in a benzene ring direct further substitution into the *ortho-* and *para*-positions, and some into the *meta*-positions (see Chapter IX, § 2 c). Then Sutton pointed out that all *ortho-para* directing substituents had positive mesomeric moments, and all *meta*-directing substituents negative ones. This provided a direct link between a physical property and chemical reactivity; and the dipolar formulae such as (6) to (8), which account for the mesomeric moments, are also a guide to chemical reactivity.

Values for bond moments can be obtained (Table 4); the absolute values are somewhat uncertain, but the relative values are reliable. The order C—O < C—I < C—Br < C—Cl (in each case carbon is the positive end of the dipole) shows the extent to which these single bonds are dipolar. The *inductive effect* of a group is the extent, relative to hydrogen, to which it attracts or repels electrons when it is bound to carbon. Thus the bond moments quoted above may be taken as evidence that the inductive effects increase in the order O < I < Br < Cl.

TABLE 4. *Bond dipole moments*

(The more electronegative atom is on the right)

Bond	Moment	Bond	Moment	Bond	Moment
H—C	0·4	C—N	0·22	C=O	2·3
H—S	0·68	C—O	0·74	C=S	2·6
H—Br	0·78	C—S	0·9	C≡N	3·5
H—Cl	1·08	C—I	1·19	$N^+\equiv C^-$	3·0
H—N	1·31	C—Br	1·38	N=O	2·0
H—O	1·51	C—F	1·41		
H—F	1·94	C—Cl	1·46		

From Smyth, *Dielectric Behaviour and Structure*, McGraw-Hill, 1955.

The bond moments can help one to understand chemical reactivity. Thus the sign of the moment for C=O is in the sense $\overset{\delta+\;\;\delta-}{C=O}$, so that it is not surprising that an anion (e.g. CN⁻) attacks the carbon atom. Moreover, multiple bonds have larger moments than the corresponding single bonds: this shows the greater extent of charge transfer, and hence heightened reactivity, of multiple bonds.

Although the carbon-hydrogen bond is weakly polar, saturated hydrocarbons have no dipole moment. This is to be expected, if all the C—H bonds have the same moment, and all the bond angles are tetrahedral. For, in propane, one terminal methyl group will have a moment along the direction of the carbon-carbon bond equal in magnitude to that of one C—H bond (cos 109° 28′ = −1/3). Then the second carbon atom has this moment, and in addition the resolved part of the moments of two C—H bonds, which amounts to the moment of one C—H bond acting in the opposite direction to the moments of the three C—H bonds of the terminal methyl group, along the line joining this last methyl group to the remainder of the molecule. Thus, the total dipole moment is zero; this argument can be extended to any paraffin.

The dipole moments of members of a homologous series, from this argument, should all be the same. This does not hold good. Thus, the values for the dipole moments of alkyl chlorides are: CH_3Cl, 1·86; CH_3CH_2Cl, 2·00; $(CH_3)_2CH.Cl$, 2·15. Now in a C—Cl dipole, chlorine is the more electronegative atom, and so the increase in dipole moment as the homologous series is ascended, due to some interaction between the C—H bonds and the C—Cl bond, shows that *a methyl group is electron-repelling relative to a hydrogen atom*. This conclusion is often helpful in discussing the course of reactions.

(b) *Bond lengths*. The sizes and shapes of molecules are determined by bond lengths, bond angles, and the distances between non-bonded atoms. The lengths of most covalent bonds can be simply expressed in terms of covalent bond radii; thus the distance between two carbon atoms, linked by a single bond, is usually 1·54 Å, and so the covalent, single-bonded radius of carbon is given as 0·77 Å. Similarly, from the C—O distance of 1·43 Å (in, say, methanol), the covalent single-bond radius of oxygen is $1·43 - 0·77 = 0·66$ Å. Multiple bonds are invariably shorter than the corresponding single bonds, as there are four (or six) electrons bonding the positively charged nuclei. The distance between two carbon atoms linked by a double bond is usually 1·34 Å, and so the double-bond radius of carbon is 0·67 Å. Such is the basis of the figures in Table 5.†

These values of the radii do not give the observed interatomic distances in mesomeric molecules. Thus, the distance between two carbon atoms in benzene is 1·40 Å. Covalent radii are useful to get an idea of expected bond lengths, but the concept of additivity is only approximate.

The type of hybrid orbital affects the bond length. Thus, in propylene, CH_3—CH=CH_2, the single bond between the carbon atom is formed from one carbon atom using sp^3 hybrid orbitals, and one using sp^2 hybrid orbitals. For single bonds between carbon atoms, a covalent radius of 0·74 Å may be assigned to a sp^2 hybridized carbon atom.

A measure of the distance between non-bonded atoms is given by the van der Waals radii in Table 5. These figures, which are only approximate, may be taken to indicate that two atoms in different molecules in a crystal will not approach much more closely than the sum of their van der Waals radii, and also that two non-bonded atoms in the same molecule will not approach much more closely. An alternative value of 0·75 Å for the van der Waals radius for hydrogen has been suggested for use in deciding whether there is steric hindrance in a given structure.‡

† For a compilation of bond lengths and angles see *Interatomic Distances*, Special Publication No. 11, London: The Chemical Society, 1958.

‡ Crombie, *Quart. Rev.* 1952, **6**, 101.

TABLE 5. *Covalent radii, and van der Waals radii (in Å)*

Element	Single-bond radius	Double-bond radius	Van der Waals radius	Triple-bond radius
Hydrogen	0·30	..	1·2	..
Carbon	0·77	0·67	2·0†	0·60
Nitrogen	0·70	0·60	1·5	0·55
Phosphorus	1·10	1·00	1·9	
Oxygen	0·66	0·55	1·4	
Sulphur	1·04	0·94	1·85	
Fluorine	0·64	0·54	1·35	
Chlorine	0·99	0·89	1·80	
Bromine	1·14	1·04	1·95	
Iodine	1·33	1·23	2·15	

† Radius of methyl group.

Note that the double-bond radius of an element is 0·1 Å less than the single-bond radius, and the van der Waals radius is 0·8 Å more than the single-bond radius.

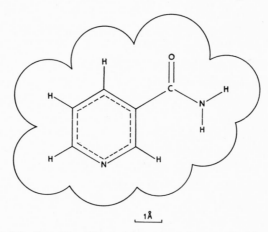

FIG. 12. Nicotinamide. The circles represent the van der Waals radii.

The principles underlying the angles between bonds have already been discussed (§ 1 *k*). Bond angles are more variable than bond lengths: roughly speaking, bending a bond requires less energy than stretching it.

To bring two non-bonded atoms with filled orbitals to a distance appreciably less than the sum of their van der Waals radii requires the expenditure of much energy; hence atoms have an effective size, and material objects are tangible. The repulsive forces brought into play are often called steric forces.

The diagram (Fig. 12) representing nicotinamide is given to show the relative magnitudes of these distances; the molecule has been drawn as if all the atoms were in one plane, but in the crystal the oxygen atom and the amide nitrogen atom are not coplanar with the pyridine ring, presumably owing to steric forces between the two nearest hydrogen atoms.

(c) *Bond strengths.*† In chemical reactions old bonds are broken and new bonds are formed, and so some idea of the strengths of bonds is useful. The most direct measure of the strength of a bond is the energy required to break it. This is called the bond dissociation energy. Thus for methane the bond dissociation energy is the change in the energy (at the absolute zero) for the reaction:

$$CH_4 \longrightarrow CH_3 + H$$

This process may be pictured as consisting of a stretching of one C—H bond, followed by breaking the bond, and finally an alteration in the shape of the methyl radical which settles down to its most stable configuration, which may well be different from that of the methyl moiety in the intact methane molecule. This separation into a series of events is purely conceptual. A few values are given in Table 6, for some C—H and C—C bonds.

In the simplest stable compounds the bond dissociation energies of the C—H and C—C bonds are about 100, and about 80 kcal/mol, respectively. The large decreases, of about 20 kcal/mol, in some of the more complex compounds listed, can be correlated with the mesomerism in the radicals formed; thus the allyl radical from but-1-ene is mesomeric between (1) and (2) (cf. § 1 q).

$$CH_2=CH-\overset{\bullet}{C}H_2 \qquad\qquad \overset{\bullet}{C}H_2-CH=CH_2$$
$$(\text{I}) \qquad\qquad\qquad\qquad (2)$$

TABLE 6

Type of bond	Molecule (the dissociating bond is shown extended)	Bond dissociation energy kcal/mol
C—H	CH_3—H	101
C—H	$H_3C.CH_2$—H	96
C—H	$(H_3C)_2CH$—H	94
C—H	$(H_3C)_3C$—H	89
C—H	m-$CH_3.C_6H_4.CH_2$—H	76
C—C	H_3C—CH_3	83
C—C	$CH_2=CH.CH_2$—CH_3	62
C—C	$Ph.CH_2$—CH_3	63
C—C	$Ph.CH_2$—CH_2Ph	47

† Cottrell, *The Strengths of Chemical Bonds*, London: Butterworth, 1958. (All the figures in this section are taken from this source, which should be consulted for a description of experimental methods.)

Few values of dissociation energies of individual bonds are available, and so the commonest measure of the strength of a bond is an average bond energy. These average bond energies (referred to henceforward simply as bond energies) are chosen so that their sum for a molecule gives its heat of formation from the atoms. The atoms are to be taken as being in the gaseous state, denoted by (g) in the formulae given below; the values refer to 25° C. Thus the heat of formation of methane from carbon and hydrogen atoms is obtained from the measured heat of combustion as shown:

$$\Delta H$$

$$CH_4(g)+2O_2(g) \rightarrow CO_2+2H_2O(g) \qquad\qquad\quad -212\cdot7$$
$$CO_2 \rightarrow C\,(graphite)+O_2 \qquad\qquad\qquad\qquad\qquad 94$$
$$2H_2O(g) \rightarrow 2H_2+O_2 \quad 2\times68\cdot3 \qquad\qquad\quad 136\cdot6$$
$$2H_2 \rightarrow 4H \qquad\qquad\quad 4\times52\cdot1 \qquad\qquad\quad 208\cdot4$$
$$C\,(graphite) \rightarrow C(g) \qquad\qquad\qquad\qquad\qquad\quad 170\cdot9$$

$$\overline{CH_4(g) \rightarrow C(g)+4H \qquad\qquad\qquad\qquad\quad 397\cdot2}$$

From this measured heat of formation, the average bond energy of the C—H bond in methane is $397\cdot2/4 = 99\cdot3$ kcal/mol. Now in ethane there are both C—H bonds and a C—C bond, so that (from the heat of combustion) we can obtain a value for the C—C bond energy, assuming that the C—H bond energies are the same as in methane. In fact, slight adjustments are made so as to get consistent values from a series of compounds. With these bond energies (Table 7), the calculated and

TABLE 7. *Bond energies (kcal/mol)*

Bond	Bond energy	Bond	Bond energy
C—H	98·7	H—O	110·6
C—C	82·6	H—S	83
C=C	145·8	H—N	93·4
C≡C	199·6	H—F	134
C—O	85·5	H—Cl	103·1
C=O	176 (aldehydes)	H—Br	87·4
C=O	179 (ketones)	H—I	71·4
C—N	72·8	F—F	37
C=N	147	Cl—Cl	57·9
C≡N	212·6	Br—Br	46·1
C—S	65	I—I	36·1
C=S	128 (in CS$_2$)	O—O	35 (in H$_2$O$_2$)
C—F	116 (in CF$_4$)	O=O	119·1 (in O$_2$)
C—Cl	81	N—N	39 (in N$_2$H$_4$)
C—Br	68	N=N	100 (in R.N=N.R)
C—I	52	N≡N	225·8 (in N$_2$)
C—Si	72 (in SiMe$_4$)	N—O	48 (in H$_2$N—OH)
C—Zn	40 (in ZnMe$_2$)	N=O	145 (in nitrites)
H—H	104·2	S—S	60 (in EtS—SEt)

observed heats of formation often agree well; this simply means that, in many cases, the assumption holds that a bond can be assigned a given energy, whatever molecule it is in. However, the observed heats of formation of *n*-pentane and neopentane (Me_4C) differ by about 4 kcal/mol; the calculated heat of formation is necessarily the same for both, and agrees with the observed value for the straight-chain isomer; if this is regarded as the norm, the branched isomer is more stable by 4 kcal/mol. In general, differences between calculated and observed heats of formation of this magnitude may depend on relatively subtle structural factors† and cannot be discussed here. But the calculated heats of formation of benzene (and other aromatic compounds) are lower than the observed values by amounts in the region of 50 kcal/mol. Such differences are significant. These aromatic compounds are mesomeric: there are no true double bonds or single bonds in benzene (§ 1 *o*), so it is not surprising that the heat of formation (calculated from values of the bond energies of C—C and C=C) should differ from the observed heat of formation. The discrepancy can be interpreted by saying that benzene is considerably more stable than the hypothetical entity containing 'normal' single and double bonds (i.e. as in ethane and ethylene): the numerical difference is often referred to as the resonance energy.

The concept of resonance energy is valuable, as it stresses that if we have reasons for thinking that a certain molecule is badly represented by a single formula and should be represented as mesomeric between this and other formulae, then the molecule will be more stable than expected from the sum of the bond energies for the one formula.

One way in which bond energies can be used is to get a rough measure of heats of reaction, especially in the gas phase. Thus, the 'keto' form of acetone can be compared with the enol form as shown (the figures are bond energies, rounded off to whole numbers):

$$CH_3\text{—}C\text{—}CH_3 \qquad\qquad CH_3\text{—}C\text{=}CH_2$$
$$\overset{\|}{O} \qquad\qquad\qquad \overset{|}{O\text{—}H}$$

keto   enol

$$(C\text{=}O)-(C\text{—}O)+(C\text{—}H)-(O\text{—}H)+(C\text{—}C)-C\text{=}C$$
$$179 \ - \ 86 \ + \ 99 \ - \ 111 \ + \ 83 \ - \ 146 = 16 \text{ kcal/mol.}$$

Thus the total bond energy of the keto form is 16 kcal/mol greater than

† Pitzer and Catalano, *J. Amer. Chem. Soc.* 1956, **78**, 4844.

that of the enol form, i.e. the keto form is considerably more stable, and hence predominates in the tautomeric mixture. This calculation may be held to account for the formation of ATP from phosphoenolpyruvate and ADP (Chapter III, § 7).

3. Hydrogen bonding

The nature of hydrogen bonding may be illustrated, in the first place, by water. The boiling-point of water is much higher than that of hydrogen sulphide, and this suggests that the molecules of water are bound to each other in the liquid state; the bond between water molecules is, of course, weak compared with the bond between the atoms on the water molecule. Two molecules of water can associate as shown in (1), or, with the valency electrons shown as dots, in (2):

<pre>
        H   H   H
        | ..   ..
  H——O----H—O   H : O : H : O :
        | ..   ..
        H   H

       (1)   (2)
</pre>

The hydrogen bond is shown by the dotted line in (1). In the alternative formula (2), the symbol H stands for the nucleus of a hydrogen atom (i.e. the proton), and the symbol O for the nucleus and inner shell electrons of an oxygen atom (see § 1 e). There is an attractive force between the proton bound to one oxygen atom, and the unshared electrons of the other oxygen atom: this is the hydrogen bond. No other element can replace hydrogen, because only with a bridging hydrogen can the unshared electrons of the oxygen atom be attracted by a nucleus without being repelled by other electrons in the inner shell of the bridging atom. The kinds of hydrogen-atom bonding with which we shall be concerned are those where the hydrogen atom bonds two oxygen atoms, as in (1), or two nitrogen atoms, as in ammonia, or one nitrogen and one oxygen atom.

The energy of a hydrogen bond is about 5 kcal/mol, which is about one-tenth that of a covalent bond. Much of the importance of hydrogen bonds derives from the fact that they are easily formed and easily broken.

The stereochemistry of the hydrogen bond may be summarized as follows. The three atoms (e.g. O—H $\cdots$ O) often, but not always, lie on a straight line; the hydrogen atom is not usually, but probably may sometimes be, midway between the other two atoms.

Hydrogen bonding may be intermolecular, as in water, or in the mutually bonded chains of desoxyribose nucleic acid. Hydrogen bonding may also be intramolecular, as in the salicylate mono-anion (3). Hydrogen bonding, which is absent in the di-anion (4), thus favours the un-ionized form of the phenolic OH and helps to lower the acidity of this

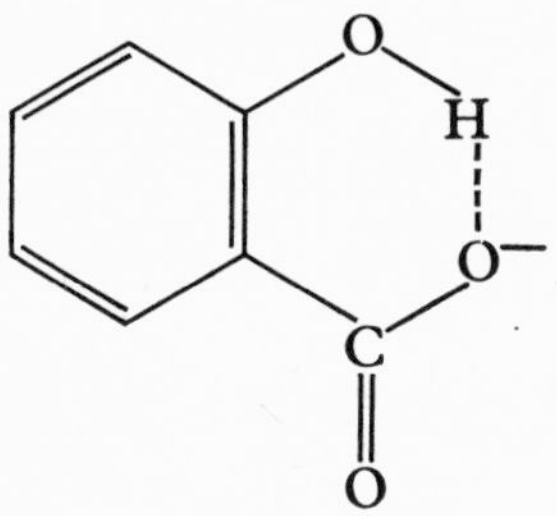

(3) 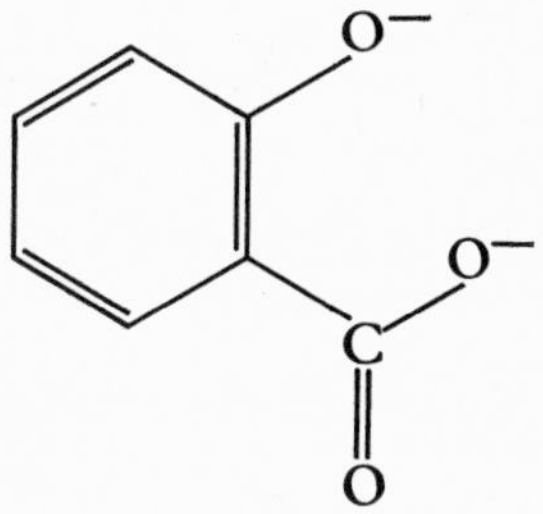   (4)

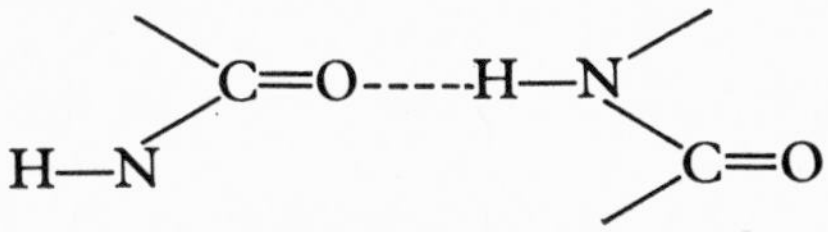

(5)

group. Hydrogen bonding† is important in proteins: the $C=O$ of one amide group forms a hydrogen bond with the H—N of another (5) (see Chapter X, § 2 e).

4. Restricted rotation about single bonds‡

The reader is assumed to be familiar with the principles of stereochemistry, but there is one important topic which must be briefly mentioned as it is not described in any but the most recent textbooks. Classical stereochemistry assumes free rotation about single bonds. This is now known to be incorrect. Spatial arrangements which can be interconverted by rotation about single bonds are called conformations. If one methyl group in ethane is twisted with respect to the

† For a general account of hydrogen bonding, see Pauling, *Nature of the Chemical Bond*, Cornell University Press, 1940, chap. ix. Many aspects are also discussed in the *Symposium on Hydrogen Bonding*, edited by Hadži, London: Pergamon Press, 1959.

‡ Barton and Cookson, *Quart. Rev.* 1956, **10**, 44; Dauben and Pitzer, in *Steric Effects in Organic Chemistry*, edited by Newman, New York: Wiley, 1956.

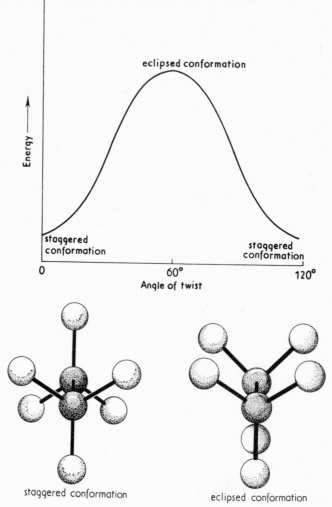

FIG. 13. Conformations of ethane.

other, the energy rises as the distance between the (non-bonded) hydrogen atoms decreases; this is shown diagrammatically in Fig. 13; the
energy is greatest when the non-bonded atoms are closest (eclipsed
conformation) and least when they are most distant (staggered conformation). The amount of energy required to convert one conformation
into another, the height of the potential barrier shown in the diagram,
is about 3 kcal/mol for ethane at room temperature;† free rotation

† For discussions about possible reasons for the magnitude of this barrier, see Bright
Wilson, *Proc. Nat. Acad. Sci.*, 1957, **43**, 816; Eyring, Stewart, and Smith, ibid. 1958, **44**,
259; Pauling, ibid., p. 211.

implies a barrier of less than about 0·6 kcal/mol (the value of RT at room temperature), as potential barriers lower than this are frequently surmounted by thermal motions. On the other hand, a potential barrier of about 20 kcal/mol is necessary to prevent rotation at room temperature, as is the case with *cis* and *trans* configurations about double bonds. Thus, the rotation about single bonds is called restricted, because it is neither completely free or completely prohibited.

Structural formulae are most frequently written without any effort at showing the relative positions of non-bonded atoms (e.g. CH₃CHO). The usual methods of representing the positions in space are by perspective or projection formulae; the latter are governed by conventions, such as that in the Fischer projections the atoms joined by horizontal lines are to be taken as pointing towards the observer (i.e. above the plane of the paper). The Fischer projections always show molecules in eclipsed conformations, which is sometimes a disadvantage, and the Newman projections are often useful alternatives. In Newman projections the view is along the C—C bond, and the bonds to the carbon atom nearer the eye are shown by lines from the centre of the circle, at 120° to each other; the bonds to the more distant carbon atom come from the circumference of the circle. The relations are shown for

| perspective view (staggered conformation) | Fischer projection (eclipsed conformation) | Newman projection (staggered conformation) |

*meso*dibrombutane. (Simple ball and spoke models, such as those obtainable from Gallenkamp, Ltd., are adequate and helpful for understanding stereochemistry.)

Conformational analysis has been applied most extensively to cyclic (particularly alicyclic) systems. The cyclohexane molecule can exist in two conformations, boat (1) and chair (2). All the adjacent carbon-hydrogen bonds are staggered in the chair form, which is the more stable.

There are two kinds of bonds in the stable form, axial bonds, and equatorial bonds, which are shown in the diagrams given below.

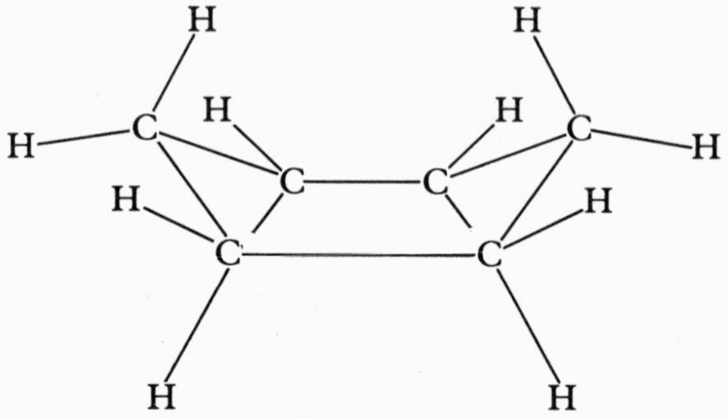

(1) boat form of cyclohexane; two
hydrogen atoms are omitted

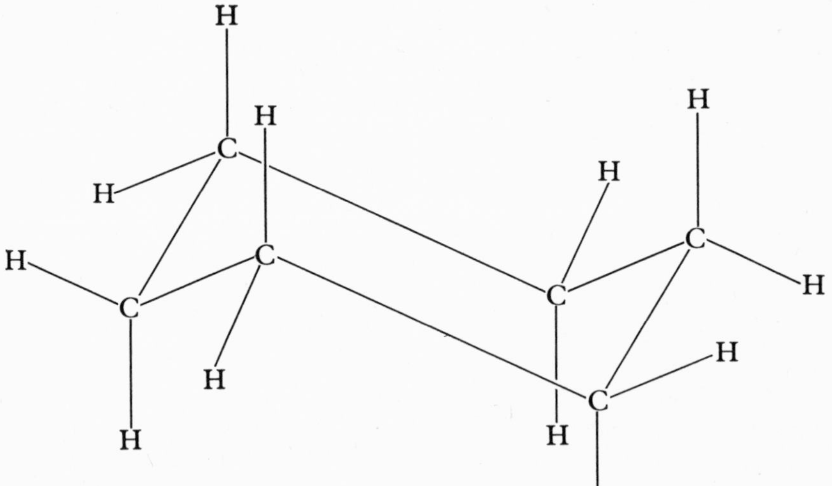

(2) chair form of cyclohexane

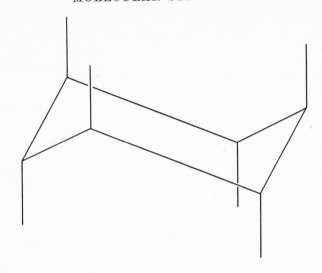

chair form; only axial bonds are shown

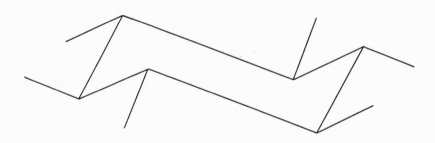

chair form; only equatorial bonds are shown

The configuration of myoinositol may be depicted as (3). This formula, in which the ring is supposed to be in a horizontal plane with the group attached to the ring either above or below the plane of the ring, suffices to show which isomer of inositol is being discussed. The shape of the molecule is, however, better represented as the chair conformation (4). The conformation (4) is preferred to the alternative (5), in which the axial and equatorial groups have been interchanged. The basis for the preference for (4) is that this conformation contains fewer axial hydroxyl groups, and in general the more stable conformation contains fewer substituents in the axial positions. The use of

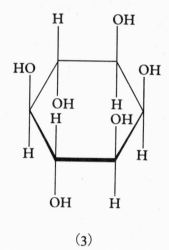

(3)

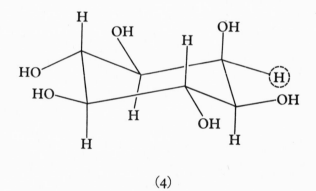

(4)

(5)

conformational analysis has led to the rule that only axial hydroxyl groups are oxidized by *Acetobacter suboxydans*, and the minimum requirements for oxidation seem to be the presence of the groups shown in (6).† The carbon atom bearing the axial hydroxyl group has an

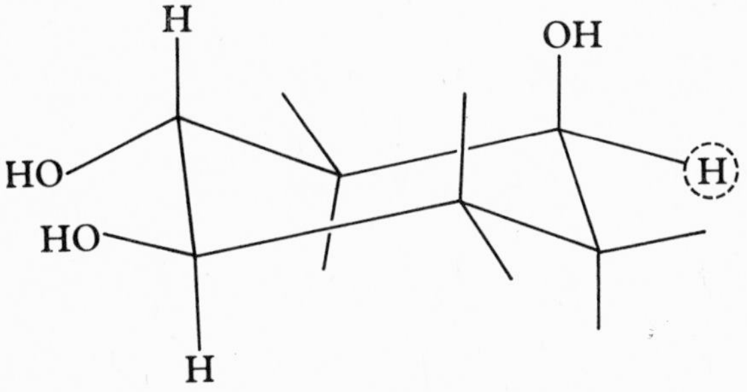

(6)

equatorial hydrogen atom, encircled in (4) and (6). Thus, the hydrogen atom attached to the carbon atom which has an axial group is actually the most exposed hydrogen atom, and it is presumably this factor which governs the selectivity of the enzymic reaction; the same feature has been observed in the (non-enzymic) oxidation of this and other alicyclic alcohols.

† Magasanik, in *Essays in Biochemistry*, p. 181, edited by Graff. John Wiley, 1956.

II

ORGANIC REACTIONS

1. Principles

(a) *Equilibria*. In a reversible chemical reaction† in solution

$$A+B \underset{k_{-1}}{\overset{k_1}{\rightleftarrows}} C+D \qquad [1]$$

a state is eventually reached at which if x molecules of A and B react in a minute to form C and D, the same number, x, molecules of C and D also react to form A and B. The reaction has then reached equilibrium, and no further net reaction occurs. So the concentrations of A, B, C, and D do not change with time; this may be expressed in the following equation:

$$-\frac{d[A]}{dt} = -\frac{d[B]}{dt} = \frac{d[C]}{dt} = \frac{d[D]}{dt} = 0. \qquad [2]$$

In this equation the symbols $[A]$, $[B]$, $[C]$, and $[D]$ stand for the concentrations of these species, and t is the time (as A and B are decomposing, the gradient in the graph of A or B plotted against time is negative). Rates, it should be noted, are defined in terms of concentrations, not of amounts, so that the rate is independent of the scale on which the reaction is being carried out.

Now chemical reactions (apart from photochemical reactions) are a consequence of molecular collisions. The frequency of collisions between molecules of A and molecules of B will be proportional to $[A][B]$, so that the rate of change of the concentration of A, as a result of reaction [1] proceeding from left to right, is given by

$$-\frac{d\overrightarrow{[A]}}{dt} = k_1[A][B]. \qquad [3]$$

The proportionality constant, k_1, in equation [3] is known as the velocity constant, or rate constant; it is the value that the rate attains when the concentrations of both $[A]$ and $[B]$ are unity. Similarly, the rate of

† Unless otherwise stated, photochemical reactions and heterogeneous reactions are not being considered. Experimentally, photochemical reactions may be recognized simply, because they do not take place in the dark. Reactions in polar solvents normally take place in solution and not exclusively on the walls of the reaction vessel. Several of the generalizations in § 1 *b* do not apply to photochemical or to heterogeneous reactions.

change of the concentration of A as a result of reaction [1] proceeding from right to left is

$$\frac{\overleftarrow{d[A]}}{dt} = k_{-1}[C][D].$$

The net rate of change of the concentration of A is then

$$-\frac{d[A]}{dt} = k_1[A][B] - k_{-1}[C][D].$$

If the concentrations at equilibrium are written $[A]_e$, $[B]_e$, etc., then from equation [2]

$$k_1[A]_e[B]_e - k_{-1}[C]_e[D]_e = 0,$$

or

$$\frac{[C]_e[D]_e}{[A]_e[B]_e} = \frac{k_1}{k_{-1}}. \qquad [4]$$

If the equilibrium constant of reaction [1] is defined by

$$K = \frac{[C]_e[D]_e}{[A]_e[B]_e},$$

then

$$\frac{k_1}{k_{-1}} = K. \qquad [5]$$

Equation [5] shows the relation between the velocity constants and the equilibrium constant for a simple reaction. Both equilibrium and velocity 'constants' are only constant for a reaction at given temperature and in dilute solution in a given medium whose properties are not materially affected by the reaction taking place.

The simplest and most important example of equilibrium processes in organic chemistry are the proton transfers of acid-base equilibria.† We shall start by defining some of the terms that will be used. An acid is a species which tends to donate a proton, and a base is a species which tends to accept a proton. The formal equation representing these tendencies is then:

$$A \rightleftarrows B + H^+$$

Hence to every acid A there is a corresponding base B. It should be noted that, although A is necessarily more positive than B by one unit, the charge of A is not restricted. Thus the formate ion (2) is the base corresponding to formic acid (1),

$$\text{H.COOH} \rightleftarrows \text{H.COO}^- + \text{H}^+$$

$$(1) \qquad\qquad (2)$$

† Bell, *Acids and Bases*, Methuen, 1952.

and the dihydrogen phosphate ion (4) is not only the base corresponding to phosphoric acid (3),

$$H_3PO_4 \rightleftharpoons H_2PO_4^- + H^+$$

$$(3) \qquad\qquad (4)$$

but also the acid corresponding to the hydrogen phosphate ion (5).

$$H_2PO_4^- \rightleftharpoons HPO_4^= + H^+$$

$$(4) \qquad\qquad (5)$$

Bases (e.g. NH_3) are defined in terms of the corresponding acids (e.g. NH_4^+),

$$NH_4^+ \rightleftharpoons NH_3 + H^+$$

Although acids and bases can thus be defined independently of any solvent, these equations do not represent chemical reactions. Ionizations take place in solution, and the proton is invariably solvated. It is the solvent to which the acid tends to donate a proton, so that the ionization of formic acid in water must be written

$$H.COOH + H_2O \rightleftharpoons H.COO^- + H_3O^+$$

The water molecule is here acquiring a proton, and acting as a base. Water may also act as an acid, e.g. when acetate ion is the base:

$$Me.COO^- + H_2O \rightleftharpoons Me.COOH + OH^-$$

Here the water molecule transfers a proton to the acetate ion. The general equation, then, defining the behaviour of an acid in water is

$$A + H_2O \rightleftharpoons B + H_3O^+ \qquad\qquad [6]$$

The equilibrium constant for this reaction is

$$K_{eq} = \frac{[B][H_3O^+]}{[A][H_2O]}.$$

It is convenient to omit the term $[H_2O]$, which will be the same for all equilibria in dilute aqueous solutions, and to define the dissociation constant of the acid A in water as:

$$K = \frac{[B][H_3O^+]}{[A]}. \tag{7}$$

The stronger the acid A, the greater will be the extent of reaction [6] in the direction $A + H_2O \rightarrow B + H_3O^+$, and the larger the dissociation constant. In particular, if an acid is much stronger than H_3O^+ its dissociation constant will be much greater than unity, so that in effect the only acidic species in a solution of a strong acid (e.g. HCl) will be the hydrated proton, H_3O^+.

It is convenient to express the strengths of bases in terms of the dissociation constants of the corresponding acids; the same equations, of the type of equation [7], then serve for both acids and bases. Thus for ammonia in water:

$$NH_4^+ + H_2O \rightleftharpoons NH_3 + H_3O^+$$

and the dissociation constant is given by

$$K = \frac{[NH_3][H_3O^+]}{[NH_4^+]}.$$

In practice it is customary to replace the dissociation constant by the pK, where p$K = -\log_{10} K$ (cf. pH $= -\log_{10}[H^+]$). So for a base, the larger the value of the pK, the stronger the base. For an acid, the smaller the value of the pK, the stronger the acid, just as the lower the value of the pH, the more acid is the solution.

So far the only solvent mentioned has been water. But the strengths of acids and bases depend greatly on the solvent. Thus, the ionization of acetic acid in water,

$$Me . COOH + H_2O \rightleftharpoons Me . COO^- + H_3O^+,$$

is far from complete, and

$$K = \frac{[MeCOO^-][H_3O^+]}{[MeCOOH]} \ll 1.$$

But the ionization of acetic acid in the basic solvent, liquid ammonia,

$$\text{Me.COOH} + \text{NH}_3 \rightleftarrows \text{Me.COO}^- + \text{NH}_4^+,$$

is effectively complete, and

$$K = \frac{[\text{MeCOO}^-][\text{NH}_4^+]}{[\text{MeCOOH}]} \gg 1.$$

In general, acids are more highly ionized in a basic solvent, and bases are more highly ionized in an acidic solvent, e.g. acetic acid. In the extremely acidic solvent, sulphuric acid, acetic acid itself is a base:

$$\text{Me—C}\underset{\text{OH}}{\overset{\text{O}}{\Big\langle}} + \text{H}_2\text{SO}_4 \rightleftarrows \text{Me—C}\underset{\text{OH}}{\overset{\overset{+}{\text{OH}}}{\Big\langle}} + \text{HSO}_4^-$$

Many organic reactions are carried out in acid solution (i.e. are acid-catalysed) and *the first step in most such reactions is the transfer of a proton on to an oxygen (or nitrogen, or sulphur) atom of the reacting species.*

The equilibrium constant is related to the *standard* free energy change (ΔG^0)[†] for a reaction by the equation[‡]

$$\Delta G^0 = -RT \ln K. \tag{8}$$

In equation [8] R is the gas constant ($R = 1 \cdot 986$ cal deg^{-1} mol^{-1}) and T is the temperature, expressed in degrees absolute. The change in free energy in an actual case depends on the concentrations of the reactants and products; ΔG^0 is the free energy change, per mol converted, if the chemical species are present throughout in the same standard states used to specify K. The standard free energy change may be regarded as depending on two factors. One is the amount of heat given out $(-\Delta H^0)$ or taken up (ΔH^0) when the reaction is carried out under standard conditions; the other is the change in entropy (ΔS^0). These factors are related by the equation

$$\Delta G^0 = \Delta H^0 - T\Delta S^0. \tag{9}$$

From equations [8] and [9] we may write

$$K = e^{-\Delta H^0/RT} . e^{\Delta S^0/R}. \tag{10}$$

† See Everett, *An Introduction to the Study of Chemical Thermodynamics*, Longmans, 1959.

‡ ln K stands for the logarithm of K to the base e, and log K for the decadic logarithm.

Equation [10] shows that a reversible reaction,

$$\text{Me.COOH} + \text{H}_2\text{O} \rightleftharpoons \text{Me.COO}^- + \text{H}_3\text{O}^+,$$

will proceed to a greater extent the more exothermic (or the less endo-thermic) it is, and the greater the increase (or the smaller the decrease) in entropy. The entropy is a measure of the 'randomness' of a system. The ionization of acetic acid is attended by a decrease in entropy; this may be attributed to the solvation of the ions being formed. The solvation means that some water molecules have given up their relatively unconstrained, random, thermal motion in order to interact with the ions, and so the entropy change is negative.

The variation of the equilibrium constant with the temperature is given by

$$\frac{d}{dT}(\ln K) = \frac{\Delta H^0}{RT^2}. \qquad [11]$$

Hence the equilibrium constant may either increase or decrease with temperature: if the reaction is exothermic, the equilibrium constant is decreased by raising the temperature; if endothermic, increased.

(b) *Factors governing the rates of reactions.* When the velocity constant of a reaction is measured at different temperatures it is found, qualita-tively, that the velocity constant increases with the temperature, and quantitatively, that a straight line is usually obtained if the logarithm of the velocity constant (k) is plotted against the reciprocal of the abso-lute temperature (T) (Fig. 14).

Now, for two molecules to react with each other, they have to collide. The kinetic theory of gases leads to a value for the number of collisions between two molecules, but this value is some 10^{11} times larger than common values of the velocity constant k. So there are many collisions, but only a few lead to reaction. Moreover, the number of collisions does not increase with temperature nearly as rapidly as the velocity constant does. Only relatively few molecules at any one instant, then, seem to be reactive. It is reasonable to assume that the reactive molecules are those possessing exceptional amounts of energy, e.g. those moving most rapidly. On this assumption, the fraction of the molecules possessing energy greater than a certain amount (E) is, approximately, proportional to $e^{-E/RT}$, and so the velocity constant should also be proportional to $e^{-E/RT}$, i.e.

$$k = Ae^{-E/RT},$$

so that

$$\log k = \log A - \frac{E}{2 \cdot 3 RT}. \qquad [12]$$

The idea that chemical reactions are a consequence of collisions between molecules possessing exceptionally large energies thus leads to the linear relation between $\log k$ and $1/T$ which is observed. Equation [12], known as the Arrhenius equation, has one theoretical interpretation (and another

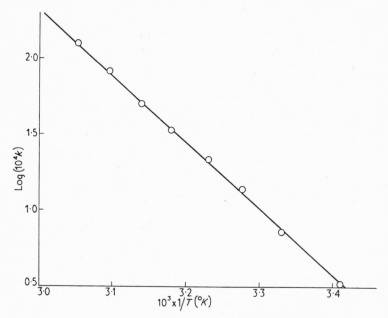

FIG. 14. Arrhenius plot for the reaction $CN^- + MeI \rightarrow MeCN + I^-$. (From the results of Marshall and Moelwyn-Hughes, *J. Chem. Soc.* 1959, p. 2640.)

is about to be given), but values for A (the frequency factor) and E (the energy of activation) quoted later are those derived from experimental measurement of the velocity constant at different temperatures. In a plot of $\log k$ against $1/T$ (Fig. 14) the gradient and the intercept give E and A. The parameter A in equation [12] is sometimes, but not always, of the same order of magnitude as the calculated collision number.†

The Arrhenius equation is also interpreted by the transition state theory, which throws light on how bonds are formed and broken in chemical reactions. By way of example, consider the reaction of chloride ion with methyl bromide, in acetone solution:

$$Cl^- + CH_3Br \rightleftharpoons CH_3Cl + Br^-$$

† Moelwyn-Hughes, *The Kinetics of Reactions in Solution*, Clarendon Press, Oxford, 1947; Frost and Pearson, *Kinetics and Mechanism*, Wiley, New York, 1953.

In this reaction a C—Br bond is broken and C—Cl bond is formed. Now there is an intermediate state, called the transition state, in which both halogens are partially bound to the carbon:

$$Cl^- + CH_3Br \rightleftharpoons [Cl\text{-----}CH_3^-\text{-----}Br] \rightleftharpoons ClCH_3 + Br^-$$
transition state

The transition state differs from an ordinary molecule in that there is one direction (here called the reaction path), the Cl—C—Br line, along which each vibration causes fission of the C$\cdots$Br partial bond. Hence the lifetime of the transition state is of the order of 10^{-14} sec, which is much shorter than the usual time interval between collisions. Any ordinary molecule may have the choice of reacting in two ways, according to which of two species it collides with; but a species in the transition state will decompose too rapidly to be able to avail itself of such a choice. This 'choice of reaction' criterion is the most powerful method of distinguishing between an ordinary molecular species and a species in the transition state. The transition state, in fact, represents a free energy barrier, and once this has been surmounted, no additional free energy is required. The height of this barrier, the excess of free energy of the transition state over that of the initial species, is called the free energy of activation, and is denoted by $\overrightarrow{\Delta G^\ddagger}$. Starred symbols refer to the properties of the transition state, and the arrow stresses the point that the height of the barrier is sufficient to characterize the rate of the reaction proceeding from left to right. Similarly, in the reverse direction (the reaction of bromide ion with methyl chloride) the rate is only governed by $\overleftarrow{\Delta G^\ddagger}$. The situation may be depicted as in Fig. 15.

The transition-state theory views rates as closely related to equilibria, and the difference between the free energies of activation in the forward and reverse directions is simply the free energy change during the reaction

$$\overrightarrow{\Delta G^\ddagger} - \overleftarrow{\Delta G^\ddagger} = \Delta G^0. \tag{13}$$

According to these ideas, then, the free energy of activation (or the height of the free energy barrier) governs the rate of a reaction. The results of experimental measurements are expressed by the velocity constant, k. The relation between the free energy of activation and the velocity constant is of the form:

$$k = Be^{-\Delta G^\ddagger/RT}. \tag{14}$$

The parameter B has the same value for all reactions (at a given temperature) and will be mentioned again shortly. The relative rates of two reactions may thus be expressed:

$$\frac{k_1}{k_2} = e^{-(\Delta G_1^{\ddagger} - \Delta G_2^{\ddagger})/RT}$$

or

$$\log(k_1/k_2) = -\frac{(\Delta G_1^{\ddagger} - \Delta G_2^{\ddagger})}{2 \cdot 3 RT}. \qquad [15]$$

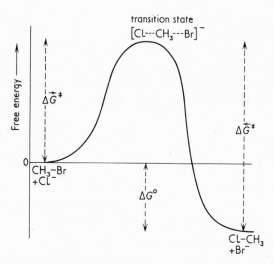

FIG. 15. Change of free energy in the reaction $Cl^- + CH_3 . Br \rightarrow CH_3Cl + Br^-$. The initial system is taken as the origin. The free energy of the final system is obtained from the equilibrium constant, and that of the transition state from the velocity constant. No other values are experimentally accessible, so the precise shape of the curve is unknown.

As we shall be more often concerned with the relative rate of two (related) reactions than with the absolute rate of either, equation [15], which enables us to find the *difference* between the free energies of activation, usually suffices. The value of $2 \cdot 3RT$ at ordinary temperatures is approximately $1 \cdot 4 \, \text{kcal/mol}$. Hence a difference of $1 \cdot 4 \, \text{kcal/mol}$ between the free energies of activation of two reactions corresponds to a tenfold ratio of velocity constants. It will be recalled that the magnitude of covalent bond energies is around $50 \, \text{kcal/mol}$ (Chapter I, § 2 c), and of hydrogen bonds around $5 \, \text{kcal/mol}$. Thus a relatively small change in energy may affect the rates of reactions markedly.

If the two reactions in equation [15] are the forward and reverse steps in a reversible change, equations [13] and [15] give

$$\frac{k_1}{k_{-1}} = e^{-(\overrightarrow{\Delta G^{\ddagger}} - \overleftarrow{\Delta G^{\ddagger}})/RT} = e^{-\Delta G^0/RT}.$$

But, from equation [8], $e^{-\Delta G^0/RT}$ is the equilibrium constant, K, and so the present treatment of rates in terms of free energy barriers also shows that the ratio of the velocity constants in the forward and reverse directions is the equilibrium constant (equation [5]).

The value of the parameter B in the equation [14] for the velocity constant is given by the transition-state theory† as $\mathbf{k}T/h$, where $\mathbf{k}$ is Boltzmann's constant, and h is Planck's constant. Hence, by the use of equation [14], the free energy barrier may be obtained from the measured velocity constant. Moreover, the free energy of activation may be regarded as made up of a heat of activation ($\Delta H^\ddagger$) and an entropy of activation (ΔS^*) (cf. equation [9]):

$$\Delta G^\ddagger = \Delta H^\ddagger - T\Delta S^\ddagger, \qquad [16]$$

and so equation [14] may now be written (cf. equation [10]):

$$k = Be^{-\Delta H^\ddagger/RT} \cdot e^{\Delta S^\ddagger/R}. \qquad [17]$$

Here the heat of activation, $\Delta H^\ddagger$, corresponds approximately to the initial kinetic energy which colliding molecules have to possess in order to react.

The chief value of the transition-state theory in organic chemistry is the picture it gives of how a reaction takes place. Most discussions of the mechanisms of organic reactions are thus presented in terms of the transition-state theory. *Indeed, the attempt to find a mechanism of a given reaction is essentially an attempt to define the one or more transition states between the starting material and the products.*

It may be noted that for a reaction between two molecules the greatest possible rate is given simply by the number of collisions in unit time; the rate of the reaction is then limited by diffusion. This upper limit of the velocity constant is of the order of 10^{12} litre mol^{-1} sec^{-1}.

Perhaps the fastest bimolecular reaction in solution is

$$H_3O^+ + OH^- \longrightarrow 2H_2O;$$

the velocity constant is $1 \cdot 3 \times 10^{11}$ l. mol^{-1} sec^{-1} at 20° C. Other reactions of the type

$$H_3O^+ + \text{base} \longrightarrow \text{acid} + H_2O,$$

when the proton is being transferred from the H_3O^+ to an oxygen or

† Glasstone, Laidler, and Eyring, *Theory of Rate Processes*, McGraw-Hill, 1941.

nitrogen atom (see § 1 e), are nearly as fast, i.e. are controlled by diffusion.†

(c) *Principle of microscopic reversibility.* The application of this general principle to a chemical reaction is as follows. If the reaction can take place by several paths (e.g. enzymic and non-enzymic), then at equilibrium the number of molecules of product (B) formed from A in a given time by each route must be the same as the number of molecules of A formed from B by the reverse of each route:

$$A \underset{k_{-1}}{\overset{k_1}{\rightleftharpoons}} B$$

$$A + E \underset{k_{-2}}{\overset{k_2}{\rightleftharpoons}} X \underset{k_{-3}}{\overset{k_3}{\rightleftharpoons}} B + E$$

whence

$$\frac{k_1}{k_{-1}} = \frac{k_2 k_3}{k_{-2} k_{-3}} = K.$$

This result emphasizes the point that the position of equilibrium is unaffected by the mechanism of the reaction, a conclusion that also follows from the fact that the change in free energy (and hence the equilibrium constant) depends only on the initial and final states.

The principle of microscopic reversibility can be applied to the mechanisms of forward and back reactions. This is often very useful (see, for example, Chapter IV, § 3 c; Chapter V, § 7 c). If, under one set of conditions, the conversion of A to B proceeds exclusively by the catalysed mechanism (via X) and not by the direct mechanism, then the reverse reaction of B to A will also proceed by X. This is reasonable on the basis of the transition state theory: the path shown in Fig. 15 will hold in whichever direction the reaction is proceeding, and the transition state is the same from whichever side it is approached. Thus, in general, if the conditions are the same, the mechanism of the forward and back reactions are the same.

The principle of microscopic reversibility does not apply to photochemical reactions, such as the addition of bromine to an ethylenic double bond, which may be promoted by light. Bromine absorbs light, and the amount of energy in a quantum of visible light (of the order of 70 kcal/mol) is such that the excited bromine molecule, whose electrons are no longer in the lowest electronic level, may dissociate into bromine atoms, which fly apart. The transformation of radiant energy into kinetic energy is irreversible, so that the reverse step takes place by a

† Bell, *Quart. Rev.* 1959, **13**, 169.

different mechanism: the bromine atoms combine by thermal collision, without emission of light.

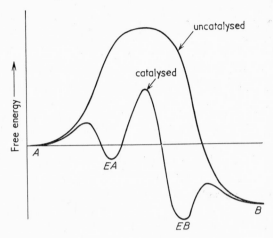

FIG. 16. Comparison of free energy changes in a catalysed and an uncatalysed reaction.

(d) *Rates and equilibria*. The transition-state theory suggests a possible parallelism between rates and equilibria, and indeed this is one of its most important consequences. A parallelism of this kind between two reactions is, in fact, sometimes encountered, and an example of a correlation between relative rates of hydrolysis and equilibria in ionization is given later (§ 2 e). There may, however, be a different kind of interplay between rates and equilibria. In one reaction, either kinetic or thermodynamic factors may sometimes decide the outcome. The product that is formed most rapidly may be less (thermodynamically) stable than an alternative product. The composition of the mixture when the reaction is terminated (i.e. the reaction mixture is worked up) will then depend on whether the conditions are such as to permit equilibration (see Chapter IV, § 3 d).

(e) *Catalysis*. The phenomenon of catalysis provides the most striking example of the lack of parallelism between rates and equilibria, as a catalyst affects the rate but not the equilibrium. A comparison between a catalysed and an uncatalysed reaction (proceeding in a homogeneous solution) is illustrated in Fig. 16. Such a picture might apply to the reactions:

(i) uncatalysed: $A \rightleftharpoons B$

(ii) catalysed: $A + E \rightleftharpoons EA \rightleftharpoons EB \rightleftharpoons B + E$

The catalyst *takes part in the reaction*, but emerges unscathed. In fact, a catalyst does not so much aid a reaction as provide an easier alternative one. How it does so is at first sight obscure; after all, there are more stages in the catalysed reaction, and each step has to be more rapid, than in the uncatalysed one.

The two main factors which contribute to the height of the free energy barrier (i.e. which govern the rate) are the work that has to be done to bring two molecules close enough to react, and the work that has to be done in stretching the bond that is to be broken; the former is usually the more important. Now the most common type of catalysis in (ionic) organic reactions involves the transfer of a proton (acid-base catalysis). The work that has to be done to bring a proton close to another atom is relatively small, because the repulsion between two atoms is a consequence of forces exerted by the electrons in one atom on the electrons in the other atom, and the proton has no electrons. In general terms, then, acids and bases commonly act as catalysts because the proton transfer stage is often fast, and because the loss or gain of a proton is accompanied by a change in the structure of the substrate.

About enzymes as catalysts only a few tentative generalizations can be made at this stage. Several types of hydrolysis which are catalysed by enzymes are also catalysed by both acids and bases, and part of the effectiveness of enzymes as catalysts may be ascribed to their functioning as both acids and bases. In some cases the various stages in enzymic reactions have been disentangled: there is first a complex formed between the enzyme and the specific substrate; this is followed by the reaction proper, which leads to a molecule in which there is a covalent bond between the enzyme and the substrate; finally the free enzyme is liberated again. Examples of most of the main types of enzymic reactions are discussed in detail later.

2. Experimental methods of investigating reaction mechanisms

A stage has now been reached at which the status of reaction mechanisms in general can be discussed. A mechanism is a hypothesis about the course the reaction takes. One or more transition states (which can never be isolated) are described by the mechanism. If there is more than one transition state, then there is at least one intermediate, but these intermediates are usually too reactive to be isolated. In a sense, the mechanism sums up all the experimental work that has been done on the nature of the reaction, and often reveals further experiments that ought to be done. Inferences drawn from experiments are either consistent with a given mechanism (and thus, to a varying extent, confirm it), or they refute it: experiments are designed primarily to eliminate plausible alternatives. A mechanism can be tested, but it can never be proved.

(a) *Nature of intermediates and products.* An organic reaction that gives but one product is the welcome exception rather than the general rule. Hence the importance, and often the difficulty, of the first phase in the study of a reaction, the determination of the stoichiometric equation. If the product can exist in more than one stereoisomeric form the nature of the product may be particularly revealing. For example, the hydrolysis of an optically active halide may give the racemic alcohol, and this is an important clue to the mechanism of the hydrolysis (Chapter III, § 2 a). Conversely, the retention of optical activity in the migrating group in the Hofmann degradation is one of the observations on which the mechanism is based (Chapter VIII, § 3 a). Many other examples of the usefulness of stereochemical information will be encountered later; moreover, a knowledge of which reactions are stereospecific has proved extremely useful in organic synthesis. Inferences from stereochemical observations are also proving valuable in the study of enzymic reactions (e.g. aldolase, Chapter V, § 9).

Sometimes a suspected intermediate may be isolated; alternatively, the possible intermediate may be prepared independently and studied. As usual, negative evidence is the most clear-cut; what was thought to be an intermediate may turn out to be too unreactive to fulfil the role.

An intermediate, although too unstable to be isolated, may sometimes be detected by its physical (or, less often, chemical) properties. A coloured intermediate is easy to observe. During the oxidation of thiols to disulphides, in the presence of metals, the solution is often intensely coloured, and the intensity of the colour has been used to assess the concentration of the reactive intermediate.†

An intermediate may also be detected by a change in the ultra-violet or infra-red absorption spectrum during the reaction, and free radicals may be detected by electron resonance spectroscopy.‡

The chemical detection of unstable intermediates depends on their high reactivity. For example, the enols formed on decarboxylation of β-keto acids have been trapped by reaction with iodine (Chapter VII, § 2 a) and free radicals may be detected by their ability to initiate the polymerization of vinyl compounds (Chapter X, § 1 a).

† Lamfrom and Nielsen, *J. Amer. Chem. Soc.* 1957, **79**, 1966.
‡ Whiffen, *Quart. Rev.* 1958, **12**, 250.

(*b*) *The kinetic equation.* The importance of the kinetic equation as a guide to the mechanism of a reaction is well illustrated by the classical work of Lapworth on the bromination of acetone.† The reaction of bromine with acetone was shown to give bromoacetone, and the stoicheiometric equation is

$$Br_2 + CH_3.CO.CH_3 \longrightarrow CH_3.CO.CH_2Br + HBr. \qquad [1]$$

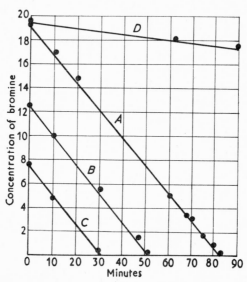

FIG. 17. Graph of the concentration of bromine plotted against time, in the reaction of bromine with acetone. (From Lapworth, *J. Chem. Soc.* 1904, **85**, 30.)

The reaction was very slow in dilute aqueous solution, but was hastened by acids. The experiments described below were therefore carried out in the presence of acid (0·4M H_2SO_4).

The reaction was followed by determining the amount of bromine remaining after various times: the initial concentration of acetone was considerably greater than the initial concentration of bromine, so that the concentration of acetone did not change appreciably during the course of the reaction. Fig. 17 shows the results of several different runs. The plots are linear, so that the rate of disappearance of bromine does not depend on the bromine concentration, which, of course, decreases during any one run. This point is also brought out by a comparison of three runs at different initial concentrations of bromine: the lines (*A, B, C*) are parallel, i.e. the rates are the same. Thus, for a fixed

† Lapworth, *J. Chem. Soc.* 1904, **85**, 30.

concentration of acetone and acid,

$$-\frac{d[\mathrm{Br_2}]}{dt} = k'. \qquad [2]$$

The upper line (D) in Fig. 17 shows the results of an experiment carried out at a lower initial concentration of acetone. This change clearly *does* affect the rate. A series of experiments (still at the same concentration of acid) showed that the rate was proportional to the concentration of acetone, i.e.

$$-\frac{d[\mathrm{Br_2}]}{dt} = k''[\mathrm{CH_3COCH_3}]. \qquad [3]$$

Finally, the acid concentration was varied: the rate was measured at a fixed initial concentration of acetone, and various concentrations of sulphuric acid. The rate was found to be proportional to the concentration of acid so that, as the acid is completely ionized, we may write

$$-\frac{d[\mathrm{Br_2}]}{dt} = k'''[\mathrm{H^+}]. \qquad [4]$$

The partial equations [2], [3], and [4] may now be combined to give the complete kinetic equation, which shows how the rate is affected by the concentrations of all three species (acetone, bromine, and acid):

$$-\frac{d[\mathrm{Br_2}]}{dt} = k[\mathrm{CH_3COCH_3}][\mathrm{H^+}]. \qquad [5]$$

The bromination of acetone is then described as being first-order with respect to acetone, first-order with respect to hydrogen ion, and zero-order with respect to bromine, as the powers to which the concentrations of these three species are raised in equation [5] are one (acetone), one (hydrogen ion), and zero (bromine).

The interpretation of the kinetic equation proceeds as follows. The bromination is zero-order with respect to bromine, so that the mechanism must consist of at least two stages, one of which does not involve bromine; moreover, the stage in which bromine *is* involved must be relatively rapid. Lapworth suggested that the enol might be an intermediate, so that, in outline, the mechanism would then be:

$$\text{acetone} \xrightarrow[\text{slow}]{\mathrm{H^+}} \text{enol} \xrightarrow[\text{fast}]{\mathrm{Br_2}} \text{bromoacetone}$$

A mechanism along these lines can be seen to account for the results shown in Fig. 17: the rate-determining step is formation of the enol; bromine is not involved in this step.

We must now put forward a definite mechanism, and show how to derive the kinetic equation from the mechanism, for comparison with the observed kinetic equation [5]. This mechanism must, of course, take into account the catalysis by acid. The following steps may be suggested:

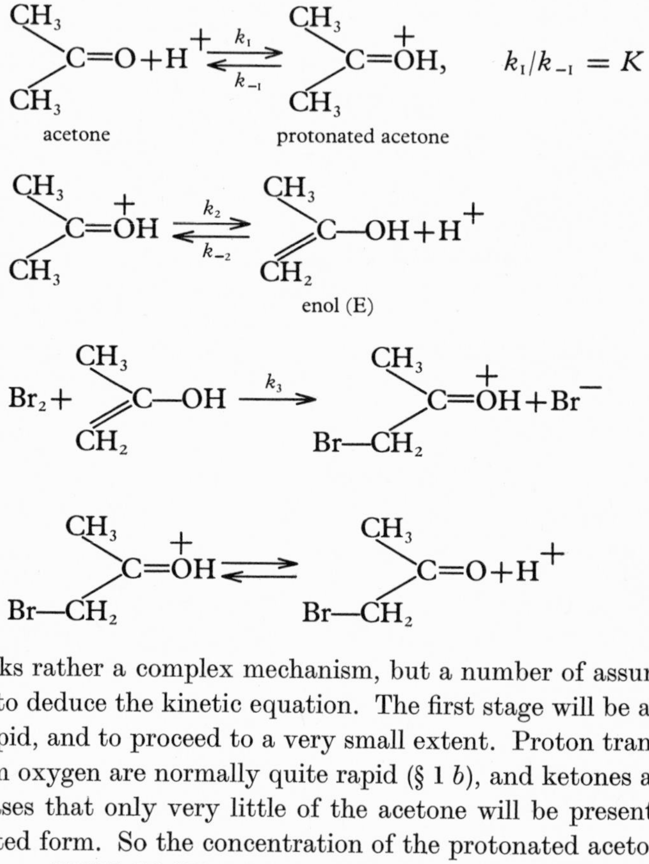

This looks rather a complex mechanism, but a number of assumptions help us to deduce the kinetic equation. The first stage will be assumed to be rapid, and to proceed to a very small extent. Proton transfers to and from oxygen are normally quite rapid (§ 1 b), and ketones are such weak bases that only very little of the acetone will be present in the protonated form. So the concentration of the protonated acetone may be taken as $K[CH_3COCH_3][H^+]$.

The main helpful assumption is the stationary-state approximation. This is applicable when an intermediate (here the enol, E) is very reactive. The concentration of the enol then remains low throughout the reaction, as, on the average, each molecule of enol is decomposed soon after it has been formed. The rate of change of the concentration of the enol is given by

$$\frac{d[E]}{dt} = Kk_2[H^+][\text{acetone}] - k_{-2}[E][H^+] - k_3[Br_2][E].$$

If the concentration of the enol is to remain low, its rates of formation and decomposition must nearly balance. The approximation, then, is to set $d[E]/dt$ equal to zero, which at once enables us to find $[E]$,

$$Kk_2[\text{H}^+][\text{acetone}] - k_{-2}[E][\text{H}^+] - k_3[\text{Br}_2][E] = 0,$$

therefore
$$[E] = \frac{Kk_2[\text{H}^+][\text{acetone}]}{k_{-2}[\text{H}^+] + k_3[\text{Br}_2]}. \qquad [6]$$

The reaction is followed by the disappearance of bromine, and the rate of this step is given by

$$-\frac{d[\text{Br}]}{dt} = k_3[\text{Br}_2][E]. \qquad [7]$$

The value of $[E]$, from equation [6], may be substituted into equation [7]:

$$-\frac{d[\text{Br}_2]}{dt} = \frac{Kk_2 k_3[\text{H}^+][\text{acetone}][\text{Br}_2]}{k_{-2}[\text{H}^+] + k_3[\text{Br}_2]}. \qquad [8]$$

We will now make another assumption, that the enol reacts much more rapidly with bromine than it reverts to the protonated ketone, i.e. that $k_{-2}[\text{H}^+] \ll k_3[\text{Br}_2]$, and so we drop the first term from the denominator in equation [8], and thus arrive at the final expression:

$$-\frac{d[\text{Br}_2]}{dt} = Kk_2[\text{H}^+][\text{acetone}],$$

which tallies with the kinetic equation [5] found by experiment. This constitutes powerful support for the mechanism. The methods used here to deduce a kinetic equation from a suggested mechanism will be found useful in many later chapters.

As already mentioned, the symbol H^+ is written for brevity; in aqueous solution the proton is solvated (i.e. present as H_3O^+), and the second and fourth steps in the mechanism probably involve a water molecule. On this basis, all the steps could be classed as bimolecular, but as it is difficult to determine the molecularity with respect to the solvent it is more convenient to omit the solvent in classifying the molecularity of a reaction.†

To summarize: the procedure in the use of kinetics to investigate mechanisms consists in: (a) determining the kinetic equation, (b) writing down a mechanism, (c) working out what kinetic equation is entailed by this mechanism, (d) comparing the observed and calculated kinetic equations.

† Unimolecular, bimolecular, and termolecular refer to the suggested mechanism, and describe the number of molecules (exclusive of solvent) which we think must collide for the reaction to occur; i.e. these terms specify the number of molecules in the transition state. The terms first-order, second-order, etc., on the other hand, refer to the observed kinetic equation. The term pseudo-unimolecular denotes a bimolecular reaction which has first-order kinetics, usually because excess of one of the reactants is present.

We can see rather more clearly the nature of the stationary-state approximation by considering an example that can be solved formally. For this purpose, two successive first-order reactions will be taken:

$$A \xrightarrow{k_1} X$$

$$X \xrightarrow{k_2} C$$

The differential equations are:

$$-d[A]/dt = k_1[A],$$
$$d[X]/dt = k_1[A] - k_2[X].$$

If the concentration of A at the start of the reaction is A_0, and the concentrations of X and C are zero, the solutions are

$$A = A_0 e^{-k_1 t}, \tag{9}$$

$$X = \frac{A_0 k_1}{k_2 - k_1} (e^{-k_1 t} - e^{-k_2 t}), \tag{10}$$

and
$$C = A_0 \left\{ 1 + \frac{1}{k_1 - k_2} (k_2 e^{-k_1 t} - k_1 e^{-k_2 t}) \right\}. \tag{11}$$

Two examples of the variations of A, X, and C with time have been worked out, and are shown in Figs. 18 and 19.

In Fig. 18, where k_2 is only one-fifth as large as k_1, X builds up to a concentration of about two-thirds that of A, after about 15 minutes; the half-life of A is about 7 minutes. X is here a stable intermediate. In Fig. 19, k_2 is twenty times as large as k_1, and here X reaches its maximum concentration after less than a minute, and its concentration is never more than about 5 per cent. of that of A. Here X is an unstable intermediate, and the stationary-state approximation will be valid. If we use this approximation, we may obtain the expression given below:

$$d[X]/dt = k_1[A] - k_2[X] = 0,$$

$$[X] = \frac{k_1[A]_0}{k_2} e^{-k_1 t}. \tag{12}$$

Now, by comparing the exact equation [10] and the approximation [12], we can see just what we are doing in using the steady-state approximation. And it will be seen that equation [10] reduces to equation [12] if $k_2 \gg k_1$, and if $t \gg 1/k_2$. By differentiation of equation [10] it can also be seen that X reaches its maximum value at a time

$$t_{max} = \frac{1}{k_2 - k_1} \ln \frac{k_2}{k_1}.$$

When $k_2/k_1 = 20$, as in Fig. 19, the induction period is quite short and the steady-state approximation is satisfactory. Conversely, special methods have to be used to follow the initial, pre-steady-state, phase of such reactions.

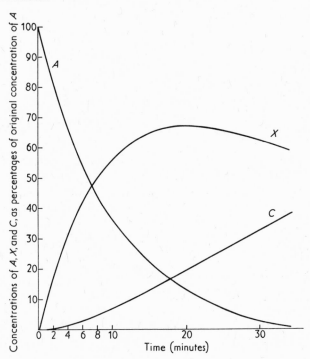

FIG. 18. Variation of the concentrations of the three species with time in the reaction $A \xrightarrow{k_1} X \xrightarrow{k_2} C$, when $k_1 = 0{\cdot}1$ min^{-1} and $k_2 = 0{\cdot}02$ min^{-1}.

(c) *Variation of observed velocity constant with temperature.* The suggested mechanism of a reaction tends to be based on the simplest interpretation of the evidence from kinetics. The variation of the observed velocity constant (k_{obs}) with temperature sometimes reveals the inadequacy of the simplest mechanism. The true velocity constant varies with temperature in the way shown in Fig. 14 (p. 52). Sometimes, however, a plot of $\log(k_{obs})$ against $1/T$ is somewhat curved (concave upwards) as shown in Fig. 20, consisting more or less of two intersecting straight lines.

If there are two competing reactions, the observed velocity constant, in the simplest case, will be the sum of two true velocity constants:

$$k_{obs} = k_I + k_{II}.$$

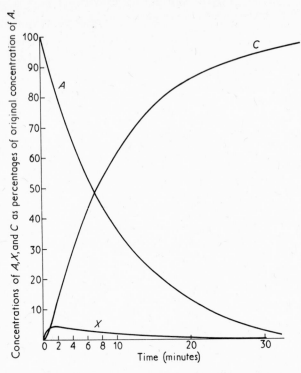

FIG. 19. Variation of the concentrations of the three species with time in the reaction $A \xrightarrow{k_1} X \xrightarrow{k_2} C$, when $k_1 = 0 \cdot 1$ min^{-1} and $k_2 = 2$ min^{-1}.

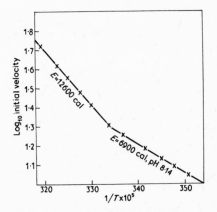

FIG. 20. Arrhenius plot for the enzyme-catalysed conversion of fumaric acid into malic acid. (From Massey, *Biochem. J.* 1953, **53**, 72.)

The Arrhenius equations for k_I and k_{II} may be written:

$$k_I = A_I e^{-E_I/RT}, \qquad k_{II} = A_{II} e^{-E_{II}/RT}.$$

Now it quite often happens that the parameters A and E both increase (or decrease) in related reactions;† thus suppose in our example that $A_I > A_{II}$, then $E_I > E_{II}$. If so, then at low temperatures $k_I \gg k_{II}$, and at high temperatures $k_I \ll k_{II}$. The energy of activation often controls the rate, and the situation is then like that on the right-hand side of the figure, with k_I predominating. If we call the reaction whose velocity constant is k_I the main reaction, then the proportion of by-products will increase with increasing temperature, as is often observed. The two lines intersect at a temperature

$$T = (E_I - E_{II})/2 \cdot 3 R \log(A_I/A_{II}).$$

The opposite type of curvature (i.e. concave downwards) in a $\log k$–$1/T$ plot could arise when there are successive, rather than competing, reactions.‡ Both types of curvature have been encountered in enzymic reactions.§

A more striking indication of a complex reaction is when the rate decreases with increasing temperature. This can be accounted for by supposing that the observed velocity constant is a composite function of a true velocity constant and an equilibrium constant; the equilibrium constant (K) must then decrease with temperature more rapidly than the velocity constant increases with temperature. If the reaction whose stoicheiometric equation was

$$A \longrightarrow B$$

gave an observed first-order constant which decreased with temperature, then a simple possible mechanism might be

$$A \rightleftharpoons X$$

$$X \longrightarrow B$$

If the equilibrium is rapidly established, and effectively maintained,

$$[X] = K[A]$$

and so $\qquad\qquad d[B]/dt = kK[A].$

---

† For a discussion of this tendency, see Blackadder and Hinshelwood, *J. Chem. Soc.* 1958, p. 2728; Leffler, *J. Org. Chem.* 1955, **20**, 1202.

‡ Christiansen, *Adv. Catalysis*, 1953, **5**, 311.

§ Dixon and Webb, *Enzymes*, p. 163, Longmans, Green, 1958; Koshland, *J. Cell Comp. Physiol.* 1959, **54**, suppl. 1, p. 245.

This type of behaviour has been observed in the polymerization leading to certain polypeptides.†

(d) *Variation of rate with environment*. The variation of the rate with the acidity of the medium is often one of the most useful procedures in the investigation of the mechanisms of reactions. The rate may be relatively high in acid and alkaline solution and low in neutral solution (e.g. the hydrolysis of carboxylic esters), or there may be a pH optimum (e.g. hydrolysis of phosphoric esters). In acid-catalysed reactions the variation of the rate with pH has been used to find out whether a solvent molecule should be formulated in the transition state. This method is not discussed here, as there is considerable doubt whether it is reliable.‡

The effect of the polarity of the medium on ionic reactions may be summarized as follows. Work has to be done to separate unlike charges, or to bring nearer together like charges. This work is lessened if the medium is made more effective at interacting with the ions; this may result from changing the solvent, or from raising the total concentration of ions in the solution. So a reaction between oppositely charged ions,

$$Cl^- + Me{-}\overset{+}{S}Me_2 \longrightarrow MeCl + Me_2S, \qquad [13]$$

will proceed more rapidly in a less polar medium, and one way of decreasing the polarity is to lower the concentration of ions. As reaction [13] proceeds the ionic concentration is lowered (since the reactants are charged but the products are not) and so the observed velocity constant increases during the reaction.§ This can be avoided by carrying out the reaction in the presence of sufficient added salts (which must be chosen so that they do not take part in the reaction) to keep the ionic concentration effectively constant.

(e) *Variation of rate with structure of the reactant*. The relation between structure and reactivity is a large subject, and what follows is only an introductory sketch. When the values of ionization constants of various *meta*- and *para*-substituted benzoic acids‖ (Table 8) are examined, some of the compounds are seen to be stronger acids than benzoic acid itself, and some weaker. This can be expressed numerically by the difference in the pK values, or, what is arithmetically the same, by the logarithm

† Waley and Watson, *Proc. Roy. Soc.* A, 1949, **199**, 499; Ballard and Bamford, ibid. 1954, **223**, 495.

‡ Long, *Proc. Chem. Soc.* 1957, 220; Whalley, *Trans. Faraday Soc.* 1959, **55**, 799; Koskikallio and Whalley, ibid., p. 815; Archer and Bell, *J. Chem. Soc.* 1959, 3228.

§ Swain and Kaiser, *J. Amer. Chem. Soc.* 1958, **80**, 4089.

‖ McDaniel and Brown, *J. Org. Chem.* 1958, **23**, 420.

TABLE 8

Compound	pK	Compound	pK
p-Aminobenzoic acid	4·86	p-Chlorobenzoic acid	3·97
p-Methoxybenzoic acid	4·47	m-Chlorobenzoic acid	3·83
p-Toluic acid	4·37	m-Cyanobenzoic acid	3·64
m-Toluic acid	4·27	p-Cyanobenzoic acid	3·54
Benzoic acid	4·20	m-Nitrobenzoic acid	3·49
m-Methoxybenzoic acid	4·08	p-Nitrobenzoic acid	3·42

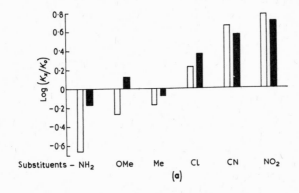

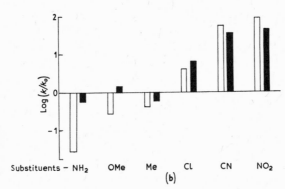

FIG. 21. Comparison of the effects of the substituents on the ionization
of an acid and on the rate of hydrolysis of its ethyl ester.

(a) Ionization of substituted benzoic acids.
      □ para-substituted   ■ meta-substituted

(b) Relative rates of alkaline hydrolysis of esters of substituted benzoic acids.
      □ para-substituted   ■ meta-substituted

of the ratio of the ionization constants. The extent to which a substituent
(X) affects the ionization constant is then assessed by $\log(K_x/K_0)$, where
K_x is the ionization constant of the particular substituted benzoic acid
and K_0 is the ionization constant of benzoic acid under the same conditions. The values of $\log(K_x/K_0)$ are shown in Fig. 21 (a). Now we know
from the values of the dipole moments (Chapter I, § 2 a) just which

substituents are electron-repelling when attached to the benzene ring, and which are electron-attracting. And it appears that electron-attracting groups are acid-strengthening when attached to the benzene ring in the *para*-position; these groups stabilize the anion relative to the uncharged molecule.

The rates of some reactions can be treated similarly. Thus Fig. 21 (*b*) shows the values of the relative rates, expressed as $\log(k/k_0)$, for the alkaline hydrolysis of some *meta*- and *para*-substituted ethyl benzoates; here k is the velocity constant for the substituted ester, and k_0 that for ethyl benzoate itself. There is a clear parallelism between the values for the relative rates of reaction in Fig. 21 (*b*) and those for the relative extents of ionization in Fig. 21 (*a*). In fact, there is a simple proportionality, and so

$$\log(k/k_0) = \rho \log(K/K_0),$$

where ρ is a constant which, since the relation holds for any of the members of the series, must be the same for all of them. This constant (the reaction constant), ρ, depends on the nature of the reaction, and measures how susceptible the reaction is to the effect of changing the substituent; by convention, $\rho = 1$ for the ionization of benzoic acids. The term $\log(K/K_0)$, however, does not depend on the nature of the reaction, but only on the particular substituent: this term, then, is called the substituent constant, and is denoted by the symbol σ, and so we may now write

$$\log(k/k_0) = \rho\sigma.$$

This quantitative relation between structure and reactivity is often referred to as Hammett's equation.†

The next questions are, How widely does such a correlation hold, and how precise is it ? Hammett's equation, it turns out, holds to an average precision of about 15 per cent. for some 3,000 reactions. But these are 'side-chain' reactions of *m*- and *p*-substituted benzene derivatives of the type:

† Hammett, *Physical Organic Chemistry*, McGraw-Hill, New York, 1940; Jaffe, *Chem. Rev.* 1953, **53**, 191.

The variable substituent R is not near to the reaction centre, and so the size of the group R will not normally affect the rate of the reaction directly. That a bulky group close to the reaction centre may affect the rate (e.g. by interfering with the approach of the reagent in a bimolecular reaction) is reasonable, and has long been known under the name of steric hindrance. The effect of structure upon reactivity in *meta*- or *para*-substituted benzene derivatives is simplified by the absence of steric effects and by the rigidity of the system.

From Fig. 21 (*b*), electron-withdrawing substituents aid alkaline hydrolysis of the benzoic ester (i.e. $\rho > 0$); this result will be discussed later when the mechanism of ester hydrolysis is being considered (Chapter VI, § 1 *c*); it is, in fact, one of the features of the reaction that any satisfactory mechanism has to account for.

Although Hammett's equation cannot be directly applied to the reactions of aliphatic compounds, Taft has worked out a procedure for disentangling polar and steric effects which has quite wide applicability; it would, however, take us too far afield to discuss this topic here.†

(*f*) *Use of isotopes.* The use of isotopes as tracers is one of the most powerful methods for exploring the mechanism of an organic reaction. An example is the pyrolysis of ethyl pyruvate to give ethyl acetate and carbon monoxide: the carbon monoxide has been shown to originate from the ethoxycarbonyl group, not from the keto group.‡

$$CH_3 - {}^{14}C - COOEt \xrightarrow{110°} CH_3 - {}^{14}C - OEt + CO$$
$$\underset{O}{\|} \qquad\qquad\qquad\qquad \underset{O}{\|}$$

Another example is provided by the hydrolysis of amyl acetate in water enriched in ${}^{18}O$: the amyl alcohol contained no excess of isotope, and so the position of fission is as shown:§

When isotopes are being used as tracers the results are interpreted on the assumption that replacement of an atom by its isotope will not affect the outcome of the reaction. Quantitatively, this assumption does not hold. Replacement of an atom by its heavier isotope generally

† Taft, in Newman, *Steric Effects in Organic Chemistry*, chap. 13, John Wiley, New York, 1956; Taft, Deno, and Skell, *Ann. Rev. Phys. Chem.* 1958, **9**, 287.
‡ Calvin and Lemmon, *J. Amer. Chem. Soc.* 1946, **69**, 1232.
§ Polanyi and Szabo, *Trans. Faraday Soc.* 1934, **30**, 508.

slows a reaction, if the bond to the atom is being broken in the rate-determining step. This effect (the kinetic isotope effect)† may be quite large: replacement of H by deuterium (D) may decrease the rate by a factor of about five, and replacement of H by tritium (T) by a factor of about twenty. The effect is much smaller with heavier atoms.

The kinetic isotope effect can be used to test whether a particular bond is broken in the rate-determining step; thus several benzene derivatives are nitrated at the same rate whether hydrogen or tritium is being replaced: the rate-determining step, it has been concluded, is not severance of the carbon-hydrogen bond‡ (Chapter IX, § 2 b).

It sometimes happens that replacement of H_2O by D_2O as solvent causes an increase in the overall rate. This can be explained by the existence of an equilibrium before the rate-determining step, so that the observed velocity constant is the product of a velocity constant and an equilibrium constant (as on p. 67). It is known from independent experiments (in the case of acid-catalysed reactions) that the change in equilibrium constant when H_2O is replaced by D_2O is such as to facilitate reaction.§

3. Classification of reactions and reagents

(a) *Types of bond-breaking.* A covalent bond between two atoms X and Y may be broken in two, formally distinct, ways. If the shared electrons which form the bond are represented by dots, then the alternatives may be written:

$$X:Y \rightarrow X:^- + Y^+, \quad \text{or} \quad X^+ + :Y^- \quad \text{Heterolysis}$$
$$X:Y \rightarrow X \cdot + \cdot Y \quad\quad\quad\quad\quad\quad\quad \text{Homolysis}$$

In heterolysis the bond breaks so that one or the other atom has both of the electrons which were formerly shared; in homolysis each atom has one of the two electrons. The direction of heterolysis is conveniently shown by a 'bent arrow':

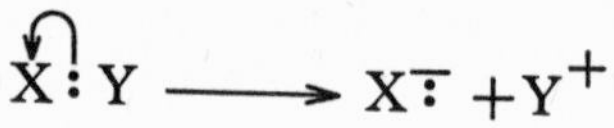

$$\overset{\curvearrowleft}{X} : Y \longrightarrow X \overline{:} + Y^+$$

For example, the ionization of acetic acid in water can be written as:

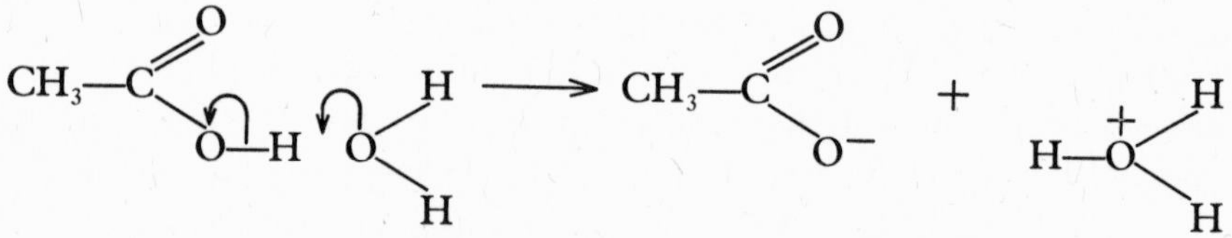

† Wiberg, *Chem. Rev.* 1955, **55**, 713.
‡ Melander, *Arkiv Kemi*, 1950, **2**, 213; Zollinger, *Experientia*, 1956, **12**, 165.
§ Bell, *Acid-Base Catalysis*, Clarendon Press, Oxford, 1941.

and the reverse reaction as:

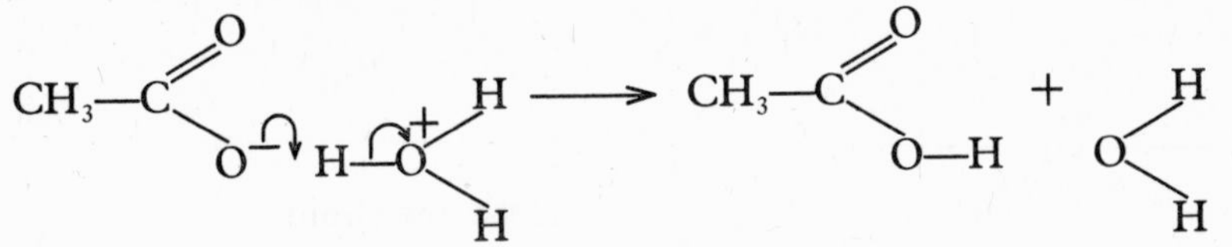

The difficulty that is sometimes experienced in the use of the bent arrow (which is often due to the fact that unshared electrons are not shown in structural formulae) can be resolved if the valency electrons are written as dots:

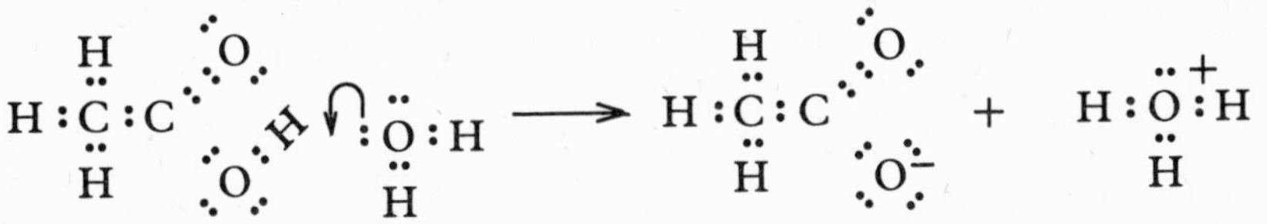

If the electrons are counted, the signs of the charges can easily be found (Chapter I, § 1 e, p. 7).

Homolysis necessarily leads to the formation of species with unpaired electrons: these (in organic chemistry) are called free radicals, and homolytic reactions are often referred to as free radical reactions. Although the distinction between homolysis and heterolysis refers to the mechanism of the breaking of a bond, considered as an isolated stage, in practice all the stages of a reaction are nearly always either homolytic or heterolytic. This is because the bimolecular reaction of a free radical with a species which is not a free radical yields another free radical. Thus, the reaction whose stoicheiometric equation is

$$X:Y + P:Q \rightarrow X:P + Q:Y$$

might proceed by the stages:

$$X:Y \rightarrow X\cdot + \cdot Y$$
$$X\cdot + P:Q \rightarrow X:P + \cdot Q$$
$$Q\cdot + \cdot Y \rightarrow Q:Y$$

In the second stage one free radical ($X\cdot$) disappears, and another ($Q\cdot$) is formed. In a few cases (particularly rearrangements) the attempt to make the distinction between homolytic and heterolytic reactions becomes unprofitable.

Experimentally, free-radical reactions can often be recognized by such properties as their being initiated by other radicals (including oxygen), or by light, or by being greatly retarded by traces of inhibitors. In heterolytic reactions the net charge of one of the products is decreased by one unit, and of the other increased by the same amount, and so these reactions are often called polar or ionic reactions. The presence of ions as reactants or products is not adequate as a basis for classifying the mechanism, as free radicals may be ions (e.g. $Me_2\dot{C}$—O^-): it is the presence of unpaired electrons which is the criterion for homolysis. Sometimes (but fortunately not very often) a reaction proceeds by a free-radical mechanism under one set of conditions and by a polar mechanism under another set of conditions (e.g. the addition of hydrogen bromide to olefines, Chapter IV).

(b) *Types of reaction.* It is convenient to classify organic reactions under four main headings:

(i) Substitution $A+B \rightarrow C+D$
(ii) Addition $A+B \rightarrow C$
(iii) Elimination $C \rightarrow A+B$
(iv) Rearrangement $A \rightarrow B$

The same sort of classification has been applied to enzymic reactions.† This division should be regarded as a helpful guide rather than as a rigid system.

(c) *Types of reagent.* The classification we are about to describe is concerned with heterolytic reactions. Consider the reaction of chloride ion with methyl bromide:

$$Cl^- + CH_3\!\!-\!\!Br \longrightarrow CH_3\!\!-\!\!Cl + Br^-$$

The bromine atom acquires unit negative charge (i.e. gains an electron) and departs with both of the electrons which once formed the bond with carbon. The chloride ion must then make up the deficiency: such reagents are called nucleophilic (or anionoid): they tend to donate electrons to another nucleus. All bases are nucleophilic species for the following reason. A base tends to combine with a proton,

$$H^+ + :NH_3 \longrightarrow NH_4^+,$$

here the ammonia donates electrons to the proton, and so ammonia is a nucleophilic reagent. Reducing agents are also nucleophilic,

$$6Fe^{++} + 6H^+ + PhNO_2 \longrightarrow 6Fe^{+++} + PhNH_2 + 2H_2O,$$

† Hoffmann-Ostenhof, *Adv. Enzymol.* 1952, **14**, 219.

as in a reduction-oxidation the reducing agent donates electrons to the oxidizing agent.

Conversely, reagents which tend to accept electrons are called electrophilic (or cationoid). Boric acid reacts as an (uncharged) electrophilic reagent when it combines with glycerol:

$$2 \begin{array}{l} CH_2OH \\ | \\ CHOH \\ | \\ CH_2OH \end{array} + B(OH)_3 \longrightarrow \begin{array}{l} CH_2OH \\ | \\ CH-O \\ | \\ CH_2-O \end{array} \overset{}{\underset{B}{}} \begin{array}{l} CH_2OH \\ | \\ O-CH \\ | \\ O-CH_2 \end{array}$$

$$+ H^+ + 3H_2O$$

The boron atom in boric acid, which is surrounded by only six valency electrons (Chapter I, § 1 e), accepts electrons and acquires a negative charge in this reaction, and thus the boron atom attains an 'inert gas' electronic configuration. Another example is the coupling reaction of a diazonium salt, which may be formally written

$$Ar.N \overset{+}{\equiv} N + Ar'-H \longrightarrow Ar.N = N.Ar' + H^+$$

Here the diazonium salt is an electrophilic reagent: it accepts both of the electrons of the Ar'—H bond, and the proton parts with none. Any acid XH is an electrophilic species because in liberating a proton it accepts both electrons of the X—H bond. And all oxidizing agents are electrophilic, e.g.

$$I_2 + 2R \cdot SH \longrightarrow R \cdot SS \cdot R + 2H^+ + 2I^-$$

The thiol is oxidized, and the iodine atoms have accepted electrons, acquired a negative charge, and become iodide ions.

As with acid-base, or reduction-oxidation, nucleophilic and electrophilic are 'reciprocal' terms: if one species donates electrons, the other member of the pair accepts them. So, if we are to combine our classification of reactions, and of reagents, we must make a conventional distinction between reagents and the substrates which are acted upon by reagents. Thus, in the first example cited in this section, methyl bromide is called the substrate, and the chloride ion is the reagent. The reaction is a substitution, and so it is a substitution by a nucleophilic reagent: the symbol S_N is often used for brevity.

The carbonyl group (as in ketones) and the ethylenic double bond (as in olefines) are the two most important substrates in addition reactions. It has long been known that most of the reagents which add to one do not add to the other. There is, of course, an obvious difference: the double bond in olefines unites two atoms of carbon, that in ketones unites an atom of carbon with one of oxygen. Now it turns out that the typical reagents for ketones belong to the nucleophilic class, and they react with the carbon atom. The polarization in a ketone can be shown as $\overset{\delta+}{C}=\overset{\delta-}{O}$ (Chapter I, § 2 a), and so the electron-donating nucleophilic reagent will become attached to the carbon atom. No comparable effect can be present in olefines, which may be symmetrical (e.g. ethylene).

Olefines react with electrophilic reagents: that is, olefines donate electrons to reagents which tend to accept them. As a result of donating electrons, the olefine acquires a partial positive charge. Since olefines do not react with most nucleophilic reagents, a carbon atom seems more reluctant to carry a negative charge than to carry a positive one. This conclusion, which is general and important, was seen clearly by Lapworth, some forty years ago, who correlated it with the observation of J. J. Thomson that only cations (and not anions) derived from hydrocarbons appear in vacuum tubes.

NUCLEOPHILIC SUBSTITUTION

1. Introduction

NUCLEOPHILIC substitution (or displacements) are of great importance in chemistry and biochemistry: they are of frequent occurrence, and more is known about the mechanism of these reactions than about other types of reactions. A few examples of nucleophilic substitution reactions are listed below:

$$EtO^- + CH_3\text{—}Br \longrightarrow CH_3OEt + Br^-$$

$$(CH_3)_3N + CH_3\text{—}I \longrightarrow (CH_3)_4N^+ + I^-$$

$$HO^- + CH_3\text{—}S^+(CH_3)_2 \longrightarrow CH_3OH + (CH_3)_2S$$

$$(EtOOC)_2CH^- + CH_3\text{—}Br \longrightarrow CH_3CH(COOEt)_2 + Br^-$$

$$HO^- + CH_3\text{—}N^+(CH_3)_3 \longrightarrow CH_3OH + (CH_3)_3N$$

In these examples carbon-nitrogen, carbon-oxygen, carbon-sulphur, or carbon-halogen bonds are broken. Reference to the table of bond dipole moments (Chapter I, § 2 a, Table 4) shows that in each case the moment is in the sense $\overset{\delta+}{C}\text{—}\overset{\delta-}{X}$, where X stands for a nitrogen, oxygen, sulphur, or halogen atom. Heterolysis of the C—X bond thus takes place in the sense C—X, i.e. the X atom departs with both of the electrons that formerly constituted the C—X bond; if the X atom bears a positive charge, this tendency will be enhanced. The carbon atom forms a new bond with a species that tends to donate electrons, i.e. a nucleophilic species. The nucleophilic species that we are concerned with here all contain an unshared pair of electrons. Many organic compounds contain carbon-nitrogen, carbon-oxygen, carbon-sulphur, or carbon-halogen bonds, and so nucleophilic substitutions are common.

In these reactions the carbon atom is breaking one bond and forming another one. We must now consider the timing of these events. If the old bond is broken before the new one is formed, the mechanism is called S_N1 (substitution, nucleophilic, unimolecular). If the new bond is being formed while the old bond is being broken, the mechanism is called S_N2 (*s*ubstitution, *n*ucleophilic, *b*imolecular).† The alternative mechanisms may be illustrated for the hydrolysis of methyl bromide (S_N2) and of tertiary butyl bromide (S_N1):

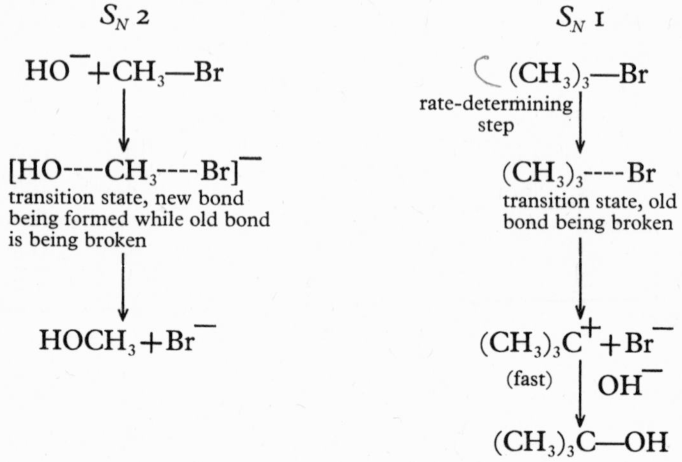

S_N2

$$HO^- + CH_3\!-\!Br$$

$$\downarrow$$

$$[HO\text{----}CH_3\text{----}Br]^-$$

transition state, new bond being formed while old bond is being broken

$$\downarrow$$

$$HOCH_3 + Br^-$$

$S_N\text{ I}$

$$(CH_3)_3\!-\!Br$$

rate-determining step $\downarrow$

$$(CH_3)_3\text{----}Br$$

transition state, old bond being broken

$$\downarrow$$

$$(CH_3)_3\overset{+}{C} + Br^-$$

(fast) $\Big|\ OH^-$

$$\downarrow$$

$$(CH_3)_3C\!-\!OH$$

Note that the transition state for the S_N2 mechanism contains *two* species (OH^- and CH_3Br) but that the transition state in the rate-determining step for the S_N1 mechanism contains only *one* species.

The evidence for these mechanisms comes partly from kinetics, and partly from stereochemistry. The stereochemical features are particularly clear-cut for reactions proceeding by the S_N2 mechanism, and so we start by discussing the stereochemical course of these reactions. The S_N1 mechanism introduces carbonium ions, which are intermediates in many important reactions. The reactions listed above are all nucleophilic displacements on carbon; many enzymic reactions are nucleophilic displacements on phosphorus, e.g.

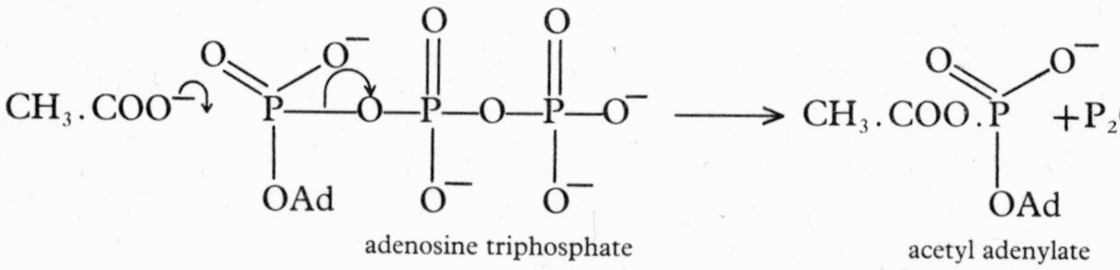

$$CH_3.COO^- \quad P\!-\!O\!-\!P\!-\!O\!-\!P\!-\!O^- \longrightarrow CH_3.COO.P \quad + P_2O_7^{4-}$$

adenosine triphosphate   acetyl adenylate

The next step‡ is a nucleophilic displacement on carbon:

† Hughes, *Trans. Faraday Soc.* 1941, **37**, 603; *Quart. Rev.* 1951, **5**, 245; Ingold, *Structure and Mechanism in Organic Chemistry*, chap. 7, Cornell University Press, 1953. Unless otherwise stated, the results are taken from the papers of Ingold, Hughes, and their collaborators.

‡ Both steps are catalysed by one enzyme, and the acetyl adenylate is probably an enzyme-bound intermediate. The thiol (coenzyme A) is shown as the anion, for convenience.

$$CoA.S^- \quad \overset{O}{\underset{|}{\overset{||}{C}}} - \overset{O}{\underset{|}{\overset{||}{O}}} - P - OAd \longrightarrow CoA.S - \overset{O}{\underset{|}{\overset{||}{C}}} + \bar{O} - \overset{O}{\underset{|}{\overset{||}{P}}} - OAd$$

acetyl adenylate　　　　　　　　　　　　　acetyl coenzyme A

(CoA.SH is coenzyme A)

Thus a sequence of two nucleophilic displacements converts acetate ions into the form in which they are metabolized.

2. $S_N 2$ mechanism

(a) *Walden inversion.* About sixty-five years ago Walden showed that an optically active compound could be converted into its enantiomer by a succession of reactions, e.g.

$$(-) \text{ malic acid } \xrightarrow{\text{PCl}_5} (+) \text{ chlorosuccinic acid } \xrightarrow[\text{Ag}_2\text{O}]{\text{H}_2\text{O}} (+) \text{ malic acid.}$$

The sign shown in brackets relates to the direction of the optical rotation measured with a polarimeter, but what we want to know is the configuration. The direction of rotation does not indicate the configuration, and so we cannot say whether the conversion of the laevorotatory ($-$) malic acid to dextrorotatory ($+$) chlorosuccinic acid has inverted the configuration, or whether the hydrolysis of the dextrorotatory chlorosuccinic acid, giving dextrorotatory malic acid, has inverted the configuration. The fact that the direction of rotation changes in the first stage, but not in the second, does not help us to decide at which stage (configurational) inversion has occurred. But the enantiomers, laevorotatory and dextrorotatory malic acids, must have opposite configurations. As there are only two stages in the interconversion, one stage must invert the configuration, and the other stage must leave it unchanged. The whole difficulty is to identify the stage at which inversion occurs. It is now known that the sequence of events is:†

$$
\begin{array}{ccccc}
\text{COOH} & & \text{COOH} & & \text{COOH} \\
| & & | & & | \\
\text{HO---C---H} & \xrightarrow{\text{PCl}_5} & \text{H---C---Cl} & \xrightarrow[\text{(Ag}_2\text{O)}]{\text{H}_2\text{O}} & \text{H---C---OH} \\
| & & | & & | \\
\text{CH}_2\text{COOH} & & \text{CH}_2\text{COOH} & & \text{CH}_2\text{COOH}
\end{array}
$$

† Thickened lines represent bonds projecting above the plane of the paper; dotted lines represent bonds projecting below this plane.

The first stage is a substitution in which the configuration of the asymmetric carbon atom is inverted: such a reaction is called a Walden inversion.

We will now consider another series of reactions in which a compound is converted into its enantiomer, and here the stage at which the Walden inversion occurs may be identified; the rotations are given below the formulae:

PhCH$_2$·CH·Me $\xrightarrow{\text{Me·C}_6\text{H}_4\text{·SO}_2\text{Cl}}$ PhCH$_2$·CH·Me

|

OH   O·SO$_2$·C$_6$H$_4$·Me

(1) $\alpha = +33°$ (2) $\alpha = +31°$

                                          $\downarrow$ Me·COO$^-$

PhCH$_2$·CH·Me $\xleftarrow{\text{OH}^-}$ PhCH$_2$·CH·Me

OH   O·COMe

(4) $\alpha = -32°$ (3) $\alpha = -7·1°$

The three stages convert the alcohol (1) into its enantiomer (4).[†] Hence an odd number of Walden inversions has been effected. Now the alcohol (1) owes its optical activity to the presence of an asymmetric carbon atom. A Walden inversion can only occur if one of the bonds formed by this carbon atom is broken. But the first stage, in which the alcohol is converted into its p-toluenesulphonate (2), is a nucleophilic displacement on sulphur and does not break the C—O bond. The last stage is the hydrolysis of a carboxylic ester, and here too none of the bonds to the asymmetric carbon atom are broken (Chapter VI, § 1 a). So this leaves the second stage; this is a nucleophilic displacement on carbon. Here, therefore, nucleophilic substitution leads to a Walden inversion. Study of other examples has shown this to be general: nucleophilic substitutions of this type ($S_N 2$ mechanism) are attended by inversion.

The connexion between inversion and substitution in these reactions has been securely established by kinetic studies. Optically active s-octyl iodide is racemized by iodide ions; this may be taken to be the result of successive, inverting substitution reactions:

† Phillips, *J. Chem. Soc.* 1923, **123**, 44.

$$\star I^- + C_6H_{13}\cdot \underset{\underset{I}{|}}{CH}\cdot Me \; \rightleftharpoons \; C_6H_{13}\cdot \underset{\underset{\star I}{|}}{CH}\cdot Me + I^-$$

When isotopically-labelled iodide ions ($\star I^-$) are used, the rate of the substitution reaction can be followed, and compared with the rate of inversion. Similarly, the rates of inversion and substitution have been compared in the reactions of bromide ion with α-phenylethylbromide, and with bromopropionic acid, and the results[†] show that each individual act of substitution causes inversion of configurations in these examples. The inversion is a consequence of the stereochemistry of the transition state. In the transition state five groups are clustered round the carbon atom, and stable species of this type (e.g. PCl_5) have the shape of trigonal bipyramids (5). In so far as the transition state may be regarded as a pentacovalent species, a trigonal bipyramid is the expected configuration.[‡] In other words, the reagent approaches the carbon atom from the side opposite to that of the group being displaced (rearward attack). The three other groups are forced back, until they are coplanar in the transition state. Finally, the leaving group is expelled, and the configuration of the carbon atom is inverted. This scheme is often likened to an umbrella being blown inside out in a gale, e.g.

$$HO^- + C_6H_{13}\cdot CHMe\cdot Br \rightarrow C_6H_{13}\cdot CHOH\cdot Me + Br^-$$

transition state
(5)

The general conclusion is that whenever a nucleophilic substitution proceeds through a transition state of the type shown ($S_N 2$ mechanism) the product will have the opposite configuration from the starting material, i.e. a Walden inversion occurs. The inversion is thus a consequence of the mechanism. So that if by other criteria (§ 3 d) we can

† Hughes, Juliusberger, Masterman, Topley, and Weiss, *J. Chem. Soc.* 1935, p. 1525; Hughes, Juliusberger, Scott, Topley, and Weiss, ibid. 1936, p. 1173; Cowdrey, Hughes, Nevell, and Wilson, ibid. 1938, p. 209.

‡ Cowdrey, Hughes, Ingold, Masterman, and Scott, ibid. 1937, p. 1252.

assign this $S_N 2$ mechanism to a given reaction we may assume that inversion occurs. This is a very important conclusion; it has been applied to enzymic reactions by Koshland (Chapter V, § 4).

(*b*) *Effect of structure on reactivity.* The displacement reaction may be written in the general form:

$$A + B\!\!-\!\!C \longrightarrow A\!\!-\!\!B + C$$

There are thus three groups to consider: the entering group (A), the departing group (C), and the group (B) on which displacement occurs. And the three groups fall into two classes: A and C either make or break bonds, but B does both. Hence the effect of structural variation on the reactivities of A and C is simpler than the effect of structural variation on the reactivity of B (compare Chapter II, § 1 *d*).

We shall consider first one aspect of the effect of the structure of the departing group on its reactivity. The charge of the group is an important factor. Alkyl bromides may be prepared from alcohols by the use of hydrobromic acid and concentrated sulphuric acid. The function of the acid is to protonate the alcohol, and it is the protonated alcohol which then reacts with bromide ion:

$$EtOH + H^+ \longrightarrow Et\overset{+}{O}H_2$$
$$Br^- + Et\overset{+}{O}H_2 \longrightarrow EtBr + H_2O$$

The bromide ion will not react with the alcohol itself; this would demand expulsion of the hydroxide ion, and the hydroxide ion cannot normally be displaced from carbon, although the neutral water can. The heterolysis in the sense $C\!\!-\!\!\overset{+}{O}H_2$ is greatly aided by the positive charge on the oxygen. There is an analogy here with the methyl group transfers in biological systems which take place with ammonium and sulphonium compounds (§ 6), by heterolysis in the sense $C\!\!-\!\!\overset{+}{N}\!\!<$, or $C\!\!-\!\!\overset{+}{S}\!\!<$.

We come now to the comparison of entering groups, i.e. the relative reactivities of nucleophilic reagents. The average relative rates for a number of displacements are given in Table 9; the least reactive ion, the nitrate ion, is taken as the standard.

It is interesting that the same order usually holds for the halogens, whether they are entering or leaving groups: in each case the largest ion is the most reactive. The figures in Table 9 also show that the mercaptide anion has the highest nucleophilic activity of any of the compounds

TABLE 9

Entering group	Logarithm of the relative rate
NO_3^-	0
$MeCO \cdot O^-$	1·3
Cl^-	1·9
PhO^-	2·6
Br^-	2·7
EtO^-	3·0
I^-	3·6
BuS^-	5·8

From Streitweiser, *Chem. Rev.* 1956, **56**, 571.

listed;† the alkoxide anion is less reactive, so that here, too, the larger anion is the more reactive. This effect has been attributed to the greater polarizability of the larger anions: in effect, this means that the electrons of the larger group (e.g. I^-) are more ready to change from being unshared (in the ion) to shared (in the molecule).

The effect of the structure of the alkyl group on the rate of nucleophilic substitutions proceeding by the $S_N 2$ mechanism will now be briefly discussed. Steric hindrance is the main topic here. In the $S_N 2$ mechanism there are five groups bonded to the central carbon atom in the transition state; if the alkyl groups are sufficiently bulky there will be congestion in the transition state.

The first example is the reaction of iodide ions with alkyl bromides; the solvent is acetone (Finkelstein reaction):

$$I^- + R\!-\!Br \longrightarrow R\!-\!I + Br^-$$

The alkyl group breaks a C—Br bond and forms a C—I one; in the transition state, the alkyl group is partially bound to each halogen atom. Two series of alkyl bromides have been studied: one in which the members differ in the number of α-methyl groups, and the other in which the members differ in the number of β-methyl groups. The rates in the first series follow the order:

| methyl bromide | ethyl bromide | isopropyl bromide | tertiary butyl bromide |
| MeBr | EtBr | Pr^{i}Br | Bu^{t}Br |

† The reaction of the SH groups in certain enzymes with alkyl halides (e.g. iodoacetamide) depends on the high nucleophilic reactivity of thiols; see Dixon and Webb, *Enzymes*, p. 377, Longmans, Green, 1958; Cecil and McPhee, *Adv. Protein Chem.* 1959, **14**, 255.

Each member reacts more rapidly than the next by a factor of 10^2 to 10^3. The last member of the series, as is true of tertiary alkyl compounds in general, tends to react by elimination rather than by substitution in bimolecular reactions (Chapter IV, § 1 e). The main cause of the drop in reactivity along the series is steric hindrance. Energy has to be expended to bring two non-bonded atoms into positions such that their distance apart is much less than the sum of their van der Waals radii. The sum of the van der Waals radii of an iodine atom and a methyl group is over 4 Å (Chapter I, § 2 b), and the iodide ion must approach to a distance of less than 3 Å from a methyl group to get to the transition state. In other words the hydrogen atoms in an α-methyl group will hinder the approach of the iodide ion.

$$I^- + \overset{H}{\underset{CH_3}{H{\Rightarrow}C}}{-}Br \longrightarrow \left[I{-}{-}{-}\overset{\overset{H}{\underset{|}{}}\overset{H}{\diagup}}{\underset{CH_3}{C}}{-}{-}{-}Br \right]^- \longrightarrow I{-}C{\overset{H}{\underset{CH_3}{\diagup}}} + Br^-$$

transition state

The members of the other series differ in the number of β-methyl groups; here, too, the rates drop along the series:

$$\overset{H}{\underset{H}{H{-}\overset{|}{C}{-}CH_2Br}} \sim \overset{H}{\underset{H}{CH_3{-}\overset{|}{C}{-}CH_2Br}} > \overset{H}{\underset{CH_3}{CH_3{-}\overset{|}{C}{-}CH_2Br}} \gg \overset{CH_3}{\underset{CH_3}{CH_3{-}\overset{|}{C}{-}CH_2Br}}$$

| ethyl bromide | n-propyl bromide | isobutyl bromide | neopentyl bromide |

In this series (in contradistinction to the earlier one) all the members are primary bromides. Neopentyl compounds are particularly unreactive in reactions proceeding by the $S_N 2$ mechanism; the β-methyl group hinders the approach of the nucleophilic reagent particularly effectively:

$$I^- + \quad \overset{H}{\underset{CH_3{-}\underset{CH_3}{\overset{|}{C}}{-}CH_3}{\overset{H}{\diagdown}C{-}Br}} \longrightarrow \left[\overset{H\quad H}{I{-}{-}\underset{\underset{CH_3\ CH_3}{\overset{|}{C}}}{C}{-}{-}{-}Br} \right]^- \longrightarrow I{-}\overset{H}{\underset{\underset{CH_3}{C}{\underset{CH_3}{\overset{C{-}CH_3}{}}}}{C}} + Br^-$$

transition state

A result of the steric hindrance in the reactions of neopentyl halides is that the iodide ion probably approaches somewhat obliquely, and not exactly along the C—Br axis; this conclusion is based on calculations of the factors contributing towards steric hindrance.†

The general conclusion reached about the reactivities of simple alkyl bromides in reactions proceeding by the $S_N 2$ mechanism is that compounds which are branched near to the reaction centre react less rapidly than straight-chain compounds. We now come to another effect. Unsaturation in the alkyl group of a primary halide markedly enhances the reactivity, when the multiple bond is in the β,γ-position. For example, in the reaction

$$I^- + R—Cl \longrightarrow RI + Cl^-$$

the sequence of reactivities is

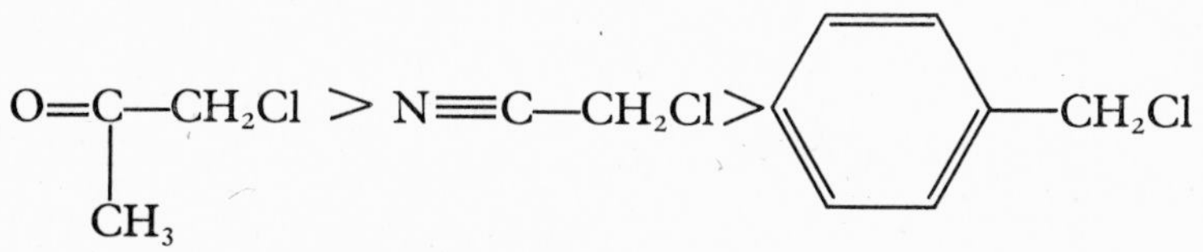

$$O{=}C—CH_2Cl \ > \ N{\equiv}C—CH_2Cl >$$

$$\underset{CH_3}{|}$$

chloroacetone   chloroacetonitrile   benzyl chloride

$$> \ CH_2{=}CH—CH_2Cl \ > \ CH_3CH_2Cl$$

allyl chloride   ethyl chloride

The causes of the enhanced reactivity of these unsaturated compounds are not well understood. One point is that multiple bonds contain π-electrons, which are relatively mobile and can thus accommodate themselves to the changes brought about in the formation of the transition state. In particular, the reactivity of chloro-acetone may be a result of partial conjugation of the carbonyl group in the transition state.‡

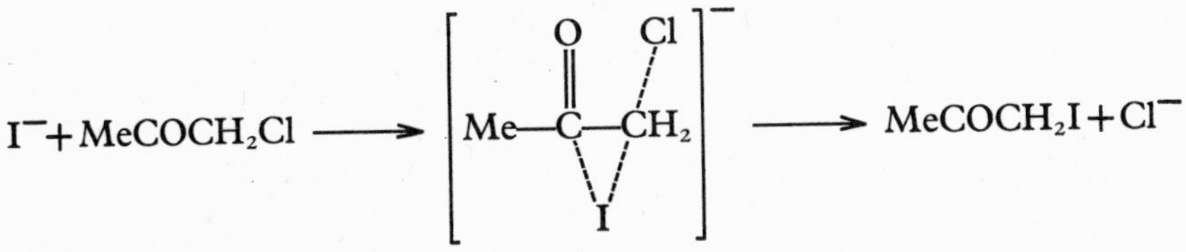

$$I^- + MeCOCH_2Cl \longrightarrow \left[Me—C—CH_2 \right]^- \longrightarrow MeCOCH_2I + Cl^-$$

† Ingold, *Quart. Rev.* 1957, **11**, 1.
‡ Bartlett and Trachtenberg, *J. Amer. Chem. Soc.* 1958, **80**, 5808.

The situation is quite different when the double bond is nearer to the reaction centre: vinyl chloride ($CH_2{=}CH{-}Cl$) and chlorobenzene are quite unreactive, and so stand in sharp contrast to allyl chloride and benzyl chloride. Nucleophilic substitution at an unsaturated centre is described later.

The examples discussed above have been limited to reactions of a negatively charged ion with an uncharged halide. In other examples both the reactants are uncharged, and both products are ions:

$$(CH_3)_3N{+}CH_3{-}I \longrightarrow (CH_3)_3\overset{\delta+}{N}{-}{-}{-}CH_3{-}{-}{-}\overset{\delta-}{I} \longrightarrow (CH_3)_4\overset{+}{N}{+}I^-$$

transition state

The formation of the transition state is attended by the separation of unlike charges (see Chapter II, § 2 d) and this type of reaction proceeds more rapidly in more polar solvents (e.g. alcohols) than in non-polar ones (e.g. hydrocarbons).

The energy of activation for reactions of tertiary amines with primary alkyl halides (in polar solvents) is generally about 14 kcal/mol, which is considerably lower than the value (about 23 kcal/mol) for the reactions of anions with primary alkyl halides in aqueous or alcoholic solution. On the other hand, the reactions of amines with alkyl halides have lower entropies of activation. A factor in the reaction of ions is the energy of detaching solvent from the ion, and indeed this may account for most of the energy of activation in the reactions of hydroxyl ions with methyl halides.† The low entropy of activation in the reactions of uncharged molecules is attributed to the dipolar character of the transition state; here the transition state will be extensively solvated (Chapter II, § 2 d).

3. $S_N 1$ mechanism

(a) *Evidence for $S_N 1$ mechanism.* The unimolecular ($S_N 1$) mechanism for nucleophilic substitution has been set out at the beginning of the chapter. The essence of this mechanism is that carbonium ions are intermediates, and that ionization is the rate-determining step. We now come to the evidence for this mechanism.

The order of reactivities of the alkyl bromides in a reaction proceeding by the $S_N 2$ mechanism was: MeBr > EtBr > Pr^{i}Br > Bu^{t}Br. Now the order for the reactions of these alkyl bromides with 0·1N-sodium hydroxide in aqueous ethanol is Bu^{t}Br > MeBr > EtBr > Pr^{i}Br (Fig. 22). Clearly some novel effect makes its appearance in the reaction carried

† Bathgate and Moelwyn-Hughes, *J. Chem. Soc.* 1959, p. 2642.

out in the aqueous medium: the tertiary halide now becomes the most reactive member of the series, and not the least reactive.

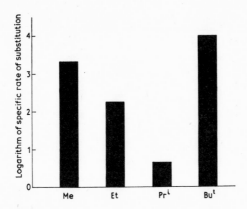

Fig. 22. Specific rate of substitution of alkyl bromides in 0·1 N-NaOH.

These are the rates of substitutions. Some olefine is also formed from isopropyl bromide and from tertiary butyl bromide. The substitutions are themselves complex, as the hydroxyl ion reacts with ethanol:

$$HO^- + EtOH \rightleftharpoons EtO^- + H_2O$$

Both OH$^-$ and OEt$^-$ are thus present, and so both alcohol

$$HO^- + RBr \longrightarrow ROH + Br^-$$

and ether

$$EtO^- + RBr \longrightarrow ROEt + Br^-$$

are formed.

Moreover, there is a difference in the kinetics: the rates of reaction of methyl and ethyl bromides are proportional to the concentration of alkali, but the rate of reaction of tertiary butyl bromide is *independent of the concentration of alkali*. In other words, the kinetics are second-order for the primary halides, and first-order for the tertiary halide. It is possible to imagine that tertiary butyl bromide undergoes a bimolecular reaction with the solvent; the reaction would have first-order kinetics:

$$H_2O + (CH_3)_3C-Br \longrightarrow H_2\overset{+}{O}-C(CH_3)_3 + Br^-$$
$$HO-C(CH_3)_3 + H^+$$

This is most improbable. The tertiary halide is unreactive in bimolecular reactions, and H_2O is a less reactive nucleophilic species than ${}^-OH$. The high reactivity of tertiary butyl bromide would be inexplicable on this basis. The tertiary alkyl halide must be reacting by a different mechanism. In this ($S_N 1$) mechanism, the old (C—Br) bond is broken before the new (C—O) bond is formed. The rate-determining step is ionization:

$$(CH_3)_3C—Br \longrightarrow (CH_3)_3C^+ + Br^-$$

a carbonium ion

This is followed by the rapid reaction of the carbonium ion with the solvent. The $S_N 1$ mechanism is favoured for the tertiary butyl bromide partly because tertiary carbonium ions are especially stable (§ 3 b) and partly because the tertiary halide is unreactive by the $S_N 2$ mechanism.

The role of the solvent has yet to be mentioned. The solvent plays a most important part on the rate-determining step in the $S_N 1$ mechanism, as in other ionizations. In aqueous solution, for example, water molecules interact with (solvate)—and hence stabilize—both cations and anions. Both the incipient carbonium ion (the cation) and the incipient bromide ion are solvated in the transition state of the rate-determining step; the formation of the ions would not be energetically feasible without solvation. The solvent in the $S_N 1$ mechanism thus does not play the same part as the nucleophilic reagent in the $S_N 2$ mechanism, but its part, although different, is just as important. Solvents differ enormously in the extent to which they interact with ions, and the rates of reactions proceeding by the $S_N 1$ mechanism are greatly affected by the solvent. In aqueous formic acid, for example, the order of reactivity of the alkyl bromides is $Bu^tBr \gg Pr^iBr > EtBr \sim MeBr$. This solvent is so effective at stabilizing ions that the reactions of the secondary and tertiary halides, which proceed by the $S_N 1$ mechanism, are the most rapid. The solvation of carbonium ions is discussed again later (§ 3 c); meanwhile we shall continue (as is customary) to omit the solvent from the equations for the $S_N 1$ mechanism, but its essential role should be borne in mind.

Further evidence for the $S_N 1$ mechanism will now be presented. Carbonium ions are extremely reactive (§ 3 b), and react rapidly with most solvents. However, carbonium ions may also react with other species. If calcium formate is added to a solution of tertiary butyl chloride in aqueous formic acid, the addition of the salt does not increase the rate of reaction of the tertiary butyl chloride, but the products now include much tertiary butyl formate. *A change in the composition of the medium has thus affected the rate and the products differently.* There must, then, be (at least) two steps, a rate-controlling step and a product-controlling step. This type of experiment constitutes an important part

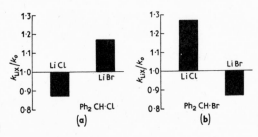

Fig. 23. Relative rates of reaction of diphenylmethyl chloride (*a*), and diphenylmethyl bromide (*b*), in aqueous acetone; k_{LiX} is the initial rate constant with added lithium halide, and k_0 is the initial rate constant in the absence of added salt.

of the evidence for the $S_N 1$ mechanism, according to which the results are interpreted as shown below:

$$(CH_3)_3C\!-\!Cl$$

rate-determining step; unaffected by $HCOO^-$

$$(CH_3)_3C^+ + Cl^-$$

product-controlling steps; affected by $HCOO^-$

H_2O $HCOO^-$

$$(CH_3)_3C\!-\!OH \qquad\qquad (CH_3)_3C\!-\!O\!-\!CHO$$

Since carbonium ions react with anions, the first step in the $S_N 1$ mechanism is reversible,

$$RX \rightleftharpoons R^+ + X^-$$

Addition of the anion X^- may thus retard the decomposition of RX, by increasing the rate of the reverse of the heterolysis. Addition of a salt yielding any other anion, however, should increase the rate of decomposition of RX, by increasing the polarity of the medium. These expectations are fulfilled by the results obtained for the hydrolysis of diphenylmethyl chloride and diphenylmethyl bromide (Fig. 23). The reaction of Ph_2CHCl is retarded by the addition of LiCl and hastened by the addition of LiBr. And the reaction of Ph_2CHBr is retarded by the addition of LiBr and hastened by the addition of LiCl.† These results thus support the $S_N 1$ mechanism:

$$Ph_2CH \cdot X \rightleftharpoons Ph_2CH^+ + X^-$$

$$Ph_2CH^+ + H_2O \longrightarrow Ph_2CH \cdot \overset{+}{O}H_2 \rightleftharpoons Ph_2CH \cdot OH + H^+$$

The same two halides have been used in another test of the $S_N 1$ mechanism. Here sodium azide was added to the halide in aqueous acetone. Now if the carbonium ion is an intermediate it will have the choice of reacting with azide ion or with water. The composition of the mixture of products, however, will be the same whichever halide is used, for the product-determining steps consist of reactions of the carbonium, Ph_2CH^+, and the same ion is formed from both halides. The results‡ are shown in the table.

In aqueous acetone containing 0·1 M-NaN$_3$ *k* (sec^{-1})	*Diphenylmethyl chloride* Ph$_2$CHCl 12·4 × 10^{-5}	*Diphenylmethyl bromide* Ph$_2$CHBr 416 × 10^{-5}
Ph$_2$CHOH in products	66%	66·5%
Ph$_2$CHN$_3$ in products	34%	33·5%

Although the rates of reaction of the two halides differed greatly, the products were formed in the same proportions. This, too, is strong evidence for the $S_N 1$ mechanism:

$$Ph_2CH \cdot Cl \rightleftharpoons Ph_2CH^+ + Cl^-, \quad \text{and} \quad Ph_2CH \cdot Br \rightleftharpoons Ph_2CH^+ + Br^-,$$

followed by

$$Ph_2CH^+ + H_2O \longrightarrow Ph_2CH \cdot \overset{+}{O}H_2 \rightleftharpoons Ph_2CH \cdot OH + H^+$$

and

$$Ph_2CH^+ + N_3^- \longrightarrow Ph_2CH \cdot N_3$$

(b) *Stability of carbonium ions.* The $S_N 1$ mechanism postulates the formation of carbonium ions. Although carbonium ions resemble ammonium ions in being positively charged, ammonium ions (and oxonium ions) have a completed octet of electrons, whereas carbonium ions have only a sextet: hence their reactivity towards nucleophilic reagents.

† Benfey, Hughes, and Ingold, *J. Chem. Soc.* 1952, p. 2488; see also Pocker, ibid. 1959, p. 3939.

‡ Ingold, *Structure and Mechanism in Organic Chemistry*, p. 355, Cornell University Press, 1953.

Carbonium ions are, in general, very reactive species, and hence, in the $S_N 1$ mechanism, the second step is faster than the first.

Some carbonium salts, however, can be isolated (e.g. (1)), and one (tropylium bromide, (2)) is actually stable in aqueous solution.

There is also experimental evidence from physical measurements (e.g. conductivity, freezing-point depressions, and light absorption) for the existence of other carbonium ions.†

$$[Ph_3C]^+[ClO_4]^-$$

(1)

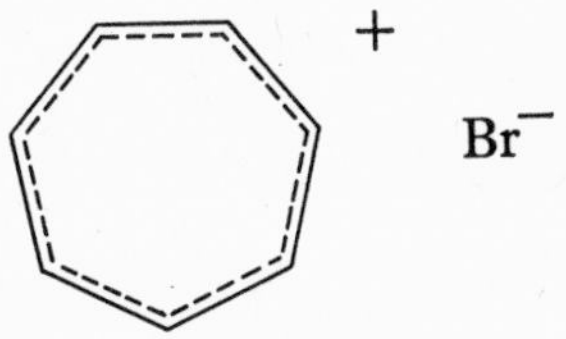

(2)

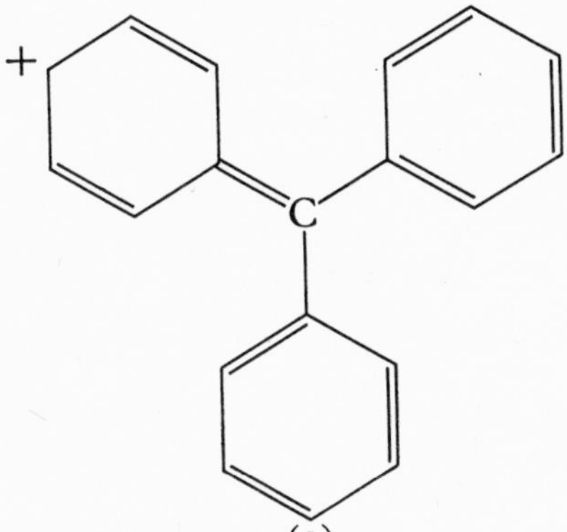

Br^-

(3)

The carbonium ions (1) and (2) are stabilized by mesomeric charge delocalization. Thus the triphenylmethyl cation in (1) can be written in nine other ways with the positive charge in the *ortho-* or *para-*positions of the three rings, e.g. (3). The charge is therefore spread over all these positions. Charge delocalization results in considerable stabilization of the ion, and is also important for aliphatic carbonium ions. Thus in the tertiary butyl carbonium ion, the stabilization may amount to 80 kcal/mol‡ (Chapter I, § 1 *r*).

The isopropyl cation is also stabilized, but not to so great an extent as the tertiary butyl cation, and the ethyl cation is stabilized to an

---

† Burton and Praill, *Quart. Rev.* 1952, **6**, 302; Gold and Tye, *J. Chem. Soc.* 1952, p. 2172; Bethell and Gold, *Quart. Rev.* 1958, **12**, 173; Grace and Symons, *J. Chem. Soc.* 1959, p. 958; Leffler, *The Reactive Intermediates of Organic Chemistry*, Interscience, New York, 1956.

‡ Muller and Mulliken, *J. Amer. Chem. Soc.* 1958, **80**, 3489.

even smaller degree. *It is a useful general rule that the order of decreasing stability of carbonium ions is: tertiary, secondary, primary.*

The stability of carbonium ions is closely connected with the rates of reactions which proceed by the $S_N 1$ mechanism. There is a partial positive charge on the carbon atom in the $S_N 1$ transition state, so that a substituent which can interact with the charge and allow it to be delocalized stabilizes the transition state and increases reactivity. This is the reason why tertiary butyl bromide reacts by the $S_N 1$ mechanism under conditions in which methyl bromide reacts by the $S_N 2$ mechanism. Another example is chlorodimethylether (4), which reacts very rapidly with ethanol by the $S_N 1$ mechanism:

$$\text{MeO·CH}_2\text{·Cl} \longrightarrow \text{MeO·CH}_2^+ \xrightarrow{\text{EtOH}} \text{MeO·CH}_2\text{·OEt} + \text{H}^+$$

$$(4) \qquad\qquad\qquad +\text{Cl}^-$$

The reaction is about 10^{14} times more rapid than the corresponding reaction of methyl chloride.† The ion is mesomeric between (5) and (6); the positive charge is shared between the oxygen and carbon atoms, and the same effect is present in the transition state.

$$\overset{+}{\text{MeO}}\!-\!\text{CH}_2 \qquad\qquad \text{Me}\overset{+}{\text{O}}\!=\!\text{CH}_2$$

$$(5) \qquad\qquad\qquad (6)$$

Ionization of halides may also be facilitated by silver or mercuric salts, as in the reaction of benzyl bromide with silver acetate:

$$\text{PhCH}_2\text{Br} + \text{Ag}^+ \longrightarrow \text{PhCH}_2^+ + \text{AgBr}$$

$$\text{PhCH}_2^+ + \bar{\text{O}}\text{COMe} \longrightarrow \text{PhCH}_2\text{OCOMe}$$

(c) *Steric factors.* It will be recalled that one of the most important features of the $S_N 2$ mechanism is the inversion of the configuration of the carbon atom on which substitution takes place. So the question arises: What will happen in the $S_N 1$ mechanism ? Now the configuration of a carbonium ion, with its sextet of electrons, will be planar, i.e. the three groups will lie in the same plane as the carbon atom to which they are bound, and in a symmetrical ion (R_3C^+) the bond angles will be 120°:

† Ballinger, de la Mare, Kohnstam, and Presst, *J. Chem. Soc.* 1955, p. 3641.

So the carbonium ion from $R^1R^2R^3CX$ cannot retain the asymmetric configuration of the carbon: on this basis, the S_N1 mechanism entails racemization.

In practice, there is some racemization, but also some inversion, in reactions proceeding by the S_N1 mechanism. This can be understood when solvation of the carbonium ion is considered.† It is convenient to picture two kinds of solvated carbonium ion. Thus, the hydrolysis of s-octyl bromide may be written:

(1)   (2)

The solvation of the bromide ion has been omitted for the sake of simplicity. The alcohol formed from the asymmetrical ion pair structure (1) will have the inverted configuration, but the alcohol from the symmetrical 'fully solvated' carbonium ion (2) will be racemic. Asymmetry will thus be preserved when the carbonium ion is so reactive that it is solvated by, and then reacts with, water, before the bromide ion has moved far away: the departing group shields, as it were, its face of the tetrahedron. If the carbonium ion is more stable it will be symmetrically solvated (structure (2)) before reaction. As carbonium ions in which the charge is on a tertiary carbon atom are more stable than those in which the charge is on a secondary one, it is reasonable that s-octyl bromide should undergo hydrolysis with about 40 per cent. loss of optical activity, whereas methyl ethyl isohexyl carbinyl chloride is hydrolysed with about 80 per cent. loss of optical activity. The general result in the S_N1 mechanism, then, is racemization and inversion: how much of each depends on the stability of the carbonium ion. There is, however, an important class of reactions in which the configuration is retained (§ 4).

† Doering and Zeiss, J. Amer. Chem. Soc. 1953, 75, 4733; Grunwald, Heller, and Klein, J. Chem. Soc. 1957, p. 2604.

Optically active alcohols react with thionyl chloride (under certain conditions) to give alkyl chlorides of the same configuration as that of the alcohol:

$$
\begin{array}{c}
\text{Me} \\
H\!\!-\!\!C\!\!-\!\!OH \xrightarrow{\;\text{SOCl}_2\;} \\
\text{Et}
\end{array}
\qquad
\begin{array}{c}
\text{Me} \\
H\!\!-\!\!C\!\!-\!\!Cl \\
\text{Et}
\end{array}
\tag{3}
$$

$$
\begin{array}{c}
\text{Me} \\
H\!\!-\!\!C\!\!-\!\!O\!\!-\!\!S(Cl)\!\!=\!\!O \\
\text{Et}
\end{array}
\tag{4}
\qquad\qquad
\begin{array}{c}
\text{Me} \\
H\!\!-\!\!C\!\!-\!\!O\!\!-\!\!S(Cl)\!\!=\!\!O \\
\text{Et}
\end{array}
\tag{5}
$$

The chlorosulphite (4) is an intermediate, and it has been suggested that it reacts by the mechanism shown in (5). This mechanism is referred to as $S_N i$ (substitution, nucleophilic, internal). The chlorosulphite (4) decomposes to a chloride (3) in a first-order reaction, with retention of configuration, but only if dioxan is the solvent. In toluene, the alkyl chloride is formed with inversion of configuration; in other solvents, the results are intermediate between these extremes.† The term $S_N i$ is perhaps unnecessary, since the results may well be due to successive displacements, without any 'front–side displacement' as in (5). In the scheme given below, the dioxan is shown as S:, as it is the unshared electrons on the oxygen atom which interact with the carbonium ion:

$$
\begin{array}{c}
\text{Me} \\
H\!-\!C\!-\!OH \\
\text{Et}
\end{array}
\longrightarrow
\begin{array}{c}
\text{Me} \\
H\!-\!C\!-\!O\!-\!S(Cl)\!\!=\!\!O \\
\text{Et}
\end{array}
\longrightarrow
\left[
\begin{array}{c}
\text{Me} \\
H\!-\!C\!\cdots\!O\!\!=\!\!S\!\!=\!\!O \\
\text{Et}
\end{array}
\right]^{+}
\xrightarrow{\;S:\;}
\left[
\begin{array}{c}
\text{Me} \\
S\!-\!C\!-\!H \\
\text{Et}
\end{array}
\right]^{+}
$$

$$
\Big\downarrow \text{Cl}^{-}\qquad\qquad\qquad\qquad\qquad\Big\downarrow \text{Cl}^{-}
$$

$$
\begin{array}{c}
\text{Me} \\
Cl\!-\!C\!-\!H \\
\text{Et}
\end{array}
\qquad\qquad\qquad\qquad
\begin{array}{c}
\text{Me} \\
H\!-\!C\!-\!Cl \\
\text{Et}
\end{array}
$$

chloride, with 'inverted' configuration　　　　chloride, with 'retained' configuration

† Lewis and Boozer, *J. Amer. Chem. Soc.* 1952, **74**, 308; 1953, **75**, 3182.

We have been discussing the configurational result in reactions proceeding by the S_N1 mechanism; the rate of reaction also depends on
steric factors. It will be recalled that the reaction of highly-branched
alkyl halides by the S_N2 mechanism was abnormally slow. This was
ascribed to steric hindrance; the bulky groups get in the way of the
approaching group. This should not happen in the S_N1 mechanism.
Now the S_N1 mechanism is favoured in aqueous formic acid, and it is
found that neopentyl bromide and ethyl bromide are decomposed in
this solvent at much the same rate. Here both alkyl halides are reacting
by the S_N1 mechanism, and the highly-branched neopentyl bromide
ionizes just as readily as ethyl bromide does. Indeed, the highly-
branched tri-t-butyl carbinyl chloride (6) is decomposed in aqueous
ethanol several hundred times more rapidly than t-butyl chloride; this
is probably because the methyl groups will be farther away from each
other in the planar carbonium ion (7) than they are in the tetrahedral
alkyl chloride (6), so that congestion in the starting material is lessened
in the transition state. This idea has been called steric assistance:

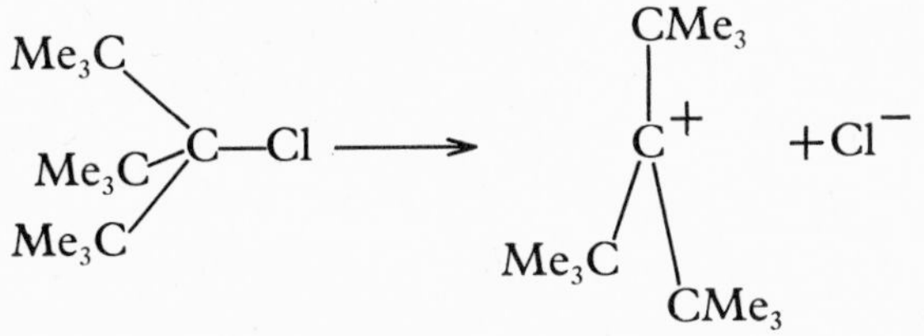

(6)   (7)

it is the counterpart of steric hindrance. A possibility to be borne in
mind is that steric assistance may play a part in some enzyme-catalysed
reactions.

There is an interesting example where a particular steric configuration
leads to complete unreactivity. The alkyl chloride (8) is completely

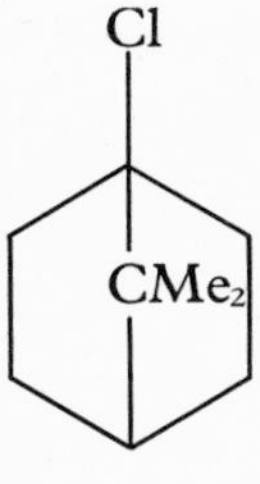

(8)

unreactive towards nucleophilic reagents, nor does it ionize on prolonged boiling with alcoholic silver nitrate.† Reaction by the ordinary S_N2 mechanism is evidently impossible, as the reagent cannot approach the carbon atom carrying the chlorine atom from the direction of the face of the tetrahedron opposite to that of the chlorine atom. Reaction by the S_N1 mechanism is not subject to steric hindrance, but is prevented by two factors: one is that the carbonium ion from (8) could not be planar without large distortion of bond angles, and the other is that the solvent could not aid ionization by solvation of the incipient carbonium ion on the 'back-side'.

(d) *Transition between S_N1 and S_N2 mechanisms.* The distinction between S_N1 and S_N2 mechanisms is of great value, but these mechanisms are the extreme cases. Under some experimental conditions the distinction is difficult to make‡ and we have also to consider what happens in the region when the mechanism is apparently changing, as in the reaction isopropyl bromide in alkaline aqueous ethanol. The experimental results are that the rate of substitution is independent of the concentration of alkali under weakly alkaline conditions (0 to 0·005 N-NaOH), but that under strongly alkaline conditions (N-NaOH) the rate is proportional to the concentration of alkali. (These are the rates of the substitution reaction; in N-NaOH about half the product consists of olefine.) Under intermediate conditions (e.g. 0·1 N-NaOH) the kinetics are between first- and second-order. The question then is whether some of the molecules react by the one pathway, and others by the other, or whether they all react by an intermediate mechanism. On the latter assumption, the bromide ion cannot depart from isopropyl bromide without *some* assistance from the nucleophilic reagent (the hydroxyl ion), but less assistance is required by isopropyl bromide than is required by methyl bromide. This seems quite reasonable, but it is difficult to correlate the structure of the transition state with the observed kinetics. If the transition state contains a hydroxyl ion, then the rate should depend on the frequency of collisions between hydroxyl ions and isopropyl bromide, and the rate should be proportional to the concentration of hydroxyl ions; whereas if the hydroxyl ion is omitted from the transition state, then the rate should be independent of the concentration of hydroxyl ions. It is not clear how one should formulate a single transition state for the reaction of isopropyl bromide with 0·1 N-NaOH, where the kinetics lie between first- and second-order. The

† Bartlett and Knox, *J. Amer. Chem. Soc.* 1939, **61**, 3184.
‡ Swain and Pegues, ibid. 1958, **80**, 812.

alternative viewpoint is that unimolecular and bimolecular substitutions are proceeding concurrently. This viewpoint is simpler, and there is some experimental evidence for it.†

(e) *Experimental criteria for distinction between $S_N 1$ and $S_N 2$ mechanisms.* As the mechanism has to be inferred from observations, it may be convenient to summarize the experimental criteria which are useful for this purpose:

(i) Second-order kinetics indicate the $S_N 2$ mechanism; but if the nucleophilic reagent is present in excess, the reaction may proceed by the $S_N 2$ mechanism with first-order kinetics.

(ii) First-order kinetics are the usual consequence of the $S_N 1$ mechanism, but no simple order is observed if the rate of the reversal of the heterolysis is comparable with the rate of further reaction of the carbonium ion. Under these conditions, too, a 'common-ion effect' may be observed in reactions proceeding by the $S_N 1$ mechanism.

(iii) Lack of parallelism between rates and compositions of products is a feature of the $S_N 1$ mechanism.

(iv) Configurational inversion is characteristic of the $S_N 2$ mechanism, and some racemization of the $S_N 1$ mechanism.

(v) Steric hindrance (in particular, unreactivity of the neopentyl compound) is characteristic of the $S_N 2$ mechanism.

4. Participation by neighbouring groups

This section deals with a particular effect of the structure of certain substrates. This effect results in either an enhanced rate of substitution, or an unexpected stereochemical outcome, or both. It is especially important as it sheds some light on enzyme action.

The $S_N 2$ mechanism, it will be recalled, leads to inversion of configuration, and the $S_N 1$ mechanism leads to racemization and inversion. Now the α-bromopropionate ion is hydrolysed in alkaline solution at a rate proportional to the concentrations of both the organic anion and the hydroxyl ion, and the lactate formed has the opposite configuration from the starting material:

† Pocker, *J. Chem. Soc.* 1959, pp. 3939, 3944, and references cited there.

So this is as expected for an $S_N 2$ reaction. But in weakly alkaline solution, the rate becomes independent of the concentration of hydroxide ion, and the lactate has the same configuration as the starting material.†
This last result may be interpreted by supposing that there are two nucleophilic substitution reactions; the first one, which controls the rate, is the intramolecular attack of the carboxylate anion to give an unstable α-lactone, which is then hydrolysed: both substitutions invert, so that the final product has the same configuration as the starting material:

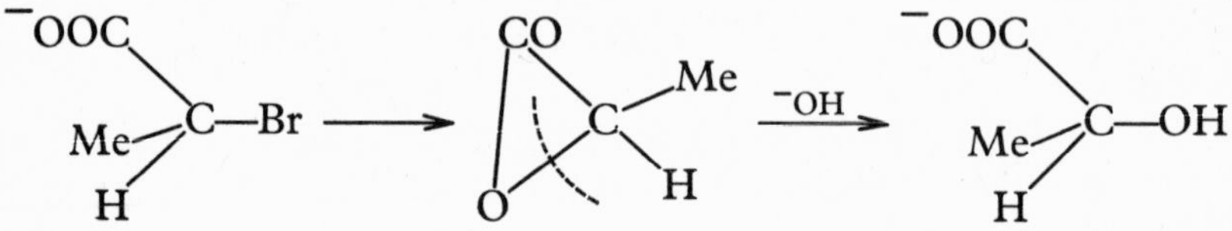

(1)

The reaction of an alkyl halide with a carboxylate ion is, of course, a well-known method of preparing esters. The postulated intermediate (1) is an α-lactone; although α-lactones have not been isolated, β-lactones are known, and they undergo hydrolysis with cleavage of the alkyl-oxygen bond (the carbon-oxygen bond marked in (1)), as is demanded by this mechanism (Chapter VI, § 1 f).

Another example of neighbouring group participation is met in the reaction of 2-bromo-n-butan-3-ol (2) with hydrogen bromide:‡

$$Me{\cdot}CHBr{\cdot}CHOH{\cdot}Me + HBr \longrightarrow Me{\cdot}CHBr{\cdot}CHBr{\cdot}Me + H_2O$$

(2)

Such displacements normally proceed by two stages:

$$ROH + HBr \longrightarrow R\overset{+}{O}H_2 + Br^- \quad \text{(i)}$$

$$R\overset{+}{O}H_2 + Br^- \longrightarrow RBr + H_2O \quad \text{(ii)}$$

The bromobutanol (2) contains two dissimilar asymmetric carbon atoms, so that there are two pairs of enantiomers in such cases. One pair is called threo (3) and the other erythro (4) (these terms are derived from the sugars; erythro means having a configurational analogy with

† Cowdrey, Hughes, and Ingold, *J. Chem. Soc.* 1937, p. 1208.
‡ Winstein and Lucas, *J. Amer. Chem. Soc.* 1939, **61**, 1576, 2845.

erythrose, and threo with threose). It will also be noticed that only the erythro isomers have a possible conformation with *two* similar groups eclipsed.

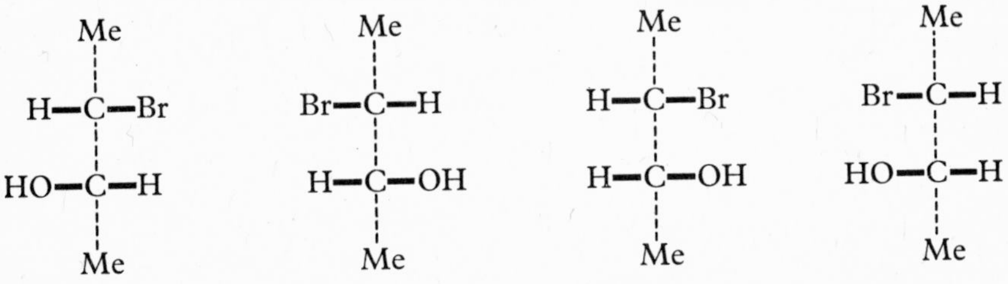

<pre>
      Me   Me   Me   Me
      | | | |
  H—C—Br   Br—C—H   H—C—Br   Br—C—H
      | | | |
  HO—C—H   H—C—OH   H—C—OH   HO—C—H
      | | | |
      Me   Me   Me   Me

        threo (3)   erythro (4)
</pre>

The stereochemistry of the product of the reaction, 2 : 3-dibromobutane, is similar to that of tartaric acid: there are two similar asymmetric carbon atoms, so there is a meso form (5) and a pair of enantiomers (6):

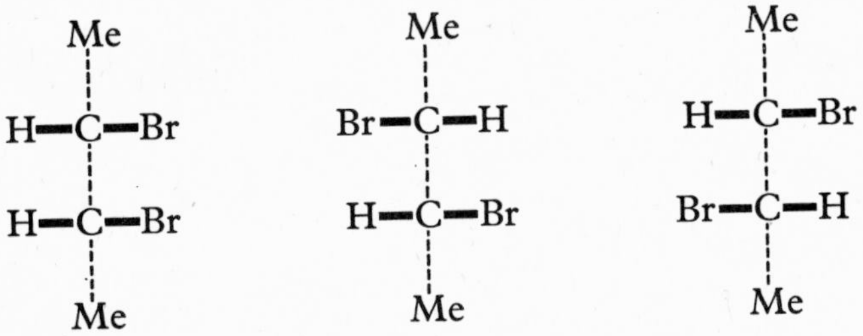

<pre>
      Me   Me   Me
      | | |
  H—C—Br   Br—C—H   H—C—Br
      | | |
  H—C—Br   H—C—Br   Br—C—H
      | | |
      Me   Me   Me

   meso form (5)   DL form (6)
</pre>

It was found that from an optically active bromobutanol, one of the pair of threo enantiomers (3), the product was the optically inactive DL form (6) of dibromobutane; no meso form (5), however, was obtained. The significance of this result is made clearer if the positive and negative signs are used to denote the configurations of the two carbon atoms:

$$\mp \rightarrow \pm \text{ and } \mp$$

The experimental result then means that the reaction must proceed through an intermediate whose properties are such that: (*a*) each carbon atom has an equal chance of eventually having either configuration, (*b*) the two carbon atoms must have opposite configurations. This amounts to saying that there is an equal chance that either both or neither carbon atom will be inverted.

The following mechanism accounts for these stereochemical observations; it is an elaboration of reaction (ii) given above. The bromine atom that is already present in the bromobutanol participates: it reacts with the neighbouring carbon atom by an intramolecular nucleophilic substitution, with inversion of configuration, to give a bromonium ion (7) (such are known); this may then react with a bromide ion in one of two ways, both of which proceed with inversion of configuration:

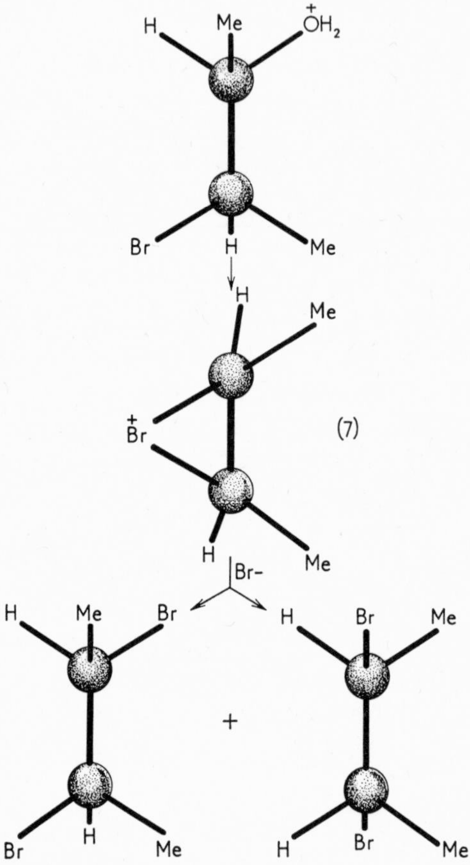

As the postulated intermediate (7) has a plane of symmetry, the product is a racemic mixture. So this mechanism explains how the active threo bromobutanol gives the racemic dibromobutane; the same argument can be applied to the other finding, that the erythro isomer of 2-bromo-butan-3-ol gives meso-2:3-dibromobutane.

We now come to an example where there is kinetic evidence for neighbouring group participation. Mustard gas ($\beta:\beta'$-dichlorodiethyl sulphide) (8) reacts with several reagents at the same high rate, a rate of the order of a million times greater than that expected for a primary alkyl chloride. The molecule has its own 'built in' nucleophilic substituent: no added reagent (X^-) can compete with the sulphur:

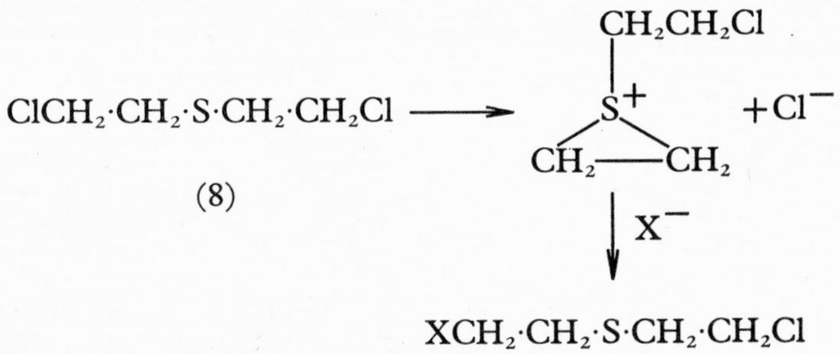

CH₂CH₂Cl
ClCH₂·CH₂·S·CH₂·CH₂Cl
S+
+Cl⁻
CH₂ CH₂
X⁻
XCH₂·CH₂·S·CH₂·CH₂Cl

(8)

Several added reagents may compete with each other, however; their relative effectiveness may be gauged from the composition of the products. The values of the relative reactivities of added nucleophilic reagents† are similar to the values given in Table 9 (p. 83).

Another example of neighbouring group participation is provided by cholesterol. Here it is the double bond that interacts with the reaction centre, so that replacement reactions at C-3 of cholesterol commonly take place relatively rapidly, and with retention of configuration, although in the absence of the double bond (as in cholestanol and its derivatives) inversion occurs.‡ The reactions of the cholesterol derivatives presumably take place with the intervention of a mesomeric carbonium ion (only part of the molecule is given in the structures written below):

Me
H
Cl
3
4
5
6
OAc⁻
AcOH
Me
H
+
Me
H
AcO

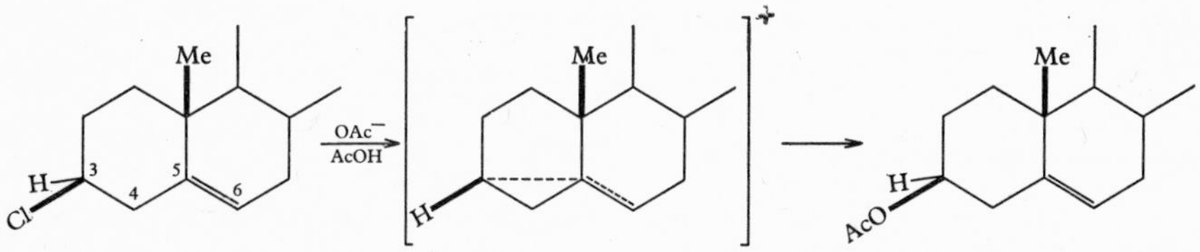

The positive charge in the intermediate is shared between C-3 and C-6.

The most striking example of acceleration caused by the participation of a double bond is the acetolysis of *anti*-norborn-7-enyl toluene-*p*-sulphonate (9).§ This proceeds more rapidly (with retention of configuration) than the reaction of the saturated compound (10) by a factor of 10^{11}. The neighbouring groups that participate in these reactions fall into two classes: either they have unshared (p) electrons (e.g. the thio ether),

† Ogston, Holiday, Philpot, and Stocken, *Trans. Faraday Soc.* 1948, **44**, 45.
‡ Shoppee, *J. Chem. Soc.* 1946, p. 1147.
§ Winstein, Shatarsky, Norton, and Woodward, *J. Amer. Chem. Soc.* 1955, **77**, 4183.

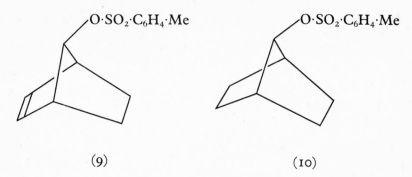

$$(9) \qquad\qquad\qquad (\mathrm{10})$$

or they have the π-electrons of a C$=$C double bond. This ('p-π') analogy holds quite widely, and we shall see in the next chapter that olefines are nucleophilic reagents.

5. Nucleophilic substitution at unsaturated centres

All the reactions that have been described so far have been substitutions at singly-bound carbon atoms in the tetrahedral sp^3 state of hybridization. There are several interesting differences in nucleophilic substitutions at doubly-bound carbon atoms.† Instead of two there are here three main mechanisms, of which only the first is closely similar to that of the substitutions at saturated centres.

(a) S_N1 *mechanism*. This mechanism is relatively uncommon, but the reactions of diazonium salts form an important example. The kinetically important step is of the type:

$$\mathrm{Ph}\!-\!\overset{+}{\mathrm{N}}\!\!\equiv\!\!\mathrm{N} \longrightarrow \mathrm{Ph}^{+}+\mathrm{N}_2$$

The phenyl cation may then react with water to give phenol, or with iodide ion to give iodobenzene. The lack of correlation between rate and proportions of products in the presence of varying concentrations of halide ions points to the S_N1 mechanism. The diazonium ion is an especially good leaving group, owing to the stability of the nitrogen molecule. The importance of diazonium salts in preparative work arises partly because other organic groups cannot in general be readily displaced from aromatic rings, and partly because the high reactivity of phenyl cations enables many different transformations to be carried out.‡

(b) *Bimolecular mechanism*. Aromatic halogen compounds (e.g. chlorobenzene (1)) are, of course, unreactive unless electron-withdrawing

† Bunnett, *Quart. Rev.* 1958, **12**, 1; de la Mare, *Progress in Stereochemistry*, 1958, **2**, 65.
‡ Cowdrey and Davies, *Quart. Rev.* 1952, **6**, 358.

groups are present in the *ortho-* or *para*-positions to the halogen atom. Thus the compounds shown form a graded series, in which the reactivity towards nucleophilic reagents (e.g. the hydroxyl ion) increases markedly.

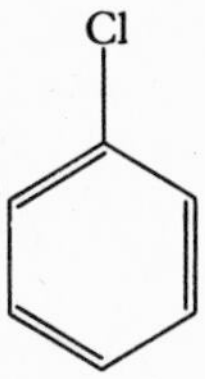

(1)    (2) 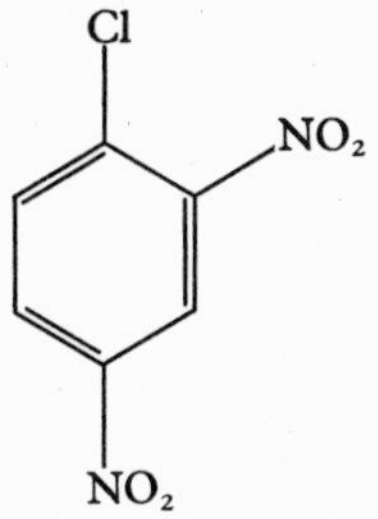   (3) 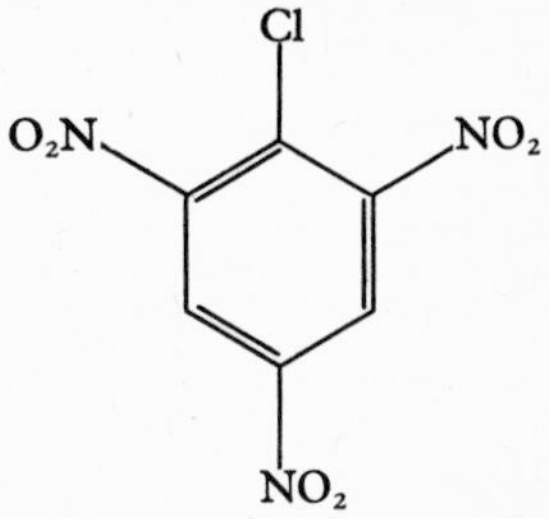   (4)

Now the electron-withdrawing nitro groups will aid the formation of a bond between the OH⁻ and the carbon-carrying chlorine atom, but will hinder rather than aid the breaking of the carbon-chlorine bond. As the nitro groups in fact facilitate the reaction, we must envisage a mechanism in which bond-making is more important than bond-breaking. This idea is consistent with the observation that the fluoro compound (5) is more reactive than the chloro compound (3), a result

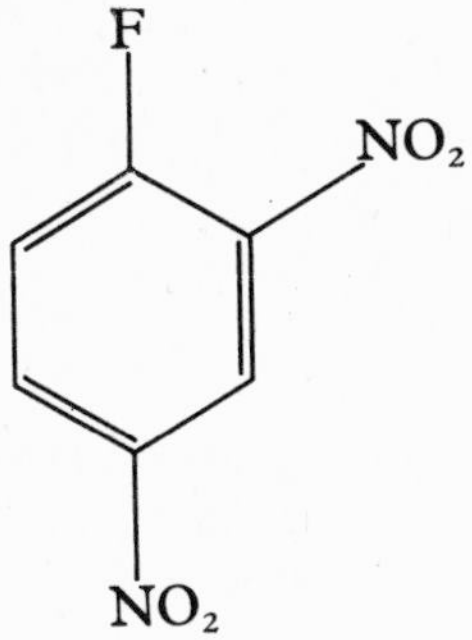

(5)

which is different from that observed with *alkyl* halides, where the order of halogen reactivity is $I > Br > Cl > F$ (§ 2 b). The high reactivity of 1-fluoro-2:4-dinitrobenzene (5) towards amines is the basis for the usefulness of this aryl halide in 'labelling' the amino groups of proteins.

An important clue to the mechanism of these reactions is provided by the isolation in certain cases of adducts, e.g. (6), which can be prepared by either of the reactions shown on the next page.

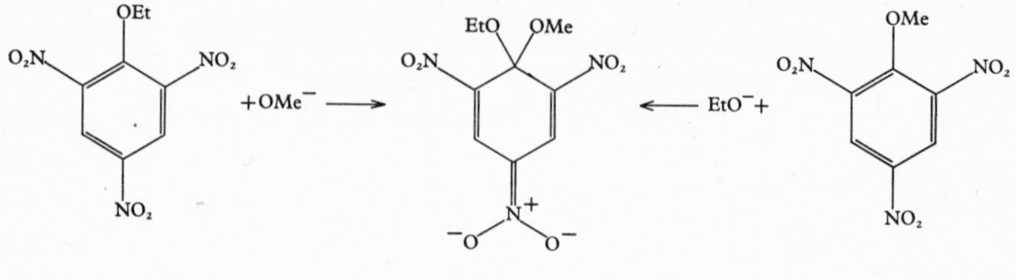

(6)

There is clearly extensive charge delocalization in the anion (6), which has been written with the charge on one nitro group, but in fact the charge will be shared between the three nitro groups. We will now assume a mechanism in which adducts similar to (6) are intermediates, which are, in general, too unstable to be isolated. Thus, for the reaction of *p*-nitrochlorobenzene with hydroxyl ions:

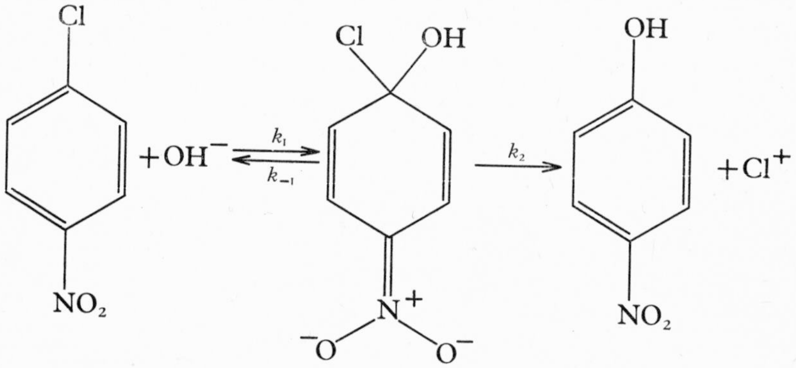

(7)

This mechanism clearly accounts for the activating effect of nitro groups. It is essentially a bond-making mechanism, in the sense that frequently the formation of the adduct, in which the new bond is formed, is rate-determining, and thus this mechanism allows an order of reactivity among halogens in which fluorine is the most reactive. Whether bond-breaking is important depends on the relative values of the velocity constants; if $k_2 \gg k_{-1}$, bond-breaking is no longer kinetically important (the kinetics can be worked out by the method given in Chapter II, § 2 *b*). This contrasts with the S_N1 and S_N2 mechanisms of aliphatic substitution, in both of which (but to varying degrees) bond-breaking is important.

This conclusion may be put briefly in the following way. Whereas the most useful division of nucleophilic substitutions at saturated centres is into a unimolecular two-step mechanism ($S_N 1$) and a bimolecular one-step mechanism ($S_N 2$), nucleophilic substitutions in activated aromatic compounds commonly take place by a bimolecular two-step mechanism.

The same mechanisms account for the reactivity of some heterocyclic halides. Thus, 2-chloropyridine (8) and 4-chloropyridine (9) are nearly as reactive as 2-chloronitrobenzene or 4-chloronitrobenzene, but 3-chloropyridine (10) is unreactive; the mechanism for the hydrolysis of 4-chloropyridine is shown below; the charge delocalization is somewhat similar to that suggested in vitamin B_6 derivatives in some enzymic reactions discussed later (Chapter V, § 20):

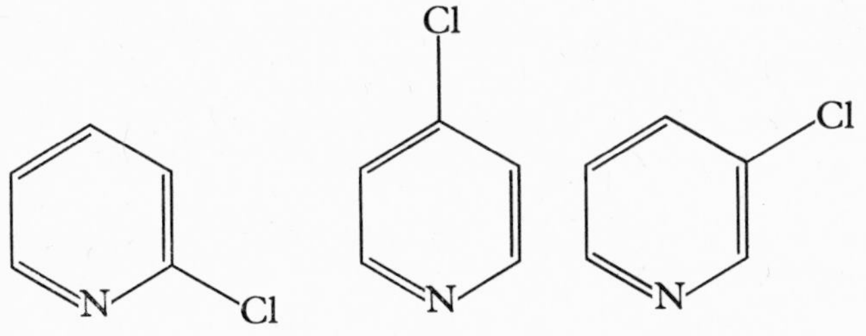

(8)   (9)   (10)

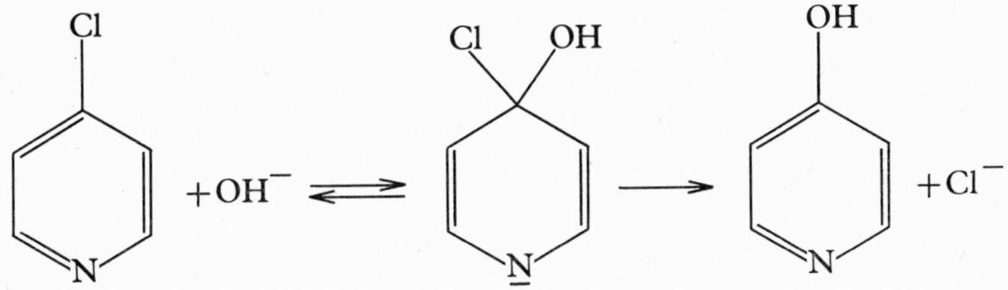

Nucleophilic substitutions at unsaturated centres are most common with, but not restricted to, activated aromatic systems. An example in a non-cyclic system is the reaction of ethyl chlorocrotonate with sodium thiophenoxide.†

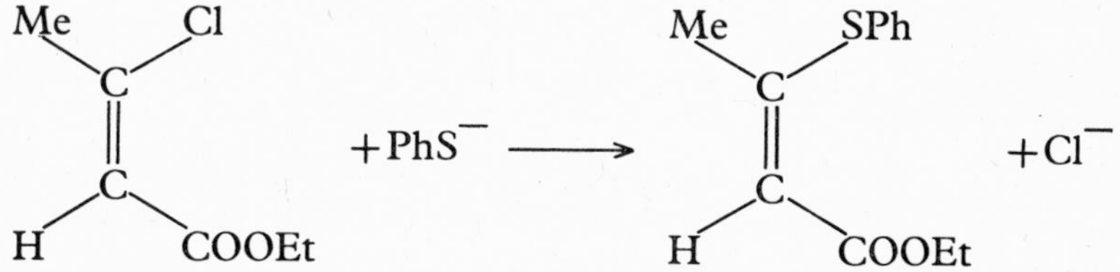

† Jones and Vernon, *Nature* 1955, **176**, 791.

(c) *Benzyne mechanism.* Halogen atoms which are not activated can be displaced from aromatic rings by powerful nucleophilic reagents. One mechanism for this displacement is the elimination-addition, or benzyne, mechanism.†

o-Bromoanisole (1) and *m*-bromoanisole (2) on treatment with potassium amide in liquid ammonia both gave *m*-anisidine (3). This result could arise if both halides lost hydrogen bromide to give a common intermediate, and there is good evidence for formulating the intermediate as a 'benzyne' (4):

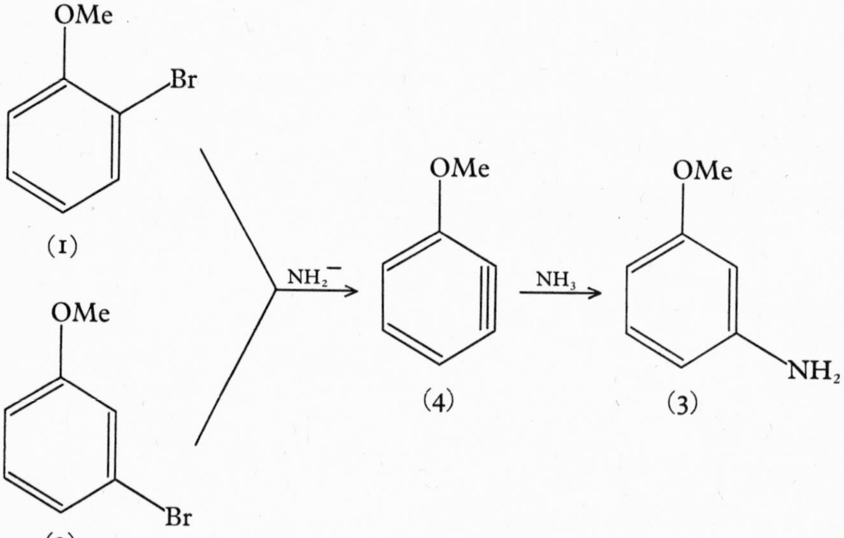

p-Bromoanisole (5) gives both *m*-anisidine, and *p*-anisidine (6); here the benzyne (7) is different from (4), and so a different result is quite reasonable.

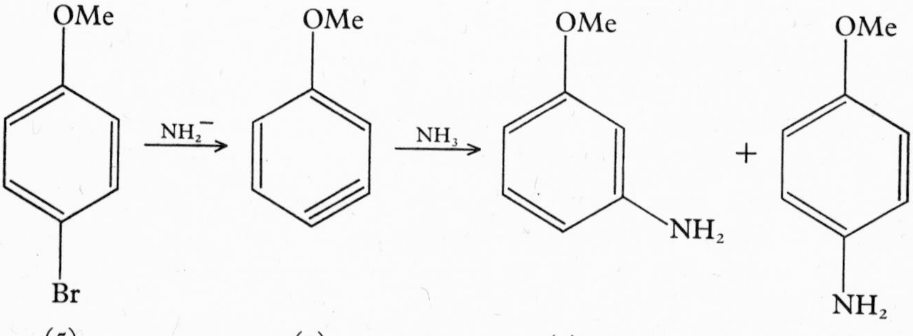

† Roberts, *Chemical Soc. Symposium, Bristol,* p. 115, London, The Chemical Society, 1958.

This mechanism predicts that chloro-[1-^{14}C]benzene should give equal amounts of [1-^{14}C]aniline and [2-^{14}C]aniline:

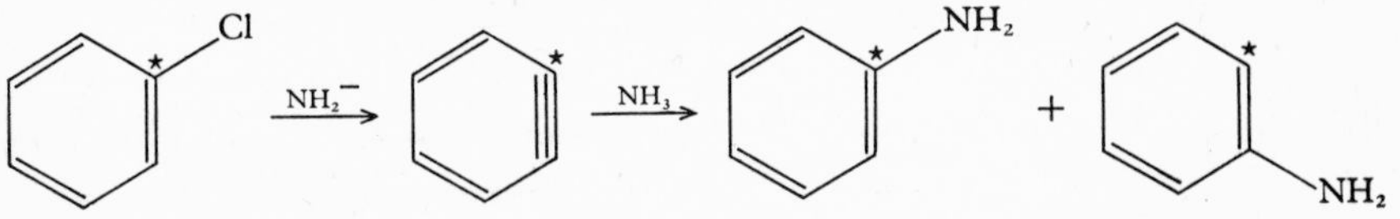

This was the result obtained, except that the amounts of (8) and (9) were not quite the same, probably owing to a kinetic isotope effect.

The triple bond in the postulated intermediate benzyne (10) is conjugated with the two double bonds; in any ordinary compound with a triple bond the bond angles are 180° (although an excited form of acetylene has an angular shape), so that there is some strain in benzyne, which is consistent with its high reactivity.

6. Transmethylation reactions

$$HS \cdot CH_2 \cdot CH_2 \cdot \underset{\underset{NH_3}{\overset{+}{|}}}{CH} \cdot COO^- \qquad CH_3 \cdot S \cdot CH_2 \cdot CH_2 \cdot \underset{\underset{NH_3}{\overset{+}{|}}}{CH} \cdot COO^-$$

homocysteine   methionine

$$HS \cdot R \qquad\qquad\qquad CH_3 S \cdot R$$

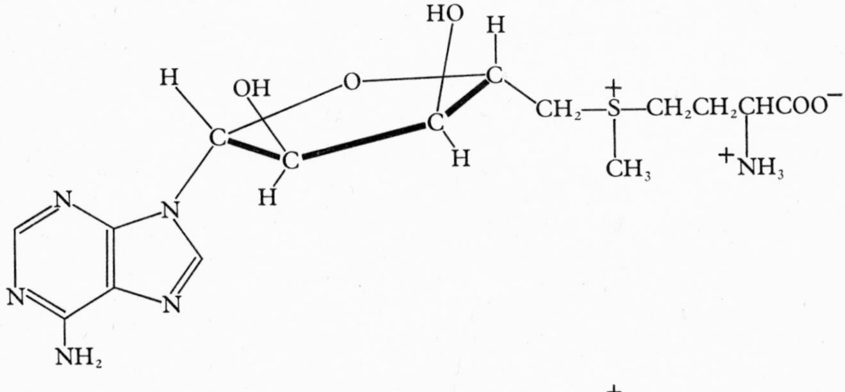

S-adenosylmethionine $Ad \underset{\underset{CH_3}{|}}{\overset{+}{-S}} - R$

The enzymic reactions which we now discuss fall into two classes. In the first class, homocysteine is methylated to give methionine.† The next step in the biological transfer of methyl groups is the conversion of methionine into S-adenosylmethionine; we are not concerned with this reaction here. The subsequent reactions of S-adenosylmethionine form the second class of transmethylation reactions. The abbreviations used in this section are shown on the preceding page.

Betaine, or the analogous dimethylthetin, reacts with homocysteine to give methionine; the enzymes are present in liver. The reactions, which are probably virtually irreversible, may be written:

$$RS^- + CH_3 - \overset{\curvearrowright}{N}{}^+(CH_3)_2CH_2COO^- \longrightarrow RSCH_3 + (CH_3)_2NCH_2COO^-$$

betaine   methionine

$$RS^- + CH_3 - \overset{\curvearrowright}{S}{}^+(CH_3)CH_2COO^- \longrightarrow RSCH_3 + CH_3SCH_2COO^-$$

dimethylthetin   methionine

These are typical nucleophilic substitutions. The carbon-nitrogen, or carbon-sulphur, bond is broken; the electrons depart with the hetero-atom, which decreases its covalency and regains electrical neutrality. As mentioned in § 2 b, this is why these 'onium' compounds are suited to function as methyl donors: their charge makes them better leaving groups.

The thiol, homocysteine, is written as an anion in the reactions given above only because the anionic form will be more nucleophilic than the uncharged form. The enzymes catalysing these reactions are specific for homocysteine but can utilize a variety of methyl donors. The enzymes may act as bases and convert homocysteine to the anion, and they may also bind the two components so that they are close in space. The extent to which this would be expected to facilitate reaction may be gauged by the comparison with the neighbouring-group participation in mustard gas (p. 100): the comparison is brought out in the diagrams:

$$-S\underset{CH_2}{\diagdown}\diagup^{CH_2-\overset{\curvearrowright}{Cl}} \qquad\qquad -S\diagdown\underset{enzyme}{}\diagup CH_3-\overset{\curvearrowright}{X}$$

---

† Maw, *Biochem. J.* 1956, **63**, 116; 1958, **70**, 168; Durell, Anderson, and Cantoni, *Biochim. Biophys. Acta*, 1957, **26**, 270; Ericson, *Nature*, 1960, **185**, 465; Durrell and Sturtevant, *Biochim. Biophys. Acta*, 1957, **26**, 282.

In the second class of transmethylation reactions, S-adenosylmethionine reacts with nicotinamide, dimethylaminoethanol, or glycocyamine; this last example is illustrated below:

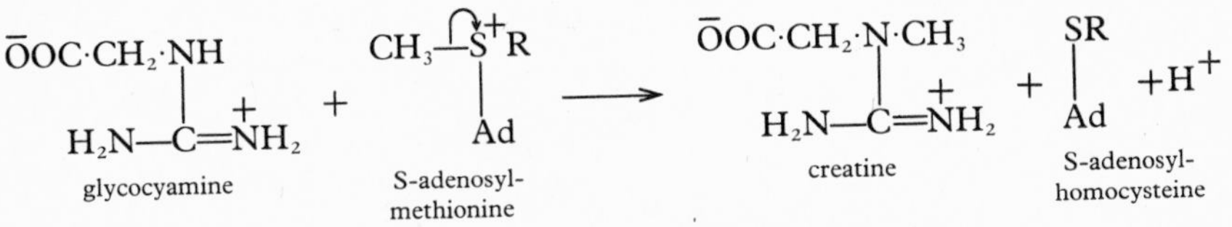

$\overline{O}OC \cdot CH_2 \cdot NH$
$H_2N{-}C{=}\overset{+}{N}H_2$
glycocyamine

$CH_3{-}\overset{+}{S}{-}R$
Ad
S-adenosyl-
methionine

$\overline{O}OC \cdot CH_2 \cdot \overset{\cdot}{N} \cdot CH_3$
$H_2N{-}C{=}\overset{+}{N}H_2$
creatine

SR
Ad
S-adenosyl-
homocysteine

$+H^+$

The nucleophilic reagents in all these reactions contain a nitrogen atom, and the reactivity is associated with the unshared pair of electrons on the nitrogen atom (compare § 1). The analogy between the catalytic effect of the enzyme and neighbouring-group participation will also apply to these transmethylases, as amino groups function effectively as neighbouring groups.

7. Phosphate transfer

The reactions of adenosine triphosphate (ATP)† are, of course, of great importance in energy transformations *in vivo*;‡ an example of one of the ways in which ATP reacts was given at the beginning of this chapter, and two more examples follow:

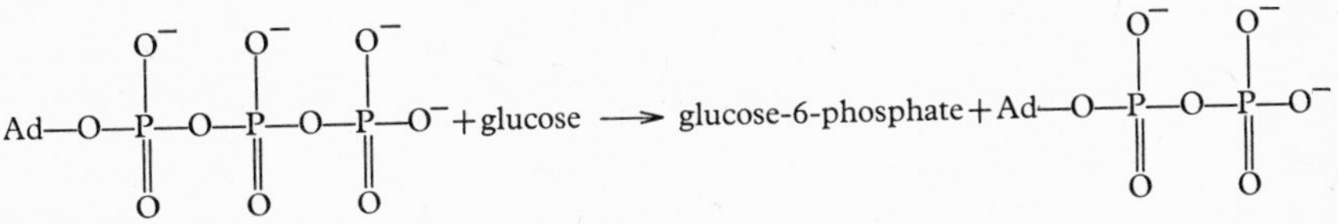

(1)   (2)

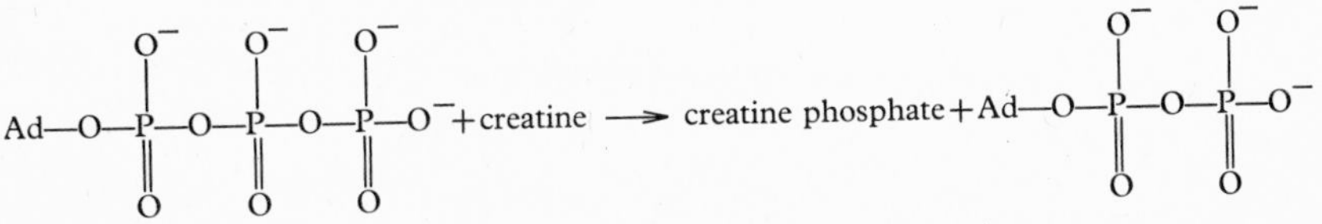

(3)

The creatine phosphate formed in the second reaction contains an

† The structure of ATP is given at the beginning of this book, facing page 1.
‡ Krebs and Kornberg, *Ergebnisse der Physiologie*, 1957, **49**, 212.

N—P bond, and we will begin by considering the factors which play a part in determining the reactivity of these phosphates.

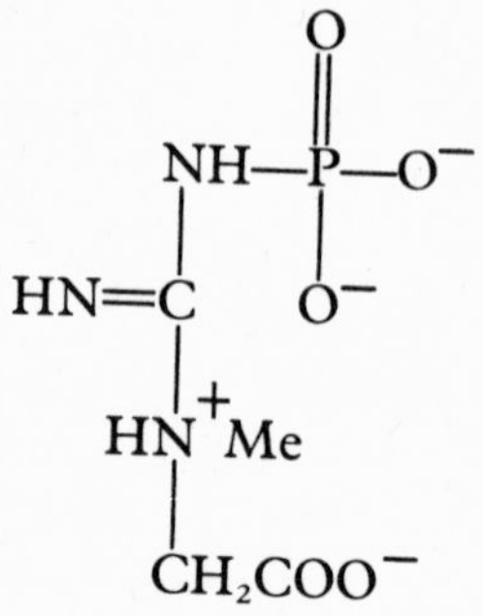

creatine phosphate (3)

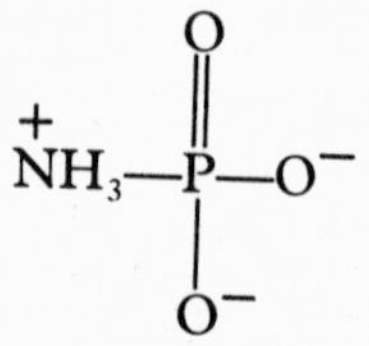

phosphoramidic acid (4)

The simplest substance of this type, phosphoramidic acid, is extremely stable in alkali, where it is present as the dianion, $H_2N \cdot PO_3^{2-}$, but in more acidic solution, in the dipolar form (4), it is reactive. Thus phosphoramidic acid phosphorylates glyoxalines (imidazoles),† forms pyrophosphate from phosphoric acid, and forms the di- and triphosphates (ADP and ATP) from the monophosphate (AMP).‡

Now phosphoramidic acid is unreactive towards nucleophilic substitution in alkaline solution, probably because the amino group is no longer charged. The ionized amino group will be a much better leaving group, just as was found for 'onium' compounds, because heterolysis in the sense $P\text{—}\overset{\curvearrowleft}{N}{}^+$ is aided by the positive charge on the nitrogen atom. Thus the reaction of a negatively charged nucleophilic species (X^-) with a phosphoramidic acid derivative may be written:

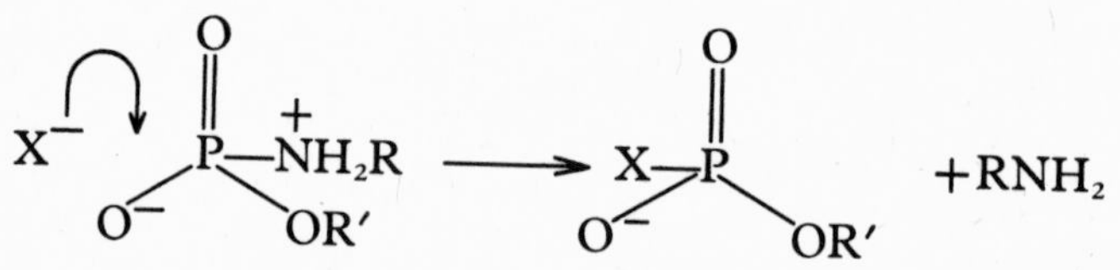

The same set of factors will be found to be important in the hydrolysis

---

† Rathler and Rosenberg, *Arch. Biochem.* 1956, **65**, 319.
‡ Chambers and Khorana, *J. Amer. Chem. Soc.* 1958, **80**, 3749.

of phosphates (Chapter VI, § 2). It is obviously possible to write an ionic form for creatine phosphate (5) of this kind:

$$\overset{+}{N}H_2\!-\!\overset{\displaystyle O}{\underset{\displaystyle O^-}{\overset{\|}{P}}}\!-\!O^-$$

$$HN\!=\!C$$

$$NMeCH_2COO^-$$

(5)

and such a form will be of importance in the non-enzymic reactions of creatine phosphate, such as that with glucose.†

We must now consider the reactivity of adenosine triphosphate (ATP). The anion (1) will be mesomeric (Chapter I, § 1 p), and so could be represented as (6).‡

$$Ad\!-\!O\!-\!\overset{\displaystyle O^-}{\underset{\displaystyle O}{P}}\!-\!O\!-\!\overset{\displaystyle O^-}{\underset{\displaystyle O}{P}}\!-\!O\!-\!\overset{\displaystyle O^-}{\underset{\displaystyle O}{P}}\!-\!O^-$$

(1)

$$Ad\!-\!O\!-\!\overset{\displaystyle O^{\frac{1}{2}-}}{\underset{\displaystyle O^{\frac{1}{2}-}}{P}}\!-\!O\!-\!\overset{\displaystyle O^{\frac{1}{2}-}}{\underset{\displaystyle O^{\frac{1}{2}-}}{P}}\!-\!O\!-\!\overset{\displaystyle O^{\frac{2}{3}-}}{\underset{\displaystyle O^{\frac{2}{3}-}}{P}}\!-\!O^{\frac{2}{3}-}$$

(6)

There are two main ways in which ATP reacts with nucleophilic reagents: either adenosine diphosphate (ADP) or the (inorganic) pyrophosphate anion is split off from ATP. Thus the reaction of glucose with ATP, catalysed by hexokinase, takes the course

$$\text{glucose} + \text{ATP}^{4-} \rightarrow \text{glucose-6-phosphate}^{2-} + \text{ADP}^{3-} + \text{H}^+.$$

When the reaction is carried out in water enriched with $H_2^{18}O$, neither the ADP nor the glucose-6-phosphate is labelled: this suggests cleavage between the terminal phosphorus atom and the linking oxygen atom.§

† Morton, *Biochem. J.* 1958, **70**, 150.
‡ Kalckar, *Chem. Rev.* 1941, **28**, 71; Oesper, *Arch. Biochem.* 1950, **27**, 255; Hill and Morales, *J. Amer. Chem. Soc.* 1951, **73**, 1656; *Arch. Biochem.* 1950, **29**, 450; Grabe, *Biochim. Biophys. Acta*, 1958, **30**, 560.
§ Cohn, *Biochim. Biophys. Acta*, 1956, **20**, 92.

The glucose functions as a nucleophilic reagent by virtue of the unshared electrons on the oxygen atom of the primary hydroxyl group. The reaction may thus be formulated as a nucleophilic attack on the terminal phosphorus atom of ATP (7). The ATP is shown in the extended conformation, as the negative charges on the oxygen atoms repel each other.

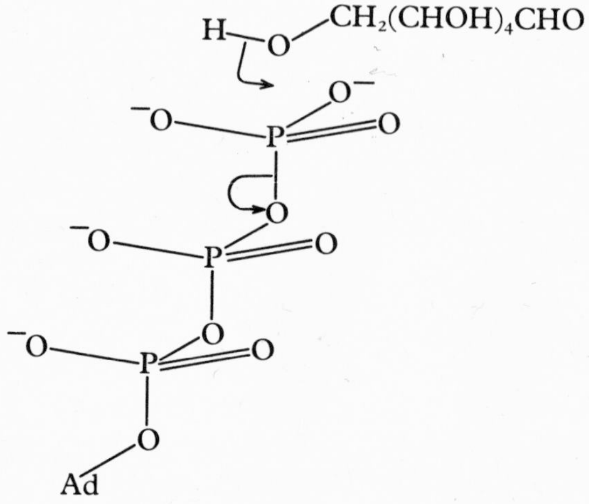

$$CH_2(CHOH)_4CHO$$

(7)

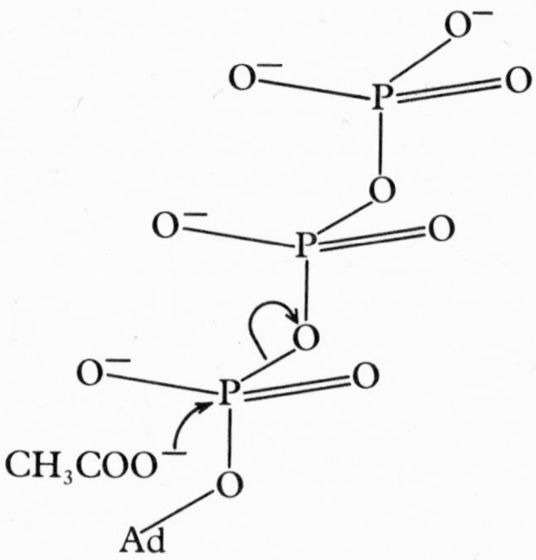

(8)

The second mode of cleavage of ATP is illustrated by the reaction with acetate,† catalysed by acetic thiokinase; here the pyrophosphate ion is

† Boyer, Koeppe, Luchsinger, and Falcone, *J. Amer. Chem. Soc.* 1956, **78**, 356; Berg, *J. Biol. Chem.* 1956, **222**, 991.

liberated (8). Nearly all the enzymic reactions of ATP fall into one of these two categories;[†] the 'middle' phosphorus in ATP seems less prone to attack. This may be due to the fact that a nucleophilic reagent approaching the middle phosphorus atom would probably be repelled to a greater extent by the negatively charged oxygen atoms.

The enzymic reactions of ATP are affected by metal ions, and some non-enzymic reactions are also catalysed by metal ions. The trans-phosphorylation:

$$\text{ATP} + \text{orthophosphate} \rightleftarrows \text{ADP} + \text{pyrophosphate}$$

is catalysed by manganous ions;[‡] this reaction can be regarded as the attack of a nucleophilic reagent (HPO_4^{2-}) on the terminal phosphorus atom, and is thus similar to the reaction of ATP with glucose. It is possible to see, in a general way, why the attack of a nucleophilic reagent on ATP should be catalysed by divalent metal ions. For one thing, the metal ion will partially neutralize the negative charges on the oxygen atoms that hinder the approach of the nucleophilic reagent. Moreover, the metal ion will confer a partial positive charge on the 'linking' oxygen atom, and thus add heterolysis in the sense $\overset{\frown}{\text{P}—\text{O}}$.

This discussion so far has deliberately concentrated on the *reactivity* of phosphates, i.e. on the kinetic aspect. It is, of course, important to know the equilibrium constants of such reactions as (i) and (ii).

$$\text{ATP} + \text{glucose} \rightarrow \text{glucose-6-phosphate} + \text{ADP} \quad \text{(i)}$$

$$\text{ATP} + \text{creatine} \rightarrow \text{creatine phosphate} + \text{ADP} \quad \text{(ii)}$$

It turns out that the equilibrium constants of these two reactions are very different; the equilibrium constant of the second reaction is of the order of unity (at pH 7 and 30° C), whereas that of the first is of the order of 10,000. This situation is general, in that the reactions forming (naturally-occurring) phosphates from ATP (directly, or formally) generally have either rather small or rather large equilibrium constants. The compounds in the former group are customarily called 'high energy' phosphates, and the latter 'low energy' phosphates, for the following reason. The standard free energy change in the hydrolysis of ATP is 8

---

† Cohn, *J. Cell. Comp. Physiol.* 1959, **54**, suppl. 1, 17.
‡ Lowenstein, *Biochem. J.* 1958, **70**, 222.

     I

to 10 kcal/mol (at pH 7 and 30° C; the pH specified in the standard state has a large effect on this value); that of creatine phosphate is of the same order, but that of glucose-6-phosphate is only about 3 kcal/mol. The term 'high energy', then, refers to the free energy change on hydrolysis. Similarly the term 'high energy bond' (or 'energy-rich bond') means, in this connexion, that it is convenient to imagine that the high free energy change on hydrolysis of a compound can be ascribed to the presence in this compound of a particular kind of bond. It should be noted that this meaning† runs counter to the ordinary chemical meaning of bond energy (Chapter I), and it is only in its chemical sense that the term bond energy is used here. It is perhaps better to think of the two classes of phosphates in terms of the equilibrium constants of the reactions in which they are formed from ATP, as described above.

The central importance of ATP in metabolism makes it important to know which organic phosphates are capable of reacting with ADP to form roughly equimolar amounts of ATP at equilibrium. One such phosphate is phosphoenol pyruvate (9) and its reaction with ADP can be formally divided into steps:

$$
\begin{array}{c}
\text{CH}_2 \\
\parallel \\
\text{C}-\text{O}-\overset{\displaystyle \text{O}}{\underset{\displaystyle \text{O}^-}{\overset{\parallel}{\text{P}}}}-\text{O}^- \; +\text{ADP} \longrightarrow \quad \text{CH}_2 \\
\mid \\
\text{COO}^-
\end{array}
\qquad
\begin{array}{c}
\text{CH}_2 \\
\parallel \\
\text{C}-\text{OH} \; +\text{ATP} \\
\mid \\
\text{COO}^-
\end{array}
$$

(9)

$$
\begin{array}{c}
\text{CH}_2 \\
\parallel \\
\text{C}-\text{OH} \\
\mid \\
\text{COO}^-
\end{array}
\longrightarrow
\begin{array}{c}
\text{CH}_3 \\
\mid \\
\text{C}=\text{O} \\
\mid \\
\text{COO}^-
\end{array}
$$

The second step is just a keto-enol tautomerization (Chapter V), and it is largely because the equilibrium here is so much towards the keto form that the equilibrium of the overall reaction is favourable for the phosphorylation of ADP by phosphoenol pyruvate (see Chapter I, § 2 c).

† Gillespie, Maw, and Vernon, *Nature*, 1953, **171**, 1147; George and Rutman, *Progress in Biophysics and Biophysical Chemistry*, 1960, **10**, 1; see also Gutfreund, *Disc. Faraday Soc.* 1959, **27**, 226.

The same structural feature is present in the acetylating agent, iso-propenyl acetate (10).

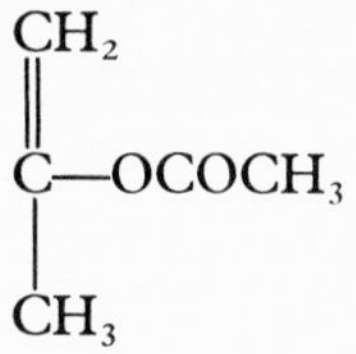

$$CH_2$$
$$\|$$
$$C\text{---}OCOCH_3$$
$$|$$
$$CH_3$$

(10)

There is sometimes a parallel between equilibria and rates in such reactions. In, for example, the attack of a nucleophilic reagent on the terminal phosphorus atom of ATP, the leaving group is ADP. A reactive species may be described as one that contains a good leaving group, and a good leaving group is often the anion corresponding to a quite strongly acid species. The low affinity of the anion of ADP (ADP^{3-}) for a proton markedly affects the extent of reaction of ATP with, say, glucose. Hence the fact that ADP is quite a strong acid will affect both the rate and extent of reaction with a nucleophilic species. It is, in fact, generally true that the hydrolysis of an acid anhydride proceeds both more rapidly, and to a greater extent, than the hydrolysis of an ester.

OLEFINE-FORMING ELIMINATIONS AND ADDITIONS TO OLEFINIC DOUBLE BONDS

1. Olefine-forming eliminations

(a) *Relation to nucleophilic substitution.* This chapter deals with some of the ways in which double bonds between two carbon atoms are formed, and how they react. These reactions are of widespread importance. Thus they are used in the determination of the structure (and estimation) of, for example, unsaturated acids and carotenoids, and the reactions are also much used in synthesis. Moreover, these reactions feature in glycolysis, and in the Krebs (citric acid) cycle.

A typical elimination is

$$CH_3 \cdot CH_2 \cdot CHBr \cdot CH_3 + NaOEt \longrightarrow CH_3 \cdot CH = CH \cdot CH_3 + EtOH + NaBr$$

$$(1) \hspace{5cm} (2)$$

The alkyl bromide (1) loses HBr to give the olefine (2). These reactions are sometimes referred to as β-eliminations, because the essence of the reaction may be depicted as:

$$H - \overset{\beta}{C} - \overset{\alpha}{C} - Br \longrightarrow \overset{\beta}{C} = \overset{\alpha}{C} + HBr$$

The carbon atom carrying the halogen atom is called α, and the one carrying the hydrogen atom which is to be eliminated is called β.

There is a plurality of possible pathways open to s-butyl bromide (1) under these conditions. Nucleophilic substitution gives the ether (3), and substitution and elimination commonly occur concurrently. Furthermore, elimination gives both the structural isomers, but-1-ene (4) and but-2-ene (2). Finally, either (or both) of the stereoisomers, i.e. the *cis* (5) or the *trans* (6), of but-2-ene may be formed:

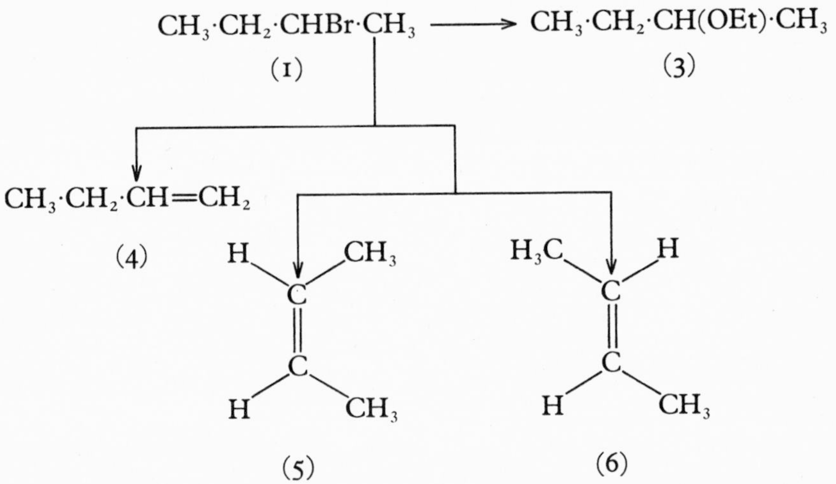

$$CH_3 \cdot CH_2 \cdot CHBr \cdot CH_3 \longrightarrow CH_3 \cdot CH_2 \cdot CH(OEt) \cdot CH_3$$
$$(\text{1}) \qquad\qquad\qquad\qquad\qquad (\text{3})$$

$$CH_3 \cdot CH_2 \cdot CH{=}CH_2$$
$$(\text{4})$$

(5)   (6)

The pathway chosen is one of the guides to the mechanism of the reaction, and, conversely, a knowledge of the mechanism may enable one to predict the pathway in other cases.†

(b) *E-2 mechanism.* In many cases the formation of an olefine from an alkyl halide and a base is a second-order reaction,

$$CH_3 \cdot CHBr \cdot CH_3 + OEt^- \longrightarrow CH_3 \cdot CH{=}CH_2 + EtOH + Br^-,$$

and the same often applies to another common type of elimination, from an ammonium or sulphonium ion:

$$HO^- + PhCH_2 \cdot CH_2 \cdot \overset{+}{N}Me_3 \longrightarrow PhCH{=}CH_2 + NMe_3 + H_2O$$

The simplest mechanism to account for the observed second-order kinetics is a bimolecular mechanism (called *E-2*; elimination, bimolecular). Here the base (OEt⁻ or OH⁻ in the examples cited) forms a bond with the β-hydrogen atom which is being eliminated, and this new bond is being formed while the old bond to the departing group is being broken. Thus, the detailed picture according to the *E-2* mechanism is

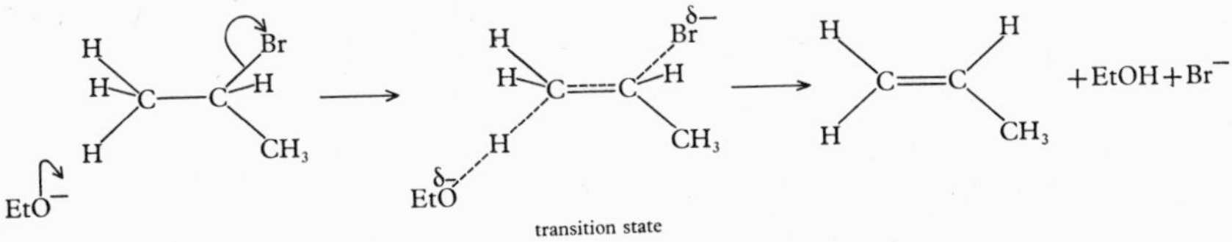

transition state

† For a detailed account of these reactions, see Ingold, *Structure and Mechanism in Organic Chemistry,* chap. viii, Cornell University Press, 1953.

This bimolecular (*E*-2) mechanism may be compared with the bimolecular (S_N2) mechanism of substitution and, as mentioned, the processes frequently compete. The main difference is that in an elimination the base attacks a hydrogen atom, and in a substitution, a carbon atom. Hence one of the factors governing the ratio of elimination to substitution (i.e. the proportion of olefine in the products) is the affinity that a given base has for carbon, relative to the affinity that it has for hydrogen. The affinity of several reagents for carbon (nucleophilic activity) has been given in Chapter III (§ 2 b, Table 9). A highly basic anion has, by definition, a high affinity for a proton, and often turns out not to have a correspondingly high affinity for carbon: thus the highly basic hydroxyl ion leads to more elimination than the less basic acetate ion. This differentiation can be used in syntheses.

Another possible mechanism which leads to second-order kinetics consists of a rapid 'pre-equilibrium', followed by a relatively slow loss of halide ion from the carbanion:

$$PhCH_2\cdot CH_2Br + OH^- \rightleftharpoons Ph\bar{C}H\cdot CH_2Br + H_2O$$

$$Ph\bar{C}H\cdot CH_2Br \longrightarrow PhCH{=}CH_2 + Br^-$$

This mechanism entails the incorporation of deuterium into the alkyl bromide during the course of the reaction when the basic species is OD^-:

$$PhCH_2\cdot CH_2Br + OD^- \rightleftharpoons Ph\bar{C}H\cdot CH_2Br \rightleftharpoons PhCHD\cdot CH_2Br + OH^-$$

This has been tested in the example given, and no deuterium was incorporated, so that this mechanism is here ruled out.†

The bimolecular (*E*-2) mechanism of elimination, like the S_N2 mechanism, is stereospecific. *The two leaving groups are on the opposite sides of the developing double bond in the transition state.* This general rule of *trans* elimination was put forward some time ago;‡ an example is that the elimination of HBr from meso-dibromosuccinic acid (1) gives bromomaleic acid (2), and DL-dibromosuccinic acid (3) similarly gives bromofumaric acid (4). The stereochemical demands are actually rather more exacting than this; not only should the departing groups be *trans*, but they should also lie in the same plane as the two carbon atoms which are to be doubly bound,§ as is shown in the formulae opposite.

† Skell and Hauser, *J. Amer. Chem. Soc.* 1945, **67**, 1661.
‡ Frankland, *J. Chem. Soc.* 1912, p. 654.
§ Barton and Miller, *J. Amer. Chem. Soc.* 1950, **72**, 1066; for a theoretical interpretation, see Stewart and Eyring, *J. Chem. Educ.* 1958, **35**, 550.

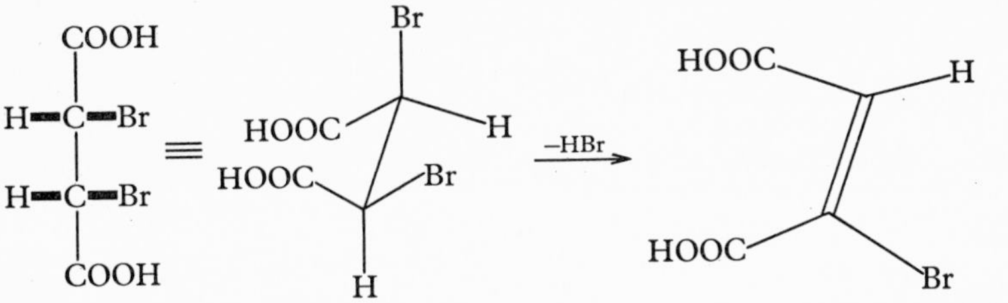

(1)   (2)

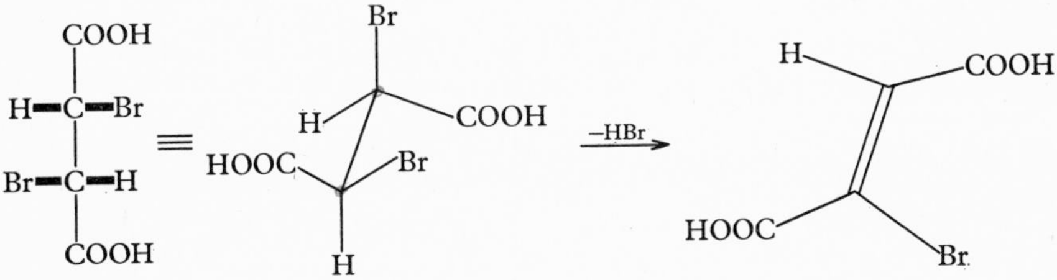

(3)   (4)

These principles may be applied to the sequence of reactions in the conversion of a *trans*-olefine into a *cis*-olefine:†

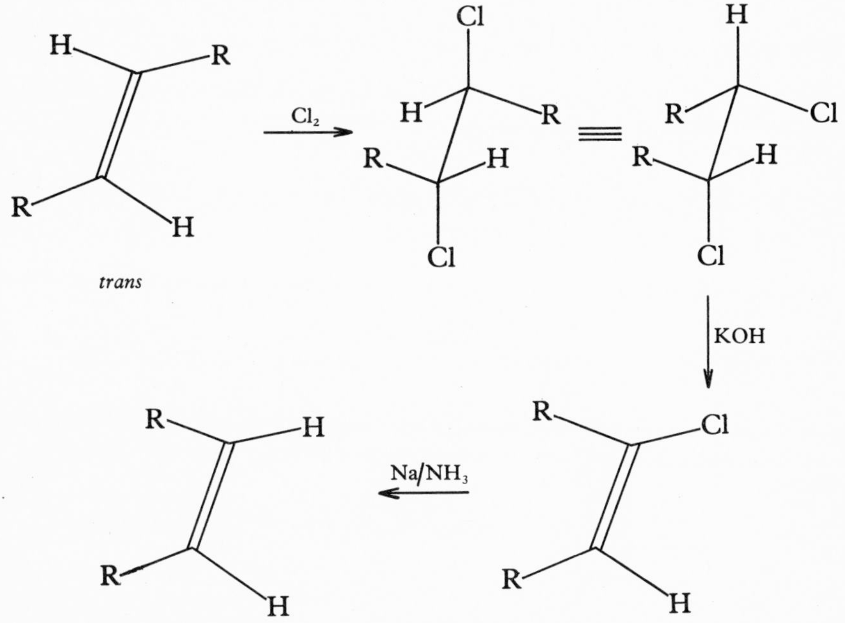

trans

Cis

† Hobb, Greenlee, and Boord, *J. Amer. Chem. Soc.* 1951, **73**, 3329.

The preference for *trans* elimination is confirmed by the following experiments. The rate of elimination of HCl from five of the isomers of benzene hexachloride has been studied: they all react at roughly comparable rates except one, and this one was found to be the one isomer (5) in which no two neighbouring carbon atoms carried a hydrogen atom and a chlorine atom in the *trans* position; this isomer reacted at about 1/10,000th the rate of the other isomers.†

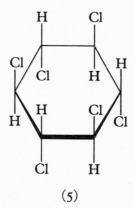

(5)

That the preference for *trans* elimination is contingent upon the departing groups being coplanar with the developing double bond is suggested by the observation that the elimination of HCl from the compounds (6) and (7) proceeds at comparable rates. Although (6) can undergo *trans* elimination, the hydrogen and chlorine atoms cannot become coplanar with the carbon atoms shown as such.‡

(6)   (7)

(c) *Orientation in bimolecular eliminations.* When s-butyl bromide is treated with potassium hydroxide in ethanol both possible olefines are formed (§ 1 a), but in this E-2 reaction the but-2-ene represents about 80 per cent. and the but-1-ene about 20 per cent. of the mixture of olefines. The major product is the one in which the β-hydrogen atom

† Cristol, Hause, and Meek, *J. Amer. Chem. Soc.* 1951, **73**, 674.
‡ Cristol and Hause, ibid. 1952, **74**, 2193.

that is eliminated comes from the carbon atom carrying the lesser number of hydrogen atoms: this is usually known as Saytzeff's rule. (It has also been reported that the but-2-ene formed under these conditions is largely the less stable *cis* stereoisomer, which is somewhat unexpected.)† A mixture of olefines is, in fact, usually formed. The difference between the free energies of activation of the reactions leading to but-1-ene and but-2-ene is less than 1 kcal/mol, which is quite small; it is, therefore, relatively difficult to track down the factors responsible for the predominant orientation.

The usual result is that the more stable olefine is the major product, and the most alkylated olefine (e.g. but-2-ene, rather than but-1-ene) is commonly the most stable isomer. However, a tertiary butyl group in the *cis* position to a methyl group is unfavourable: the molecule is overcrowded, as can be seen from the overlap of the van der Waals radii of the methyl groups, one of which is at one end of the double bond, and the other of which is part of the tertiary butyl residue.

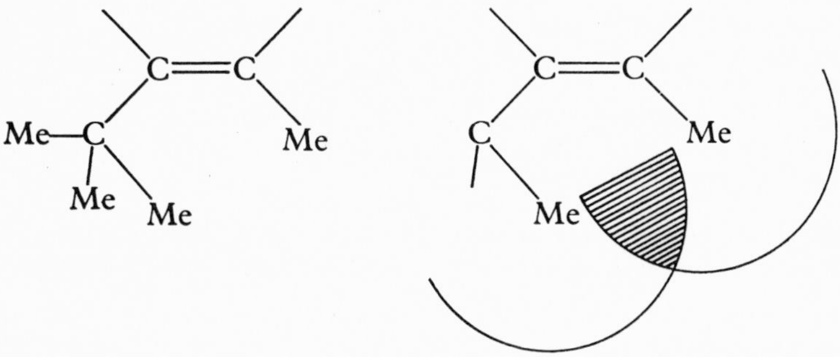

Hence the more alkylated olefine (1) is less stable than its isomer (2),

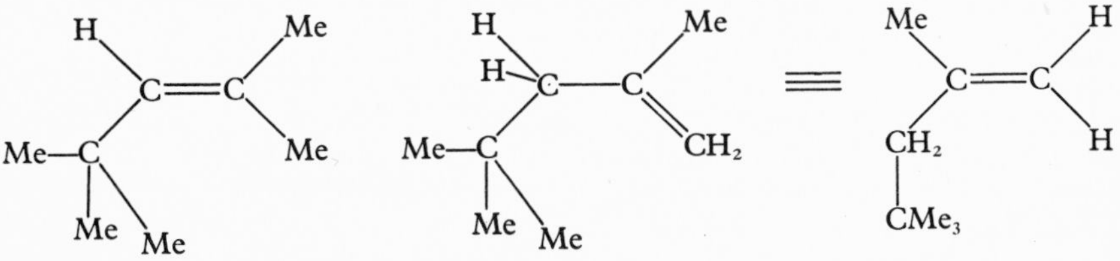

(1)   (2)

and so the latter (2) is the major product formed in the elimination of HBr from $Me_3C.CH_2.CMe_2Br$.‡

† Dhar, Hughes, and Ingold, *J. Chem. Soc.* 1948, p. 2058.
‡ Brown, *J. Chem. Soc.* 1956, p. 1248; Brown and Moritani, *J. Amer. Chem. Soc.* 1956, **78**, 2203.

Although the more stable olefine is the main product in the examples given hitherto, the important factor is the stability of the transition state relative to the initial state. In some eliminations, notably from

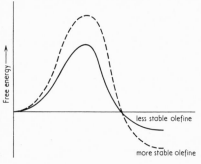

FIG. 24. Less stable olefine is the main product

(e.g. $EtO^- + CH_3 . CH_2 . CH . CH_3$)
$$\underset{^+S(CH_3)_2}{|}$$

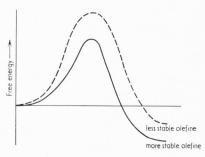

FIG. 25. More stable olefine is the main product

(e.g. $EtO^- + CH_3 . CH_2 . CH . CH_3$)
$$\underset{Br}{|}$$

sulphonium and ammonium ions, the main product is the *less* highly substituted olefine:

$$CH_3 \cdot CH_2 \cdot CH \cdot CH_3 \underset{^+SMe_2}{|} + EtO^- \longrightarrow CH_3 \cdot CH_2 \cdot CH = CH_2 + CH_3 \cdot CH = CH \cdot CH_3$$

$$74\% \qquad\qquad 26\%$$

In particular, ethylene is the main olefine formed by the decomposition of most quaternary ammonium hydroxides containing an ethyl group (Hofmann rule). In the reaction shown above, as but-1-ene is less stable than but-2-ene, the more stable transition state must correspond to the less stable product. This situation entails a 'crossing' of the energy curves (Fig. 24), as opposed to the situation in the examples cited earlier (Fig. 25).

There are several possible factors which may contribute towards the preferential formation of the less stable olefine. In olefines of the type $RCH_2 . CMe_2X$, where R is a branched alkyl group, steric factors favour the formation of the olefine with a terminal double bond, especially when the leaving group is bulky, as the $—\overset{+}{N}Me_3$ and $—\overset{+}{S}Me_2$ groups are. The E-2 mechanism requires a stereochemically well-defined transition state (§ 1 b), and the hydrogen atoms in a terminal methyl group of $RCH_2 . CMe_2X$ are more accessible to the attack by base than are the hydrogen atoms of the CH_2 group.† There is also, of course, a statistical

† Brown, *J. Chem. Soc.* 1956, p. 1248.

factor of $3:1$ which favours attack on the hydrogen atoms of the methyl groups.

The fractional charge arising from the dipole in a bond joining two atoms of differing electronegativity (the inductive effect) may influence the direction of elimination. Thus the chloride (3) gives the olefine (4):

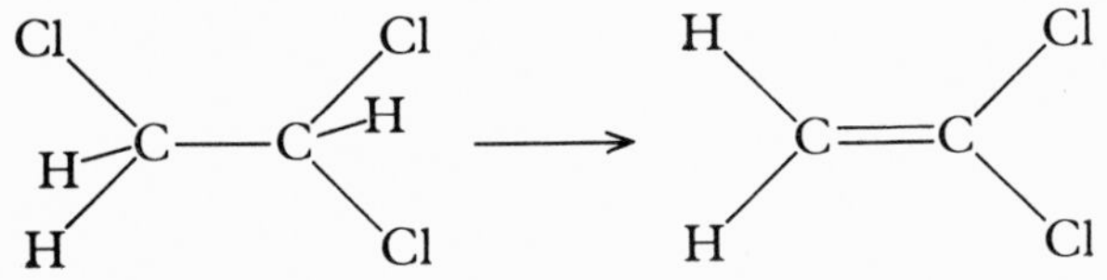

(3)   (4)

The hydrogen atom is lost from the carbon atom which carries two electron-withdrawing chlorine atoms; as the hydrogen atom departs leaving the formerly bonding pair of electrons with the carbon atom, the departure is facilitated by the movement of electrons away from the carbon atom. A similar conclusion is reached by a study of the effect of varying the substituent (X) on the rate of the reactions (i) and (ii).†

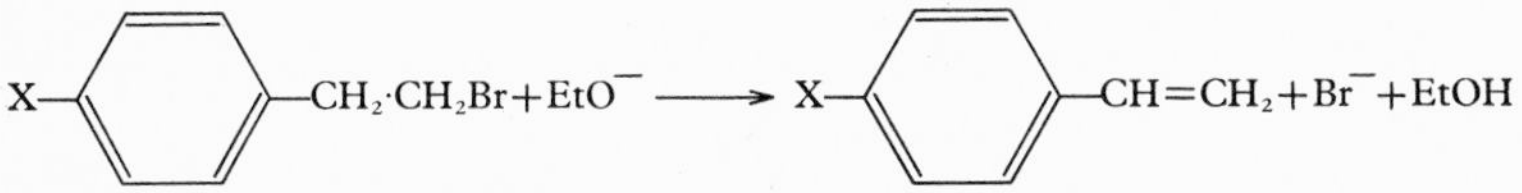

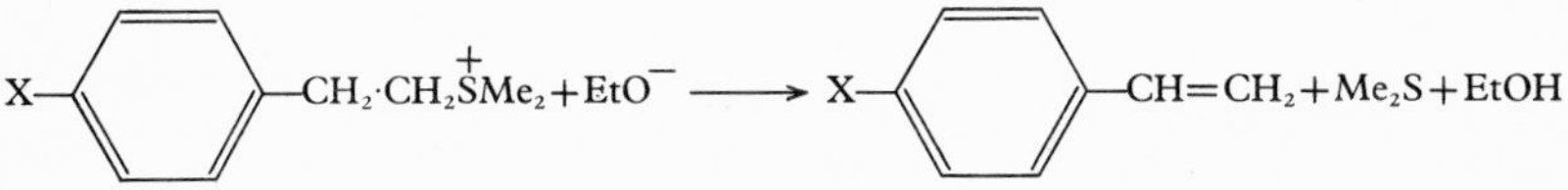

The application of Hammett's equation (Chapter II, § 2 e) gave values of the reaction constant (ρ) of $+2 \cdot 3$ for reaction (i) and of $+2 \cdot 6$ for reaction (ii). Thus electron-withdrawing substituents facilitate both reactions, and to about the same extent, essentially by lessening the work required to break the carbon-hydrogen bond. Conversely, an electron-repelling substituent acts unfavourably towards the cleavage of the C—H bond. A methyl group is (relative to hydrogen) an electron-repelling substituent, so that the reason for the preferential formation of but-1-ene from the sulphonium salt, $CH_3CH_2CH(\overset{+}{S}Me_2)CH_3$, may be connected with the electron-repelling character of the methyl group shown below:

† Saunders and Williams, *J. Amer. Chem. Soc.* 1957, **79**, 3712.

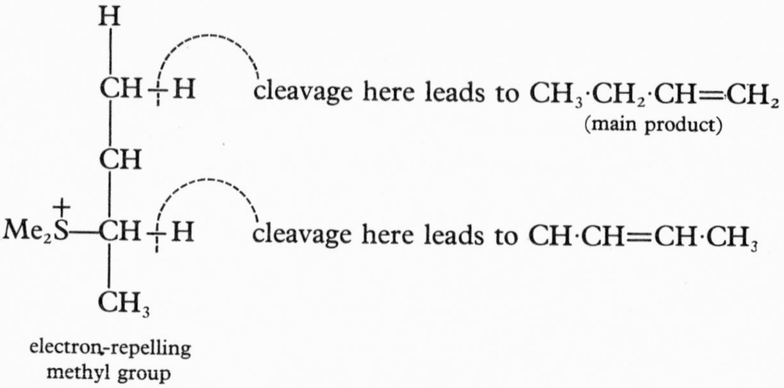

$$
\begin{array}{l}
\text{H} \\
| \\
\text{CH} \!-\!\text{H} \qquad \text{cleavage here leads to } CH_3\cdot CH_2\cdot CH{=}CH_2 \\
| \qquad\qquad\qquad\qquad\qquad\qquad\qquad \text{(main product)} \\
\text{CH} \\
| \\
Me_2\overset{+}{S}\!-\!\text{CH}\!-\!\text{H} \qquad \text{cleavage here leads to } CH\cdot CH{=}CH\cdot CH_3 \\
| \\
\text{CH}_3
\end{array}
$$

electron-repelling
methyl group

In this example, it does not seem likely that the orientation should be ascribed to steric hindrance.

(d) *E-1 mechanism.* The rate of elimination of hydrogen bromide from t-butyl bromide in ethanol is not much increased by adding approximately one molecular proportion of sodium ethoxide; the main reaction is first-order, and is by a unimolecular (*E*-1) mechanism:

$$(CH_3)_3C\!-\!Br \xrightarrow{\text{slow}} (CH_3)_3\overset{+}{C} + Br^-$$

$$(\text{I})$$

$$(CH_3)_3\overset{+}{C} \xrightarrow{\text{fast}} CH_2{=}C(CH_3)_2 + H^+$$

The intermediate (1) is a carbonium ion; it is, in fact, the same carbonium ion as is postulated in the S_N1 mechanism for nucleophilic substitution. The S_N1 and *E*-1 reactions share a common intermediate, whose formation is the rate-determining step. This intermediate, the carbonium ion, can then react in two ways, as set out on the opposite page.

Thus, if a series of t-butyl compounds, $(CH_3)_3C.X$, all react by the unimolecular mechanism, the proportion of the olefine in the total product should be the same, since the leaving group, X, has already been expelled before the product-determining stage. This has been found to hold, for example, in the reactions of t-butyl chloride, bromide, and iodide in aqueous ethanol. Similarly, the orientation (when more than one olefine can be formed) does not depend on the leaving group. In unimolecular eliminations, the main product is the most alkylated olefine (Saytzeff rule).

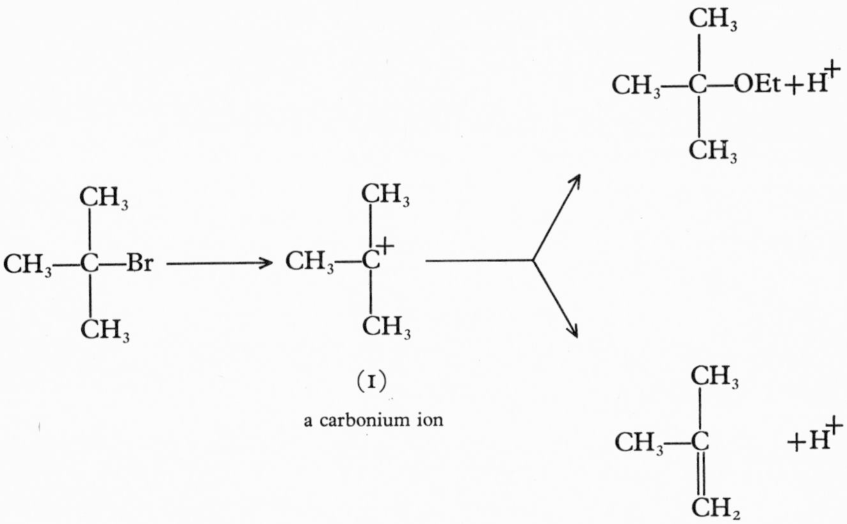

$$CH_3-\overset{\overset{\displaystyle CH_3}{|}}{\underset{\underset{\displaystyle CH_3}{|}}{C}}-OEt+\overset{+}{H}$$

$$CH_3-\overset{\overset{\displaystyle CH_3}{|}}{\underset{\underset{\displaystyle CH_3}{|}}{C}}-Br \longrightarrow CH_3-\overset{\overset{\displaystyle CH_3}{|}}{\underset{\underset{\displaystyle CH_3}{|}}{\overset{+}{C}}}$$

(I)

a carbonium ion

$$CH_3-\overset{\overset{\displaystyle CH_3}{|}}{\underset{\underset{\displaystyle CH_2}{||}}{C}} \quad +\overset{+}{H}$$

| rate-determining | product-determining |
| stage | stage |

(e) *Elimination and substitution.* Elimination and substitution frequently compete. The proportion of olefine in the products depends on
a number of factors, which are briefly discussed in this section. The
yield of olefine varies markedly with whether the compound is primary,
secondary, or tertiary. Tertiary halides give the most olefine by either
mechanism, but the difference is much more marked in the bimolecular
reaction. Here the cause is easily seen from the figures in Table 10.

TABLE 10

Alkyl halide	Substitution 10^5k (l. mol^{-1} sec^{-1})	Elimination 10^5k (l. mol^{-1} sec^{-1})	Yield of olefine (%)
Ethyl bromide	118	1·2	1
Isopropyl bromide	1·2	7·6	19
t-Butyl bromide	1	50	nearly 100

Conditions: NaOEt in EtOH at 55° C.

From: Ingold, *Structure and Mechanism in Organic Chemistry*, p. 439, Cornell University Press, 1953.

The branching of the α-carbon atom increases the rate of the elimination
and decreases the rate of the substitution (Chapter III, § 2 b), so that
the combined effect is that the yield of olefine changes sharply.

The yield of olefine also increases with increase of temperature. The
more basic the reagent, the greater the yield of olefine, if the bimolecular

mechanism is operative (§ 1 b); in the unimolecular mechanism the intermediate common to both substitution and elimination (the carbonium ion) usually reacts with the solvent, and so here the olefine yield is governed by the nature of the solvent. The solvent also affects matters in bimolecular reactions, and, in general, the yield of olefine is higher in absolute ethanol than in aqueous ethanol.

(f) *Some other eliminations.* Olefines are formed from 1,2-dibromides by the action of zinc; the reaction may be envisaged as follows (note that the order of increasing electronegativity is zinc, carbon, bromine):

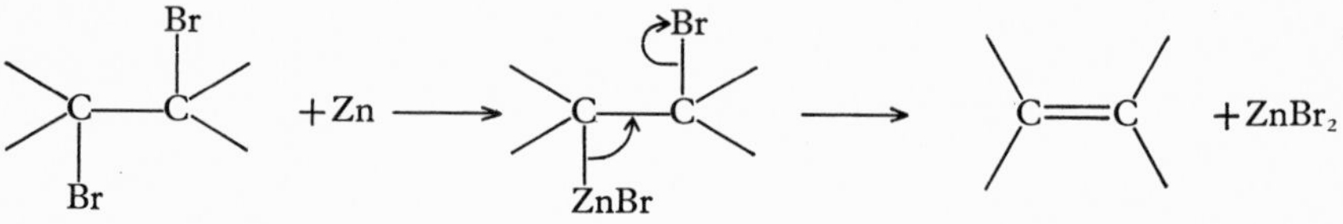

An interesting example leads to the formation of spiropentane:

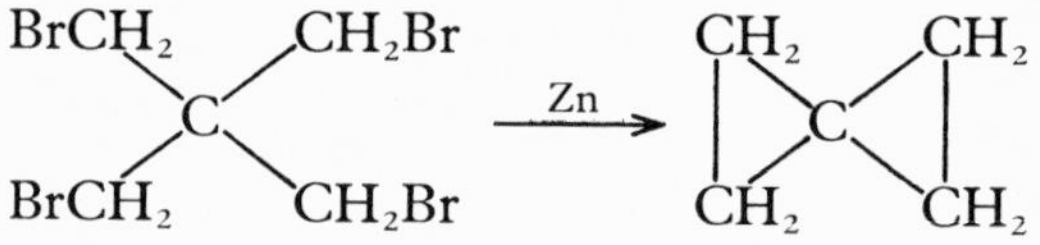

The yield was greatly improved by the addition of ethylene-diamine tetra-acetic acid, which depressed the concentration of zinc ions and lowered the rate of a metal ion-catalysed side reaction.†

The formation of olefines from dibromides and iodide ion is somewhat similar:

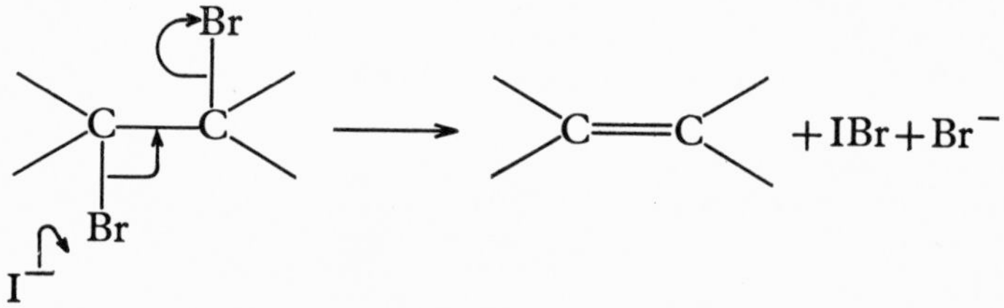

This is a bimolecular (E-2) reaction, and so the dibromide will react in that conformation in which the two carbon-bromine bonds are anti-parallel. Meso-dibromides (e.g. (1)) were found to react more rapidly than the corresponding DL-dibromides (e.g. (2)):‡

---

† Applequist, Fanta, and Henrikson, *J. Org. Chem.* 1958, **23**, 1715.
‡ Winstein, Pressmann, and Young, *J. Amer. Chem. Soc.* 1939, **61**, 1645; Young, Pressmann, and Coryell, ibid., p. 1640.

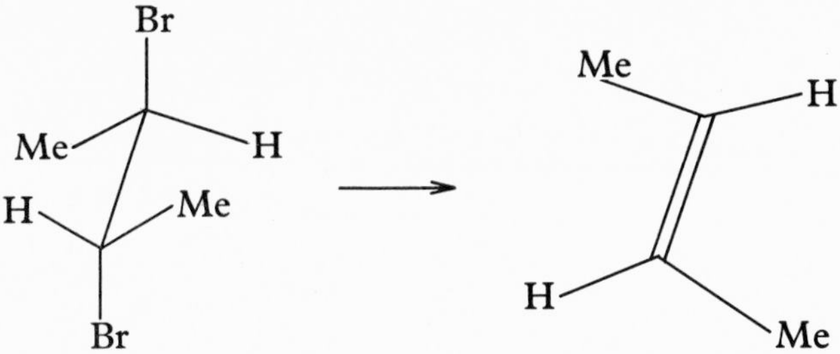

(I)   *trans*-but-2-ene

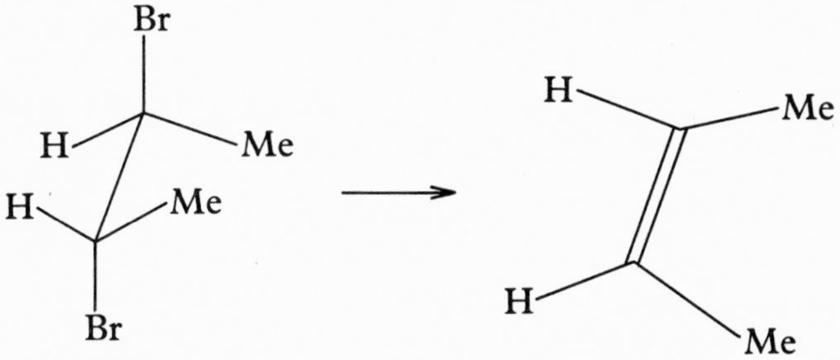

(2)   *cis*-but-2-ene

The slower reaction of (2) may be ascribed to the fact that the methyl groups are moving nearer together during the course of the reaction (the methyl groups are eclipsed in the olefine, and the double bond is shorter than the single bond), so that the transition state leading to the *cis* olefine is less stable (relative to the initial state) than that leading to the *trans* olefine. This is another example of the importance of steric effects in bimolecular eliminations.

In these reactions two halogen atoms are lost to give an olefine. A halogen atom and a hydroxyl group may also be lost, as in the stereo-selective olefine synthesis, in which one stage is as shown:†

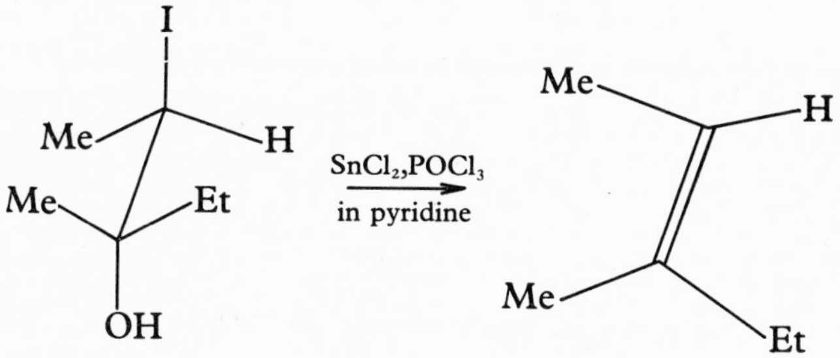

† Cornforth, Cornforth, and Mathew, *J. Chem. Soc.* 1959, p. 112.

A halogen atom and carbon dioxide may also be lost; thus cinnamic acid dibromide (3) (prepared by the *trans* addition of bromine to *trans*-cinnamic acid) loses carbon dioxide and bromide ion to give the *cis-β*-bromostyrene (4) in acetone solution, although in aqueous solution the main product is the more stable *trans* olefine.†

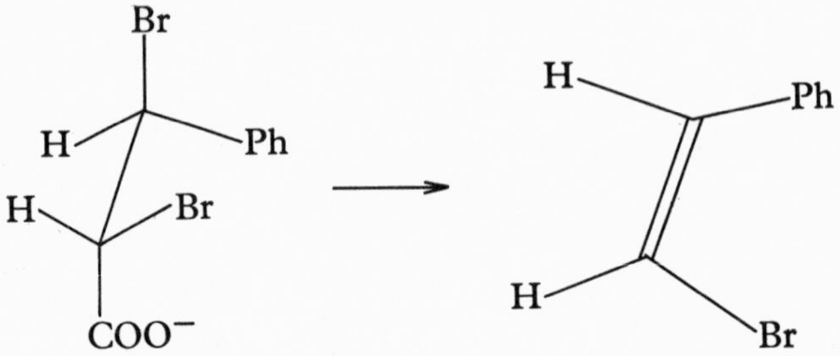

(3)   (4)

Olefines are also formed by heating esters (or halides) in the gas phase. In contradistinction to the reactions in solution, the reaction in the gas phase is usually a *cis* elimination, proceeding via a cyclic transition state.‡

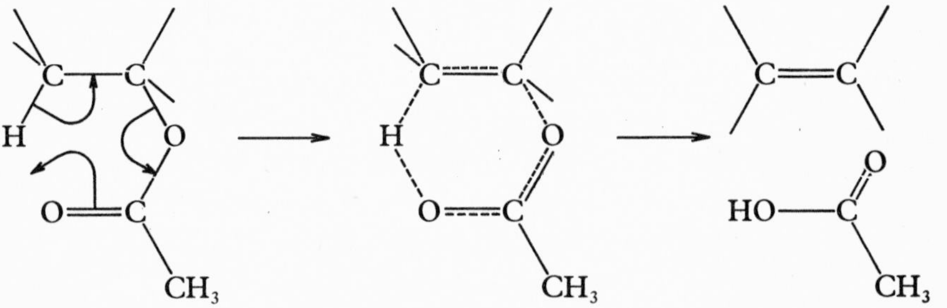

(g) α-*Eliminations*. Chloroform is decomposed in alkaline solution; the products are carbon monoxide, formate ion, and chloride ion. There is considerable evidence§ for the mechanism

$$CHCl_3 + OH^- \underset{}{\overset{fast}{\rightleftharpoons}} \bar{C}Cl_3 + H_2O$$

$$CO,\ HCOO^- \xleftarrow[H_2O]{fast} CCl_2 + Cl^-$$

dichlorocarbene

---

† Grovenstein and Lee, *J. Amer. Chem. Soc.* 1953, **75**, 2639; Cristol and Norris, ibid., p. 2645.

‡ Cram, in Newman's *Steric Effects in Organic Chemistry*, Wiley, 1956, p. 304; MacColl, *J. Chem. Soc.* 1958, p. 3398.

§ Hine, *J. Amer. Chem. Soc.* 1950, **72**, 2438, and later papers.

Here the hydrogen and chlorine atoms, which are eliminated in the conversion of chloroform into dichlorocarbene, were both bound to the same carbon atom, and so this is referred to as an α-elimination. The reactive intermediate, dichlorocarbene, is one of the few examples of a divalent carbon compound; there is an unshared pair of electrons on the carbon atom and the species is often classed as a diradical. Dichloro-carbene is a probable intermediate in several reactions of chloroform in alkaline solution (e.g. Reimer–Tiemann reaction). There is also evidence that the parent hydrocarbon, carbene (or methylene), CH_2, is formed on pyrolysis of diazomethane. Carbene is an even more reactive species.[†]

2. Some eliminations catalysed by enzymes

The enzymes which catalyse the formation of a carbon-carbon double bond by elimination of water, or ammonia, are discussed in § 4. Here we may first note dimethylpropiothetin dethiomethylase, the enzyme which catalyses an olefine-forming elimination from a sulphonium salt:[‡]

$$\overset{+}{Me_2}S \cdot CH_2 \cdot CH_2 \cdot COOH \longrightarrow Me_2S + CH_2{=}CHCOOH + \overset{+}{H}$$

The non-enzymic reaction takes place readily with cold alkali. Compounds containing a thiol group (e.g. glutathione) are required in the enzymic reaction; it seems possible that a basic group in the enzyme helps to detach the proton from the thetin.

The second elimination catalysed by an enzyme discussed in this section is a step in the biosynthesis of steroids:[§]

mevalonic acid
pyrophosphate

isopentenyl
pyrophosphate

† See, for example, Hine and Prosser, *J. Amer. Chem. Soc.* 1958, **80**, 4282; Kirmse, *Angew. Chem.* 1959, **71**, 537.

‡ Challenger and Simpson, *J. Chem. Soc.* 1948, p. 1591; Cantoni and Anderson, *J. Biol. Chem.* 1956, **222**, 171.

§ Bloch, Chaykin, Phillips, and de Waard, *J. Biol. Chem.* 1959, **234**, 2595; Lynen, Eggerer, Henning, and Kessel, *Angew. Chem.* 1958, **70**, 738; Agranoff, Eggerer, Henning, and Lynen, *J. Amer. Chem. Soc.* 1959, **81**, 1254.

In this reaction the carbon-carbon double bond is formed by the elimination of water and carbon dioxide. If we assume that the function of ATP is to phosphorylate the tertiary hydroxyl group, then the reaction may be shown in outline as:

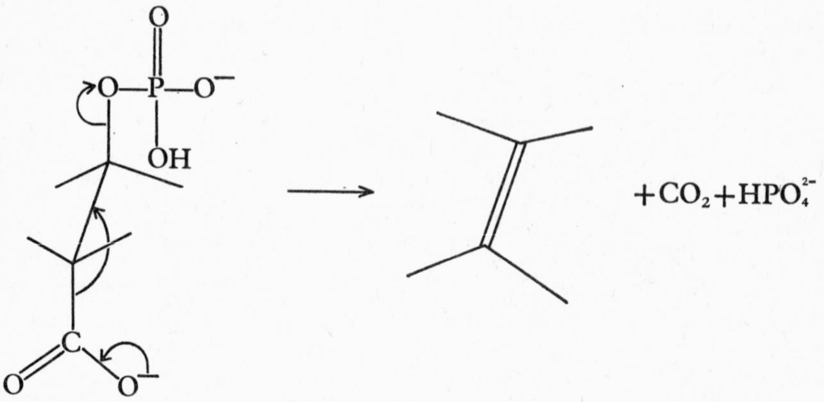

$$+CO_2+HPO_4^{2-}$$

The reaction is thus quite similar to the elimination of carbon dioxide and bromide ion from cinnamic acid dibromide discussed above, and shown again below:

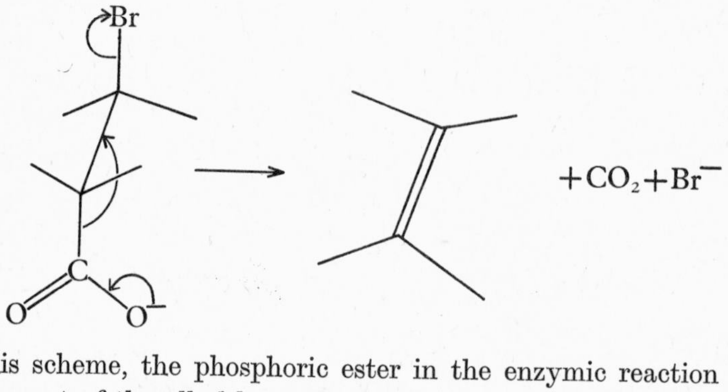

$$+CO_2+Br^-$$

On this scheme, the phosphoric ester in the enzymic reaction is the counterpart of the alkyl bromide in the non-enzymic reaction (cf. the reactions of glucose-1-phosphate, Chapter VI, § 2 a). It seems quite likely that the adenosine triphosphate does phosphorylate the tertiary hydroxyl group: the resulting phosphoric ester would lose phosphoric acid much more readily than the alcohol would lose ⁻OH, and indeed the phosphoric ester might well be very unstable. The formation of olefines from esters, including phosphoric esters, is a well-known reaction.†

† See especially Linstead, Owen, and Webb, *J. Chem. Soc.* 1953, pp. 1211, 1218.

3. Additions to olefines

The reactions which we are now going to discuss are of the type:

$$CH_2{=}CH_2 + Br_2 \longrightarrow BrCH_2 \cdot CH_2Br$$

$$HOOC \cdot CH{=}CH \cdot COOH + H_2O \longrightarrow HOOC \cdot CHOH \cdot CH_2 \cdot COOH$$

These additions are obviously the reverse of the eliminations described in the last section. The addition of water (§ 3 c) is usually a readily reversible reaction: the equilibrium can be approached from either side. The additions of halogens, or halogen acids, however, are not carried out under the same conditions as are used for the corresponding eliminations, and so we cannot assume that a similar mechanism holds for the addition and the elimination.

The main point about the reagents which add to olefines is that they are electrophilic, in contrast to the nucleophilic reagents which add on to ketones (Chapter V).

(a) *Addition of halogens.* The addition of halogens to olefines is a heterolytic reaction (we are not here concerned with the photochemical reaction, mentioned in § 5). One of the results which points to this conclusion is that if the addition of bromine to ethylene is carried out in aqueous solution containing chloride ions, both $Br \cdot CH_2 \cdot CH_2 \cdot Br$ and $Cl \cdot CH_2 \cdot CH_2 \cdot Br$ are formed. This result can be accounted for by a two-stage mechanism:

$$CH_2{=}CH_2 + Br_2 \longrightarrow BrCH_2 \cdot \overset{+}{C}H_2 + Br^-$$

$$BrCH_2 \cdot \overset{+}{C}H_2 + Br^- \longrightarrow BrCH_2 \cdot CH_2Br$$

$$BrCH_2 \cdot \overset{+}{C}H_2 + Cl^- \longrightarrow BrCH_2 \cdot CH_2Cl$$

That the bromine molecule is acting as an electrophilic reagent in the first stage, i.e.

$$CH_2{=}CH_2 \quad Br{-}Br$$

is shown by the fact that a negative charge (as in $CH_2{=}CH \cdot COO^-$) increases reactivity towards bromine, and a positive charge diminishes it. A detailed kinetic study of the addition of bromine to stilbene in methanol has shown that the overall reaction

$$Ph \cdot CH{=}CH \cdot Ph + Br_2 + MeOH \longrightarrow Ph \cdot CHBr \cdot CH(OMe)Ph + HBr$$

proceeds by two stages: the rate-determining step is mainly the reaction of the olefine with the electrophilic bromine molecule.†

The stereochemistry of the process gives some information about the intermediate formed in the first stage. The addition of bromine to maleic acid (1) gives the racemic dibromide (2), while fumaric acid (3) gives the meso dibromide (4):

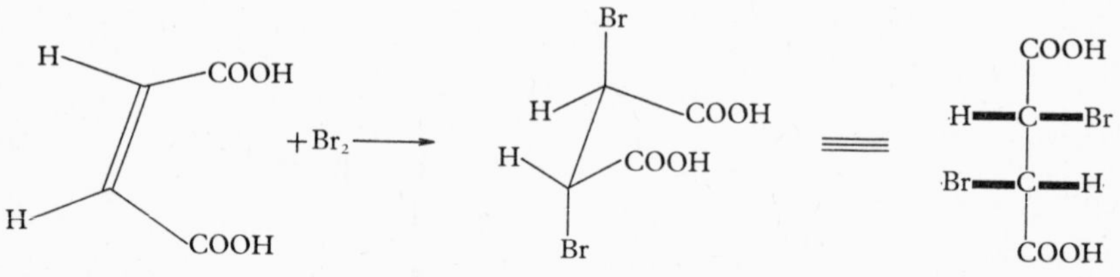

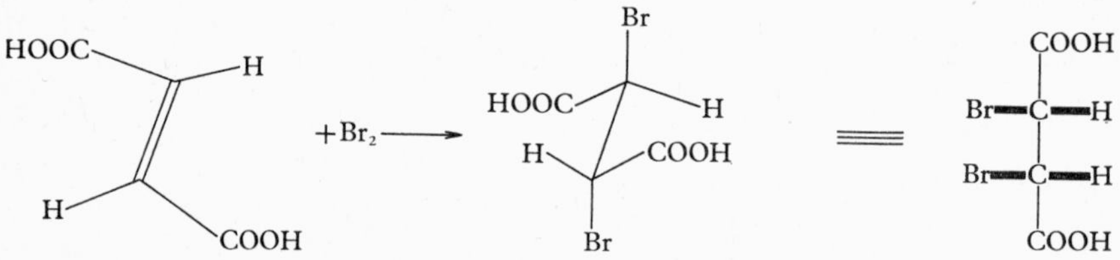

These reactions are clearly *trans* additions, akin to the *trans* eliminations discussed earlier.

The requirements of an electrophilic addition in two stages, which results in *trans* addition, were first accommodated by the following mechanism:‡

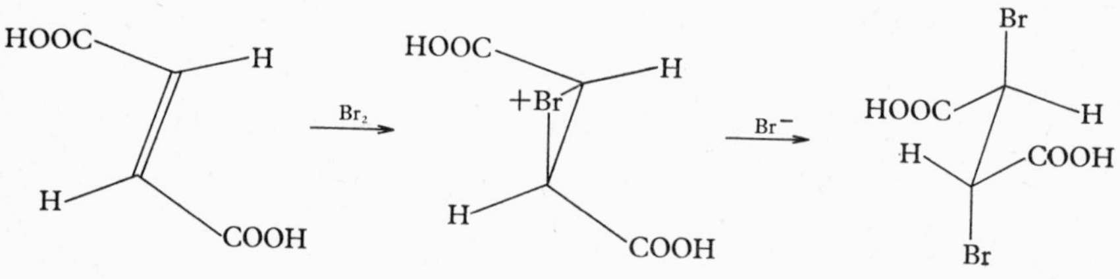

The postulated intermediate (5) is a bromonium ion which, in the second stage, reacts with bromide ion with inversion of configuration of the carbon on which displacement is taking place. This inversion is

† Bartlett and Tarbell, *J. Amer. Chem. Soc.* 1936, **58**, 466.
‡ Roberts and Kimball, ibid. 1937, **59**, 947.

quite reasonable, as this stage is a nucleophilic substitution (Chapter III, § 2 *a*), and it is this inversion which gives rise to the *trans* addition. We have, in fact, already met an intermediate such as (5) in discussing participation of neighbouring groups (Chapter III, § 4). The intermediate (5) has been represented as if the positive charge were exclusively located on the bromine atom: the structure may also be expressed as mesomeric between

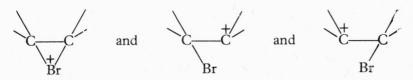

(*b*) *Addition of halogen acids.* Here the reagent is unsymmetrical, so that if the olefine is also unsymmetrical, there are two possible products; in fact, the problem of orientation arises, just as it did in elimination reactions. The main experimental result is that usually only one product is formed in the addition of halogen acids to compounds with one carbon-carbon double bond. This may be contrasted with the situation in eliminations where several products are usually formed. Thus propene (1) and hydrogen iodide give isopropyl iodide (2), and not n-propyl iodide (3).

$$Me \cdot CH{=}CH_2 + HI \longrightarrow Me \cdot CHI \cdot Me, \quad not \quad Me \cdot CH_2 \cdot CH_2 I$$

$$(1) \qquad\qquad\qquad (2) \qquad\qquad\qquad (3)$$

In these additions to unsaturated hydrocarbons the orientation is such that the product contains the halogen bound to the carbon atom carrying the smaller number of hydrogen atoms; this is Markownikoff's rule, advanced nearly a century ago.

The orientation can be discussed in terms of the stability of the carbonium ion, which may be taken as the best approximation to the structure of the transition state for the rate-determining step which can be expressed in conventional formulae. The carbonium ion leading to the formation of isopropyl iodide from propene is then the isopropyl carbonium ion, which is more stable than the n-propyl carbonium ion (Chapter III, § 3 *b*). Similarly, the addition of hydrogen iodide to vinyl chloride (4) gives (5) and not (6):

$$CH_2{=}CH \cdot Cl + HI \longrightarrow CH_3 \cdot CHICl, \quad not \quad I \cdot CH_2 \cdot CH_2 Cl$$

$$(4) \qquad\qquad\qquad (5) \qquad\qquad\qquad (6)$$

The carbonium ion related to the observed product is mesomeric between (7) and (8), i.e. the charge is delocalized:

$$CH_3{-}\overset{+}{C}H{-}Cl \qquad CH_3{-}CH{=}\overset{+}{C}l \qquad \overset{+}{C}H_2{-}CH_2{-}Cl$$

$$(7) \qquad\qquad (8) \qquad\qquad (9)$$

Such mesomerism is not possible for the carbonium ion (9). The addition of hydrogen bromide to acrylic acid (10) gives the β-bromopropionic acid (11); here there is a carbonyl group conjugated with the olefinic double bond (see § 3 e for other reactions of such compounds), and the most stable ion now has the proton on the oxygen atom and is mesomeric between (12) and (13); this formulation accounts for the observed orientation.

$$CH_2{=}CH{-}COOH \ + \ H{-}Br \longrightarrow Br{\cdot}CH_2{\cdot}CH_2{\cdot}COOH$$

$$(10) \qquad\qquad\qquad\qquad\qquad (11)$$

$$CH_2{=}CH{-}C\!\!\begin{array}{c}\overset{+}{\diagup}OH\\[2pt]\diagdown OH\end{array} \quad \text{and} \quad \overset{+}{C}H_2{-}CH{=}C\!\!\begin{array}{c}\diagup OH\\[2pt]\diagdown OH\end{array}$$

$$(12) \qquad\qquad\qquad\qquad (13)$$

While hydrogen iodide invariably, and hydrogen chloride nearly always, adds in the direction expected from the application of these ideas, hydrogen bromide frequently does not. The orientation in the additions of hydrogen bromide seemed capricious, until, as a result of the work of Kharasch and Mayo, it was established that the reactive species in the additions of hydrogen bromide could be a bromine atom.† This usually results in the 'abnormal' addition of hydrogen bromide, i.e. addition giving an opposite orientation from that observed in the addition of hydrogen chloride or hydrogen iodide. Thus propene and hydrogen bromide give isopropyl bromide ('normal' addition) in the absence of air and in the presence of an antioxidant, but in the presence of peroxide a more rapid reaction leads to n-propyl bromide (only about 1 per cent. of a molecular proportion of the antioxidant, or of the peroxide, is used):

$$CH_3{\cdot}CHBr{\cdot}CH_3 \xleftarrow[\text{HBr}]{\text{antioxidant}} CH_3{\cdot}CH{=}CH_2 \xrightarrow[\text{HBr}]{\text{peroxide}} CH_3{\cdot}CH_2{\cdot}CH_2Br$$
'normal'   'abnormal'

† Mayo and Walling, *Chem. Rev.* 1940, **27**, 351.

The 'abnormal' addition in the presence of peroxides (sometimes called the peroxide effect) must result from a reaction of peroxides with hydrogen bromide (rather than with the olefine), as other hydrogen halides do not show the effect. Oxidation to molecular bromine is not important, as small quantities of bromine do not affect the addition of hydrogen bromide. However, bromine atoms can react by a chain reaction:

$$Br\bullet + CH_3\!-\!CH\!=\!CH_2 \longrightarrow CH_3\!-\!\overset{\bullet}{C}H\!-\!CH_2Br$$

$$CH_3\!-\!\overset{\bullet}{C}H\!-\!CH_2Br + HBr \longrightarrow CH_3\!-\!CH_2\!-\!CH_2Br + Br\bullet$$

Hence a small quantity of a peroxide (or oxygen) can affect the course of a reaction, provided that both reactions written above are rapid compared with the rate of the heterolytic reaction. As olefines form peroxides on exposure to air, 'abnormal' addition was frequently encountered before its cause was realized. Just as the peroxides function by generating bromine atoms, so the anti-oxidants (e.g. phenols) function by reacting with them.

Thus there are two quite distinct mechanisms for the addition of hydrogen bromide to an olefine: a heterolytic mechanism, and a homolytic (bromine atom) one. It is not necessary that the two mechanisms should give different products in every case. The orientation in the 'abnormal' addition can be accounted for by considering the relative stability of the various possible free radicals, in the same way as the orientation in the heterolytic reaction was discussed in terms of the stabilities of carbonium ions. Thus, addition of a bromine atom to propene could give either (14) or (15):

$$CH_3\!-\!\overset{\bullet}{C}H\!-\!CH_2Br \qquad\qquad CH_3\!-\!CHBr\!-\!\overset{\bullet}{C}H_2$$

$$(14) \qquad\qquad\qquad\qquad (15)$$

Now the stability of alkyl radicals, like that of carbonium ions, increases markedly along the series primary $<$ secondary $<$ tertiary (Chapter I, § 1 r). So the radical (14) would be expected to be more stable than (15), and the 'abnormal' orientation follows. Abnormal orientation is not observed in the addition of hydrogen bromide to acrylic acid (or other α,β-unsaturated acids), and here the free radical leading to the formation of β-bromopropionic acid is mesomeric between

$$\text{Br—CH}_2\text{—}\overset{\bullet}{\text{CH}}\text{—C}\underset{\text{OH}}{\overset{\text{O}}{\diagup}} \qquad \text{and} \qquad \text{Br—CH}_2\text{—CH=C}\underset{\text{OH}}{\overset{\overset{\bullet}{\text{O}}}{\diagup}}$$

and the same product is expected to be favoured by either mechanism.

Hydrogen chloride hardly ever shows signs of reacting by a chlorine atom mechanism, probably because of the relatively high bond energy of the hydrogen chloride. The homolytic mechanism cannot compete with the heterolytic mechanism in the additions of hydrogen iodide because the heterolytic mechanism is so rapid, and, also, is apparently catalysed by iodine atoms.

The stereochemistry of the addition of hydrogen halides to olefines has not been studied extensively. The cyclic olefine (16) reacts rapidly with hydrogen bromide in acetic acid (a heterolytic reaction) to give exclusively the *trans* compound (17), but the isomeric olefine (18) gives 35 per cent. of the *cis* isomer of (17).

(16)   (17)   (18)   (19)

If both reactions proceeded through a carbonium ion, this would be the same (19) for both reactions, and so, if the decomposition of this carbonium ion were the product-controlling step, then the *cis* and *trans* isomers should be formed in the same proportions from both (16) and (17); moreover, a stable carbonium ion would decompose to give a mixture of isomers. It is possible that the carbonium ion reacts without being 'free', or that it interacts with the solvent in such a way as to permit stereospecific addition.†

Similarly, the homolytic addition of hydrogen bromide to olefines can proceed in a stereospecific fashion. Thus *cis*-2-bromobut-2-ene (20) gives meso-2,3-dibromobutane (21), and an analogous *trans* addition of hydrogen bromide to the *trans* isomer of (20) gives the DL-2,3-dibromobutane. Hence the free radicals formed by addition of bromine atoms to the olefines may react with hydrogen bromide so rapidly that they have no time to lose their configurational identity by rotation about the single bond.‡

† Hammond and Mevitt, *J. Amer. Chem. Soc.* 1954, **76**, 4121.
‡ Goering and Larsen, ibid. 1957, **79**, 2653.

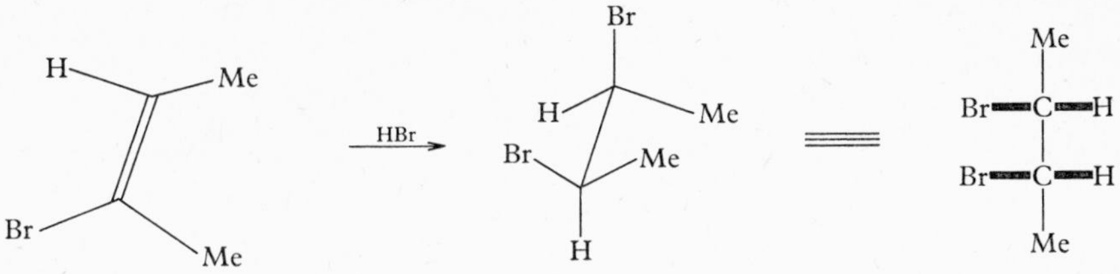

(20)   (21)

$$\xrightarrow{\text{HBr}}$$

(c) *Hydration of olefines.* Of all the reactions of the carbon-carbon double bond, the addition of water is perhaps of most direct interest to biochemists, as the enzymic reactions described in § 4 belong to this class. These reactions often proceed smoothly in aqueous solution.

The hydrations are acid-catalysed, and in effect the species that adds is the hydrated proton, H_3O^+. An example is the formation of β-hydroxy-butyric acid (2) from crotonic acid (1), in 1N-perchloric acid at 90° C:

$$CH_3 \cdot CH{=}CH \cdot COOH + H_2O \rightleftharpoons CH_3 \cdot CHOH \cdot CH_2 \cdot COOH$$

(1)   (2)

The rate of approach towards equilibrium has been studied, both for the hydration of the olefine and the dehydration of the alcohol. The rate of hydration is first-order in olefine and first-order in acid; the dehydration is also acid-catalysed, and the equilibrium constant is practically independent of the concentration of acid.† The hydration is exothermic to the extent of about 5 kcal/mol, which is close to the value calculated from the bond energies (Chapter I, § 2 c), i.e. the energy lost in breaking an O—H bond and converting a C=C into a C—C one is approximately balanced by the energy gained in forging a new C—H bond and a new C—O one.

As the hydration of olefines and the reverse reaction, the dehydration of alcohols, take place under the same conditions (i.e. the reactions are readily reversible), we may use the principle of microscopic reversibility (Chapter II, § 1 c) in discussing the mechanism. Now, the acid-catalysed dehydration of secondary and tertiary alcohols takes place by the *E*-1 (unimolecular) mechanism:

† Pressmann and Lucas, ibid. 1939, **61**, 2271.

$$\underset{\substack{|\\ \overset{}{O}H}}{Me_2C}-CH_2Me \quad + H^+ \rightleftharpoons \underset{\substack{\\ \overset{+}{O}H_2}}{Me_2C}-CH_2Me$$

(3)   (4) ⇅

$$Me_2C{=}CHMe \quad + H^+ \rightleftharpoons Me_2\overset{+}{C}-CH_2Me + H_2O$$

(6)   (5)

Thus the hydration of the olefine (6) takes place through the same intermediates, the carbonium ion (5) and the oxonium ion (4). The route in this direction is then:

$$\text{olefine} \xrightarrow{H^+} \text{carbonium ion} \xrightarrow{H_2O} \text{oxonium ion} \xrightarrow[-H^+]{} \text{alcohol}$$

The last step (loss of the proton from the oxonium ion) is likely to be fast. The carbonium ion, a highly reactive species, would be expected to react rapidly with water. Hence the first step, the formation of the carbonium ion, is probably the rate-determining step. Moreover, the olefine (7) is not converted into its more stable isomer (6) during the course of hydration to the alcohol (3):†

$$CH_2{=}\underset{\substack{|\\ Me}}{C}-CH_2Me \xrightarrow{H^+} Me{-}\underset{\substack{|\\ Me}}{\overset{+}{C}}-CH_2Me \xrightarrow{H_2O} Me{-}\underset{\substack{|\\ Me}}{\overset{\overset{+}{O}H_2}{C}}-CH_2Me \xrightarrow[-H^+]{} Me{-}\underset{\substack{|\\ Me}}{\overset{OH}{C}}-CH_2Me$$

(7)   (5)   (3)

Thus if, as written, a common carbonium ion (5) is formed from both olefines, it forms the oxonium ion (4) much more rapidly than it loses a proton.

The general picture of the hydration of the olefine‡ may be shown as in Fig. 26. This diagram is not meant to represent the heights of the free energy barriers at all accurately, but merely to distinguish between low barriers corresponding to fast reactions and high barriers, corresponding to the rate-determining steps in the forward and reverse reactions.

† Levy, Taft, and Hammett, *J. Amer. Chem. Soc.* 1953, **75**, 1253.
‡ Purlee and Taft, ibid. 1956, **78**, 5807, give a rather different interpretation, but see Long and Paul, *Chem. Rev.* 1957, **57**, 935.

A similar sort of picture may apply to the acid-catalysed addition of solvent (e.g. acetic acid) to 3-*p*-menthene (8). Here the olefine is optically active, but the carbonium ion (9) is symmetrical, so that its formation must be attended by loss of optical activity. The rate of

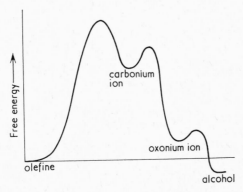

FIG. 26. Free energy profile for the reversible hydration of an olefine.

decomposition of the olefine was the same as the rate of loss of optical activity, which is consistent with the formation of the carbonium ion (9) being the rate-determining step.†

$$
\begin{array}{cc}
(8) & (9)
\end{array}
$$

(*d*) *Addition to conjugated olefinic systems.* The reactivity of compounds containing conjugated carbon-carbon double bonds (e.g. butadiene (1)) is similar in kind to that of mono-olefines, but enhanced in

$$CH_2{=}CH{-}CH{=}CH_2 \qquad BrCH_2{\cdot}CH{=}CH{\cdot}CH_2Br \qquad BrCH_2{\cdot}CHBr{\cdot}CH{=}CH_2$$

$$
\begin{array}{ccc}
\text{(1)} & \text{(2)} & \text{(3)}
\end{array}
$$

† Kwart and Weisfeld, *J. Amer. Chem. Soc.* 1958, **80**, 4670.

degree. The main feature of addition to such systems is that 1,4-addition occurs, so that one of the products from the reaction of bromine with butadiene is the 1,4-dibromide (2). Thus the double bonds interact: this is, of course, why we say that they are conjugated.

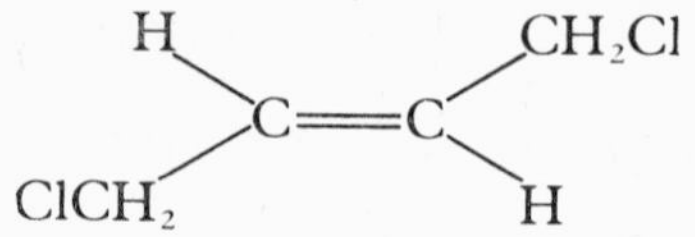

(4)

These are not, however, the sole products: 1,2-addition also occurs, leading to (3) from butadiene. We now proceed to discuss the factors governing the orientation of the addition.

Now it is the *trans* isomer (4) of 1,4-dichloro-but-2-ene which is formed by the addition of chlorine to butadiene,† so that there must be two distinct stages in the reaction. The same is assumed to be true for the addition of bromine to butadiene. The first stage is the electrophilic addition of bromine; of the four carbon atoms in butadiene, two are terminal and two non-terminal. The initial addition takes place to a terminal carbon atom because, in the transition state (5), the partial positive charge is spread over more carbon atoms than in the transition state (6) that would lead to addition to a non-terminal carbon atom.

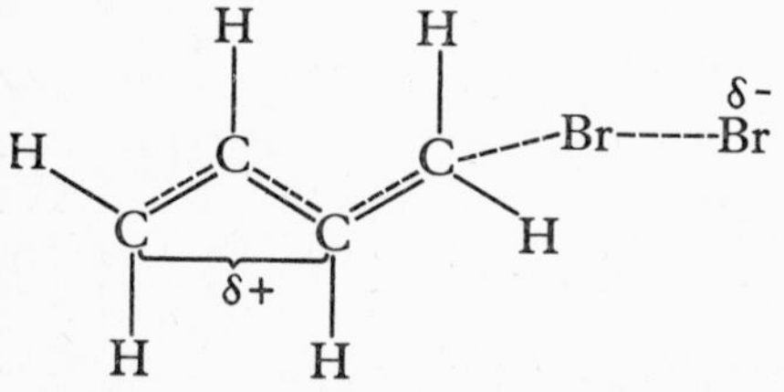

(5) 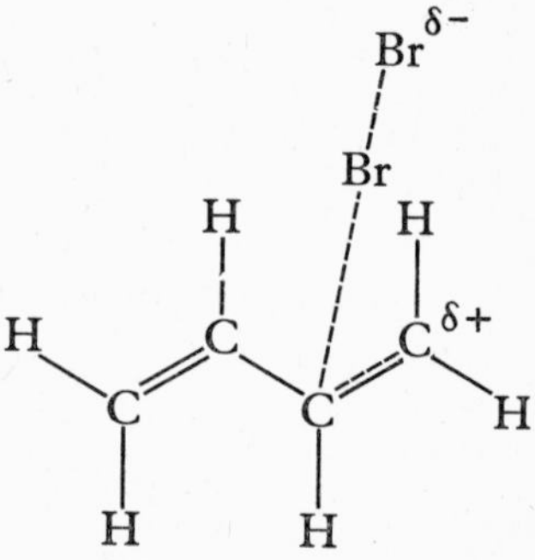   (6)

Thus the transition state (5) is more stable than (6), and so the first stage leads to the mesomeric carbonium ion (7):

† Mislow and Hellmann, *J. Amer. Chem. Soc.* 1951, **73**, 244.

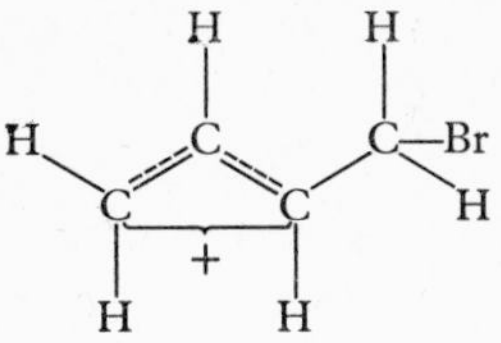

written for a species
mesomeric between

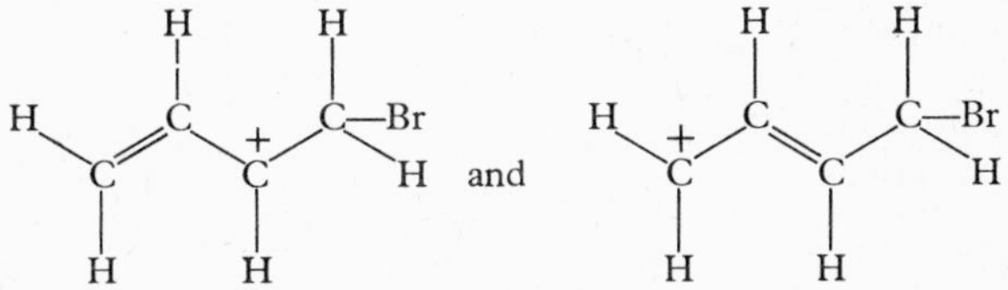

(7)

and

Addition of a bromide ion will now give the 1,2-dibromide (3) via the transition state (8), and the 1,4-dibromide (2) via (9).

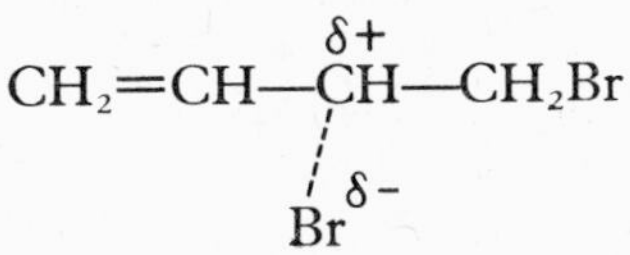

$$\underset{(8)}{\overset{\delta+}{CH_2=CH-\underset{\overset{|}{\underset{\delta-}{Br}}}{CH}}-CH_2Br} \qquad \underset{(9)}{\overset{\delta+}{CH_2-CH=CH-CH_2Br}}$$

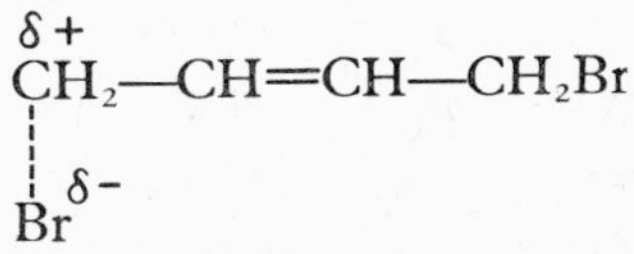

Both products are formed at about the same rate,† at −15° C.

At higher temperatures, the orientation is determined by different factors. Here the two dibromides (2) and (3) are interconvertible; in the equilibrium mixture the 1,4-dibromide (2) predominates, and under these conditions thermodynamic, not kinetic, factors decide the outcome.

Similar factors govern the addition of hydrogen halides to conjugated olefines: the proton adds to the terminal carbon, and then the halide ion adds to give finally a 1,2- or 1,4-adduct.

The Diels–Alder addition is an important reaction of conjugated dienes: this is a 1,4-addition in which the reagent which adds is either another molecule of diene (e.g. reaction (i)) or more commonly an α-β-unsaturated carbonyl compound (e.g. reactions (ii) and (iii)).

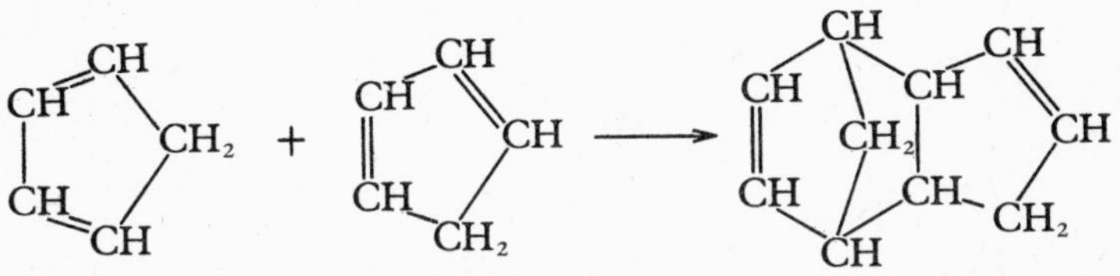

(i)

cyclopentadiene

† Hatch, Gardner, and Gilbert, ibid. 1959, **81**, 5943.

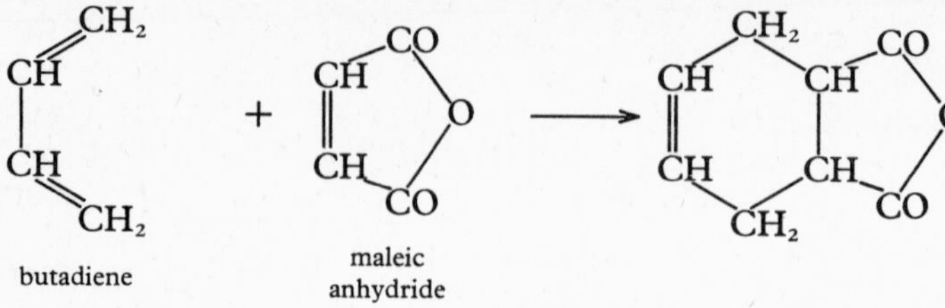

$$
\text{butadiene} \quad + \quad \text{maleic anhydride} \quad \longrightarrow \quad \tag{ii}
$$

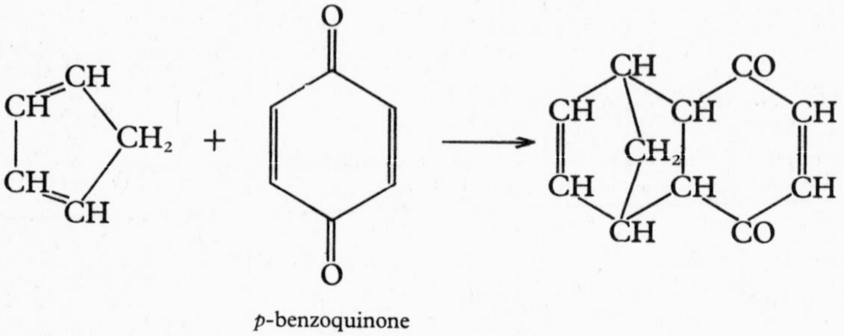

$$
\quad + \quad p\text{-benzoquinone} \quad \longrightarrow \quad \tag{iii}
$$

This reaction leads to otherwise inaccessible ring systems. The reaction is stereospecific: the addition is *cis*, so that the product of reaction (ii) is the anhydride of a *cis*-1,2-dicarboxylic acid. Moreover, it is stereospecific in another way: the product from maleic anhydride and cyclopentadiene has the *endo* configuration (10) and not the *exo* configuration (11), as if the reactive groups kept as close as possible to each other during the reaction:

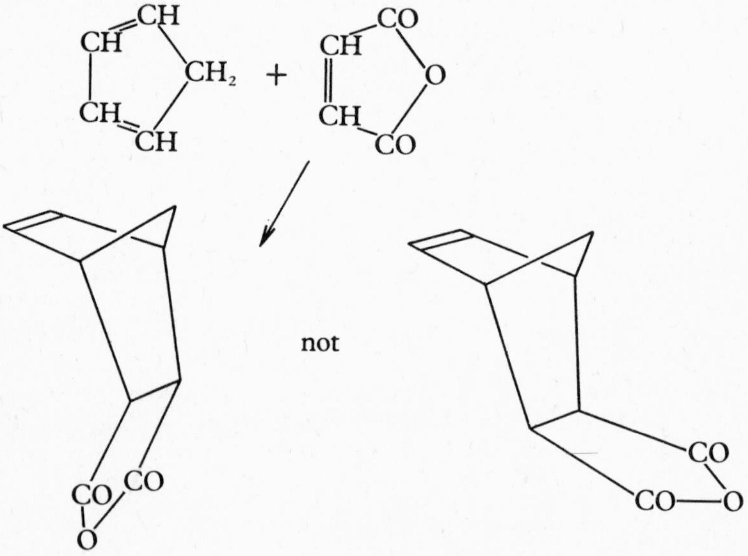

not

(10)   (11)

The reaction is reversible, and it is found that, for example, reaction (iii) has a large negative entropy of activation in the forward direction (about -30 entropy units for the reaction in benzene solution) but a small entropy of activation in the reverse direction. The fact that the entropy of activation is much greater in magnitude for the association shows that the transition state must be nearly as highly ordered as is the product. A notable feature of the kinetics of the Diels–Alder reaction is that, in several instances, the rate is the same whether the reaction is carried out in the gas phase or in any of several solvents: this shows that there is no great separation of charges in the transition state.

Thus, the essential feature of the mechanism of the Diels–Alder reaction is that in the transition state for, say, the dimerization of cyclopentadiene (reaction (i)), the two rings lie in nearly parallel planes and are quite close. Of the two new bonds, one is probably more nearly formed than the other.† This configuration facilitates the changes from double bonds between carbon atoms within one ring to single bonds connecting the rings, as in the double bonds the π-electrons are already above and below the plane of the ring; these changes may also be described as from sideways overlap to endways overlap of the p orbitals of the carbon atoms.

(e) *Additions to α,β-unsaturated carbonyl compounds.* The compounds that are to be discussed in this section contain the system $C{=}C{-}C{=}O$. The main characteristic of these compounds is that they can react with nucleophilic reagents as well as electrophilic ones. The type of reaction may be shown as:

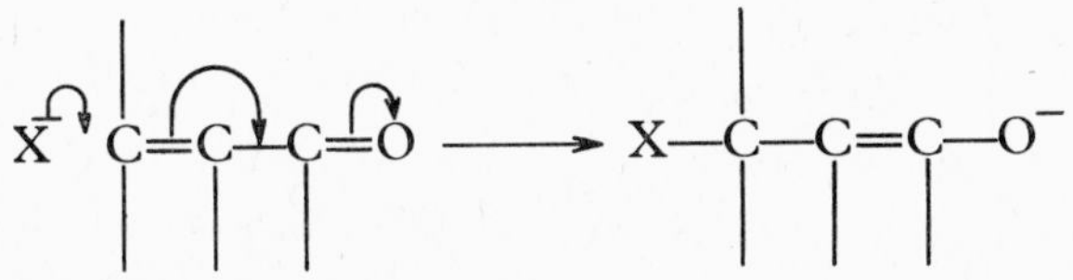

The cyanide ion is one of the nucleophilic reagents that may be used:

† Woodward and Katz, *Tetrahedron*, 1959, **5**, 70. This paper cites references to earlier work.

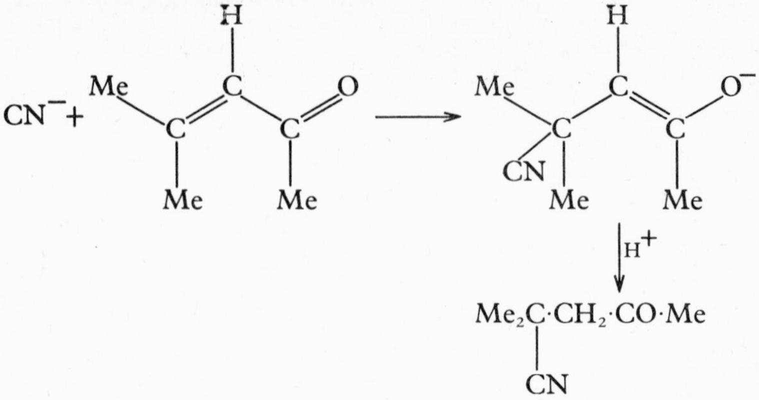

Another example of the addition of a nucleophilic species to an α,β-unsaturated carbonyl compound is provided by the analytically useful additions of mercaptans to N-ethyl maleimide:†

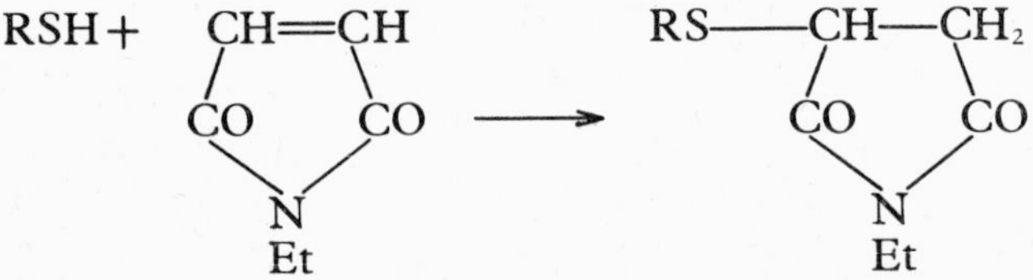

The double bonds in α,β-unsaturated carbonyl compounds interact in a way that is expressed by writing the carbonyl compounds as mesomeric between

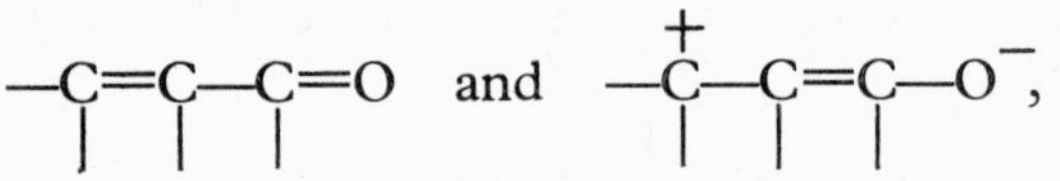

so that when a nucleophilic reagent (X^-) attacks the electrophilic carbon atom, the transition state (1) is stabilized by delocalization of the charge, and, in particular, part of the fractional negative charge can be accommodated on the oxygen atom, which is much more ready to bear a negative charge than carbon is. This, then, is the reason why nucleophilic species add to carbon-carbon double bonds only when they are conjugated with carbon-oxygen, or carbon-nitrogen or nitrogen-oxygen multiple bonds.

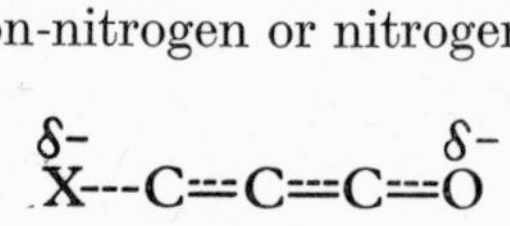

(1)

† Roberts and Rouser, *Anal. Chem.* 1958, **30**, 1291; Alexander, ibid., p. 1292.

The addition of a carbanion (an anion formed by rupture of a carbon-hydrogen bond) (Chapter V, § 7) to an α,β-unsaturated carbonyl compound is known as the Michael addition, and is one of the more important types of reaction in which new carbon-carbon bonds are formed. An example is the addition of diethyl malonate to ethyl cinnamate, in the presence of ethoxide ions:

$$CH_2(COOEt)_2 + EtO^- \rightleftharpoons \bar{C}H(COOEt)_2 + EtOH$$

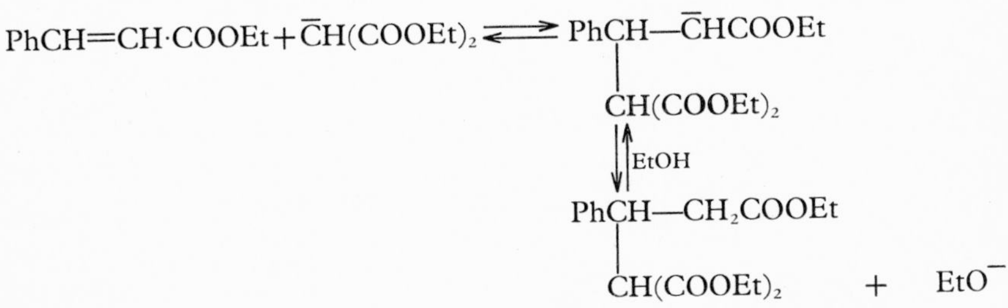

$$PhCH=CH \cdot COOEt + \bar{C}H(COOEt)_2 \rightleftharpoons PhCH\underset{|}{—}\bar{C}HCOOEt$$
$$CH(COOEt)_2$$
$$\updownarrow EtOH$$
$$PhCH\underset{|}{—}CH_2COOEt$$
$$CH(COOEt)_2 \quad + \quad EtO^-$$

4. Enzymes catalysing additions to olefinic double bonds

Three well-known enzymic reactions fall into the category of olefine hydration or, in reverse, dehydration of an alcohol: these are the reactions catalysed by fumarase, aconitase, and enolase. Some other enzymes (e.g. threonine dehydrase) require pyridoxal phosphate as coenzyme; this coenzyme is discussed in the next chapter.

(a) *Fumarase.* The kinetics of the reaction catalysed by fumarase:

| fumarate | $+H_2O \rightleftharpoons$ | L-malate |

have been studied in a particularly comprehensive manner by Alberty and his colleagues,[†] and only a brief summary of the main conclusions about the mechanism of the reaction can be given here.

† Farrar, Gulowsky, Alberty, and Miller, *J. Amer. Chem. Soc.* 1957, **79**, 3978; Alberty, Miller, and Fisher, ibid., p. 3973; Alberty and Hammes, *J. Phys. Chem.* 1958, **62**, 154.

The first step in the reaction is the combination of the enzyme with the substrate (the fumarate anion). The rate of this step is so high that it is probably limited only by the rate at which the substrate can diffuse to the enzyme (a diffusion-controlled reaction).

The bell-shaped plot of rate as a function of pH can be accounted for in terms of two groups in the enzyme, one group acting as an acid and the other as a base;[†] the acidic group will be concerned with the transfer of the hydrogen atom, if the enzymic reaction is analogous to the hydrations discussed above.

The next point concerns the spatial dispositions of the H and OH groups. As only one enantiomer (L-malate) is formed, the reaction is stereospecific at the asymmetric carbon atom carrying the OH group. The reaction is also stereospecific at the other carbon atom. For when the hydration is carried out in D_2O, the malate formed contains but one carbon-bound deuterium atom, and the remaining fumarate contains no deuterium. Now if the reaction were not stereospecific, at equilibrium there would be two deuterium atoms in the fumarate and three in the malate, simply as a result of the shuffling resulting from the forward and reverse reactions:

$$\overset{-}{O}OC\cdot CH{=}CH\cdot COO^- \ +\ D_2O \ \rightleftharpoons\ \overset{-}{O}OC\cdot CHD\cdot CHOH\cdot COO^- \rightleftharpoons \overset{-}{O}OC\cdot CD{=}CH\cdot COO^-$$

fumarate

$$\overset{-}{O}OC\cdot CDOH\cdot CD_2\cdot COO^- \rightleftharpoons \overset{-}{O}OC\cdot CD{=}CD\cdot COO^- \rightleftharpoons \overset{-}{O}OC\cdot CDOH\cdot CHD\cdot COO^-$$

trideuteromalate

Thus, since only one deuterium is actually incorporated into the malate the hydration is stereospecific: whether it is *cis* or *trans* will now be discussed.

Experimental evidence favours the view that *trans* addition occurs; this evidence is based on comparison of the enzymic product with synthetic monodeuteromalate.[‡]

[†] See Waley, *Biochim. Biophys. Acta*, 1953, **10**, 27; Dixon and Webb, *Enzymes*, Longmans, Green, 1958, for general discussions of this topic.

[‡] Gawron and Fondy, *J. Amer. Chem. Soc.* 1959, **81**, 6333.

This description is concerned with how the reaction is, as it were, organized in space. We now consider how it is organized in time, i.e. whether the H and OH are added in separate steps, and if so, which is the slower step, and which comes first. Now bonds to deuterium are normally broken more slowly than bonds to hydrogen (Chapter II, § 2f), but the dehydration of deuteromalate takes place at the same rate as that of malate. This suggests that the rate-determining step is not C—H fission, but is C—O fission. If a fast C—H fission preceded the slow C—O fission, then deuteromalate in H_2O should have lost deuterium by a rapid exchange reaction: this did not happen. Thus C—H fission in the dehydration of malate may be described as fast, but not first. This state of affairs is quite similar to the unimolecular mechanism of elimination in general, and in particular to the non-enzymic dehydration of an alcohol illustrated in Fig. 26 (p. 139).

(b) *Aspartase.* The conversion of fumarate into L-aspartate has been shown, by similar methods, to be a *trans* addition of ammonia to the double bond. Hence the configuration at both carbon atoms is the same in monodeuteromalate (formed by fumarase) and monodeuteroaspartate (formed by aspartase).†

(c) *Aconitase.*‡ The two reactions catalysed by *cis*-aconitase are also hydrations of an olefinic double bond:

$$\text{citrate} \underset{H_2O}{\overset{-H_2O}{\rightleftharpoons}} \textit{cis}\text{-aconitate} \underset{-H_2O}{\overset{H_2O}{\rightleftharpoons}} \text{isocitrate}$$

As aconitate is an unsymmetrical olefine, and water an unsymmetrical reagent, there are two possible orientations for the addition, and it turns out that both reactions are catalysed by aconitase, probably via a common intermediate. The configuration of the isocitrate formed (1)

$$
\begin{array}{c}
COO^- \\
| \\
HO-C-H \\
| \\
H-C-COO^- \\
| \\
CH_2COO^-
\end{array}
$$

(I)

---

† Gawron and Fondy, loc. cit.; Englard, *J. Biol. Chem.* 1958, **233**, 1003; Krasna, ibid., p. 1010.

‡ Gawron, Glaid, LoMonte, and Gary, *J. Amer. Chem. Soc.* 1958, **80**, 5836; Englard and Colowick, *J. Biol. Chem.* 1957, **226**, 1047; Speyer and Dickmann, ibid. 1956, **220**, 193.

shows that the elements of water have been added in a *trans* fashion to the *cis* olefine. The stereochemical features of the aconitase reaction are brought out in the scheme given below; the types of intermediates only represent possible analogues to enzyme-bound intermediates. Ferrous ions, which play a part in the reaction, may replace H^+ as the electrophilic species.

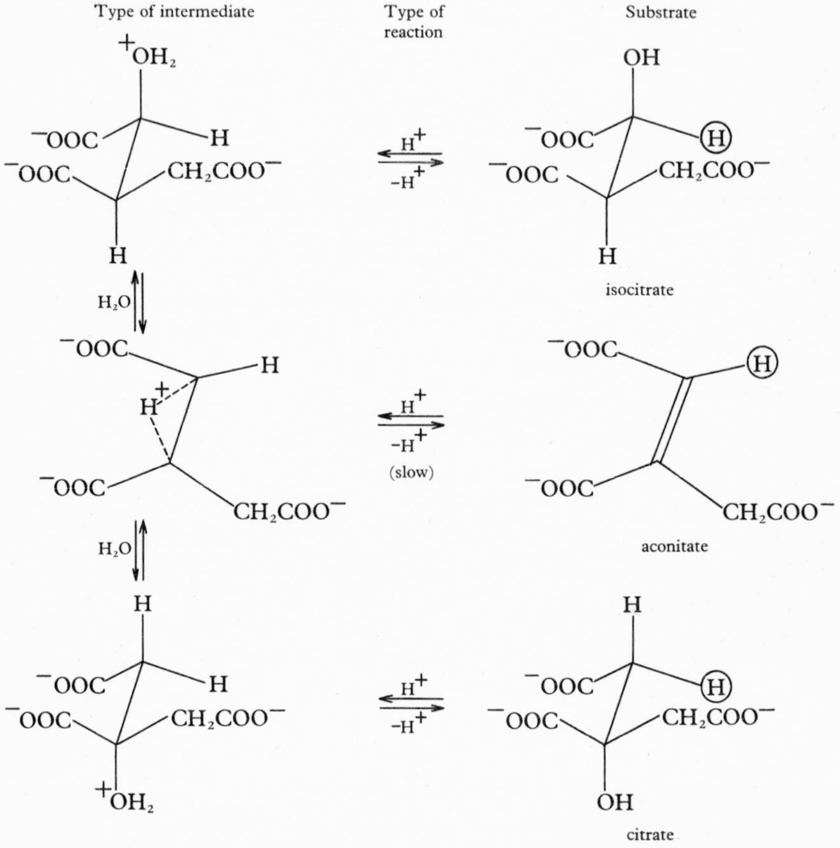

Type of intermediate	Type of reaction	Substrate

Type of intermediate (top left): $^+OH_2$ / ^-OOC, ^-OOC, H, CH_2COO^-, H

Type of reaction: $\xrightarrow{H^+}$ $\xleftarrow{-H^+}$

Substrate: isocitrate — OH / ^-OOC, ^-OOC, (H), CH_2COO^-, H

H_2O ⇅

Middle intermediate: ^-OOC, H^+, ^-OOC, H, CH_2COO^-

Type of reaction: $\xrightarrow{H^+}$ $\xleftarrow{-H^+}$ (slow)

Substrate: aconitate — ^-OOC, (H), ^-OOC, CH_2COO^-

H_2O ⇅

Bottom intermediate: H / ^-OOC, ^-OOC, H, CH_2COO^- / $^+OH_2$

Type of reaction: $\xrightarrow{H^+}$ $\xleftarrow{-H^+}$

Substrate: citrate — H / ^-OOC, ^-OOC, (H), CH_2COO^- / OH

    As with fumarase, the stereospecific nature of the reaction is shown by the observation that citrate in D_2O, in the presence of aconitase, only acquires one deuterium, and aconitate none: unspecific reaction would lead to a greater extent of deuterium uptake, as shown for fumarase. It was the possibility of such stereospecific enzymic reactions which led Ogston to point out that citrate, a symmetrical metabolite, would lose its symmetry when combined with an enzyme by a 'three-point' attachment† (see, for example, p. 183).

† Ogston, *Nature*, 1948, **162** 963; 1958, **181**, 1462.

Further consideration of this point leads to a refinement of our ideas of which elements of symmetry are important for different purposes.†
Citric acid (2) may be prepared with only one of the terminal carbon atoms labelled; subsequent enzymic reactions in the citric acid cycle preserve the distinction between the carboxyl groups; thus (3) is formed, but not (4). At first glance it hardly appears possible that the enzyme can

$^{14}COOH$	$^{14}COOH$	$^{14}COOH$
$\mid$	$\mid$	$\mid$
CH_2	CO	CH_2
$\mid$	$\mid$	$\mid$
$HO\!-\!C\!-\!COOH$	CH_2	CH_2
$\mid$	$\mid$	$\mid$
CH_2	CH_2	CO
$\mid$	$\mid$	$\mid$
$COOH$	$COOH$	$COOH$
(2)	(3)	(4)

(as it, in fact, does) distinguish between the terminal carboxyl groups. The situation in citric acid is more easily discussed, and the generality appreciated, if only the central carbon atom is considered: this is bound to four groups, of three kinds, and so the molecule may be written *Caabd*, where the small letters represent the groups. The two *a* groups, it appears, can be differentiated in an asymmetrical situation, but fortunately we can decide on the criterion for distinguishing between the *a* groups without specifying, in detail, the nature of the situation.

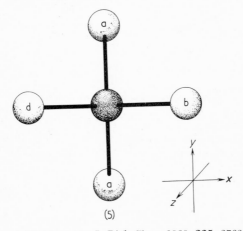

(5)

† Hirschmann, *J. Biol. Chem.* 1960, **235**, 2762.

The molecule *Caabd* certainly has one kind of symmetry. It has a plane of symmetry, the horizontal plane through the central atom and the *b* and *d* groups in (5), and so is not resolvable. The kinds of symmetry are best described in terms of the operators which act on a molecule to produce an indistinguishable species. Here the operator is: reflect in the *xz* plane. If a molecule has a centre of symmetry, the operator is: rotate through 180°, and reflect in the plane perpendicular to the axis of rotation; another operator differs only in that the angle of rotation specified is 90°. If a molecule possesses these 'reflection' types of symmetry it is not resolvable. But that does not mean that, in (5), the *a* groups are indistinguishable. For if we transpose them, by the operation of rotation about the *z* axis (the one perpendicular to the plane of the paper) by 180°, then the different groups *b* and *d* change places too, and so the final arrangement is different from the first. Whether the initial and final arrangements can be distinguished depends on the situation, i.e. whether it 'matters' exchanging the positions of *b* and *d*. The two *a* groups can thus not be distinguished if rotation about an axis by $360°/n$ (*n* is not one) brings the molecule back to an arrangement indistinguishable from the original one. Thus neither of the members of the two pairs in *Caabb* can be distinguished from its partner.

The conclusion, then, is that if one is concerned with optical activity, the relevant symmetry operator involves reflections, but that if one is concerned with differentiating groups, then the relevant symmetry operator involves only rotations.

The condition for the distinction between the two *a* groups of *Caabd* is, of course, only permissive. But distinction is possible in an asymmetric environment, such as is provided by an enzyme. The situation may be visualized in terms of a 'three-point' attachment between the enzyme and the substrate, but this picture cannot be put into more realistic terms until more is known about the structure of the catalytic site of, in this case, aconitase. Perhaps the hydroxyl group and two of the carboxyl groups of citric acid are bound by the enzyme.

There is evidence that the slow step in the interconversion of citrate and aconitate is the one where the double bond is formed or broken. The hydrogen atom marked in the formulae (p. 148) is not involved in these changes; but it is this hydrogen atom which is transferred to triphosphopyridine nucleotide in the reaction catalysed by isocitrate dehydrogenase (Chapter VII, § 2 *d*).

It will be seen that a mechanism of the type shown above does not require aconitate to be an intermediate in the conversion of citrate into isocitrate.

(d) *Enolase*. The reaction catalysed by this enzyme provides another example of a reversible dehydration of an alcohol:

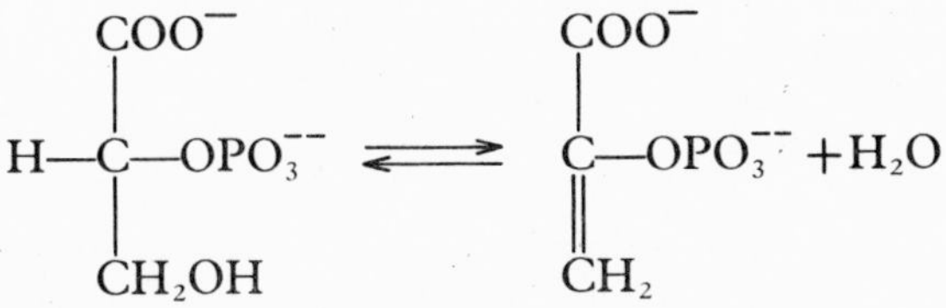

$$
\begin{array}{ccc}
COO^- & & COO^- \\
| & & | \\
H{-}C{-}OPO_3^{--} & \rightleftharpoons & C{-}OPO_3^{--} \ +H_2O \\
| & & \| \\
CH_2OH & & CH_2
\end{array}
$$

Metal ions play an important part in this reaction: both substrate and product bind metal ions, so that the apparent equilibrium constant depends on the nature and concentration of the metal ions. The kinetics suggest that the enzyme first combines with the metal and then with the substrate.[†] The enzyme plus metal combination can be regarded as behaving in the same way as acid does in the non-enzymic dehydration of alcohols; the hydroxyl group will be expelled more readily after combination with a positively charged species. The order of effectiveness of different metal ions may depend on their relative affinities for oxygen and nitrogen.[‡]

Enolase is one of the enzymes which have been shown to retain their activity after partial degradation.

5. *Cis-trans* isomerization[§]

A simple example of *cis-trans* isomerization is the conversion of maleic acid (1) into fumaric acid (2):

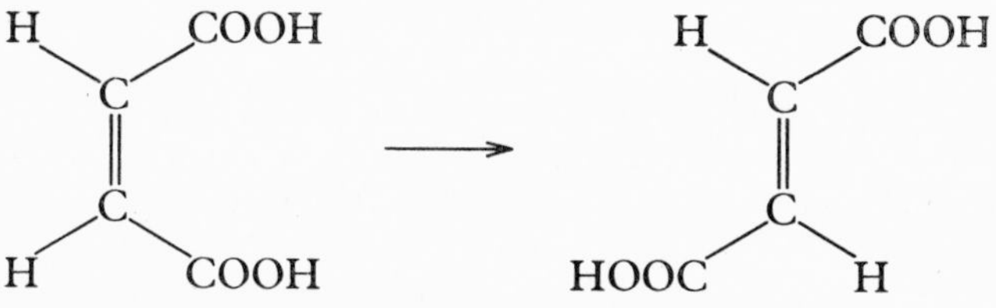

(1)   (2)

The conversion of a derivative of maleic acid into the corresponding derivative of fumaric acid (§ 6) is a step in the catabolism of tyrosine,

---

[†] Wold and Ballou, *J. Biol. Chem.* 1957, **227**, 301, 313.

[‡] Williams, *The Enzymes*, vol. 1, p. 391, Academic Press, 1959; see also Malström and Rosenberg, *Advances in Enzymology*, 1959, **21**, 131.

[§] Wyman, *Chem. Rev.* 1955, **55**, 625; Wheland, *Advanced Organic Chemistry*, chap. 7, New York, John Wiley; Dewar, *Electronic Theory of Organic Chemistry*, p. 317, Clarendon Press, 1949; Davies and Evans, *Trans. Faraday Soc.* 1955, **51**, 1506.

and a *cis-trans* isomerization has been put forward as a step in the visual cycle.

Cis-trans isomerization can be carried out in a number of ways, which may be divided into photochemical, catalytic, and thermal methods. The final product is, in general, a mixture; often the *trans* isomer predominates.

The photochemical reaction may give a mixture in which the less stable *cis* isomer predominates as radiation energy is being supplied to the reaction mixture. If *monochromatic* light of a wavelength corresponding to the first absorption band of the *trans* isomer is used to effect the reaction, this isomer will be transformed (via an excited state) to the *cis* isomer which, as it does not absorb light of this particular wavelength, will be unaffected. Thus, in favourable cases, the less stable isomer can be prepared from the more stable one by photochemical isomerization.

Light may have another kind of effect. The conversion of *cis*-stilbene (3) into the *trans* isomer (4) is catalysed by bromine, but only in the light. As visible light suffices, and (3) does not absorb visible light, the action of the light must be on the bromine. Now light causes some

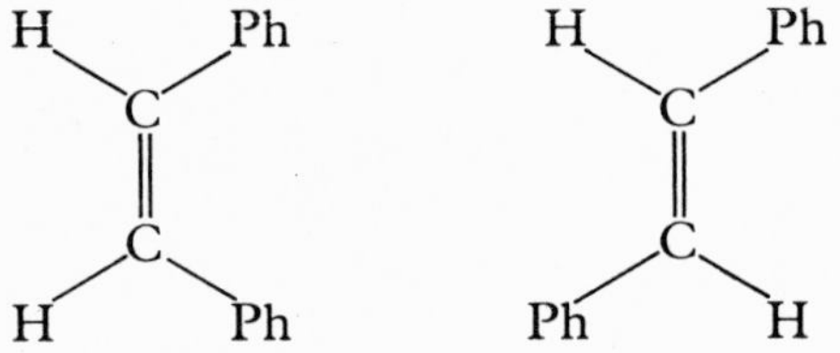

(3)   (4)

dissociation of bromine into atoms, and the reaction of bromine atoms with the olefine can cause isomerization by the steps:

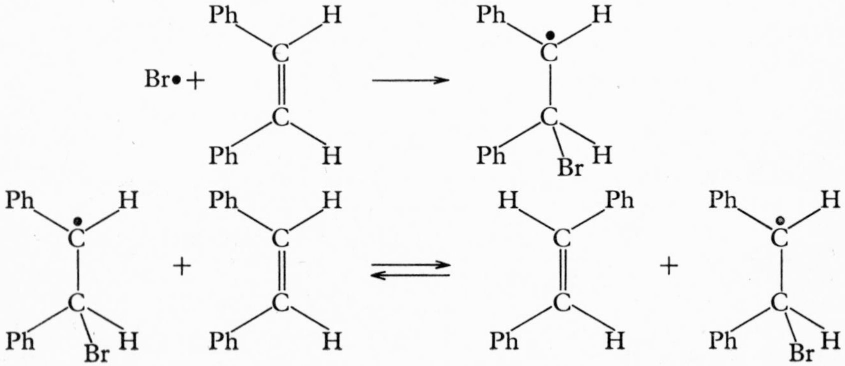

Thiols are well known as catalysts for *cis-trans* isomerizations. Thus, the thiyl radicals from methyl mercaptan catalyse the conversion of *cis*-but-2-ene into the *trans* isomer by the following mechanism:[†]

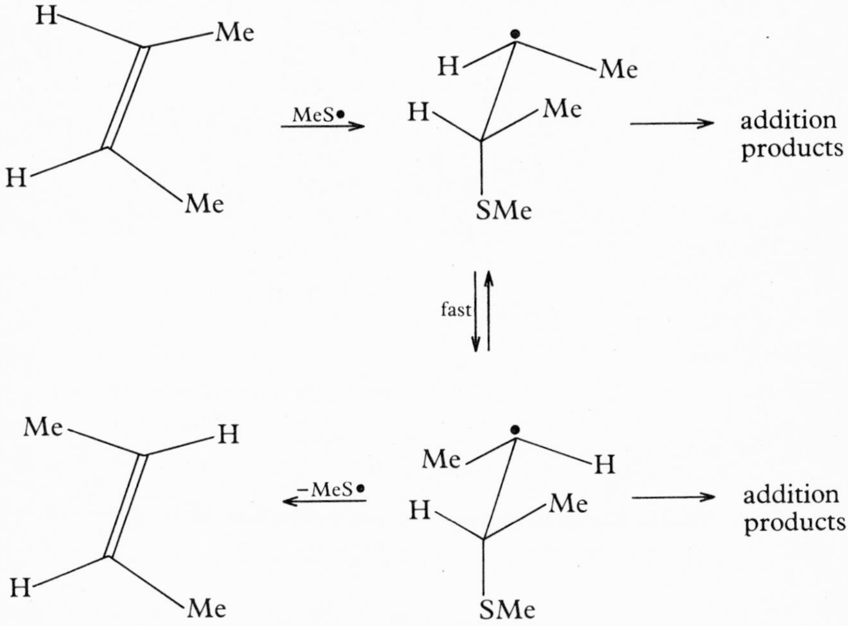

The free radical is converted into the *trans* olefine more rapidly than into addition products; this scheme explains how a reagent which adds to olefines may yet convert a *cis* olefine into a *trans* one. Thiols are effective catalysts, as thiyl radicals are readily formed and highly reactive.

Isomerization may be catalysed by ionic reagents. Thus acids are often effective, e.g. hydrogen chloride in the conversion of maleic acid into fumaric acid; the intermediate here is presumably a protonated complex.

These are the photochemical and catalysed reactions; now the thermal isomerization will be described. Those that have been examined fall into two groups. One group has a high energy of activation and a low entropy of activation; the other group has a low energy but a high negative entropy of activation. Now the isomerization must pass through a 'perpendicular' stage (5).

[†] Walling and Helmreich, *J. Amer. Chem. Soc.* 1959, **81**, 1144.

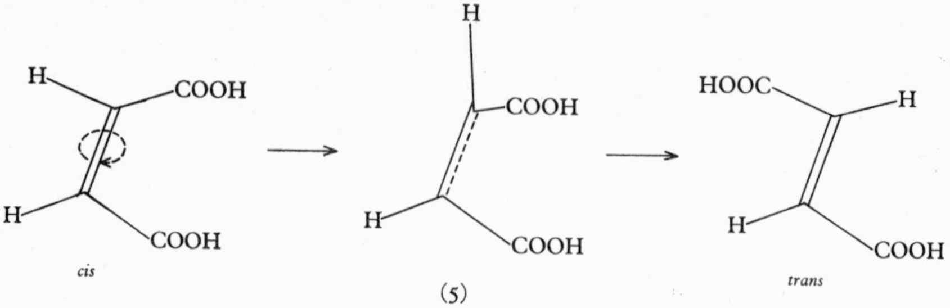

(5)

cis   *trans*

The most stable electronic arrangement for (5) is one in which the spins of the pair of π-electrons are parallel (called a triplet state), and it has been suggested that the group of isomerizations with low energy of activation proceeds via the triplet state: the large negative entropy of activation arises from the low probability of attaining a transition state in which the arrangement of the spins of the electrons differs from that in the original state. The other group of isomerizations takes place via a perpendicular transition state in which the spins of the electrons remain opposed; the attainment of this transition state requires more energy, but is not unusually improbable.

6. 4-Maleylacetoacetate isomerase

This enzyme† catalyses the conversion of a *cis* into a *trans* isomer:

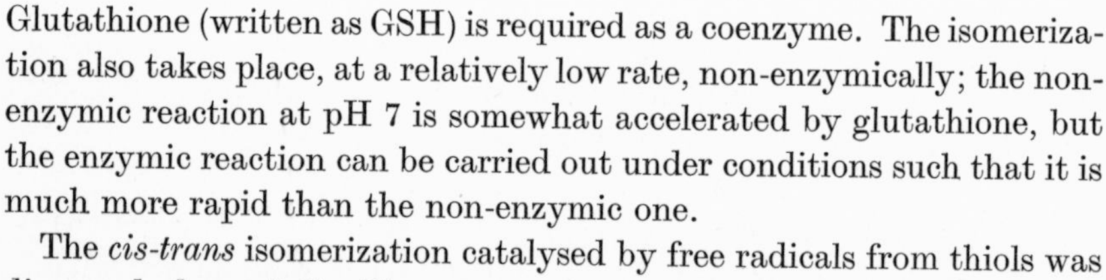

4-maleylacetoacetate   4-fumarylacetoacetate

Glutathione (written as GSH) is required as a coenzyme. The isomerization also takes place, at a relatively low rate, non-enzymically; the non-enzymic reaction at pH 7 is somewhat accelerated by glutathione, but the enzymic reaction can be carried out under conditions such that it is much more rapid than the non-enzymic one.

The *cis-trans* isomerization catalysed by free radicals from thiols was discussed above (§ 5). The non-enzymic isomerization of maleylacetoacetate, catalysed by glutathione, could take place by a similar mechanism; alternatively, the reactive species may be the anion, GS^-, the first intermediate will then be a carbanion (as described in § 3 e), written

† Knox and Edwards, *J. Biol. Chem.* 1955, **216**, 489; Edwards and Knox, ibid. 1956, **220**, 79.

as X^-, which may be converted into the *trans* form, or may pick up a proton to give the stable adduct (XH):

$$GS^- + Cis \underset{k_{-1}}{\overset{k_1}{\rightleftharpoons}} X^- \underset{k_{-2}}{\overset{k_2}{\rightleftharpoons}} trans + GS^-$$
$$k_3 \bigg\downarrow H^+$$
$$XH$$

The relative values of the velocity constants will then determine whether isomerization takes place much more rapidly than adduct formation. Although the stable adduct (XH) is not an intermediate in the enzymic reaction, the unstable carbanion (X^-) could be.

ADDITIONS TO ALDEHYDES AND KETONES

1. General nature of carbonyl addition reactions

THE reactions of aldehydes and ketones are particularly important, as they are widely used in synthesis and biosynthesis: in particular, new C—C bonds *in vivo* are nearly always formed by a carbonyl addition reaction (see Chapter X, § 1 *d*, for an alternative process).

The main feature that determines the reactivity of the carbonyl group is its polarization, symbolized as $\overset{\delta+\ \ \delta-}{C=O}$ (see Chapter I, § 1 *q*, § 2 *a*). Thus there are two points of attack: a nucleophilic reagent will attack the electrophilic carbon atom, and an electrophilic reagent will attack the nucleophilic oxygen atom. In many cases (perhaps including many enzyme-catalysed reactions) both processes occur. The electrophilic species may be a proton, which reacts with the unshared electrons on the oxygen atom of the carbonyl group:

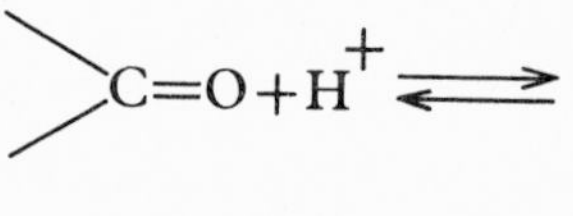

$$>\!\!C=O+H^+ \rightleftharpoons >\!\!C=\overset{+}{O}\diagdown_H$$

The electrons that form the carbon-oxygen double bond will be pulled away from the carbon atom to a greater extent in the protonated form. Protonation of the oxygen atom thus enhances the electrophilic reactivity of the carbon atom. Acid catalysis is therefore common in carbonyl addition reactions. Catalysis by bases is also common, but for a different reason: the function of the base is to generate the nucleophilic species which reacts with the carbon of the carbonyl group.

2. Addition of cyanide ion

The addition of hydrogen cyanide to an aldehyde or ketone gives a cyanohydrin,

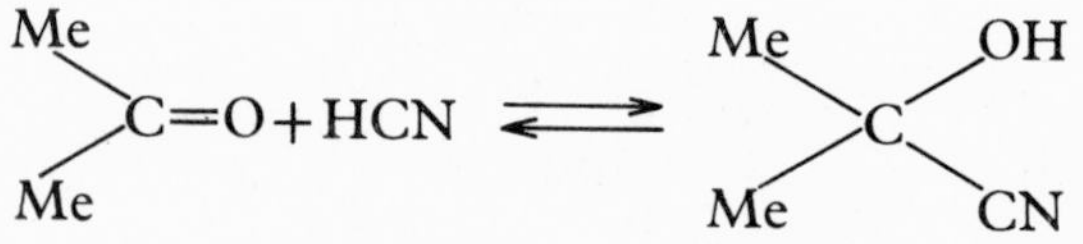

$$\underset{Me}{\overset{Me}{>}}\!\!C=O+HCN \rightleftharpoons \underset{Me}{\overset{Me}{>}}\!\!C\underset{CN}{\overset{OH}{<}}$$

acetone cyanohydrin

In an early investigation Lapworth used as the carbonyl component a yellow quinone which gave a colourless cyanohydrin, so that the progress of the reaction could be easily observed. Acids retarded, and bases greatly accelerated cyanohydrin formation. The function of the base is taken to be the generation of cyanide ions, which are the reactive species:† the cyanide ion, CN⁻, has a partial negative charge on the carbon atom, while the acid HCN has not. The mechanism is thus:‡

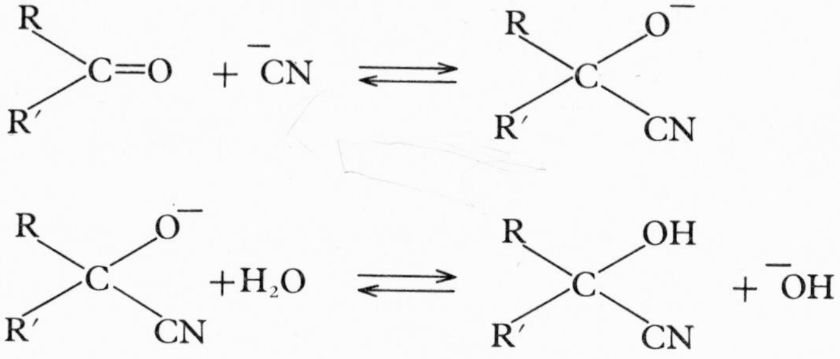

Cyanohydrin formation is reversible: the position of equilibrium has been much studied and we may instance two series of compounds. In aromatic aldehydes, *para*-substituents which can interact with the carbonyl group of the aldehyde favour dissociation of the cyanohydrin: an example of such a substituent is the dimethylamino group. The interaction can be shown by writing *p*-dimethylamino-benzaldehyde as mesomeric between (1) and (2):

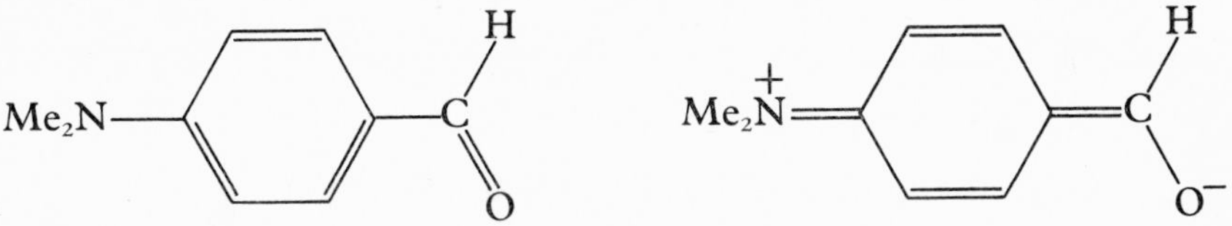

(1)   (2)

In the other series of compounds the variation in the extent of cyanohydrin formation is ascribed to steric factors. These compounds are alicyclic ketones. Here it is observed, for example, that the equilibrium constant for the formation of the cyanohydrin of cyclohexanone is about one hundred times greater than that for cycloheptanone. These differences arise because the geometry of the trigonal carbon atom in a ketone differs from that of the tetrahedral carbon atom in a cyanohydrin.§

† Lapworth, *J. Chem. Soc.* 1903, **83**, 995.
‡ See also Julien, Mousseren, and Fauche, *Bull. Soc. chim. France*, 1956, pp. 401, 408.
§ Prelog, *J. Chem. Soc.* 1950, p. 420; Brown, ibid. 1956, p. 1248.

Such steric factors, which cannot be discussed here, are often particularly noticeable in alicyclic compounds, which are more constrained than open-chain compounds.

3. Addition of water, alcohols, and thiols, and the reverse reaction

(a) *Addition of water.* The addition of water to carbonyl compounds is greatly affected by the nature of the carbonyl compound. Thus, chloral, acetaldehyde, and acetone:

$$Cl_3C \cdot CHO \qquad CH_3 \cdot CHO \qquad (CH_3)_2CO$$

chloral   acetaldehyde   acetone

form a graded series. Chloral forms a stable hydrate, acetaldehyde is about 60 per cent. hydrated at equilibrium, and acetone is hardly hydrated at all, in aqueous solution.

The hydration of acetaldehyde is catalysed by both acids and bases. The kinetics are consistent with the following mechanisms, shown for catalysis by hydrogen ions:

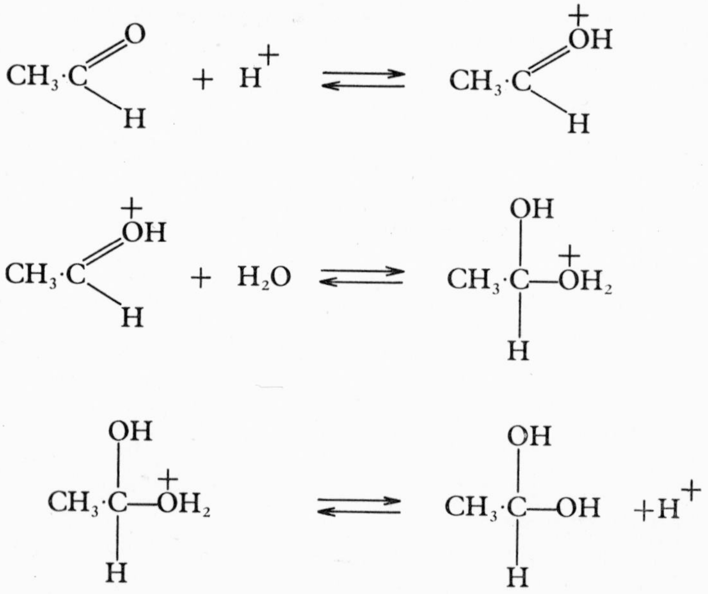

and by hydroxyl ions:

$$CH_3 \cdot C\!\!\begin{array}{c}O\\H\end{array} \;+\; \overline{O}H \;\rightleftharpoons\; CH_3 \cdot \overset{\overset{\displaystyle O^-}{|}}{\underset{\underset{\displaystyle H}{|}}{C}}\!\!-OH$$

$$CH_3 \cdot \overset{\overset{\displaystyle O^-}{|}}{\underset{\underset{\displaystyle H}{|}}{C}}\!\!-OH \;+\; \overset{+}{H} \;\rightleftharpoons\; CH_3 \cdot \overset{\overset{\displaystyle OH}{|}}{\underset{\underset{\displaystyle H}{|}}{C}}\!\!-OH$$

In the acid-catalysed case the function of the acid is to accelerate the reaction by conversion of the C=O to the more electrophilic C=$\overset{+}{O}$H (see § 1); in the second case, the reagent is made more reactive, as $\overline{O}$H is more nucleophilic than H_2O.

The rate-determining step is the second in the acid-catalysed hydration, and the first step in the base-catalysed hydration, as proton transfers to or from oxygen are rapid in aqueous solution in the presence of acids and bases.

The hydration of acetaldehyde is also subject to general acid-base catalysis.† This is found as follows. The rate is measured in a series of buffers at the same pH (and ionic strength): in general acid-base catalysis, the observed rate constant varies with the nature and concentration of the acid and base components of the buffer. This variation shows that hydrogen ions and hydroxyl ions are not the only catalysts. In general acid-base catalysis, the observed rate constant (k) is given by

$$k = k_0 + k_1[H^+] + k_2[OH^-] + k_3[\text{acid}] + k_4[\text{base}].$$

In an acetate buffer (i.e. a solution that contains both unionized acetic acid and acetate ions), this equation becomes

$$k = k_0 + k_1[H^+] + k_2[OH^-] + k_3[\text{MeCOOH}] + k_4[\text{MeCOO}^-].$$

The mechanism shown for catalysis by hydrogen ions, which did not bring in the source of the hydrogen ions, cannot apply to the reaction catalysed by, say, acetic acid; here the transition state in the rate-determining step must contain acetaldehyde, water, and acetic acid. How these molecules are arranged is not known, but it is possible that they are hydrogen-bonded as shown:

† Bell, Rand, and Wynn-Jones, *Trans. Faraday Soc.* 1956, **52**, 1093.

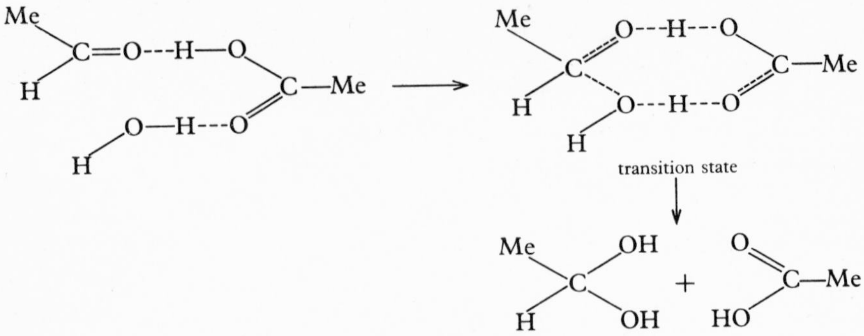

Direct study of the hydration of acetone is rendered difficult, not because the reaction is too fast, but because it occurs to such a small extent. This difficulty is overcome by determining the rate of isotopic exchange between acetone and $H_2{}^{18}O$; as the hydrate is symmetrical (apart from the isotopic distinction), it will lose either ^{16}OH or ^{18}OH at nearly the same rate. Thus, introduction of ^{18}O in acetone is accounted for by the formation and decomposition of the hydrate and so the rate of isotopic labelling of acetone in $H_2{}^{18}O$ is a measure of the rate of formation and decomposition of the hydrate:

$$Me_2C=O+H_2{}^{18}O \rightleftharpoons Me_2C\genfrac{}{}{0pt}{}{{}^{18}OH}{OH} \rightleftharpoons Me_2C={}^{18}O+H_2O$$

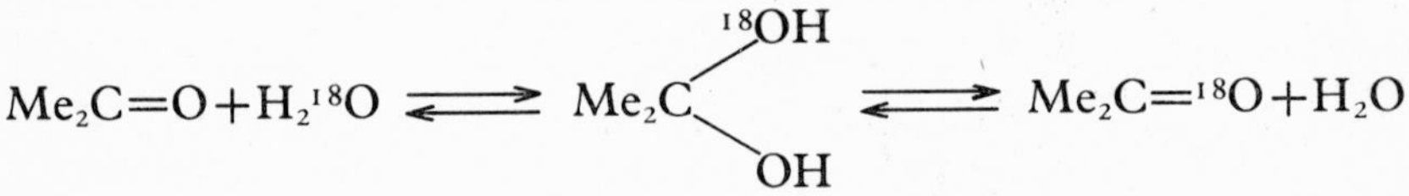

This reaction was found to be catalysed by acids and bases.

(b) *Addition of alcohols.* Alcohols react with aldehydes in the same way as water does:

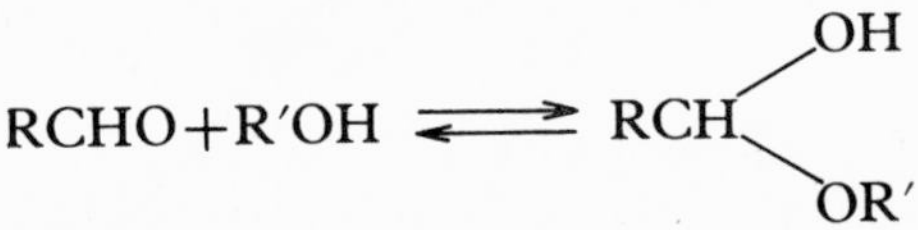

$$RCHO+R'OH \rightleftharpoons RCH\genfrac{}{}{0pt}{}{OH}{OR'}$$

The products are hemi-acetals, and are compounds of the same type as the cyclic forms of sugars. These hemi-acetals cannot usually be isolated, but evidence for their existence is provided by study of the physical properties of mixture of aldehydes and alcohols. The freezing-point-composition curve shows a maximum (higher than that of either pure component) when equimolecular amounts of the two components are present.[†] Similarly, the infra-red absorption spectra of mixtures of

† McKenna, Tartar, and Lingafelter, *J. Amer. Chem. Soc.* 1949, **71**, 729.

aldehydes and alcohols differ from the spectra of the components; in a particular case the mixture was studied by comparing its absorption with that due to the alcohol in one cell and the aldehyde in another, placed so that the radiation passed through both. The intensities of bands due to the C=O and C—H in the aldehydes decreased, but the intensity due to the OH band in the alcohol remained the same; these changes are consistent with the formation of a hemi-acetal, as the OH band in the hemi-acetal was not distinguished from the OH band in the alcohol.† Ketones do not show the same changes.

Since glucose shows many of the reactions of an aldehyde and contains hydroxyl groups situated so that cyclization can occur, the intramolecular formation of a hemi-acetal is not surprising. The specific rotation of a freshly-prepared solution of α-D-glucose is 113°, but it decreases to 52·5° on keeping; the specific rotation of β-D-glucose is 19°, and it rises to 52·5° on keeping. The preparation of the β form from the α one led to the recognition of the cyclic structure of glucose. The α and β forms differ in the configuration at C-1:

α -D-glucose   β -D-glucose   (I)

Interconversion can take place through the acyclic aldehyde form (1). On this basis, the reaction is the addition of a hydroxyl group to the aldehyde group. The reaction is catalysed by acids and bases. In water, an amphiprotic solvent, both acidic and basic species are present. But tetramethylglucose (which is more soluble in organic solvents than glucose is) undergoes mutarotation very slowly in a solvent which is basic and not acidic (pyridine), or acidic but not basic (m-cresol). In a mixture of the two solvents, however, mutarotation proceeds about twenty times more rapidly than in water.‡ When two such species are used in an inert solvent (benzene), the rate is third-order, being

† Ashdown and Kletz, *J. Chem. Soc.* 1948, p. 1454.
‡ Lowry and Faulkner, ibid. 1925, **127**, 2883.

proportional to the product of the concentration of tetramethylglucose, phenol, and pyridine. These results suggest that both the removal of a proton from one position and the addition of a proton to another position are necessary to provide the driving force to break the C—O bond. An acid (here H⁺) and a base (here OH⁻) can facilitate the heterolysis of the C—O bond, as shown:

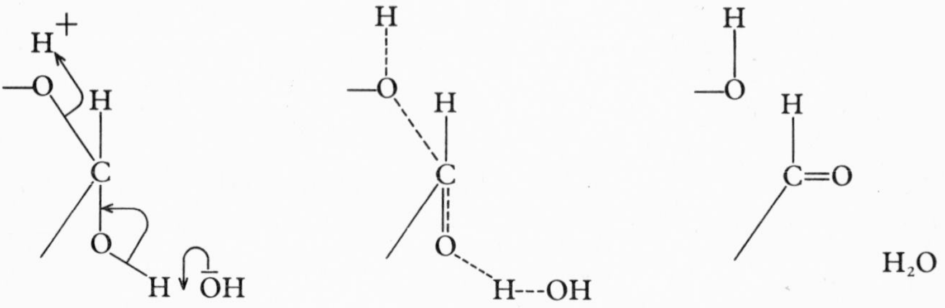

hemi-acetal (cyclic form)   transition state   aldehyde (open-chain form)

Both the acidic and basic groups can be in the same molecule. 2-Hydroxy-pyridine is a more effective catalyst than a mixture of phenol and pyridine; the effect is specific in that it is not shown by 3-hydroxy- or 4-hydroxy-pyridine.† This catalysis, which again involves a 'protonation-deprotonation' type of mechanism, may be shown as:

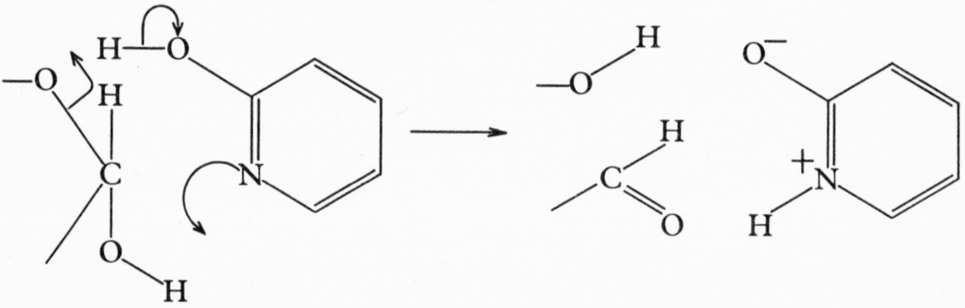

This is a striking example of catalytic efficiency. It bears some resemblance to enzymic catalysis. The catalyst and substrate form a complex, and the catalyst is, to some extent, specific. Moreover, as many enzymic reactions are those catalysed by both acids and bases, it seems likely that part of the effectiveness of enzymes as catalysts is to be attributed to their functioning as both acids and bases, just as 2-hydroxypyridine does here. Similarly, the effectiveness of carboxylic acids as catalysts

† Swain and Brown, *J. Amer. Chem. Soc.* 1952, **74**, 2534, 2538.

has been ascribed to their being able to form hydrogen bonds at two points simultaneously:[†]

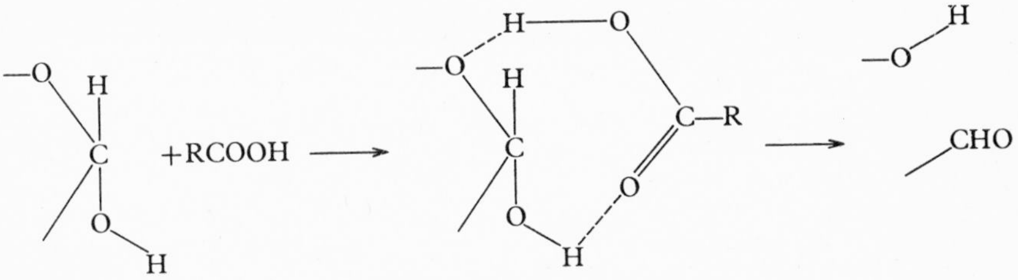

(c) *Addition of thiols.* Thiols are more ready than alcohols to combine with carbonyl groups. Thiols, for instance, react with both aldehydes and ketones, but alcohols usually react only with aldehydes. Thiols and aldehydes may give either hemi-mercaptals or (more frequently) mercaptals, depending on the conditions.

$$RCHO + R'SH \longrightarrow RCH(OH)SR'$$
hemi-mercaptal

$$RCH(OH)SR' + R'SH \longrightarrow RCH(SR')_2$$
mercaptal

Mercaptals are used in syntheses to protect carbonyl groups; the carbonyl compound can be regenerated with mercuric chloride.

The hemi-mercaptal from cysteine and formaldehyde (which cannot be isolated) cyclizes to thiazolidine-4-carboxylic acid; the reaction takes the course:[‡]

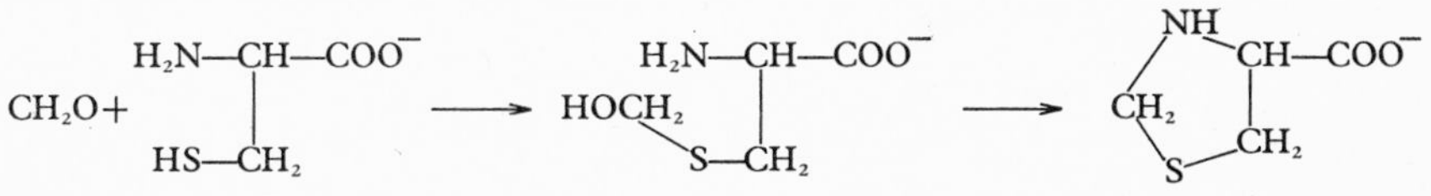

It seems generally to be true that the SH group displays greater nucleophilic reactivity than the NH_2 group. The hemi-mercaptal from glutathione and methylglyoxal is discussed in § 13. There may also be a hemi-mercaptal group in rhodopsin,[§] the protein from the retina which, on bleaching, liberates the aldehyde, retinene.

[†] Swain, di Milo, and Cordner, ibid. 1958, **80**, 5983.
[‡] Ratner and Clarke, ibid. 1937, **59**, 200.
[§] Wald, *Exp. Cell Res.* 1958, suppl. 5, p. 389.

(d) *Hydrolysis of acetals.* The hydrolysis of acetals,

$$
\underset{\text{acetal}}{CH_3-\overset{\overset{\displaystyle H}{|}}{\underset{\underset{\displaystyle OEt}{|}}{C}}-OEt} + H_2O \;\rightleftharpoons\; CH_3-C\underset{O}{\overset{H}{<}} + 2\,EtOH,
$$

is catalysed by hydrogen ions, but not by other acidic species. Thus there is general acid catalysis in the hydrolysis of hemi-acetals (§ 3 b) but specific hydrogen-ion catalysis in the hydrolysis of acetals. As hemi-acetals are probable intermediates in the hydrolysis of acetals, the slower step must be the first one:

$$
\underset{\text{acetal}}{CH_3-\overset{\overset{\displaystyle H}{|}}{\underset{\underset{\displaystyle OEt}{|}}{C}}-OEt} + H_2O \;\underset{}{\overset{\text{slow}}{\rightleftharpoons}}\; \underset{\text{hemi-acetal}}{CH_3-\overset{\overset{\displaystyle H}{|}}{\underset{\underset{\displaystyle OEt}{|}}{C}}-OH} + H_2O \;\overset{\text{fast}}{\rightleftharpoons}\; CH_3-C\underset{O}{\overset{H}{<}}
$$

The acid catalysis in the hydrolysis of acetals suggests that the reaction proceeds via the protonated acetal: the C—O heterolysis will be aided by a positive charge on the oxygen. Furthermore, the reaction proceeds more rapidly in D_2O than in H_2O, which suggests a proton transfer before the rate-determining step (Chapter II, § 2 f). Thus, the most probable mechanism is:†

$$
CH_3-\overset{\overset{\displaystyle H}{|}}{\underset{\underset{\displaystyle OEt}{|}}{C}}-OEt + H^+ \;\overset{\text{fast}}{\rightleftharpoons}\; CH_3-\overset{\overset{\displaystyle H}{|}}{\underset{\underset{\displaystyle OEt}{|}}{C}}-\overset{+}{\underset{\underset{\displaystyle H}{|}}{O}}Et \;\overset{\text{slow}}{\rightleftharpoons}\; CH_3-C\underset{\overset{+}{O}Et}{\overset{H}{<}} + EtOH
$$

(fast ‖ H_2O)

$$
EtOH + CH_3-C\underset{O}{\overset{H}{<}} \;\overset{-H^+}{\rightleftharpoons}\; CH_3-\overset{\overset{\displaystyle H}{|}}{\underset{\underset{\displaystyle \overset{+}{O}H_2}{|}}{C}}-OEt
$$

† Kreevoy and Taft, *J. Amer. Chem. Soc.* 1955, **77**, 3146.

4. Glycosidases

The two enzyme preparations, maltase and emulsin, contain gluco-sidases. Maltase catalyses the hydrolysis of α-D-glucopyranosides to α-D-glucopyranose, emulsin catalyses the hydrolysis of β-D-gluco-pyranosides to the β epimer.

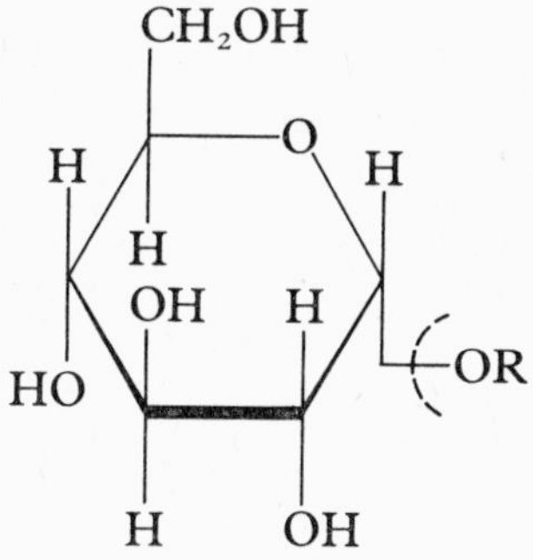

α -D-glucopyranoside 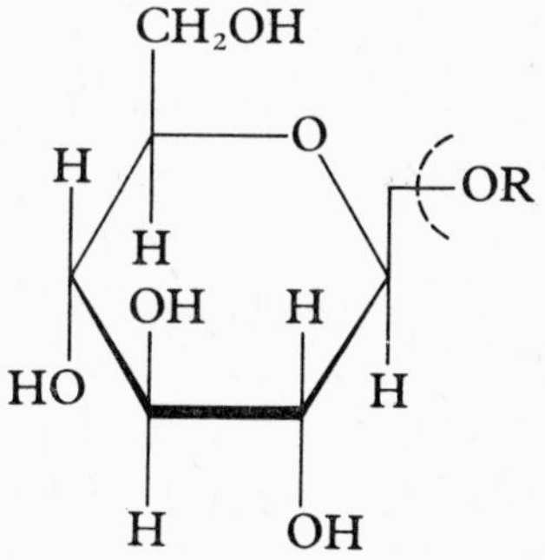   β -D-glucopyranoside

The reaction is the hydrolysis of an acetal to a hemi-acetal, and it proceeds with retention of configuration on C-1. The carbon-oxygen bond of a hemi-acetal is more labile than the other carbon-oxygen bond (the O—CH₃ bond when R = CH₃), so that the probable position of cleavage is as shown above. Moreover, these glucosidases catalyse the hydrolyses of many glucosides; the enzymes are specific if one is thinking in terms of the sugar moiety, but unspecific in that the group R can be varied widely. When an enzyme is specific for just part of a molecule, it usually happens that it is the bond nearer to that part of the molecule which is broken.† An example of the application of this rule is found in the hydrolysis of sucrose by invertase. From its specificity this enzyme may be classed as a β-D-fructofuranosidase, i.e. it is the fructose part of sucrose which combines with the enzyme. So the expected position of cleavage is as shown:

$$\text{glucose—O⫯fructose}$$

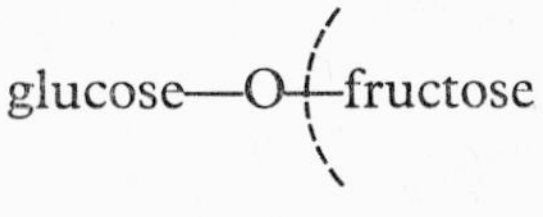

In agreement with this prediction, the enzymic hydrolysis in $H_2{}^{18}O$ gives glucose not containing any ^{18}O‡ (compare Chapter X, § 3).

---

† Koshland, *Biol. Rev.* 1953, **28**, 416; Koshland, in *Mechanism of Enzyme Action*, Johns Hopkins Press, Baltimore, 1954, p. 608.

‡ Koshland and Stein, *J. Biol. Chem.* 1954, **208**, 139.

The result, then, of this discussion is to suggest that the glucose-oxygen bond in α- and β-glucosides is broken in the enzymic hydrolyses catalysed by maltase and emulsin. Now the hydrolysis can be regarded as a nucleophilic substitution; as oxygen is more electronegative than carbon, heterolysis will be in the sense C—O, and a nucleophilic reagent will attack the carbon. We saw, in Chapter III, that nucleophilic substitutions normally proceed with inversion of configuration, and that when the configuration was retained this was usually the result of two successive inversions. Hence Koshland has suggested that a glucosyl-enzyme is formed (with inversion), and then hydrolysed (with inversion):

$$\text{α-glucoside} + \text{enzyme} \longrightarrow \text{β-glucosyl-enzyme} + \text{ROH} \qquad \text{(i)}$$

$$\text{β-glucosyl-enzyme} + H_2O \longrightarrow \text{α-glucose} + \text{enzyme} \qquad \text{(ii)}$$

Another example in which the enzyme acts as a nucleophilic reagent, and where a glucosyl-enzyme is a probable intermediate, is discussed in Chapter VI, § 2 b.

The effect of substituents on the rate of enzymic hydrolysis of phenyl glucosides has also been studied.[†] Electron withdrawing substituents (e.g. nitro group) in the benzene ring accelerate the enzymic hydrolysis and electron-repelling substituents (e.g. methoxy group) retard the reaction. This result is consistent with the rate-determining step being the breaking of the C—OR bond (reaction (i)), i.e. the nucleophilic attack of the enzyme on the glucoside.

5. Addition of sodium bisulphite

Aldehydes and some ketones (methyl ketones and alicyclic ketones) react with sodium bisulphite: the products are salts of α-hydroxy-sulphonic acids. The reaction is reversible, and the mechanism given below is derived from a study of the kinetics of the reverse reaction:[‡]

† Nath and Rydon, *Biochem. J.* 1954, **57**, 1.
‡ Blackadder and Hinshelwood, *J. Chem. Soc.* 1958, pp. 2720, 2728.

6. Addition of amino compounds

There are several reactions of the general type:

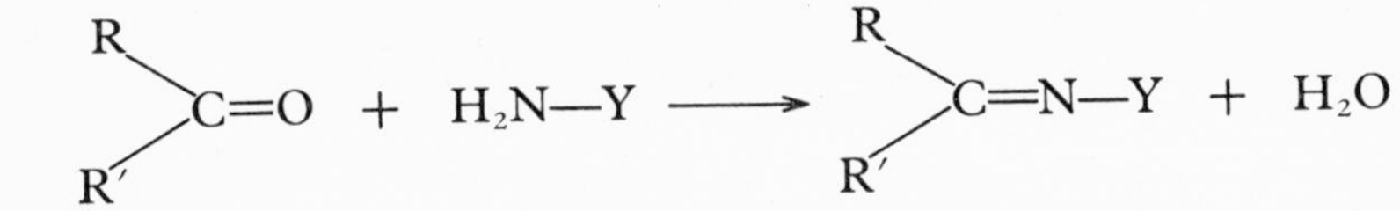

Stable compounds are formed when Y has an aromatic ring, or unshared electrons on an oxygen or nitrogen atom, conjugated with the C=N bond in the product. Two examples follow:

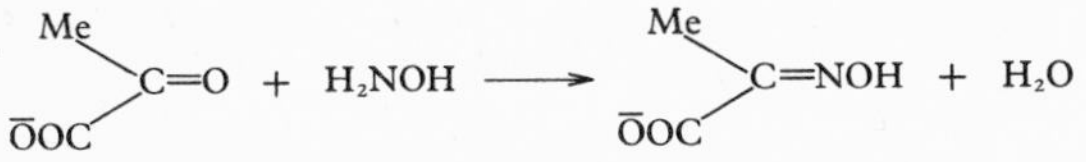

pyruvate ion   hydroxylamine   an oxime

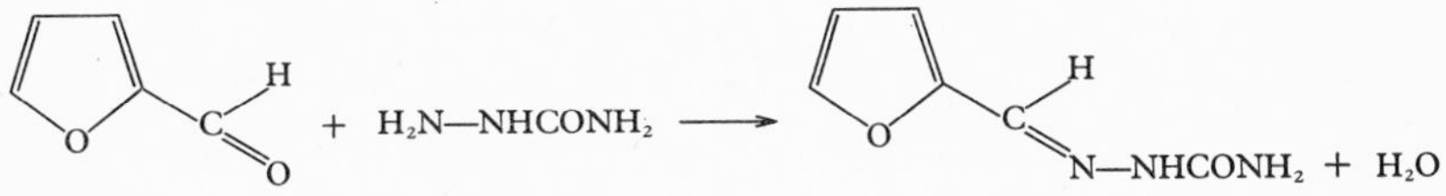

furfural   semicarbazide   a semicarbazone

The study of these reactions provides a good example of the application of spectroscopy to the investigation of a reaction. When sodium pyruvate and hydroxylamine are mixed in aqueous solution, at pH 7, the absorption band due to the keto group of the pyruvate is greatly reduced in intensity. This was observed both in the ultra-violet and infra-red regions of the spectrum. This change occurs so rapidly that it is complete by the time that the first readings are taken (thirty seconds after mixing). The formation of the oxime is considerably slower, so that there is a rapid reaction between hydroxylamine and the ketone. The most probable reaction is formation of the carbinol-amine:

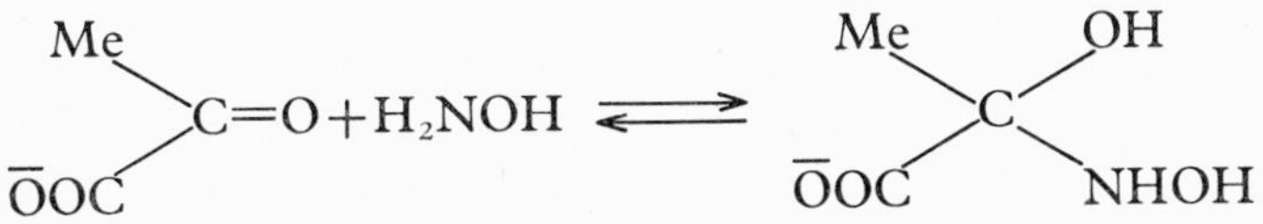

carbinolamine

As the carbinolamine lacks the ketonic carbonyl group, the formation of the carbinolamine accounts for the spectroscopic change. This reaction resembles the hydration of a carbonyl group, which is also often rapid. The second step, the formation of the oxime from the carbinol-amine by loss of water, is thus the rate-determining step. The reaction is acid-catalysed (between pH 5 and pH 7), as is commonly the case with dehydrations (see Chapter IV, § 3 c), and so we may write the rate-determining step briefly as

$$\underset{\text{-OOC}}{\overset{\text{Me}}{>}}\!C\!\underset{\underset{\text{OH}}{|}}{\overset{\text{OH}}{<}}N\!-\!H \quad \xrightarrow{\text{H}^+} \quad \underset{\text{-OOC}}{\overset{\text{Me}}{>}}C\!=\!NOH$$

The reaction is also subject to general acid catalysis. Thus, the rate increases with increase in concentration of phosphate buffer, although the pH and ionic strength are kept constant. The catalytic species is probably the acid, $H_2PO_4^-$; the transition state in the catalysis of the dehydration by $H_2PO_4^-$ may possibly be of the cyclic type

i.e.

The occurrence of general acid catalysis means that the rate of reaction depends on the nature of the buffer, and not merely on the pH, so that when two carbonyl compounds are compared, the nature of the buffer should be specified: acetone reacts more rapidly with semicarbazide than o-nitrobenzaldehyde does in an acetate buffer, but less rapidly in a chloroacetate buffer.

The main features of the reaction of pyruvate with hydroxylamine are shared by several other reactions of this type.† A characteristic feature of these reactions is that there is an optimum pH (around pH 5): the rate first increases on lowering the pH from 7 to about 5, and then the rate drops again in more strongly acidic solution. The acid-catalysed dehydration of the carbinolamine may not be slower than its formation in the more acidic solutions, so that here the rate-determining step may be the attack of the hydroxylamine upon the ketone. The decrease in rate as the pH is lowered is then due to the hydroxylamine (pK 6) becoming protonated; the protonated hydroxylamine, $^+NH_3OH$, will not attack the carbonyl group, since there is no longer a pair of unshared electrons on the nitrogen atom.

† Jencks, J. Amer. Chem. Soc. 1959, **81**, 475; references to earlier work are given here.

We have yet to consider the reversibility of the semicarbazone reaction. The rates and the equilibria often do not run together. Thus cyclohexanone semicarbazone is formed about fifty times as fast as furfural semicarbazone, but it is also hydrolysed nearly 300 times as fast; so that an equimolecular mixture of cyclohexanone, furfural, and semicarbazide gives mostly the cyclohexanone semicarbazone initially, but eventually practically the only product is furfural semicarbazone. When two pathways are possible, it is important to know whether kinetic or thermodynamic control is operating; this choice will be important in biological systems.

7. Formation of enols and enolate ions (mesomeric carbanions)

(a) *Halogenation of ketones.* We have so far considered the reactions of carbonyl compounds which are due to the group itself; but carbonyl compounds possess reactive hydrogen atoms (the replaceable atoms in what are sometimes called active methylene or methyl groups); thus acetone and bromine react to give (initially) bromoacetone:

$$Br_2 + CH_3 \cdot CO \cdot CH_3 \longrightarrow BrCH_2 \cdot CO \cdot CH_3 + HBr$$

Bromoacetone also contains reactive hydrogen atoms, and so undergoes further bromination; in alkaline solution, tribromoacetone is formed, which may then react further to give bromoform and acetate ion. The introduction of the second and third bromine atoms is relatively rapid. The reactive hydrogen atoms are those on the carbon atom next to the carbonyl carbon atom; more distant hydrogen atoms are not activated; the explanation of this is readily seen after the reasons for the reactivity have been discussed.

The reaction of bromine with acetone is catalysed by alkali. The rate of reaction, moreover, is proportional to the concentration of alkali and of acetone, but independent of the concentration of bromine. This suggests a kinetic scheme of the following type (XH is acetone and B is base):

$$XH + B \underset{k_{-1}}{\overset{k_1}{\rightleftharpoons}} X^- + BH^+$$

$$X^- + Br_2 \overset{k_2}{\longrightarrow} XBr + Br^-$$

If the ion, X^-, is an unstable intermediate and reacts with bromine much more rapidly than it reacts with the acid corresponding to the catalytic base (e.g. H_2O from ^-OH), then the kinetic equation (compare

Chapter II, § 2 b) reduces to:

$$\text{rate} = k_1[\text{XH}][\text{B}].$$

These are the conditions found, that the rate is proportional to the concentrations of acetone and base, but independent of the bromine concentration. Moreover, the rate of iodination is the same as the rate of bromination, i.e. neither the nature nor the concentration of the halogen affects the rate, as the rate-determining step is ionization of the ketone. We have yet to formulate the ion X^-. Although this ion is formed by heterolysis of a C—H bond, the greater part of the negative charge must be accommodated on the oxygen atom, and so the ion may be represented as the enolate (see Chapter I, § 1 q):

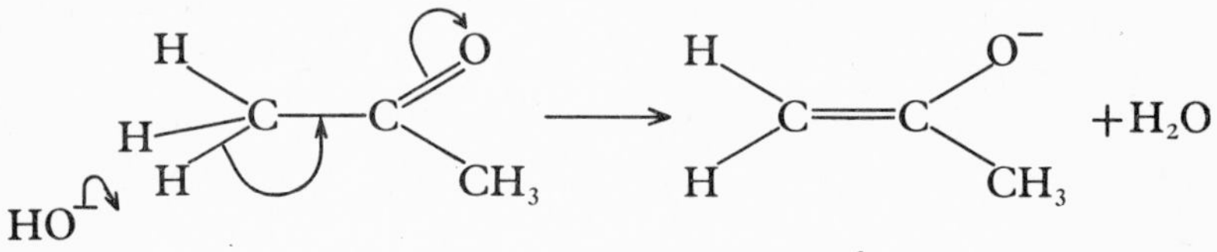

enolate

The reader will observe that this process bears some resemblance to the olefine-forming eliminations described in Chapter IV.

There are two important checks on this mechanism for the base-catalysed halogenation of ketones. One is stereochemical. The ketone (1) (phenyl s-butyl ketone)

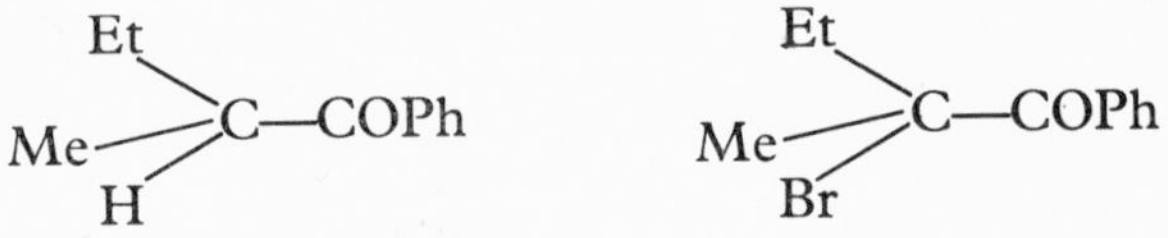

(1)   (2)

has an asymmetric carbon atom, and so may be resolved. The optically active form undergoes bromination; the product (2) is also resolvable, but is obtained in the optically inactive form. Racemization thus accompanies bromination. The crucial point is that the rate of bromination is equal to the rate of racemization.† Now the rate-determining step in the bromination is the formation of an intermediate, and so the formation of this intermediate leads to racemization. We have formulated the intermediate in the bromination of acetone as the enolate, and the formation of the enolate (3) would indeed lead to racemization as the enolate lacks the asymmetric carbon atom.

† Hsü and Wilson, *J. Chem. Soc.* 1936, p. 623.

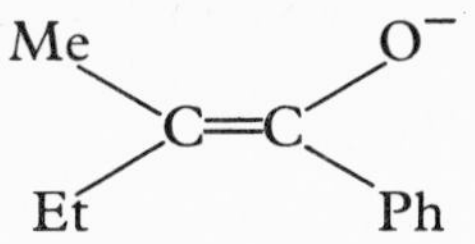

(3)

The other check makes use of tracers. The same ketone is racemized in D_2O; the rates of racemization and deuterium uptake are found to be equal.[†] In this experiment the halogen is not present, and so the ion simply reverts to the ketone, but the reaction

$$MeCH(Et)COPh + OD^- \rightleftarrows MeCD(Et)COPh + OH^-$$

can be followed by the incorporation of deuterium.

Thus, under one set of conditions the rates of bromination and racemization are equal; under another, the rates of racemization and deuterium uptake. Together, these results strongly support the mechanism in which the enolate is an intermediate.

We have assumed that the enolate ion is brominated rather than the enol itself; this is likely in alkaline solution where the ion is fairly abundant, as the ion is even more reactive towards the electrophilic bromine than the enol is, although enols also react rapidly with bromine. In the particular case of ethyl malonate, the velocity constant for the reaction of the anion with bromine is of the order of 10^{11} l. mol^{-1} min^{-1}, which is probably 10^4 to 10^6 times as large as the velocity constant for reaction of the enol with bromine. It is only in acid solution (here below pH 3) that the very low concentration of the ion outweighs its greater reactivity.[‡]

So far we have only described the mechanism of the base-catalysed bromination of ketones. The reaction is also acid-catalysed, and here the enol is the intermediate (see Chapter II, § 2 b):

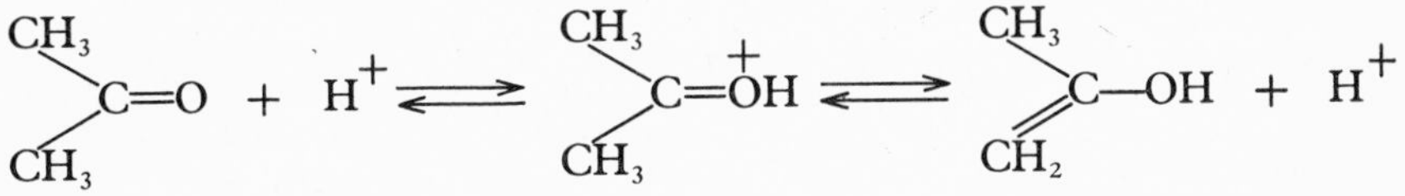

enol

To form the enol from the ketone, a C—H bond has to be broken. This

† Hsü, Ingold, and Wilson, ibid. 1938, p. 78.
‡ Bell and Spiro, ibid. 1953, p. 429.

is facilitated by the positive charge on the ion, as is brought out by the 'bent-arrow' representation:

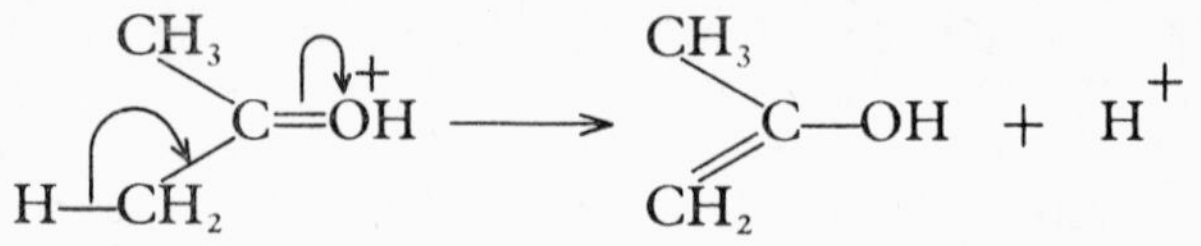

The enol contains a carbon-carbon double bond, and both the formation of the enol, and its reaction with bromine, are reactions of the types described in Chapter IV (§ 1 d and § 3 a). The double bond in the enol is especially reactive towards bromine (an electrophilic reagent) because the transition state is stabilized by accommodation of the partial positive charge on the oxygen atom:

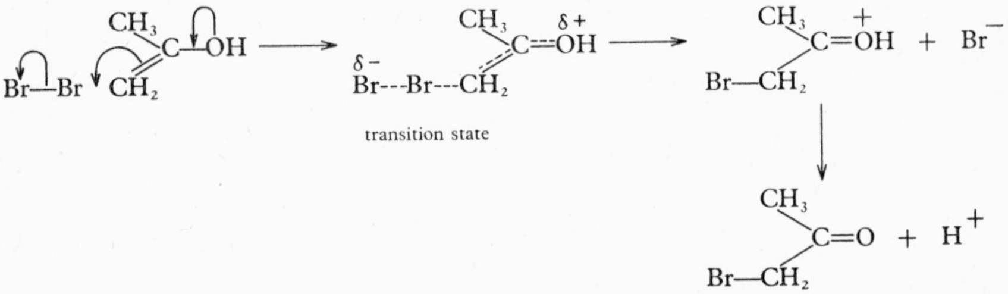

This account has been given in qualitative terms, to stress the main principles. The quantitative aspect of the acid-catalysed halogenation of ketones has been studied in great detail, in order to elucidate the mechanisms of enolization.

The kinetic equation for the enolization of acetone includes a term proportional to the concentration of (unionized) acetic acid, and another term proportional to the product of the concentrations of acetic acid and acetate ion.† The existence of a term involving CH_3COOH has been attributed (and there is considerable evidence for this view) to the steps:

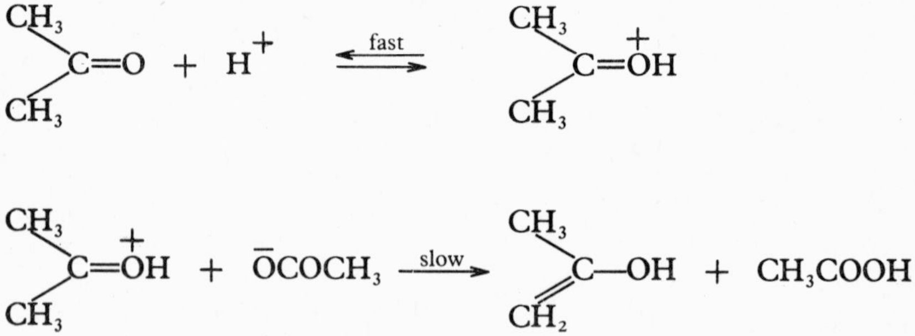

† Bell and Jones, *J. Chem. Soc.* 1953, p. 88.

These steps utilize the species H^+, $^-OCOCH_3$, rather than the unionized molecule CH_3COOH, but the mechanism still gives rise to a term proportional to the concentration of CH_3COOH in the kinetic equation, as $[CH_3COO^-][H^+] = K_A[CH_3COOH]$. There is also a term proportional to the concentration of acetate ion, and this is attributed to the attack of acetate on (unionized) acetone.

The term in the kinetic equation proportional to the product of the concentrations of carboxylic acid and carboxylate ion may arise from a cyclic, hydrogen-bonded, transition state:†

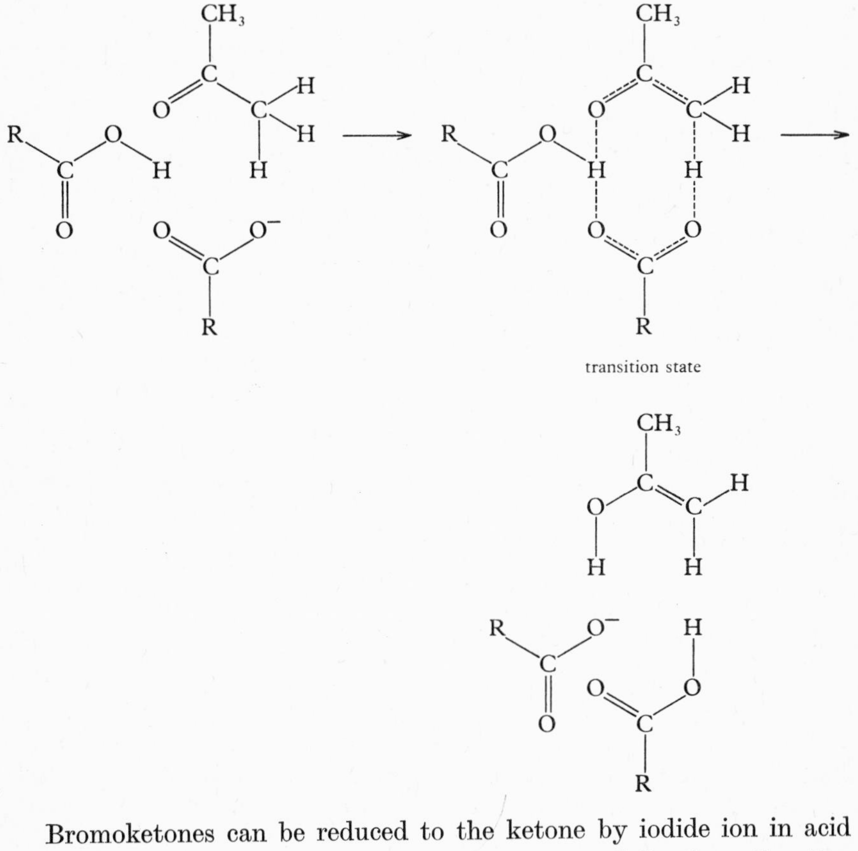

transition state

Bromoketones can be reduced to the ketone by iodide ion in acid solution; iodine is formed, and the reaction is used for the estimation of the amount of enol formed in a specimen of ethyl acetoacetate. The rate-determining step in the enolization catalysed by acetic acid was formulated above as the attack of the acetate ion on the carbon-bound hydrogen atom of the protonated ketone. By analogy, the reduction of

† Swain, di Milo, and Cordner, *J. Amer. Chem. Soc.* 1958, **80**, 5983.

bromoketone can be regarded as the attack of the iodide ion on the bromine atom:

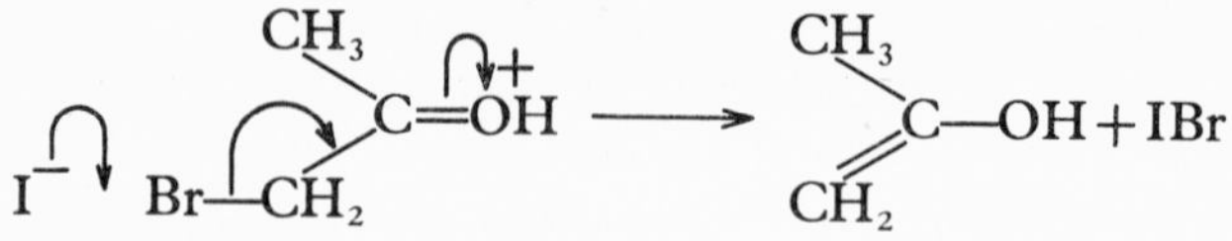

$$CH_3 \quad C=\overset{+}{O}H \longrightarrow \quad CH_3 \quad C-OH + IBr$$

$$I^- \quad Br-CH_2 \qquad\qquad CH_2$$

$$I^- + IBr \longrightarrow I_2 + Br^-$$

(b) *Tautomerism.* The conversion of a ketone into the corresponding enol, such as we have been discussing above, is an example of tauto-merism. The keto-enol change may be written:

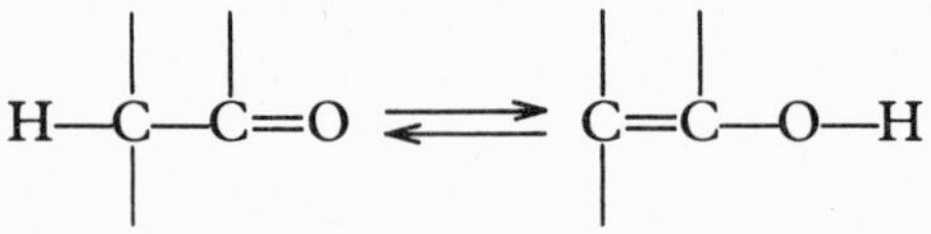

$$H-\overset{|}{\underset{|}{C}}-\overset{|}{C}=O \rightleftharpoons \overset{|}{C}=\overset{|}{\underset{|}{C}}-O-H$$

and tautomerism is an isomeric change, occurring in certain unsaturated systems, in which a group and a double bond migrate. The most impor-tant migrating group is the hydrogen atom; this kind of tautomerism is called prototropy.† The mechanism of keto-enol tautomerism has been discussed in the previous section, and we may now mention the position of equilibrium. In compounds with only one carbonyl group, not con-jugated with other groups, the equilibrium is greatly in favour of the keto form, as would be expected from the bond energies (Chapter I, § 2 c). But in acetylacetone the enol form preponderates in solvents other than water. In water the keto group can form hydrogen bonds with the solvent,

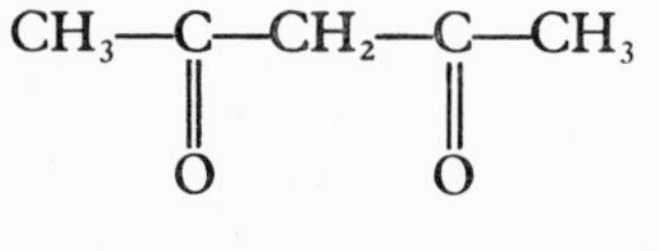

$$CH_3-\overset{|}{\underset{\overset{||}{O}}{C}}-CH_2-\overset{|}{\underset{\overset{||}{O}}{C}}-CH_3 \qquad CH_3-\overset{|}{\underset{\overset{|}{O}-H---O}{C}}=CH-\overset{|}{\underset{}{C}}-CH_3$$

keto 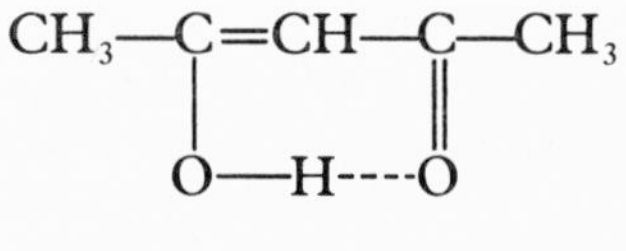   enol (hydrogen-bonded)

and so there is still 85 per cent. keto form, but in hexane about 92 per cent. is in the enol form, which is stabilized by internal hydrogen bonding.

There are several reactions in which tautomeric changes play a part. A rearrangement in the sugars (the de Bruyn–van Ekenstein reaction),

† For detailed discussion, see Ingold, *Structure and Mechanism in Organic Chemistry,* chap. x, Cornell University Press, 1953.

in which glucose, fructose, and mannose are interconverted, is usually taken to proceed through the common ene-diol, or the enolate derived from it, as written below:

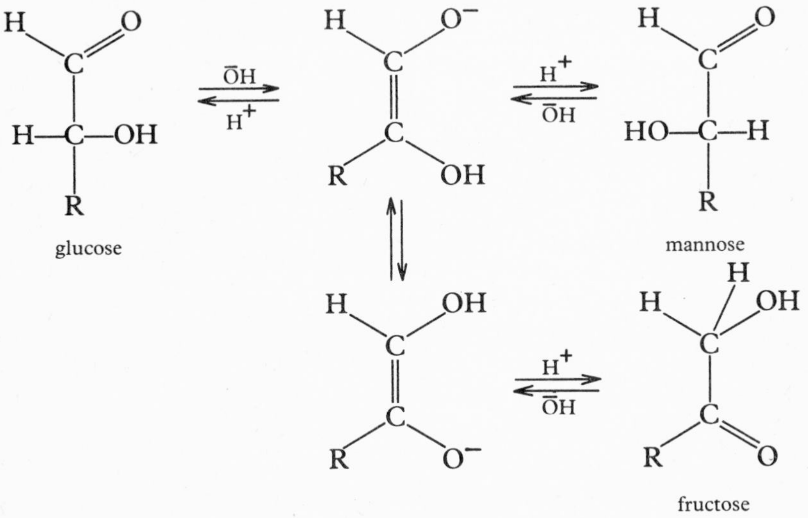

glucose   mannose

                                                                               fructose

Some evidence from experiments with isotopes is consistent with this mechanism.†

(c) *Aldol reaction*. The formation of aldol from acetaldehyde is an addition reaction of an important type, in which a new carbon-carbon bond is formed:

$$2CH_3 \cdot CHO \longrightarrow CH_3 \cdot CHOH \cdot CH_2 \cdot CHO$$

acetaldehyde   aldol

The reaction is catalysed by both acids and bases; we shall consider the base-catalysed reaction first. Now, although two acetaldehyde molecules combine (irreversibly), the rate, at relatively high acetaldehyde concentrations, is only first-order in acetaldehyde. This immediately suggests an analogy with the mechanism for the base-catalysed bromination of acetone (§ 7 a); here one molecule of acetaldehyde will play the same part as the bromine did, and act as the electrophilic species which reacts with the enolate anion:

† Topper and Stetten, *J. Biol. Chem.* 1951, **189**, 191; Sowden and Schaffer, *J. Amer. Chem. Soc.* 1952, **74**, 505.

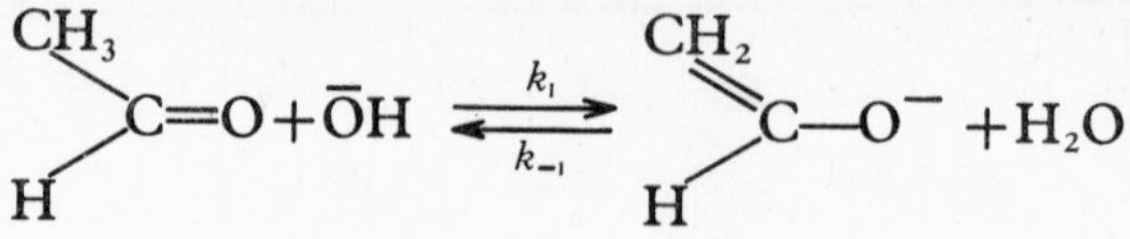

$$\underset{H}{\overset{CH_3}{>}}C{=}O + \bar{O}H \underset{k_{-1}}{\overset{k_1}{\rightleftharpoons}} \underset{H}{\overset{CH_2}{>}}C{-}O^- + H_2O$$

enolate

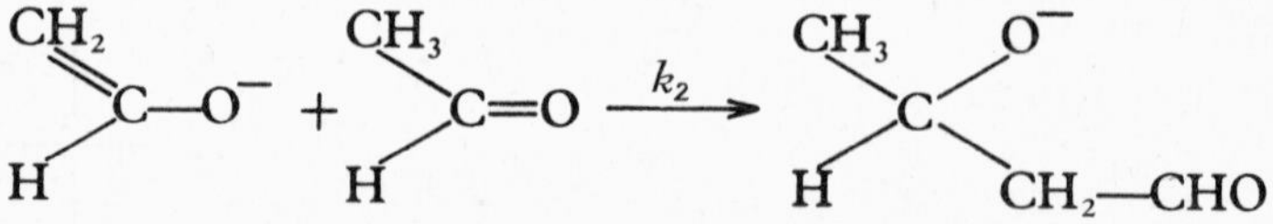

$$\underset{H}{\overset{CH_2}{>}}C{-}O^- + \underset{H}{\overset{CH_3}{>}}C{=}O \xrightarrow{k_2} \underset{H}{\overset{CH_3}{>}}C\underset{CH_2-CHO}{\overset{O^-}{<}}$$

This mechanism, on the assumption that the enolate is an unstable inter-mediate, leads to the kinetic equation (see Chapter II, § 2 b):

$$\text{rate} = \frac{k_1 k_2 [CH_3CHO]^2[OH^-]}{k_1 + k_2[CH_3CHO]}. \tag{i}$$

When the enolate reacts much more rapidly with another molecule of acetaldehyde than it reverts to CH_3CHO, i.e. when $k_2[CH_3CHO] \gg k_{-1}$, this expression reduces to:

$$\text{rate} = k_1[CH_3CHO][OH^-].$$

Moreover, this mechanism predicts that, when the reaction is carried out in D_2O, the aldol formed will not contain deuterium bound to carbon, and this is found to be so. However, when the acetaldehyde concentra-tion is low, the rate is between first- and second-order with respect to acetaldehyde, and this can be accounted for by assuming that the two terms in the denominator of equation (i) are now of the same order of magnitude. On this basis, partial reaction in D_2O should, at low con-centrations of acetaldehyde, lead to incorporation of deuterium in the unreacted acetaldehyde; this, too, is found, and indeed the extent of incorporation can be quantitatively accounted for by the mechanism given above.†

Acetone undergoes a reaction which is similar in essence but different in detail. In the first place, the dimerization of acetone to diacetone alcohol is reversible; in fact, the equilibrium is on the side of acetone itself, so that the reaction is studied in the direction:

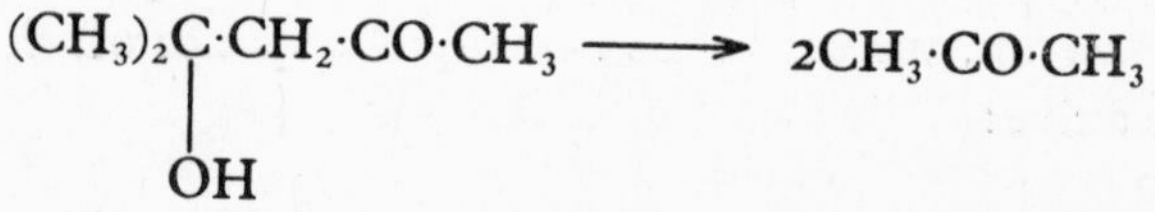

$$(CH_3)_2\underset{OH}{\overset{|}{C}}{\cdot}CH_2{\cdot}CO{\cdot}CH_3 \longrightarrow 2CH_3{\cdot}CO{\cdot}CH_3$$

† Bell and Smith, J. Chem. Soc. 1958, p. 1691.

By the principle of microscopic reversibility the mechanism is the same for the forward and back reactions; and this enables us to find the kinetics for the aldol reaction as follows. The rate of decomposition of diacetone alcohol is given by

$$v_1 = k[\text{diacetone alcohol}][\text{OH}^-]$$

and the equilibrium constant of the reaction by

$$[\text{diacetone alcohol}]/[\text{acetone}]^2 = K;$$

these equations may be combined to give the expression for the rate of formation of diacetone alcohol as

$$v_1 = kK[\text{acetone}]^2[\text{OH}^-].$$

If we assume that the mechanism is analogous to that of the aldol reaction of acetaldehyde

$$\mathrm{CH_3 \cdot CO \cdot CH_3 + \overline{O}H} \underset{k_{-1}}{\overset{k_1}{\rightleftharpoons}} \mathrm{CH_2{=}\overset{\overset{\displaystyle O^-}{|}}{C}\cdot CH_3 + H_2O}$$

$$\mathrm{CH_2{=}\overset{\overset{\displaystyle O^-}{|}}{C}\cdot CH_3 + CH_3 \cdot CO \cdot CH_3} \underset{k_{-2}}{\overset{k_2}{\rightleftharpoons}} \mathrm{(CH_3)_2\underset{\underset{\displaystyle O^-}{|}}{C}\cdot CH_2 CO \cdot CH_3}$$

$$\mathrm{(CH_3)_2\underset{\underset{\displaystyle O^-}{|}}{C}\cdot CH_2 \cdot CO \cdot CH_3 + H_2O} \rightleftharpoons \mathrm{(CH_3)_2\underset{\underset{\displaystyle OH}{|}}{C}\cdot CH_2 \cdot CO \cdot CH_3 + OH^-}$$

then the rate equation shows that here an expression of the same type as equation (i) will apply, but that now $k_{-1} \gg k_2[\text{CH}_3\text{COCH}_3]$. The prediction, that the rate of incorporation of deuterium into acetone (in alkaline D_2O) should be much greater than the rate of the aldol addition, has been confirmed. The difference between the aldol reactions of acetaldehyde and acetone shows that the carbonyl group in the aldehyde is much more reactive than that in the ketone, as is to be expected.

The decomposition of diacetone alcohol is catalysed by primary and secondary amines, but not by tertiary amines. This catalysis is probably due to the formation of imines, in which the electron-attracting nature of the positively charged nitrogen atom will aid the reaction.†

† Westheimer and Cohen, *J. Amer. Chem. Soc.* 1938, **60**, 90; Westheimer and Jones, ibid. 1941, **63**, 3283.

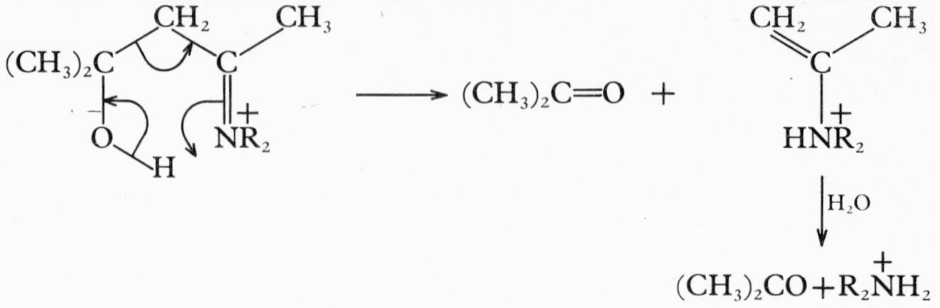

$$(CH_3)_2C=O +$$

$$\downarrow H_2O$$

$$(CH_3)_2CO + R_2\overset{+}{N}H_2$$

The acid-catalysed aldol reaction is complicated by the tendency of the alcohols to undergo dehydration in acid solution; thus benzaldehyde and acetophenone give the unsaturated ketone, phenyl styryl ketone (1), in acid solution. It seems reasonable to assume that the hydroxyketone (2) is first formed, and its dehydration is known to be sufficiently rapid for it to be an intermediate. The following mechanism has been advanced for this reaction, in dilute solution:†

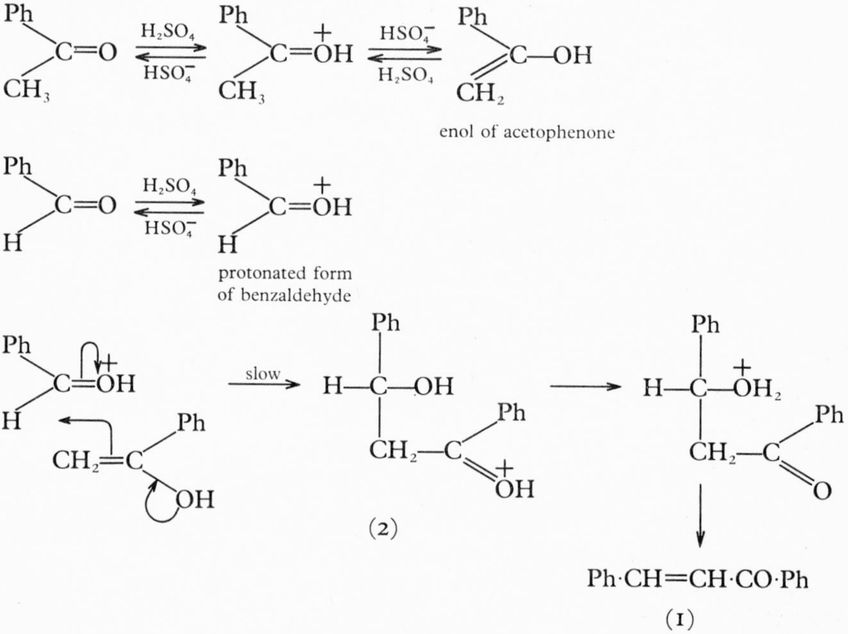

enol of acetophenone

protonated form
of benzaldehyde

(2)

$$Ph \cdot CH = CH \cdot CO \cdot Ph$$

(1)

8. Enzyme-catalysed tautomerization

The enzymic counterpart to the de Bruyn–van Ekenstein reaction, described in § 7 b, is the interconversion of D-glucose-6-phosphate and D-fructose-6-phosphate, catalysed by phosphoglucose isomerase; here

† Noyce and Pryor, *J. Amer. Chem. Soc.* 1955, **77**, 1397, 1402.

mannose phosphate is not formed, but there is a separate enzyme (phosphomannose isomerase) which interconverts mannose-6-phosphate and fructose-6-phosphate. When the phosphoglucose isomerase reaction is carried out in D_2O, the glucose phosphate formed from fructose-6-phosphate contains one atom of deuterium, bound to C-2. When the starting material is glucose phosphate with a deuterium atom bound to C-1 (1), the deuterium is not lost when the conversion into fructose-6-phosphate (2) is carried out in H_2O with phosphoglucose isomerase alone; but when both phosphoglucose isomerase and phosphomannose isomerase are present, the starting material releases some of its deuterium to the aqueous medium by the cycle $1 \rightleftarrows 2 \rightleftarrows 3 \rightleftarrows 4 \rightleftarrows 5$.

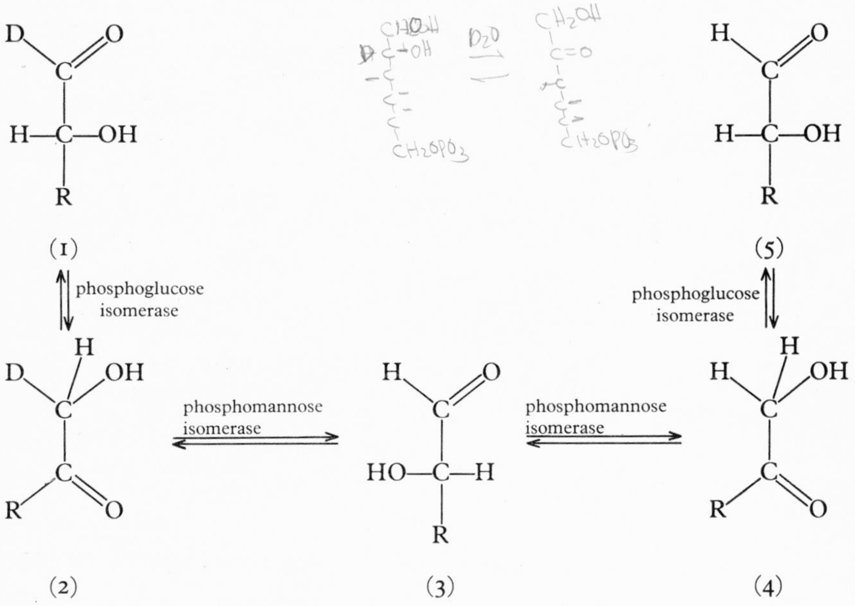

These observations can be interpreted by supposing that the two enzymes are both stereospecific, in that they both labilize just one of the two hydrogen atoms attached to the C-1 of fructose phosphate; but each enzyme must labilize a different hydrogen atom. An enzyme-bound ene-diol (or its ion) may well be an intermediate.†

Similar observations have been made with triosephosphate isomerase, which catalyses the conversion of D-glyceraldehyde-3-phosphate into dihydroxyacetone phosphate (see § 9).

† Topper, *J. Biol. Chem.* 1957, **225**, 419; Bloom and Topper, *Science*, 1956, **124**, 982; Rieder and Rose, *Fed. Proc.* 1956, **15**, 337.

9. Aldolase

A number of enzymic reactions can be classed as aldol additions, but we shall be mainly concerned with the reaction catalysed by aldolase itself, in which D-glyceraldehyde-3-phosphate and dihydroxyacetone phosphate combine to give fructose-1,6-diphosphate.

The addition proceeds (without an enzyme) in alkaline solution; here the trioses, rather than their phosphates, are used:

$$
\begin{array}{ccc}
CH_2OH & CH_2OH & CH_2OH \\
| & | & | \\
CO & CO & CO \\
| & | & | \\
CH_2OH & HO-C-H & H-C-OH \\
\xrightarrow{\text{pH 11·5}} & \quad\text{and}\quad & \\
CHO & H-C-OH & HO-C-H \\
| & | & | \\
H-C-OH & H-C-OH & H-C-OH \\
| & | & | \\
CH_2OH & CH_2OH & CH_2OH
\end{array}
$$

D-fructose   D-sorbose

The products are written in their open-chain forms for the sake of simplicity. The mechanism of the reaction is probably similar to that given for acetaldehyde, as the hexoses contain no carbon-bound deuterium when the addition is carried out in D_2O,[†] and the kinetics are first-order in total triose.[‡] Hence the 'difficult' (rate-determining) step is the formation of the mesomeric carbanion from dihydroxyacetone, and so we might guess by analogy that this step would be the one in which the enzyme intervened in the reaction of the triosephosphates. We shall see later that there is much evidence that this is so.

Even the non-enzymic reaction shows considerable stereospecificity; as two new asymmetric centres are created, four stereoisomers could be formed, but the two compounds shown (fructose and sorbose) account for over 90 per cent. of the products formed. In both these compounds the newly formed hydroxyl group on C-4 is *trans* (in the projection formula) to the hydroxyl group on C-3. This result can be interpreted if the dihydroxyacetone approaches the glyceraldehyde in a particular

† Bonhoeffer and Walters, *Z. physik. Chem.* 1938, **A 181**, 441.
‡ Berl and Feazel, *J. Amer. Chem. Soc.* 1951, **73**, 2054.

way. One possibility is that the glyceraldehyde can react in either of the conformations (1) or (2). Then if the dihydroxyacetone, reacting as the enolate ion, approaches in the way shown, the product will be either fructose, or sorbose.

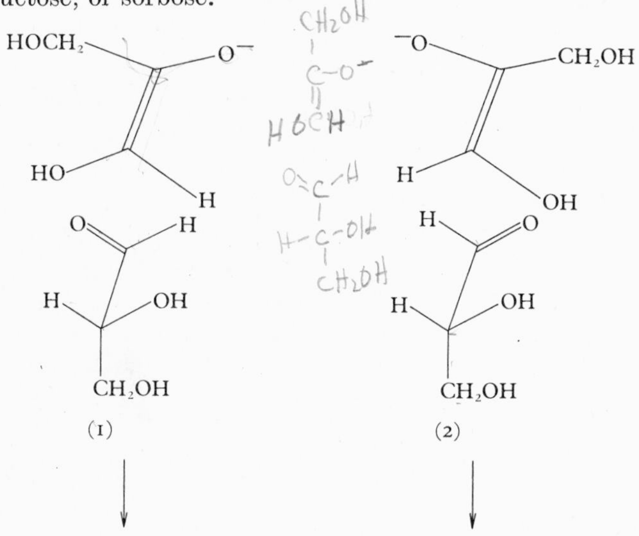

(1)   (2)

fructose   sorbose

Let us now return to the enzymic reaction catalysed by aldolase. The fact that the sole product is fructose diphosphate shows that the enzyme discriminates between the two hydrogen atoms in the CH_2OH group of dihydroxyacetone phosphate. Aldolase catalyses several aldol reactions: the aldehyde may be acetaldehyde or a tetrose,[†] but the specificity for dihydroxyacetone phosphate seems to be complete. This again suggests that the aldolase activates the dihydroxyacetone phosphate. That the two combine to give a complex is shown by the appearance of a peak in the ultra-violet absorption spectrum of mixtures of the ketone and aldolase; this peak is not observed in mixtures of glyceraldehyde phosphate and aldolase, and the addition of the aldehyde to aldolase and dihydroxyacetone phosphate causes the peak to disappear.[‡]

Further evidence is provided by experiments with isotopes. In the presence of aldolase, one carbon-bound hydrogen atom of dihydroxyacetone phosphate is replaced by tritium. The rate of the incorporation catalysed by muscle aldolase is greater than the rate of hexose diphosphate formation, but is depressed to this value when glyceraldehyde phosphate is present; the fructose diphosphate formed is not labelled.

† Hough and Jones, *J. Chem. Soc.* 1953, p. 342; Govin and Jones, ibid., p. 1537.
‡ Topper, Mehler, and Bloom, *Science*, 1957, **126**, 1287.

This hydrogen exchange reaction is stereospecific, as might be expected from the stereochemical discussion presented above. Now another enzyme, triosephosphate isomerase (§ 8), which acts on the same substrate, also catalyses the replacement of just one hydrogen atom by tritium, but here it is the other hydrogen atom that is replaced. This is shown by labelling dihydroxyacetone phosphate (3), in the presence of

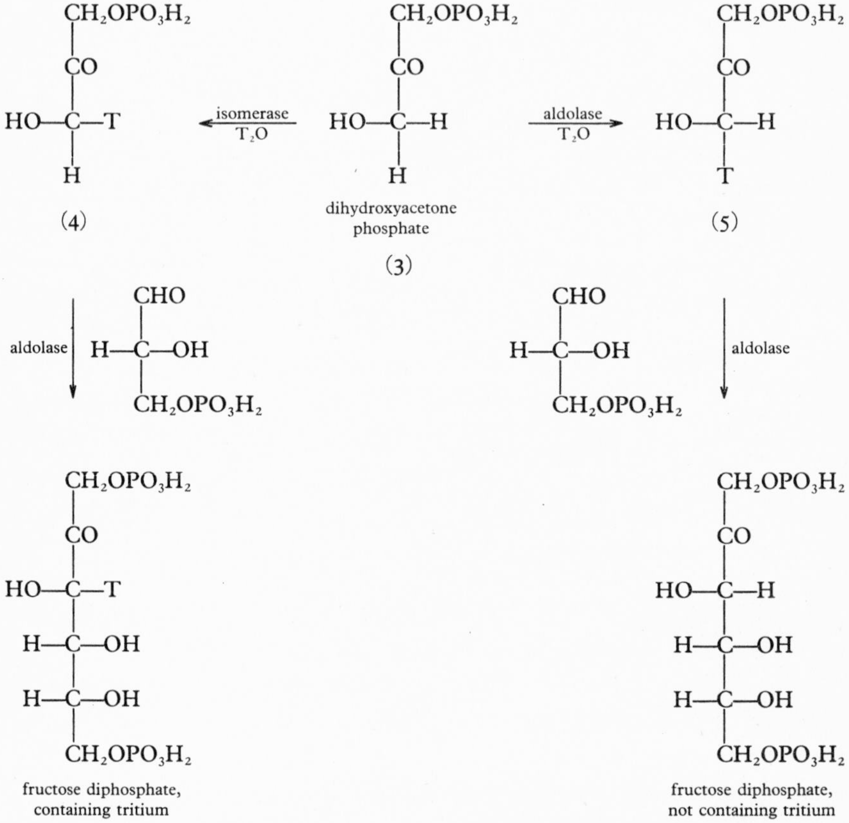

$$CH_2OPO_3H_2$$
$$|$$
$$CO$$
$$|$$
$$HO—C—T$$
$$|$$
$$H$$

(4)

$$\xleftarrow{\text{isomerase}\atop T_2O}$$

$$CH_2OPO_3H_2$$
$$|$$
$$CO$$
$$|$$
$$HO—C—H$$
$$|$$
$$H$$

dihydroxyacetone
phosphate

(3)

$$\xrightarrow{\text{aldolase}\atop T_2O}$$

$$CH_2OPO_3H_2$$
$$|$$
$$CO$$
$$|$$
$$HO—C—H$$
$$|$$
$$T$$

(5)

aldolase ↓

$$CHO$$
$$|$$
$$H—C—OH$$
$$|$$
$$CH_2OPO_3H_2$$

$$CHO$$
$$|$$
$$H—C—OH$$
$$|$$
$$CH_2OPO_3H_2$$

aldolase ↓

$$CH_2OPO_3H_2$$
$$|$$
$$CO$$
$$|$$
$$HO—C—T$$
$$|$$
$$H—C—OH$$
$$|$$
$$H—C—OH$$
$$|$$
$$CH_2OPO_3H_2$$

fructose diphosphate,
containing tritium

$$CH_2OPO_3H_2$$
$$|$$
$$CO$$
$$|$$
$$HO—C—H$$
$$|$$
$$H—C—OH$$
$$|$$
$$H—C—OH$$
$$|$$
$$CH_2OPO_3H_2$$

fructose diphosphate,
not containing tritium

either muscle aldolase, or, alternatively, triosephosphate isomerase; the labelled compound is then incubated in ordinary water with the other of the two enzymes; in neither case is the tritium released into the water. Moreover, when yeast aldolase is used to catalyse the synthesis of fructose diphosphate from glyceraldehyde phosphate and a specimen of dihydroxyacetone phosphate (4) which had been labelled in the presence of triosephosphate isomerase, the hexose contains tritium; in another experiment, similar except that the specimen of dihydroxyacetone phosphate (5) had been labelled in the presence of muscle aldolase, the hexose did not contain tritium.

Further evidence suggests that the absolute configurations of the two samples of labelled dihydroxyacetone phosphate are (4) and (5), and are related to the configurations of the carbon atoms in fructose disphosphate as shown above.

If we suppose that the enzyme, aldolase, detaches the hydrogen atom from dihydroxyacetone phosphate as a proton, and binds the enolate so formed, then the formation of D-fructose diphosphate as the sole stereoisomer could be accounted for if the stereospecific addition to glyceraldehyde phosphate took place in the manner sketched. Here it is supposed that the enzyme-bound enolate can only be approached from below, and that the carbonyl group is attacked from only one side. This is essentially a hypothetical elaboration of the route suggested in the non-enzymic reaction (§ 7 c).†

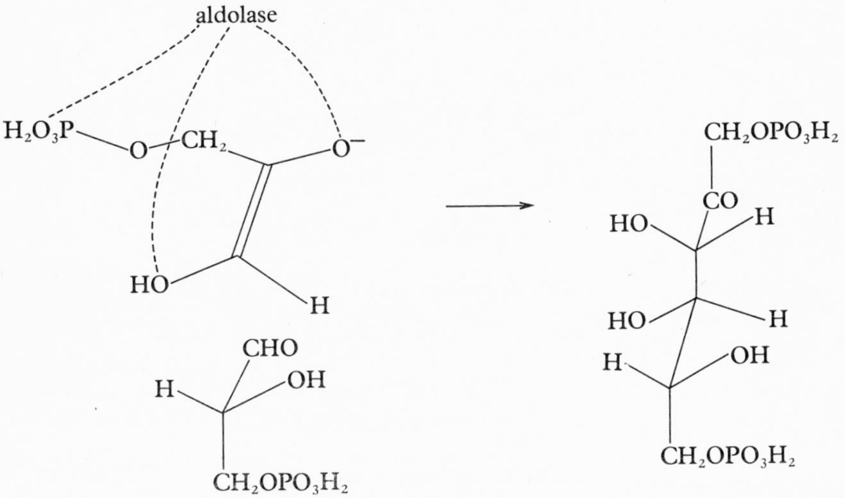

There are several differences (e.g. in the requirements for added metal ions) between yeast aldolase and muscle aldolase, but the stereochemical features seem to be common.

The rate of the aldolase-catalysed reaction is of the order of 10^3 mols/l. min, at unit enzyme concentration. This may be compared with the rate of the base-catalysed reaction of dihydroxyacetone with glyceric aldehyde, which is about 10^{-6} mols/l. min at pH 7. Thus the enzymic reaction (of the phosphates) is more rapid by a factor of the order of 10^9.

† Rose and Rieder, *J. Biol. Chem.* 1958, **231**, 315; Rose, *J. Amer. Chem. Soc.* 1958, **80**, 5835; Bloom and Topper, *Nature*, 1958, **181**, 1128; Rutter and Ling, *Biochim. Biophys. Acta*, 1958, **30**, 71.

A final point about the aldolase-catalysed reaction is that the equilibrium is in favour of the hexose: the generalization that 'synthetic' reactions are endergonic (energetically unfavourable) does not apply to reactions in which carbon-carbon bonds are synthesized; the equilibrium is also in favour of the products in the reaction catalysed by citrase, and by isocitrase.

There are several other enzymic reactions of the aldol type, e.g.

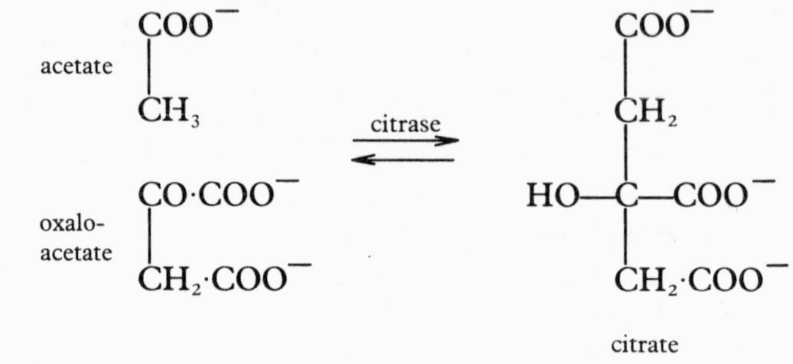

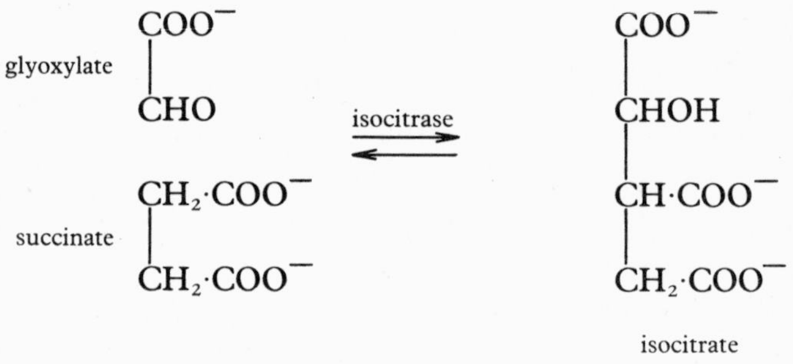

$$
\begin{array}{ll}
\text{acetate} & \begin{array}{l} \text{COO}^- \\ | \\ \text{CH}_3 \end{array} \\[2em]
\text{oxalo-} & \begin{array}{l} \text{CO·COO}^- \\ | \\ \text{CH}_2\text{·COO}^- \end{array}
\end{array}
\quad \underset{\longleftarrow}{\overset{\text{citrase}}{\longrightarrow}} \quad
\begin{array}{l}
\text{COO}^- \\ | \\ \text{CH}_2 \\ | \\ \text{HO—C—COO}^- \\ | \\ \text{CH}_2\text{·COO}^-
\end{array}
$$

citrate

$$
\begin{array}{ll}
\text{glyoxylate} & \begin{array}{l} \text{COO}^- \\ | \\ \text{CHO} \end{array} \\[2em]
\text{succinate} & \begin{array}{l} \text{CH}_2\text{·COO}^- \\ | \\ \text{CH}_2\text{·COO}^- \end{array}
\end{array}
\quad \underset{\longleftarrow}{\overset{\text{isocitrase}}{\longrightarrow}} \quad
\begin{array}{l}
\text{COO}^- \\ | \\ \text{CHOH} \\ | \\ \text{CH·COO}^- \\ | \\ \text{CH}_2\text{·COO}^-
\end{array}
$$

isocitrate

There are also the similar reactions of thiol esters, where the thiol is coenzyme A (CoA—SH), e.g.

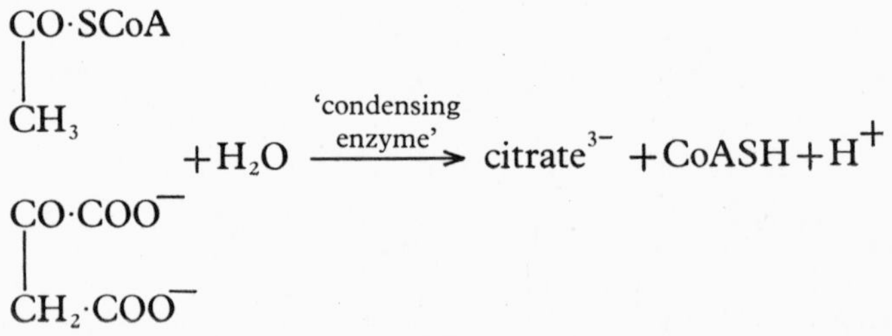

$$
\begin{array}{l}
\text{CO·SCoA} \\ | \\ \text{CH}_3 \\[1em]
\text{CO·COO}^- \\ | \\ \text{CH}_2\text{·COO}^-
\end{array}
+ H_2O \xrightarrow{\substack{\text{'condensing}\\ \text{enzyme'}}} \text{citrate}^{3-} + \text{CoASH} + H^+
$$

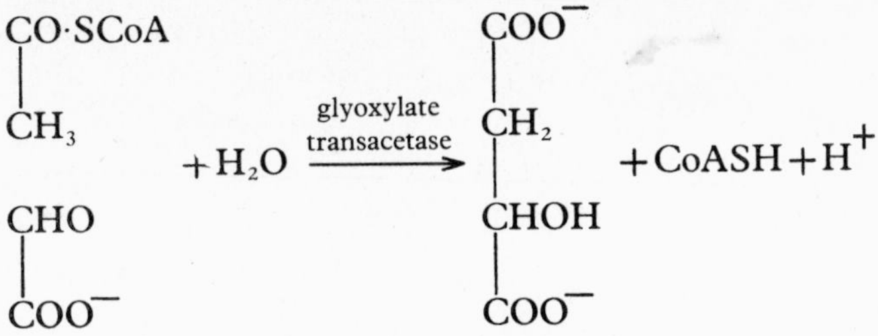

CO·SCoA $\quad\quad$ COO⁻

CH₃ $\quad$ +H₂O $\xrightarrow[\text{transacetase}]{\text{glyoxylate}}$ CH₂ $\quad$ +CoASH+H⁺

CHO $\quad\quad$ CHOH

COO⁻ $\quad\quad$ COO⁻

malate

In the reaction leading to citrate there is no appreciable incorporation of isotopically labelled hydrogen from the medium into the citrate, nor does acetyl coenzyme A acquire a labelled hydrogen atom on incubation with the enzyme. Hence the acetyl coenzyme A is not converted into free enol, or enolate ion, during the reaction.† The reactivity of thiol esters is discussed later (Chapter VII, § 3). The reaction of acetaldehyde with glycine to give threonine, or allothreonine, is formally similar, but pyridoxal phosphate (§ 20) is a coenzyme.

10. Benzoin reaction

In this reaction two molecules of an aromatic aldehyde combine to give an α-hydroxyketone, e.g.

$$2\text{Ph·CHO} \longrightarrow \text{Ph·CO·CHOH·Ph}$$

benzaldehyde $\quad\quad\quad$ benzoin

The difference between the aldol and benzoin reactions is brought out in the following skeleton formulae:

aldol

$$\begin{array}{c}\text{C} \\ | \\ \text{O}\end{array} + \begin{array}{c}\text{C—C} \\ | \\ \text{O}\end{array} \longrightarrow \begin{array}{c}\text{C—C—C} \\ |\quad\quad| \\ \text{O}\quad\ \ \text{O}\end{array}$$

benzoin

$$\begin{array}{c}\text{C} \\ | \\ \text{O}\end{array} + \begin{array}{c}\text{C} \\ | \\ \text{O}\end{array} \longrightarrow \begin{array}{c}\text{C—C} \\ |\ \ \ | \\ \text{O}\ \ \text{O}\end{array}$$

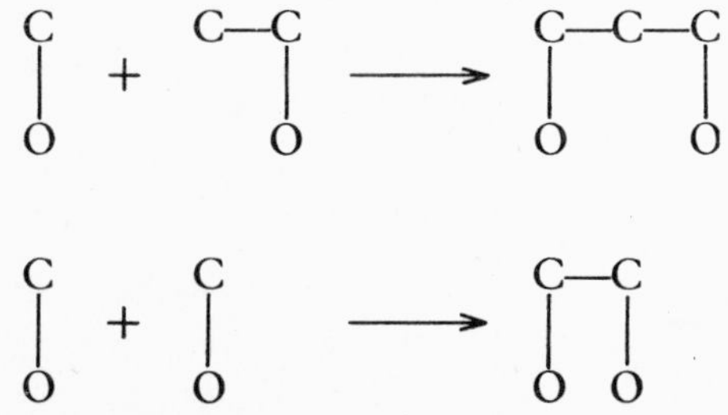

The benzoin reaction is carried out in the presence of cyanide ion. The cyanide ion is not simply acting as a base, since only a few other substances (which are discussed in the next section) can replace it. The rate

† Marcus and Vennesland, *J. Biol. Chem.* 1958, **233**, 727; Bové, Martin, Ingraham, and Stumpf, ibid. 1959, **234**, 999; England, ibid., p. 1004.

of the reaction is proportional to the concentration of the cyanide ion, and to the square of the concentration of benzaldehyde. The mechanism which is usually suggested starts with the formation of a cyanohydrin (§ 2); this then undergoes prototropic change to a carbanion, which reacts with another molecule of aldehyde in the rate-determining step:

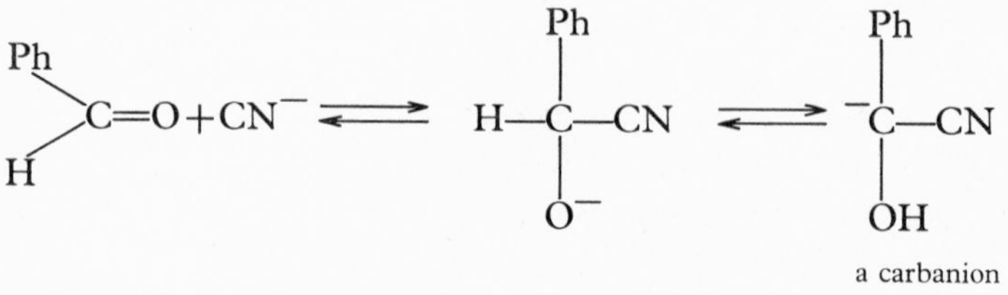

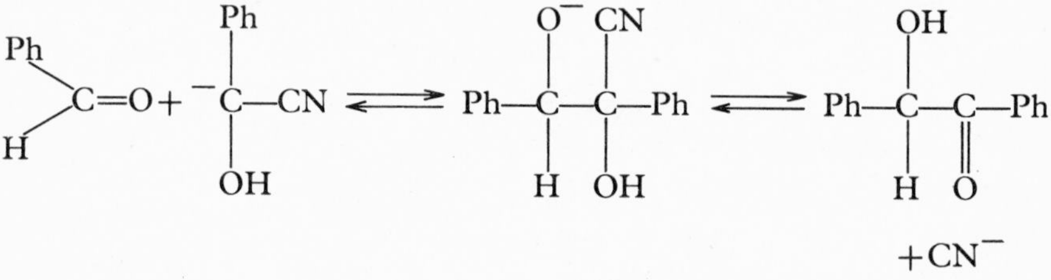

$$
\underset{H}{\overset{Ph}{>}}C{=}O + CN^- \rightleftharpoons \underset{O^-}{\overset{Ph}{H{-}C{-}CN}} \rightleftharpoons \underset{OH}{\overset{Ph}{{}^-C{-}CN}}
$$

a carbanion

$$
\underset{H}{\overset{Ph}{>}}C{=}O + \underset{OH}{\overset{Ph}{{}^-C{-}CN}} \rightleftharpoons Ph{-}\underset{H\ \ OH}{\overset{O^-\ \ CN}{C{-}C}}{-}Ph \rightleftharpoons Ph{-}\underset{H\ \ O}{\overset{OH}{C{-}C}}{-}Ph
$$

$$+ CN^-$$

The postulated carbanion would be stabilized by mesomerism, in the same way as the carbanions of carbonyl compounds that we have already discussed:

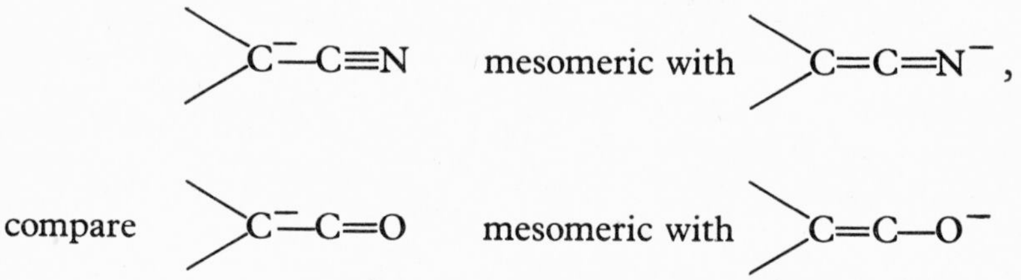

$$>C^-{-}C{\equiv}N \quad \text{mesomeric with} \quad >C{=}C{=}N^- ,$$

$$\text{compare} \quad >C^-{-}C{=}O \quad \text{mesomeric with} \quad >C{=}C{-}O^-$$

The function of the cyanide is thus to give a mesomeric carbanion.

This mechanism predicts that deuterobenzaldehyde, PhCDO, will rapidly exchange its deuterium with the solvent on carrying out the reaction in H_2O, as the formation of the carbanion must be fast compared with its reaction with the second molecule of aldehyde in order to account for the rate being second-order in benzaldehyde concentration. In fact, however, the rate of exchange is of the same order as the rate of reaction;† this observation can be accounted for if it is supposed that the proton in the carbanion is held relatively firmly, perhaps by a molecular bond

† Wiberg, *J. Amer. Chem. Soc.* 1954, **76**, 5371.

as suggested by Dewar.† An electron-repelling substituent in the benzene ring will decrease the electrophilic reactivity of the carbonyl group and *p*-dimethylaminobenzaldehyde, by itself, does not undergo the benzoin reaction (compare § 2). However, *p*-dimethylaminobenzaldehyde can act as the nucleophilic partner and react with benzaldehyde to give the expected dimethylaminobenzoin:

$$Me_2N-\underset{}{\bigcirc}-CHO + PhCHO \xrightarrow{CN^-} Me_2N-\underset{}{\bigcirc}-CO \cdot CHOHPh$$

Benzoins of this kind, with two different aromatic rings, may rearrange under the conditions of the reaction, so the product may be the isomer of the anticipated compound. The reaction is also reversible.

The benzoin reaction can also be carried out with a mixture of an α-keto acid and an aldehyde. Decarboxylation accompanies benzoic acid formation, and the rate of evolution of carbon dioxide parallels the rate of formation of cyanohydrin.‡ The following mechanism is similar to that suggested for the usual benzoin reaction, except that here the mesomeric carbanion is formed by decarboxylation (compare the decarboxylation of quinaldinic acid, Chapter VII, § 2 *b*).

$$Ar \cdot CO \cdot COO^- + CN^- \longrightarrow Ar \cdot \overset{O^-}{\underset{CN}{\overset{|}{C}}} -COO^- \xrightarrow{H^+} Ar \cdot \overset{OH}{\underset{CN}{\overset{|}{C}}}^- + CO_2$$

$$Ar \cdot \overset{OH}{\underset{CN}{\overset{|}{C}}}^- + Ar \cdot CHO \longrightarrow Ar \cdot \overset{OH}{\underset{CN}{\overset{|}{C}}} - \overset{H}{\underset{O^-}{\overset{|}{C}}} \cdot Ar \longrightarrow Ar \cdot \overset{O}{\overset{||}{C}} - \overset{H}{\underset{OH}{\overset{|}{C}}} \cdot Ar$$

Acyloin formation can sometimes be brought about with aliphatic aldehydes; an interesting example is the reaction of ethyl glyoxylate with threose to give ascorbic acid:§

† Dewar, *The Electronic Theory of Organic Chemistry*, Clarendon Press, Oxford, 1949, p. 137.
‡ Franzen and Fikentscher, *Annalen*, 1958, **613**, 1.
§ Helferich and Peters, *Ber.* 1937, **70**, 465.

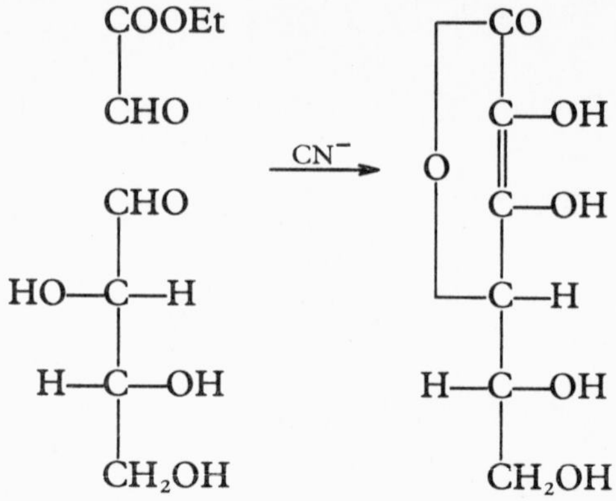

$$
\begin{array}{ccc}
\text{COOEt} & & \\
| & & \text{CO} \\
\text{CHO} & & | \\
| & & \text{C—OH} \\
\text{CHO} & \xrightarrow{\ \text{CN}^-\ } & \| \\
| & & \text{C—OH} \\
\text{HO—C—H} & & | \\
| & & \text{C—H} \\
\text{H—C—OH} & & | \\
| & & \text{H—C—OH} \\
\text{CH}_2\text{OH} & & | \\
& & \text{CH}_2\text{OH}
\end{array}
$$

Interchange reactions may also occur with benzoins which are of the general type (e.g. $X = Ph$, $Y = p\text{-Me}_2N\text{—C}_6H_4$):

$$ X\cdot CO\cdot CHOH\cdot X + 2Y\cdot CHO \;\rightleftharpoons^{\ CN^-\ }\; 2Y\cdot CO\cdot CHOH\cdot X $$

11. Some enzymic reactions for which thiamine pyrophosphate is the coenzyme

Certain carbohydrate interconversions in the pentose phosphate cycle are similar to the interchange reactions of benzoin; here the type of reaction may be written:

$$ X\cdot CO\cdot CHOH\cdot Y + Z\cdot CHO \longrightarrow X\cdot CO\cdot CHOH\cdot Z + Y\cdot CHO $$

Thus, one of the reactions catalysed by transketolase† is:

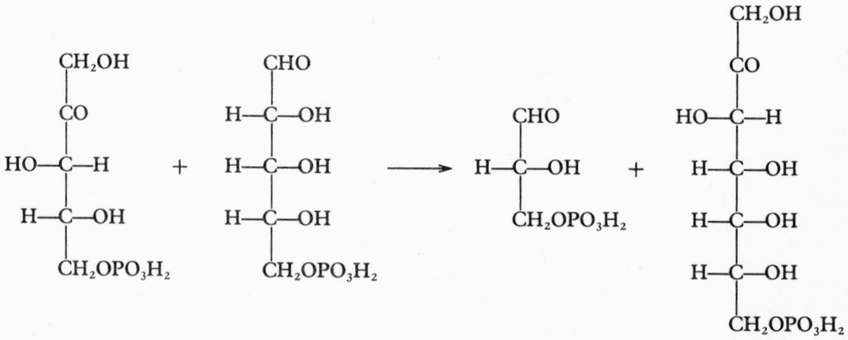

$$
\begin{array}{ccccccc}
\text{CH}_2\text{OH} & & \text{CHO} & & & & \text{CH}_2\text{OH} \\
| & & | & & & & | \\
\text{CO} & & \text{H—C—OH} & & \text{CHO} & & \text{CO} \\
| & & | & & | & & | \\
\text{HO—C—H} & + & \text{H—C—OH} & \longrightarrow & \text{H—C—OH} & + & \text{HO—C—H} \\
| & & | & & | & & | \\
\text{H—C—OH} & & \text{H—C—OH} & & \text{CH}_2\text{OPO}_3\text{H}_2 & & \text{H—C—OH} \\
| & & | & & & & | \\
\text{CH}_2\text{OPO}_3\text{H}_2 & & \text{CH}_2\text{OPO}_3\text{H}_2 & & & & \text{H—C—OH} \\
& & & & & & | \\
& & & & & & \text{H—C—OH} \\
& & & & & & | \\
& & & & & & \text{CH}_2\text{OPO}_3\text{H}_2
\end{array}
$$

D-xylulose-5-phosphate   D-ribose-5-phosphate   D-glyceraldehyde-3-phosphate   sedoheptulose-7-phosphate

† Horecker, *J. Cell. Comp. Physiol.* 1959, **54**, suppl. 1, p. 89.

This is one of the reactions in which thiamine pyrophosphate is a coenzyme.

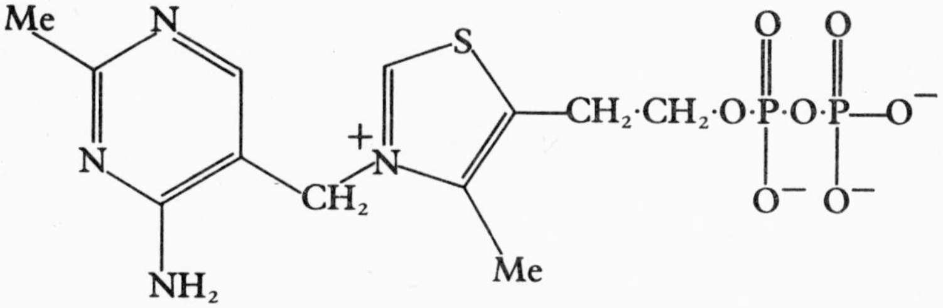

thiamine pyrophosphate

Another reaction for which thiamine pyrophosphate is a coenzyme is the formation of acetoin (acetylmethylcarbinol), MeCOCHOHMe, from acetaldehyde and pyruvic acid; the enzyme is α-carboxylase. Some interesting model experiments have been carried out with thiamine itself, and the pyrophosphate.†

Thiamine catalyses the formation of acetoin from acetaldehyde and pyruvic acid, and of benzoin from benzaldehyde. Thus, if we knew how thiamine catalysed these reactions, we should have some idea what part thiamine pyrophosphate might play in the enzymic reactions. The first step is to see whether simpler related compounds are active, and it turns out that several thiazoles, e.g.

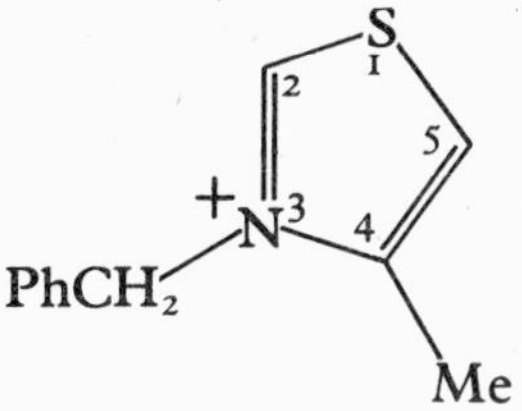

(1)

also catalyse benzoin (and, in some cases, acetoin) formation. Similar results were obtained with thiamine. Now, the compound (1) exchanged one hydrogen atom for a deuterium atom in D_2O, and thiamine or the pyrophosphate also acquired a carbon-bound deuterium atom under these conditions. Experimental evidence showed that it was the hydrogen atom attached to C-2 which was being replaced. These replacements

† Breslow, *J. Amer. Chem. Soc.* 1958, **80**, 3719; Breslow and McNelis, ibid. 1959, **81**, 3080; Westheimer, in *The Enzymes*, edited by Boyer, Lardy, and Myrbäck, vol. 1, p. 259, Academic Press, 1959; Yatco-Manzo, Roddy, Yount, and Metzler, *J. Biol. Chem.* 1959, **234**, 733; Yount and Metzler, ibid., p. 738.

are base-catalysed, and take place via the anions; the anion (2) from thiamine may be shown in a shortened form as (3):

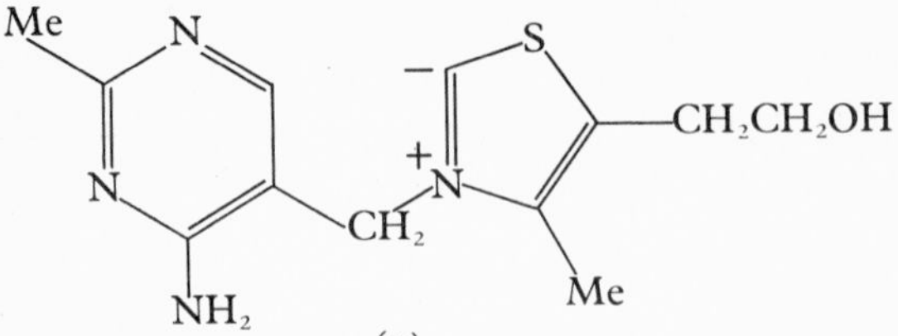

Me   N
         |
N   CH₂—N⁺—[thiazole ring]—CH₂CH₂OH
| |
NH₂   Me
        (2)

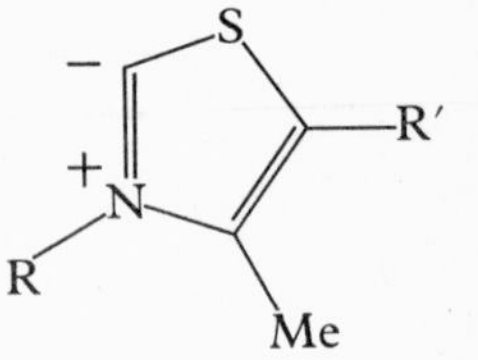

[thiazole ring] R'—... N⁺—R, Me
        (3)

The mechanism for the formation of acetoin from pyruvic acid and acetaldehyde, catalysed by thiamine, may thus be

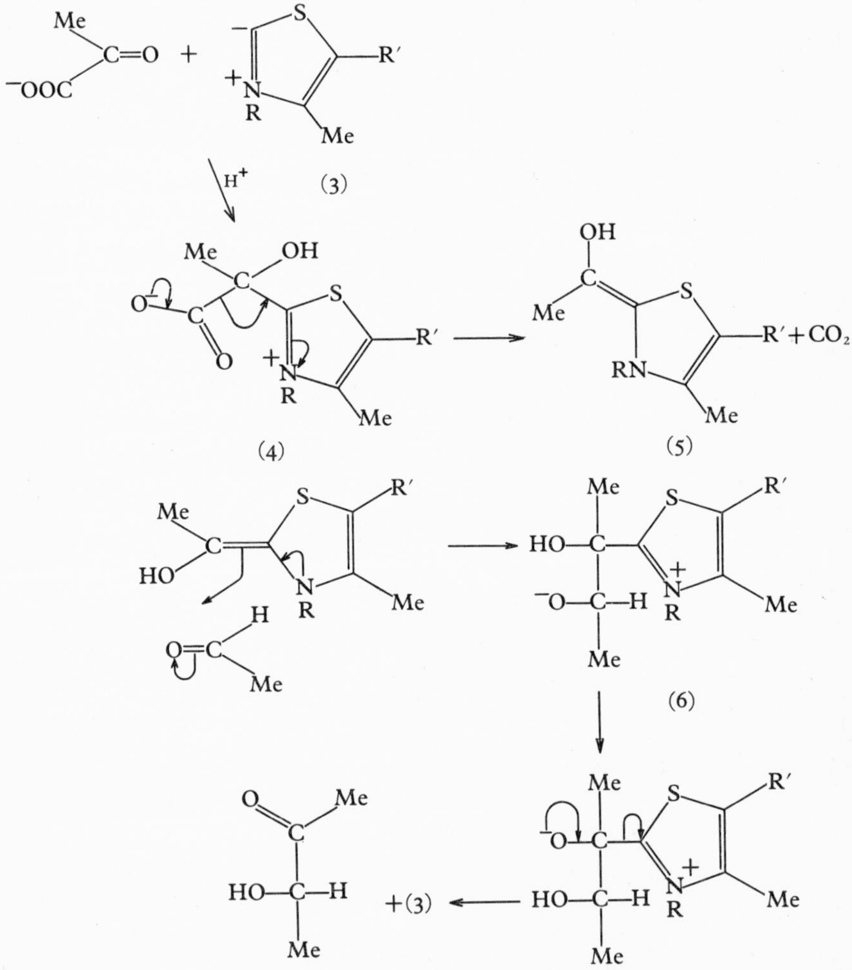

Me
  \
   C=O   +   [thiazole anion]—R'
  /   N⁺—R, Me
⁻OOC
        (3)

↓ H⁺

(4)

Me   OH
  \ |
O⁻—C—C—[thiazole]—R'
   ‖   N⁺—R, Me
   O

→

OH
 |
 C—[thiazole]—R' + CO₂
 | RN—, Me
Me
        (5)

(4)   (5)

Me
  \
   C=C—[thiazole]—R'
  /   N—R, Me
HO
      |
   O=C—H
      \
       Me

→

Me
 |
HO—C—[thiazole]—R'
 | N⁺—R, Me
⁻O—C—H
 |
Me
      (6)

(6)

O   Me
‖ /
C
 \
HO—C—H   +(3) ←
 |
Me

Me
 |
⁻O—C—[thiazole]—R'
 | N⁺—R, Me
HO—C—H
 |
Me

The first step is an addition of the thiamine anion (3) to pyruvate. The adduct loses carbon dioxide to give the species (5) (compare the decarboxylation of the substituted pyridylacetic acid described in Chapter VII, § 2 b). The nucleophilic species (5) functions as an 'active aldehyde', and, in the next stage, reacts with acetaldehyde to give (6). After proton interchange between the oxygen atoms, cleavage gives the product, acetoin, and regenerates the catalyst (3). This mechanism is closely similar to that put forward for the benzoin reaction, when an α-keto acid and an aldehyde are used (§ 10); thiamine plays the same part as the cyanide ion.

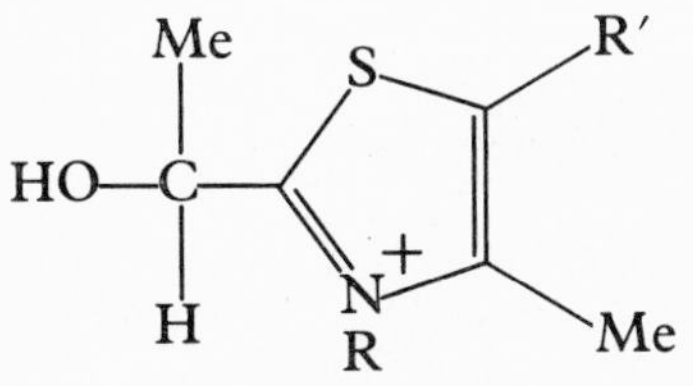

(7) 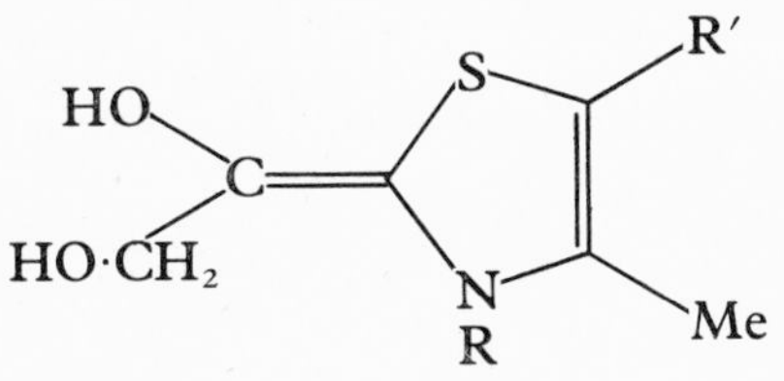   (8)

The hydroxyethyl thiamine (7), which could form (5) by loss of a proton, has been found to react with acetaldehyde to give acetoin. Moreover, the pyrophosphate from (7) (here $R' = CH_2CH_2OP_2O_6^{3-}$), which is found in cells, undergoes the enzymic reaction with acetaldehyde to give acetoin, and replaces thiamine in nutritional experiments.† It seems probable, therefore, that when thiamine pyrophosphate functions as a coenzyme, compounds such as (5) are formed. Such (nucleophilic) compounds would also be expected to react readily with the disulphide bond of lipoic acid to give thiol esters (compare the reaction of cyanide ion with disulphides), and this is the next step in the metabolism of pyruvate.‡ Similarly, in the reaction catalysed by transketolase, the intermediate corresponding to (5) would be (8).

Another reaction for which thiamine pyrophosphate is a coenzyme belongs to the small class in which the inorganic phosphate ion reacts to form an ester: the enzyme (phosphoketolase) catalyses the following reaction:§

† Krampitz, J. Cell. Comp. Physiol. 1959, 54, suppl. 1, p. 101; Carlson and Brown, J. Biol. Chem. 1961, 236, 2099.
‡ See, for example, Sanadi, Langley, and White, J. Biol. Chem. 1959, 234, 183.
§ Horecker, J. Cell. Comp. Physiol. 1959, 54, suppl. 1, p. 89.

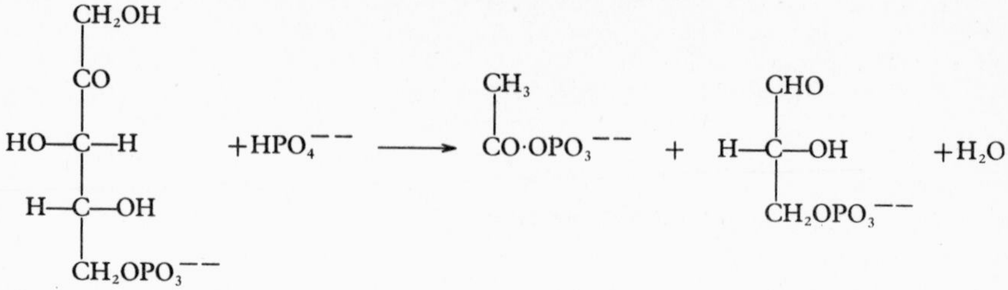

$$\begin{array}{c} CH_2OH \\ | \\ CO \\ | \\ HO-C-H \\ | \\ H-C-OH \\ | \\ CH_2OPO_3{}^{--} \end{array} \quad +HPO_4{}^{--} \longrightarrow \begin{array}{c} CH_3 \\ | \\ CO\cdot OPO_3{}^{--} \end{array} \quad + \quad \begin{array}{c} CHO \\ | \\ H-C-OH \\ | \\ CH_2OPO_3{}^{--} \end{array} \quad +H_2O$$

D-xylulose-5-phosphate   acetyl   D-glyceraldehyde-
                                           phosphate   3-phosphate

A reverse benzoin type of reaction would give glyceraldehyde phosphate and glycollic aldehyde; so we can easily account for one of the products, but the formation of the acetyl phosphate involves both esterification of orthophosphate and rearrangement. Several mechanisms seem possible, and further evidence is necessary before a choice can be made.

12. Cannizzaro reaction

The aldol reaction is contingent on the presence of a hydrogen atom in the α position to the aldehyde group, so that aromatic aldehydes cannot undergo the aldol reaction; instead, with alkali, disproportionation to the alcohol and the acid takes place:

$$2PhCHO + \bar{O}H \longrightarrow PhCH_2OH + PhCOO^-$$

This reaction also occurs with aliphatic aldehydes which have no α-hydrogen atom (e.g. $Me_3C \cdot CHO$). Excess formaldehyde and an aldehyde can be used in a 'crossed' Cannizzaro reaction:

$$ArCHO + H \cdot CHO + \bar{O}H \longrightarrow ArCH_2OH + H \cdot COO^-$$

This is a convenient method of reducing aromatic aldehydes. An aliphatic aldehyde and excess formaldehyde may undergo an aldol reaction, followed by a 'crossed' Cannizzaro reaction:

$$CH_3-CHO \xrightarrow{3H\cdot CHO} HOCH_2-\underset{\underset{CH_2OH}{|}}{\overset{\overset{CH_2OH}{|}}{C}}-CHO \xrightarrow[\substack{\text{'crossed'} \\ \text{Cannizzaro'}}]{H\cdot CHO} HOCH_2-\underset{\underset{CH_2OH}{|}}{\overset{\overset{CH_2OH}{|}}{C}}-CH_2OH$$

$$+H\cdot COOH$$

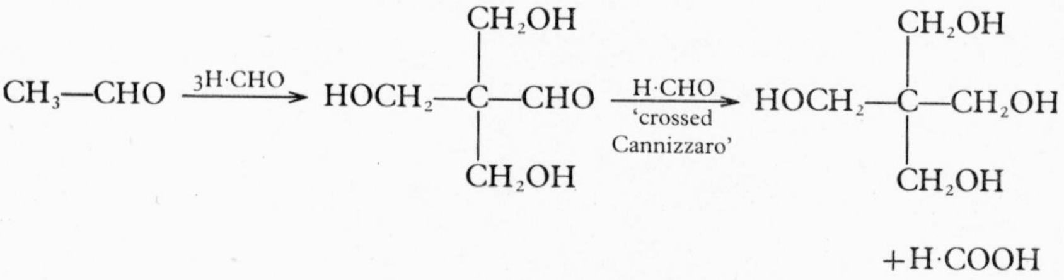

These last reactions illustrate the interplay of the two main ways in which aldehydes interact in alkaline solution.

There are probably three different mechanisms for the Cannizzaro reactions: one involving free radicals, one operating in heterogeneous mixtures, and one in homogeneous solution. Only the last will be discussed here. The kinetics may be third- or fourth-order; they are always second-order in aldehyde and may be first- or second-order in hydroxyl ion. When the reaction (with benzaldehyde) is carried out in D_2O, the benzyl alcohol formed has no carbon-bound deuterium;[†] this shows that the alcohol derives its 'extra' hydrogen atom directly from the second molecule of aldehyde, and not from the medium. The following mechanism accounts for these facts:

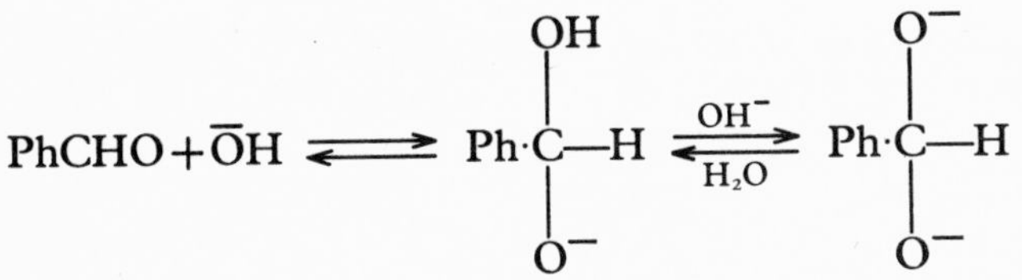

$$Ph\cdot COO^- + PhCH_2OH$$

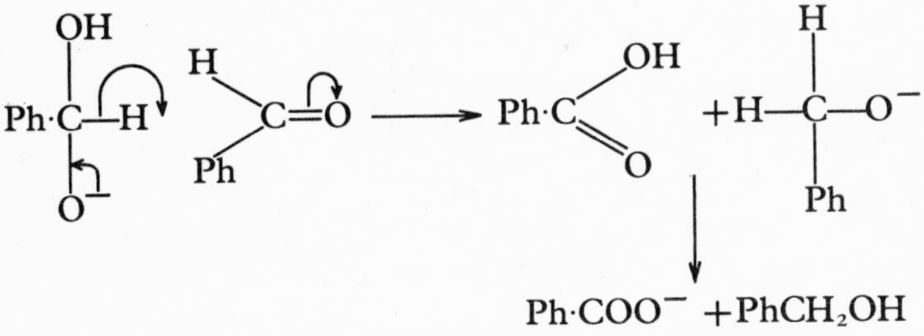

The rate-determining step must be that in which the hydrogen atom, together with its pair of bonding electrons (i.e. the hydride ion) is transferred from one molecule to the other. As written, the reaction would be third-order; when the doubly-ionized species (2) replaces the singly ionized (1) in the reaction with the carbonyl group the reaction becomes fourth-order; (2) will be less abundant, but more reactive, than (1).

α-Keto-aldehydes undergo intramolecular Cannizzaro reactions:

$$PhCO\cdot CHO + \overline{O}H \longrightarrow PhCHOH\cdot COO^-$$

† Fredenhagen and Bonhoeffer, *Z. physik. Chem.* 1938, **181 A,** 379.

The newly formed hydroxyl and carboxyl groups are now contained within one molecule. The conversion of phenylglyoxal to mandelic acid in D_2O occurs without formation of carbon-bound deuterium,[†] and the reaction is first-order in phenylglyoxal and in hydroxide ion. Moreover, $Ph\,^{14}COCHO$ gives $Ph\,^{14}CHOHCOOH$, and this shows that it is not the phenyl group which migrates from one carbon atom to the other: in other words, the original keto group is reduced, and the aldehyde group oxidized.[‡] The mechanism for the intramolecular Cannizzaro reaction is thus analogous to that for the intermolecular version:

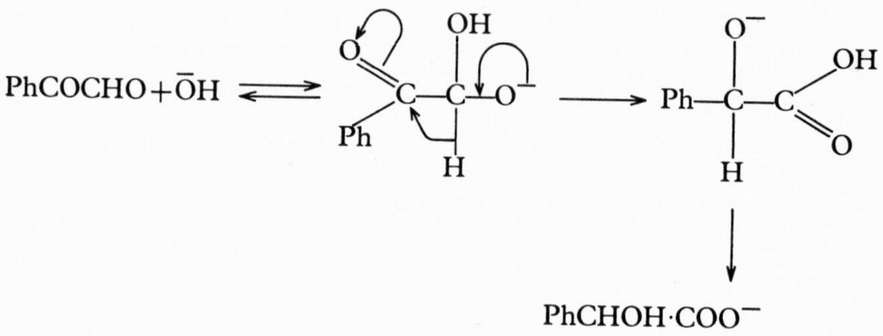

$$PhCHOH \cdot COO^-$$

13. Glyoxalase-I

This enzyme catalyses the formation of S-lactoylglutathione from methylglyoxal and glutathione (GSH):

$$Me \cdot CO \cdot CHO + GSH \longrightarrow Me \cdot CHOH \cdot CO \cdot SG$$

$$H_2N \cdot CH(COOH)CH_2 \cdot CH_2 \cdot CO \cdot NH \cdot \underset{|}{CH} \cdot CO \cdot NH \cdot CH_2 \cdot COOH$$
$$CH_2SH$$

glutathione (GSH)

There is another enzyme (glyoxalase-II) which catalyses the hydrolysis of the thiol ester, S-lactoylglutathione, to lactic acid and glutathione; the overall reaction is thus the conversion of methylglyoxal to lactic acid, an example of an enzymic intramolecular Cannizzaro reaction. It

[†] Doering, Taylor, and Schoenewaldt, *J. Amer. Chem. Soc.* 1948, **70**, 455.
[‡] Neville, ibid., p. 3499.

is the first stage with which we shall be concerned here, and some experiments with model compounds will now be described. It may be noted that, in this stage, methylglyoxal may be replaced by phenylglyoxal.

The intramolecular Cannizzaro reaction of phenylglyoxal is catalysed by a mixture of a thiol and a tertiary amine; both have to be present, and the catalysis is more efficient when both groups are present in the same molecule (cf. mutarotation, p. 161). The reaction can be carried out in neutral solution in water; in methyl alcohol, the product is the methyl ester of mandelic acid. When a variety of basic thiols was tested, the catalytic activity depended on the basicity of the thiol, and the number of carbon atoms between the sulphur and nitrogen atoms. These and other observations led to the following mechanism, in which the reaction in methyl alcohol with N-diethylcysteamine has been taken as an example:†

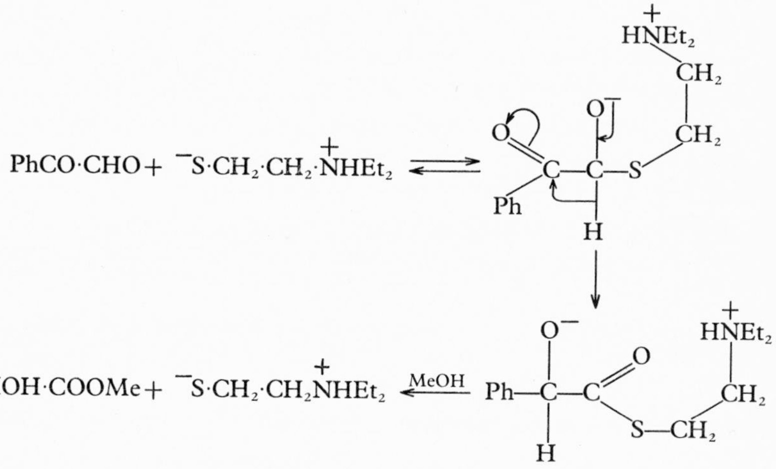

The initial formation of a hemi-thioacetal is a relatively rapid reaction; it may be seen that the positively charged nitrogen atom can be in the vicinity of the oxygen atoms, one or the other of which is negatively charged in the reaction mechanism given above.

These experiments suggest that, in the reaction catalysed by glyoxalase-I, methylglyoxal and glutathione form a hemi-thioacetal (1) which then undergoes the Cannizzaro reaction:

† Franzen, *Chem. Ber.* 1955, **88**, 1361; 1957, **90**, 623, 2036.

$$\text{MeCOCHO} + \text{GS}^- \longrightarrow \underset{\underset{\text{Me}}{}}{\overset{O}{\underset{}{\big\Vert}}}C - \overset{\overset{O^-}{\big\vert}}{\underset{\underset{H}{\big\vert}}{C}} - SG$$

(I)

$$\text{MeCHOH·CO·SG} \longleftarrow \text{Me} - \overset{\overset{O^-}{\big\vert}}{\underset{\underset{H}{\big\vert}}{C}} - C \overset{O}{\underset{SG}{\diagdown}}$$

There is also direct evidence in favour of this mechanism. In the first place, glutathione and methylglyoxal form an adduct, which is probably the hemi-thioacetal (1).† In the second place, there is kinetic evidence that the substrate for the enzyme is this adduct, rather than the free components. A general method for establishing the mode of formation of a ternary complex ESA (where S and A are the two substrates, and E the enzyme) has been described.‡ If the two substrates combine rapidly to form a species (SA) which is the true substrate for the enzyme, so that the kinetic scheme is

$$S + A \rightleftarrows SA,$$

$$SA + E \rightleftarrows ESA \rightarrow E + \text{product},$$

then the velocity of the reaction is a symmetrical function of the concentrations of A and S. So that if $[A]$ is held at a given value, and $[S]$ varied, and the velocity plotted against $[S]$, the resulting curve will be indistinguishable from that obtained by holding $[S]$ at the same value as was previously chosen for $[A]$, and now this time varying $[A]$. The application of this procedure to the glyoxalase-I reaction gave results consistent with the view that the hemi-thioacetal is the substrate for the enzyme.§

Finally, as in the non-enzymic reaction, the hydrogen atom which is transferred to the keto group being reduced does not equilibrate with the medium, which implies an intramolecular hydride-ion shift.‖

† Yamazoe, *Tokyo J. Biochem.* 1936, **23**, 319.
‡ Segal, Kachmar, and Boyer, *Enzymologia*, 1952, **15**, 187.
§ Cliffe and Waley, *Biochem. J.* 1961, **79**, 475.
‖ Franzen, *Chem. Ber.* 1956, **89**, 1020; Rose, *Biochim. Biophys. Acta*, 1957, **25**, 214.

14. Mannich reaction

This reaction is a condensation of a primary or more commonly a secondary amine with formaldehyde and a compound containing an active hydrogen atom, e.g.

$$PhCO \cdot CH_3 + CH_2O + Me_2NH \longrightarrow PhCO \cdot CH_2 \cdot CH_2 \cdot NMe_2 + H_2O$$

There are probably different detailed paths in different cases, but one mechanism postulates the initial formation of a compound from form-aldehyde and the amine, e.g. Me_2NCH_2OH in the example cited above. The similar reaction of formaldehyde with amino acids forms the basis of Sörensen's formol-titration, which is often used for following proteo-lysis.† In the Mannich reaction, which is usually carried out at a pH of about 3, or lower, dehydration to a mesomeric carbonium ion may occur:

$$Me_2N \cdot CH_2OH + H^+ \rightleftharpoons Me_2N \cdot CH_2\overset{+}{O}H_2 \rightleftharpoons Me_2\overset{+}{N}{=}CH_2 + H_2O,$$

which will then react with the third component, whose reactive form may be the anion or the enol,

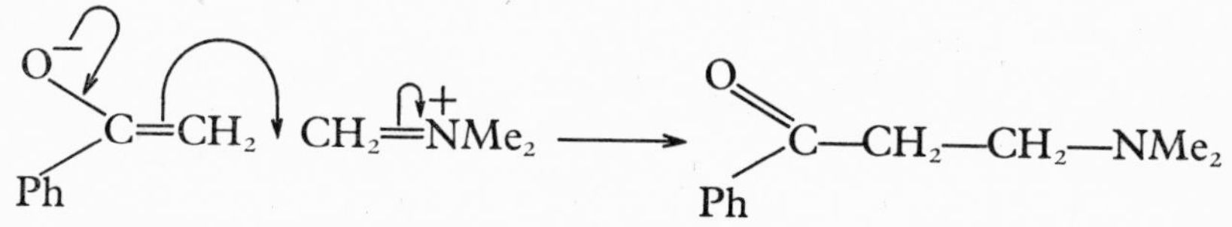

Reactions of essentially the same type occur when the active hydrogen atom is attached to a nitrogen or sulphur atom. An example of a Mannich reaction leading to a heterocyclic product is the synthesis of tropinone:‡

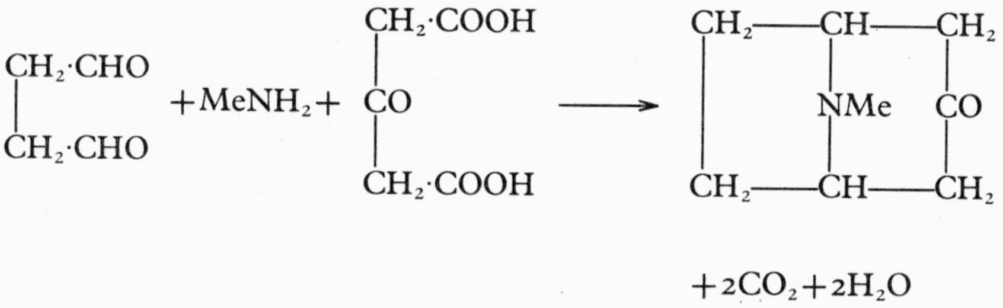

$$+ 2CO_2 + 2H_2O$$

---

† See, for example, Taylor, *Analyst*, 1957, **82**, 488.

‡ Robinson, *J. Chem. Soc.* 1917, **111**, 762; see also Robinson, *Structural Relations of Natural Products*, Clarendon Press, Oxford, 1955.

Here two rings are formed in one process. It is interesting that this synthesis was based on the view that some such process might give rise to the tropane alkaloids, which are closely related to tropinone. Experimental evidence is consistent with this hypothesis.† The main biochemical analogy of the Mannich reaction seems to be the class of reactions in which tetrahydrofolic (1) acid is the coenzyme.

15. Some enzymic reactions for which tetrahydrofolic acid is the coenzyme

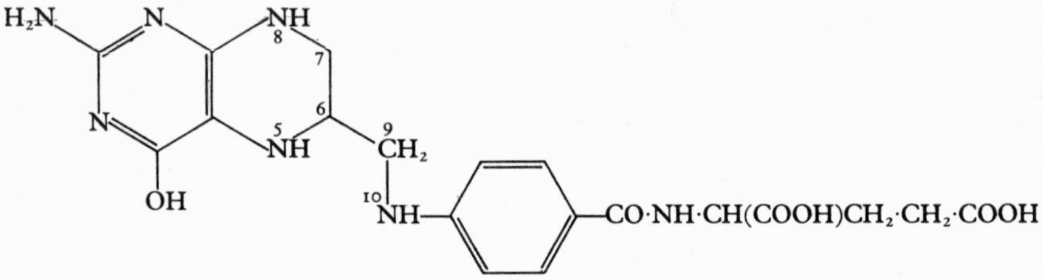

(1)

Two important examples from this class are the interconversion of serine and glycine, and purine synthesis. These reactions are often collectively referred to as 'one-carbon metabolism', and the one-carbon unit shown as $[CH_2O]$,

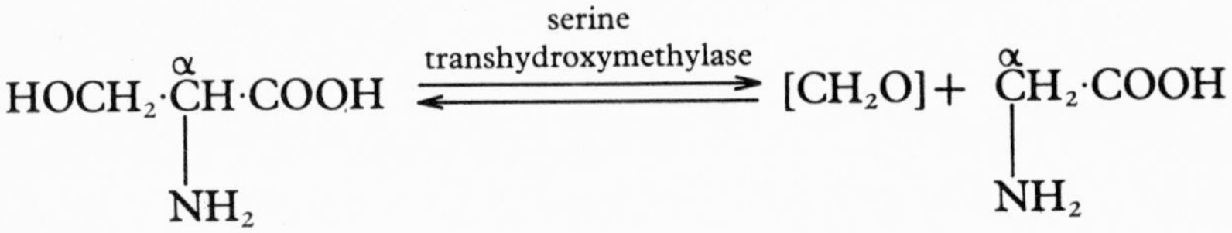

$$HOCH_2 \cdot \overset{\alpha}{C}H \cdot COOH \underset{}{\overset{\text{serine}}{\underset{\text{transhydroxymethylase}}{\rightleftharpoons}}} [CH_2O] + \overset{\alpha}{C}H_2 \cdot COOH$$

serine NH_2 glycine NH_2

The species shown as $[CH_2O]$ is probably 5-hydroxymethyltetrahydrofolic acid (2),‡ which may also be formed (non-enzymically) from formaldehyde and tetrahydrofolic acid.§ The amino acids are also 'activated' in this reaction by combination with pyridoxal phosphate (§ 20) which, judging by model experiments, forms an anil with the amino acid and confers nucleophilic activity on the α-carbon atom of the amino acids.

---

† Leete, Marion, and Spenser, *Nature*, 1954, **174**, 650; for discussions of the biosynthesis of alkaloids, see Mothes, *Symposia of the Society for Experimental Biology*, 1959, **13**, 258; Wenkert, *Experientia*, 1959, **15**, 165.

‡ Huennekens, Hatefi, and Kay, *J. Biol. Chem.* 1957, **224**, 435.

§ Blackley, *Biochem. J.* 1959, **72**, 707.

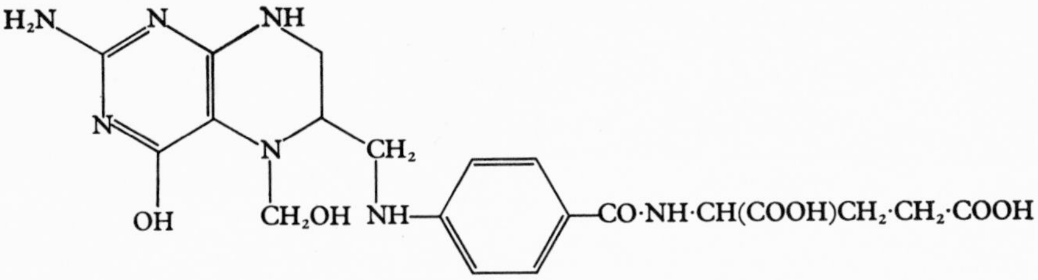

(2)

It is characteristic of tetrahydrofolic acid that the 'one-carbon unit' being transferred may be oxidized while still bound to the coenzyme;[†] only part of the coenzyme is shown in the formulae given below:

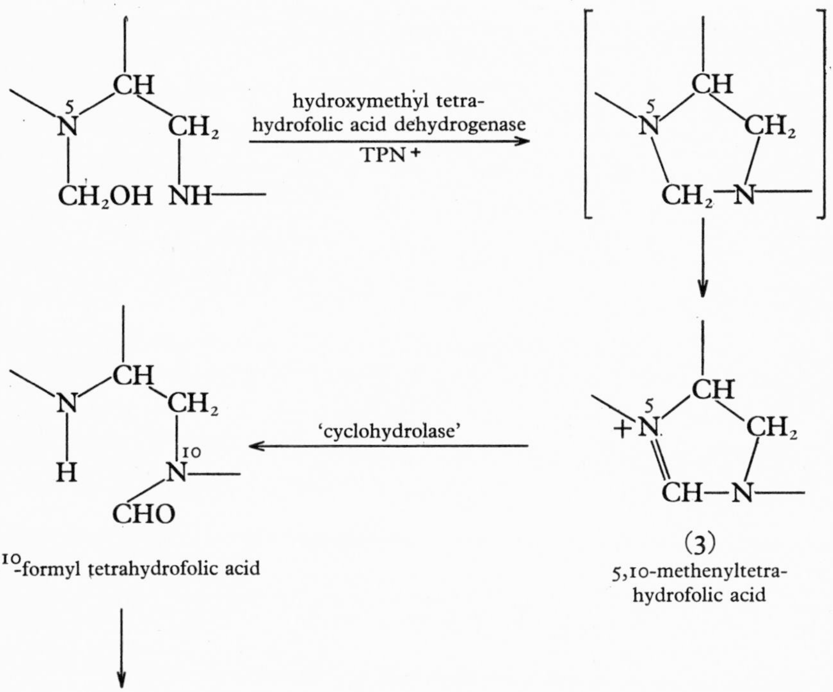

hydroxymethyl tetra-
hydrofolic acid dehydrogenase
TPN+

N^{10}-formyl tetrahydrofolic acid

'cyclohydrolase'

(3)
5,10-methenyltetra-
hydrofolic acid

tetrahydrofolic acid + H·COOH

The 10-formyl tetrahydrofolic acid can be regenerated from formate, tetrahydrofolic acid, and adenosine triphosphate.[‡]

The transferred carbon atom has a partial positive charge, in the 5,10-methenyl derivative (3), and is thus an electrophilic reagent.

[†] Hatefi, Osborn, Kay, and Huennekens, *J. Biol. Chem.* 1957, **227**, 637.
[‡] Peters and Greenberg, ibid. **226**, 329.

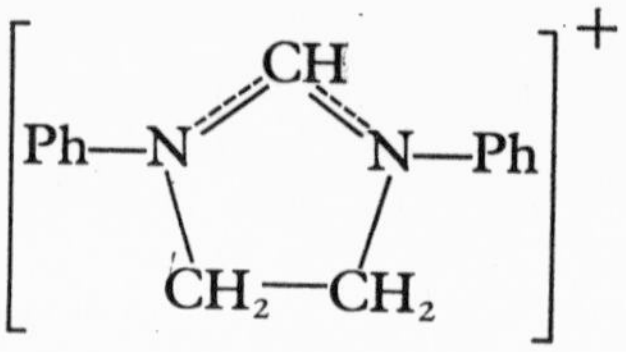

$$\left[\begin{array}{c} \text{CH} \\ \text{Ph—N} \diagup\!\!\!\diagdown \text{N—Ph} \\ \text{CH}_2\text{—CH}_2 \end{array} \right]^+$$

(4)

Model compounds of the same type, e.g. (4), also display some of the same electrophilic activity.†

16. Reaction of Grignard reagents with carbonyl compounds

The reaction of a Grignard reagent with a carbonyl compound is a widely used synthetic process:

$$\text{MeCHO} + \text{Me}_2\text{CH·MgBr} \longrightarrow \underset{\underset{\text{OH}}{|}}{\text{MeCH·CHMe}_2}$$

The essential feature in these reactions may be expressed as follows. Carbon is more electronegative than magnesium, so that a Grignard reagent undergoes heterolysis in the sense $\overset{\frown}{\text{C—Mg}}$. The alkyl (or aryl) group in the reagent thus functions as a nucleophilic reagent, and attacks the electrophilic carbon atom of the carbonyl group. In a simplified form the mechanism for the reaction given above may be represented as:

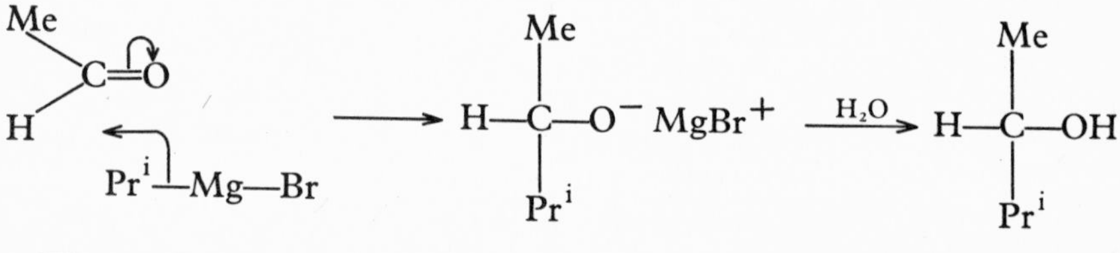

The mechanisms of these reactions are certainly more complicated than this, and, to a large extent, unknown in detail.‡ Although the Grignard reagent from a halide RX and magnesium is customarily written as RMgX, the evidence suggests that the reagent, at least in some cases, is the dialkylmagnesium, R_2Mg.§ Moreover, the solvent (usually ether) is bonded to the metal in the reagent, and the (solvated)

---

† Jaenicke and Brode, *Annalen*, 1959, **624**, 120.

‡ Franzen, *Reaktionsmechanismen*, p. 110, Hüthig, Heidelberg, 1958; Wright, in *Steric Effects in Organic Chemistry*, chap. 8, edited by Newman, Wiley, 1956.

§ Dessy, Wotiz, and Hollingsworth, *J. Amer. Chem. Soc.* 1957, **79**, 358; Dessy, Handler, Wotiz, and Hollingsworth, ibid., p. 3476.

magnesium halide may catalyse the reaction. There may also be side reactions, of which the most common with ketones is reduction to the alcohol.

17. Reduction of carbonyl compounds

(a) *Reduction by dissolving metals.* Carbonyl compounds may be reduced to alcohols in several ways. An important method, but one which will not be discussed here, is by hydrogen and a metallic catalyst. Dissolving metals reduce aldehydes and ketones; reduction by 'nascent' hydrogen may proceed by donation of electrons to the electrophilic carbon of the carbonyl group, and the products depend on the conditions. Ketones usually give the corresponding alcohol only in alkaline solution; in neutral or acidic solution dimeric alcohols (1) are formed. These results are consistent with the view that the dimeric products are formed by one-electron additions; the monomeric products may be formed by two-electron additions, or by two successive one-electron additions:

Reduction to monomeric product (by zinc and sodium hydroxide):

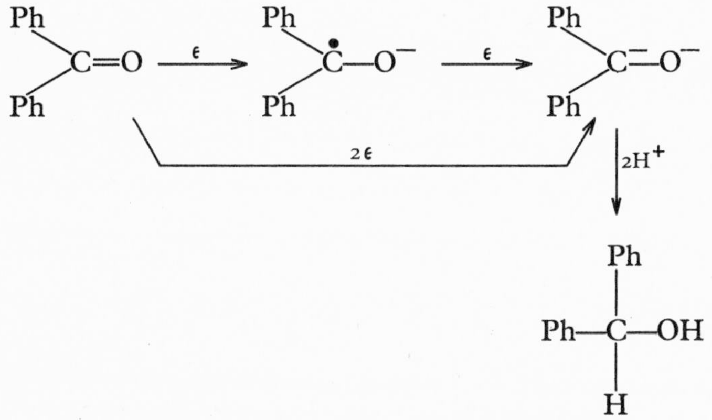

Reduction to dimeric product (by zinc and acetic acid):

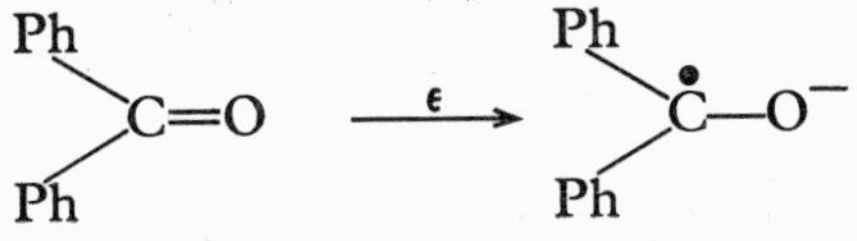

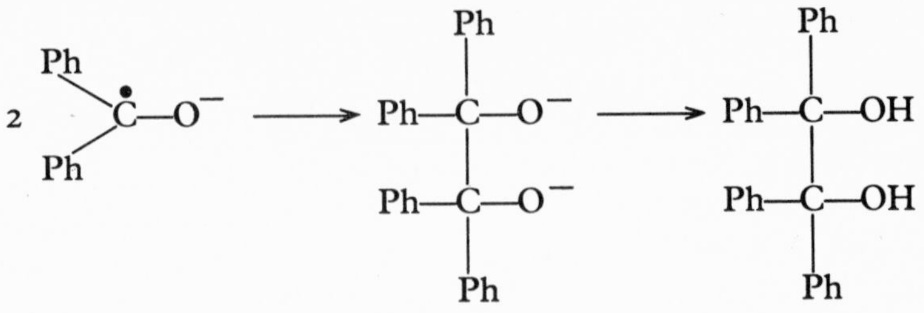

$$2 \; \underset{Ph}{\overset{Ph}{>}}\!\!\overset{\bullet}{C}\!-\!O^{-} \longrightarrow \underset{\underset{Ph}{|}}{\overset{Ph}{|}}{Ph-C-O^{-}} \longrightarrow \underset{\underset{Ph}{|}}{\overset{Ph}{|}}{Ph-C-OH}$$

(I)

(b) *Reduction by metal hydrides.* Lithium aluminium hydride ($LiAlH_4$) and sodium borohydride ($NaBH_4$) are widely used for reduction of the carbonyl group:

$$4R_2CO + NaBH_4 \longrightarrow Na[(R_2CHO)_4B]$$

The reaction of ketones with sodium borohydride is first-order in both ketone and borohydride. In a series of cyclic ketones, the rate of reaction with sodium borohydride paralleled the extent of cyanohydrin formation.† In cyanohydrin formation (§ 2) the nucleophilic cyanide ion attacks the carbonyl group, and the simplest interpretation of the borohydride reduction is that the rate-determining step is the first attack of the borohydride anion, possibly via a cyclic transition state:

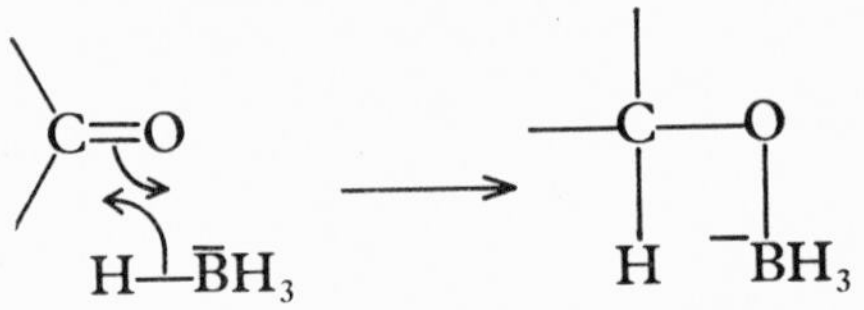

$$\underset{H-\bar{B}H_3}{\overset{\diagdown}{>}C\!=\!O} \longrightarrow \underset{H \quad {}^{-}BH_3}{\overset{|}{-}\overset{|}{C}\!-\!O}$$

In a succession of similar steps, the remaining hydrogen atoms are transferred from boron to carbon. This reaction, then, may be viewed as a hydride ion transfer (cf. Cannizzaro reaction), and it also resembles the conversion of a carbonyl compound into an alcohol by a Grignard reagent.

(c) *Reduction by metal alkoxides.* This is the reversible reaction between a carbonyl compound and an aluminium alkoxide, known as the Meerwein–Ponndorf–Verley reduction. An example which (as nitro groups are readily reduced by most reagents) shows the specificity of the reduction is:

† Brown, Wheeler, and Ichikawa, *Tetrahedron*, 1957, **1**, 214.

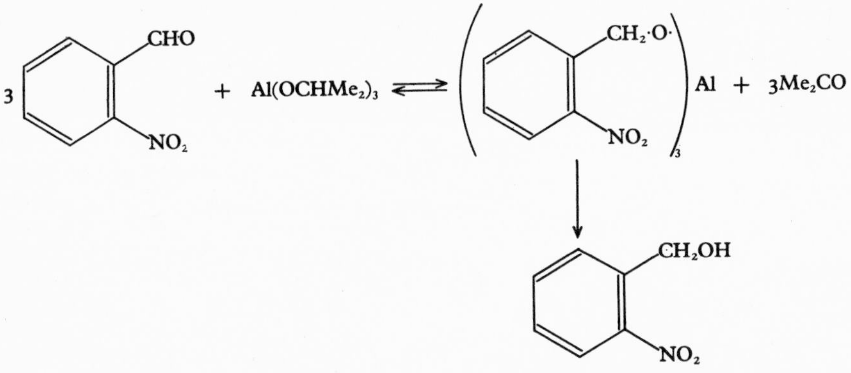

The equilibrium may be displaced to the right by distillation, as acetone is the most volatile species present. The reaction is usually carried out with aluminium isopropoxide in isopropanol, but since aluminium isopropoxide may be used in the fused state or in an inert solvent, it must be the hydrogen atom bound to the alkoxide which is transferred to the carbonyl group. Moreover, the aluminium alkoxide is not merely a source of alkoxide ions, since free alkoxide ions attack nitro groups and racemize optically active ketones, and these may be reduced without racemization by aluminium alkoxides. These observations are best interpreted by a mechanism in which the function of the aluminium is both to enhance the reactivity of the carbonyl group and to facilitate the attainment of a cyclic transition state:†

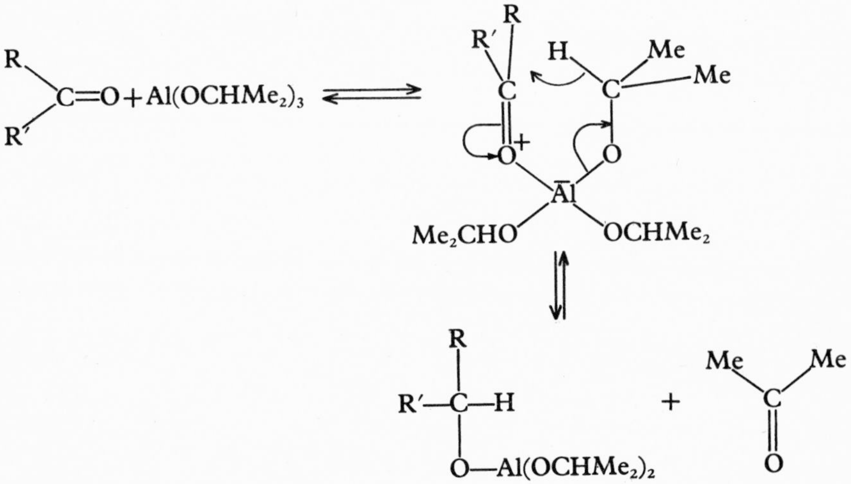

† Woodward, Wendler, and Brutschy, *J. Amer. Chem. Soc.* 1945, **67**, 1425; Jackmann and Mills, *Nature*, 1949, **164**, 789.

If the reducing alcohol is optically active, and the ketone unsymmetrical, the reduction does not give equal amounts of the enantiomers of the alcohol being formed, and the predominating enantiomer has the same configuration as the reducing alcohol.†

18. Enzymic reduction of aldehydes and ketones

These reactions are commonly of the type:

$$—CO— \ + \ DPNH \ + \ H^+ \ \rightleftharpoons \ —CHOH— \ + \ DPN^+$$

The coenzyme, diphosphopyridine nucleotide, or coenzyme I (DPN⁺), has the partial structure (1) (it is written in full in the front of the book, facing p. 1), and in some reactions is replaced by a phosphorylated analogue, triphosphopyridine nucleotide, coenzyme II (TPN+).

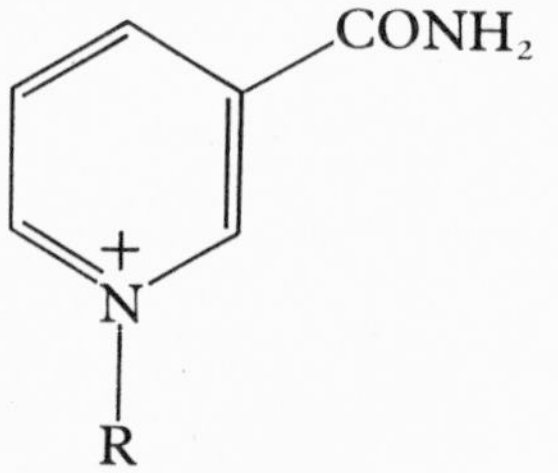

DPN⁺
(partial structure)

(1)

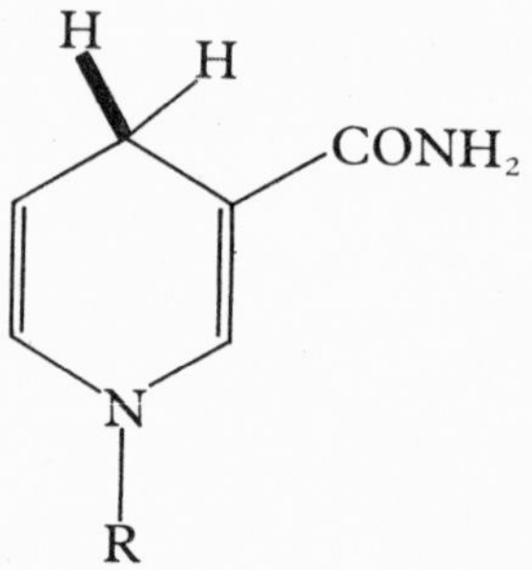

DPNH
(partial structure)

(2)

A point to be noted is that the reduced coenzyme (2) is only weakly basic, and hence not ionized at pH 7·5, owing to mesomerism of the type:

which renders the lone pair of electrons less available for combination with a proton; this is the same effect, only to a less marked degree, which is held to account for the non-basicity of pyrrole in Chapter IX. The oxidized form of the coenzyme is necessarily charged, and so in the oxidation a proton is liberated, which, of course, makes the position of equilibrium (or the redox potential) pH-dependent.

† Doering and Young, *J. Amer. Chem. Soc.* 1950, **72**, 631.

The most important aspect of the mechanism of these enzymic reductions concerns the hydrogen transfer. The knowledge gained here, by the use of deuterium as tracer, represents one of the most substantial advances towards understanding the steric course of enzyme-catalysed reactions. When dideuteroethanol, $[1\text{-}^2H_2]$-ethanol (CH_3CD_2OH), is oxidized by diphosphopyridine nucleotide and yeast alcohol dehydrogenase, the reduced coenzyme (3) contains one atom of carbon-bound deuterium:

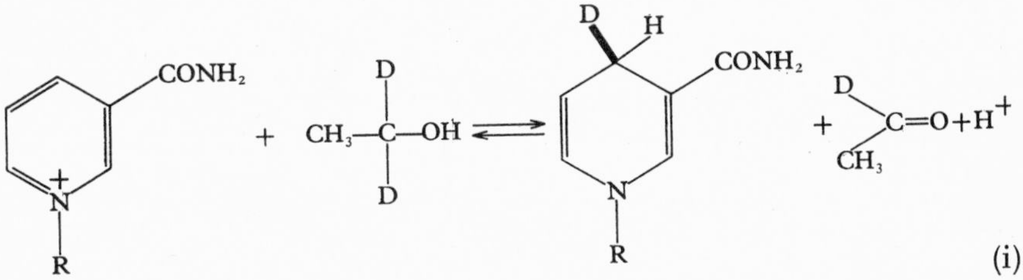

(3)

(i)

This result shows that there is 'direct hydrogen transfer' between the substrate and the coenzyme, and rules out the alternative possibility that the hydrogen newly bound to the coenzyme is provided by the aqueous medium. Moreover, the result that there is just *one* atom of carbon-bound deuterium per molecule of reduced coenzyme shows that the reverse reaction is also stereospecific. In the reverse reaction the deuterium atom, rather than the hydrogen atom, is removed from the reduced coenzyme; if this were not so, the reduced coenzyme would eventually acquire two deuterium atoms (in the 4 position), in the presence of excess dideuteroethanol.

When the deuterated reduced coenzyme (3) is enzymically oxidized with acetaldehyde, deuteroethanol, $[1\text{-}^2H_1]$-ethanol (4), is formed:

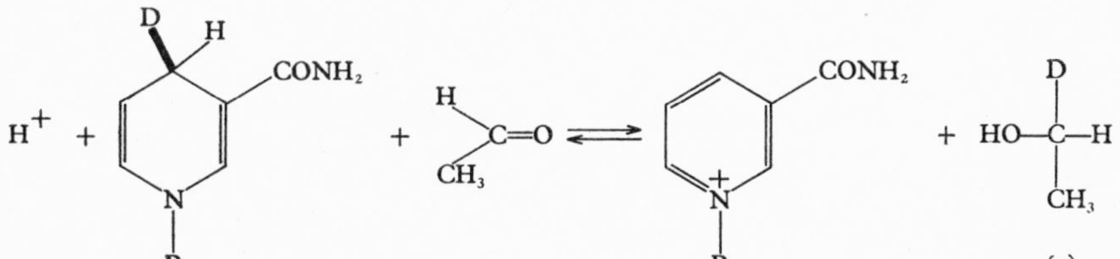

(4)

(ii)

Thus the enzyme distinguishes between the two hydrogen atoms at the 4 position of the reduced coenzyme (2), and between the two hydrogen atoms of the methylene group in ethanol. These are examples of discrimination between the two a groups in *Caabd*, discussed in Chapter IV (§ 4 c).

The monodeuterated reduced coenzyme (3), formed in reaction (i), may also be oxidized by pyruvate and the enzyme, lactate dehydrogenase; the lactate (5) so formed contains carbon-bound deuterium:

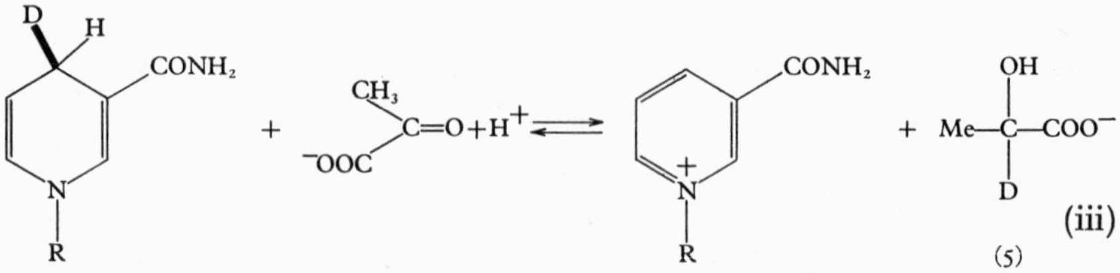

(iii)

This result shows that alcohol dehydrogenase and lactate dehydrogenase

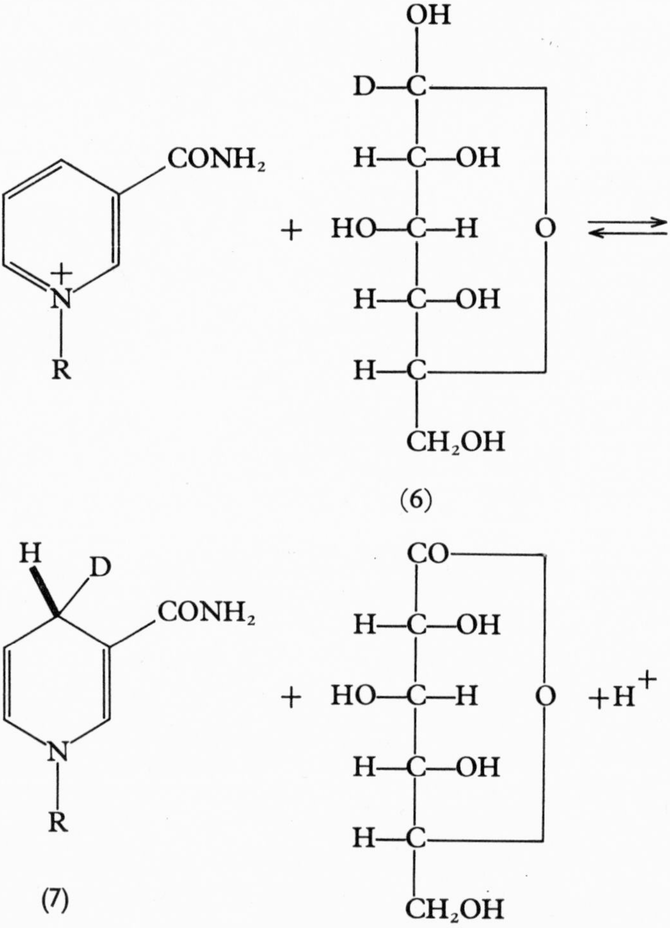

(6)

(iv)

(7)

both catalyse reactions in which the same hydrogen atom of the reduced coenzyme is transferred. This hydrogen atom is called α.

Other enzymes catalyse reactions in which the other (β) hydrogen atom is transferred. Thus, $[1\text{-}^2H_1]$-glucose (6) and glucose dehydrogenase give deuterated reduced coenzyme (7). This deuterated reduced coenzyme (7) is oxidized by pyruvate and lactate dehydrogenase to lactate (8) which is free from carbon-bound deuterium, and instead the deuterium is in the oxidized coenzyme:

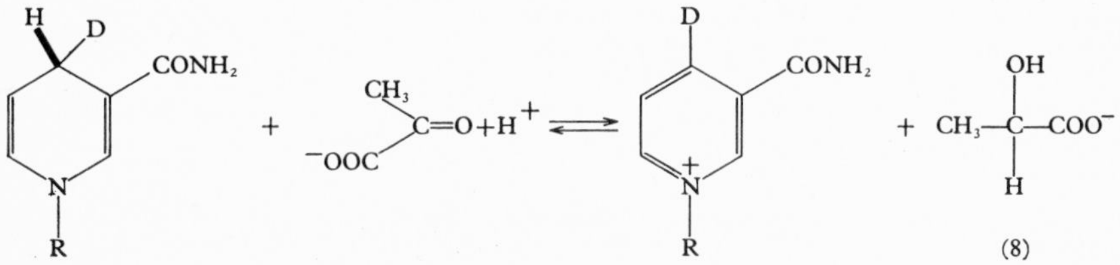

(7)   (v)

Reaction (v) must differ from reaction (iii) in the configuration of the reduced coenzyme. As the hydrogen atom transferred in reaction (iii) is called α, the other one, which is transferred in reaction (v), is called β.

There are, then, two classes of enzymes which transfer hydrogen to diphosphopyridine nucleotide, and the same has been found to hold for triphosphopyridine nucleotide. This distinction may influence 'coupling' between oxidations and reductions involving these coenzymes.†

The formulae given above for oxidized and reduced diphosphopyridine

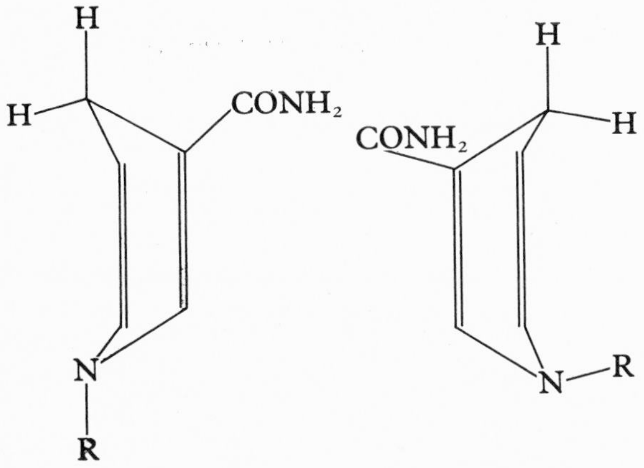

† Vennesland and Westheimer, in The Mechanism of Enzyme Action, p. 357, edited by McElroy and Glass, Johns Hopkins Press, Baltimore, 1954; Vennesland, Fed. Proc. 1958, 17, 1150; Stern and Vennesland, J. Biol. Chem. 1960, 235, 205.

nucleotide are not meant to show the shapes of the pyridine or dihydro-pyridine parts of the molecules. In the oxidized form, the pyridine ring, and the atoms directly bound to it, probably lie in a plane (see the structure of nicotinamide, Chapter I, § 2 b). In the reduced coenzyme (bottom of p. 207) there are alternative non-planar conformations possible. The differing positions of the two hydrogen atoms in the 4 position are shown in these formulae. These two conformations may not be readily interconvertible when the reduced coenzyme is bound to the enzyme.

The stereospecific direct hydrogen transfer is consistent with a hydride-ion transfer mechanism for these enzymic reactions and is analogous to the reductions brought about by aluminium alkoxides (cf. § 17 c). This means that the hydrogen atom may be transferred with the pair of

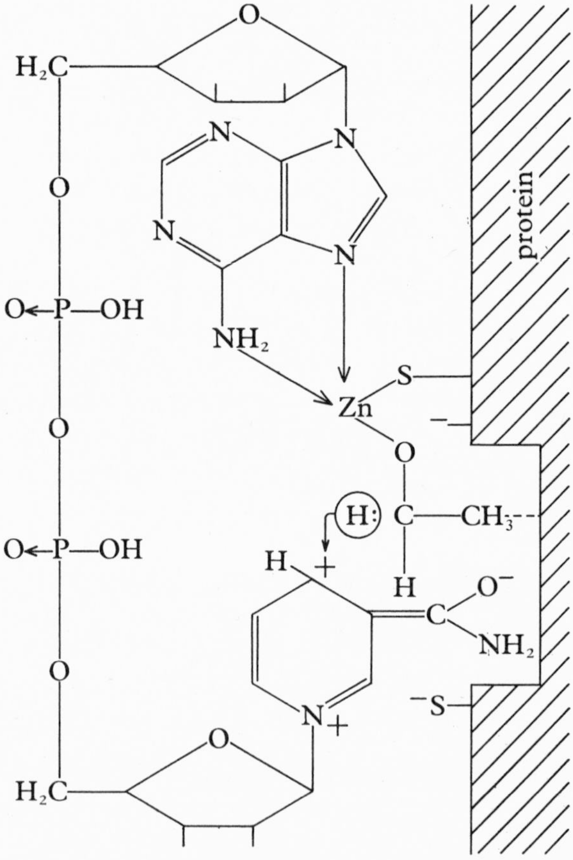

From Wallenfels, loc. cit.

bonding electrons which it formerly shared with the carbon atom. The kinetic isotope effect observed with yeast alcohol dehydrogenase† seems also to be consistent with this type of mechanism. This enzyme contains zinc, which plays a part in the reaction,‡ and there is evidence that a thiol group is also involved. The picture§ on p. 208 is meant to stress the kind of binding that might occur in the alcohol dehydrogenase reaction.

A model reaction that has been studied in detail is the reduction of thioketones. This can be effected by reduced diphosphopyridine nucleotide, or by N-benzyl dihydronicotinamide, here shown labelled with deuterium in the 4 position (9):

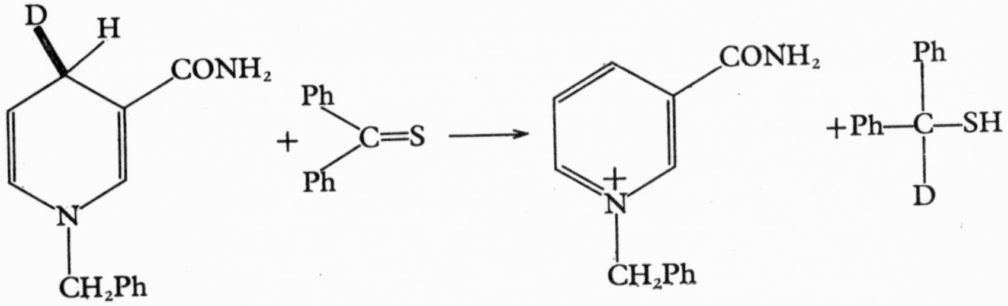

(9)

The reaction shows direct hydrogen transfer, is first-order in the dihydropyridine and in the thioketone, but the rate does not depend on the pH. There is also a kinetic isotope effect, and these observations suggest that the transition state can be shown as:

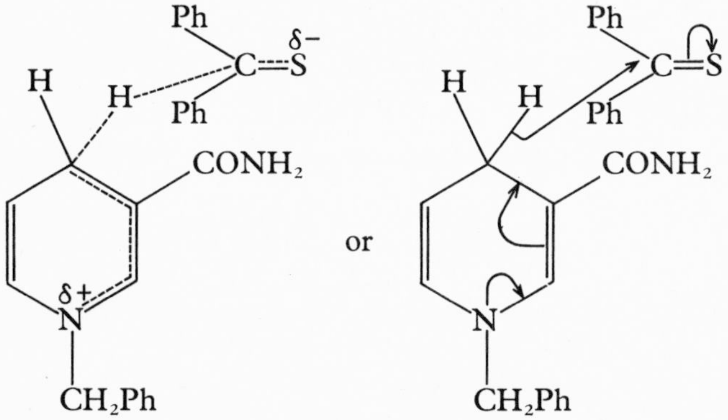

or

† Mahler and Douglas, J. Amer. Chem. Soc. 1957, **79**, 1159; for a general account of the kinetics of these reactions, see Theorell, Adv. Enzymol. 1958, **20**, 31.

‡ Vallee, Proc. 4th Int. Congr. Biochem. 1960, **8**, 138.

§ Wallenfels, in Steric Course of Microbiological Reactions, p. 32, edited by Wolstenholme and O'Connor, Ciba Foundation Study Group No. 2, Churchill, London, 1959; see also Kaplan, ibid., p. 37.

The essence of this mechanism is that it shows the shift of a hydride ion.†
Possibly in the transition state one of the phenyl groups is coplanar with,
and quite close to, the dihydropyridine ring.

19. Tautomerism of imines

The tautomerism of imines of the type

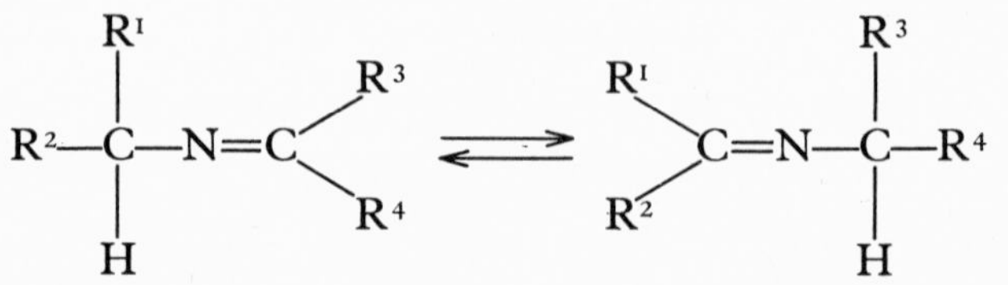

takes place under basic conditions. The main point at issue here is
whether the reaction proceeds via a carbanion, mesomeric between (1)
and (2). Note that this mesomeric carbanion would not be expected to

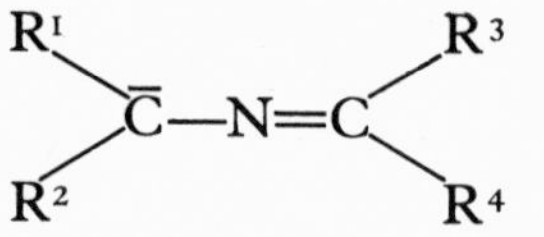

(1) 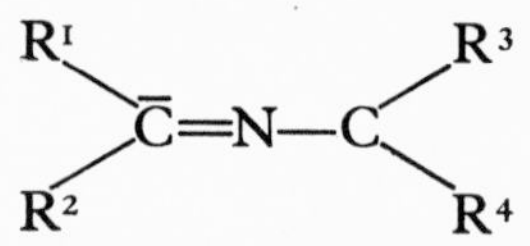   (2)

be as stable as the carbanion derived from a ketone, since here the
negative charge is not shared by the electronegative atom. As usual,
the procedure consists of postulating a mechanism, considering its consequences, and testing for them.

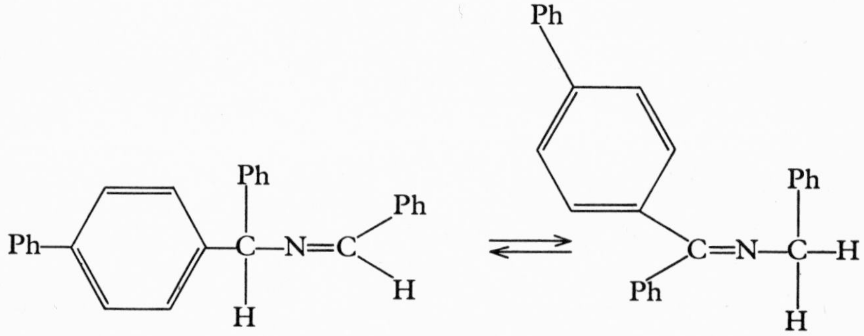

(3)   (4)

Now if the conversion of the optically active imine (3) into (4) proceeded
via a carbanion, then in general the rate of loss of optical activity of the

† Westheimer, in *The Enzymes*, vol. **1**, p. 259, edited by Boyer, Lardy, and Myrbäck,
Academic Press, New York, 1959.

system would exceed the rate of conversion of (3) into (4), if the carbanion (5) were an intermediate. This consequence arises because the carb-

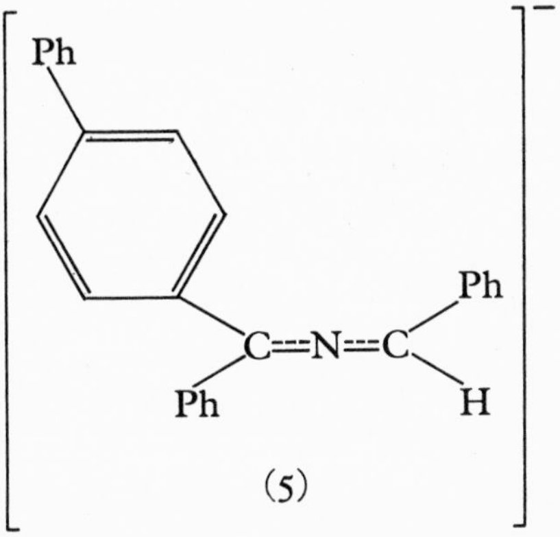

(5)

anion (5) has the choice of reverting to (3) or going forward to (4): either route leads to loss of optical activity, but only one leads to tautomerism. A similar test can be effected by carrying out the reaction in deuterated solvent (here EtOD), and comparing the initial rates of deuterium uptake and tautomerism. Here again if the carbanion (5) were an intermediate it would take up deuterium whether it reverted to (3) or went forward to (4). In fact, it was found that the rates of tautomerism, racemization, and deuterium uptake were the same.†

These results suggest that the carbanion (5) is not an intermediate in the conversion of (3) into (4), and that a hydrogen atom is transferred to one carbon atom (from the solvent) as the other hydrogen atom is being removed (by the base) from the other carbon atom. Thus the transition state, for the reaction catalysed by sodium ethoxide in ethanol, may be shown as (6): .

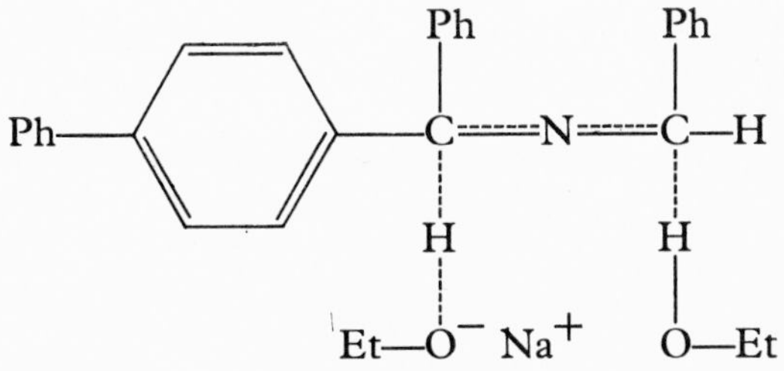

(6)

† Hsü, Ingold, and Wilson, *J. Chem. Soc.* 1935, p. 1778; Ossorio and Hughes, ibid. 1952, p. 426.

The sodium is shown in (6) as it seems reasonable that a sodium ion will be close to an ethoxide ion, and will be solvated, and that the solvating solvent molecule will contain a polarized O—H bond.

20. Some reactions in which vitamin B_6 is the coenzyme

The term vitamin B_6 has been used to refer to any of the five pyridines shown below: here the term is restricted to the phosphates (4) and (5), as these are the coenzymes in the reactions we shall discuss.

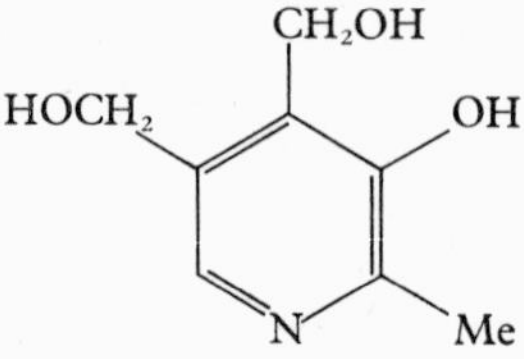

pyridoxine (1)   pyridoxal (2)   pyridoxamine (3)

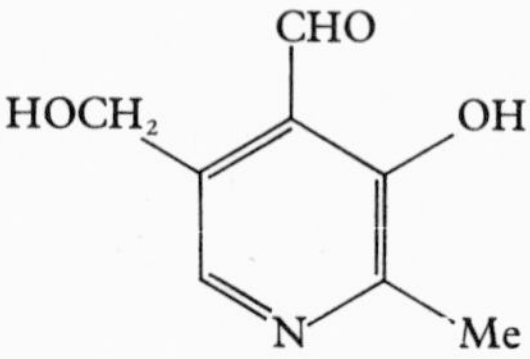

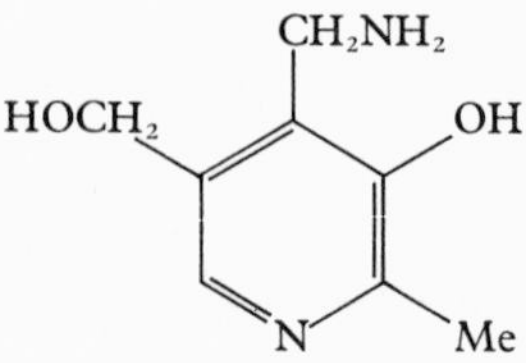

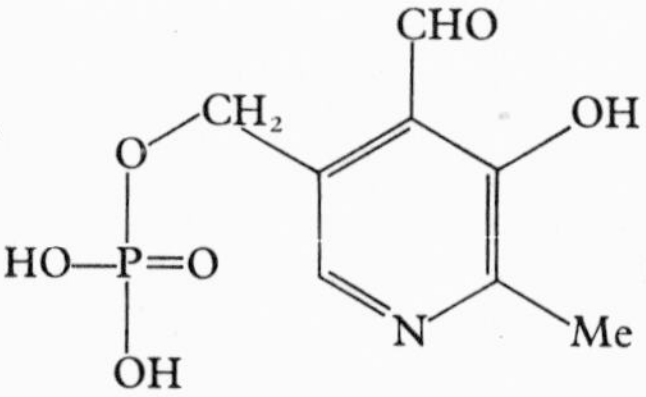

pyridoxal phosphate (4)   pyridoxamine phosphate (5)

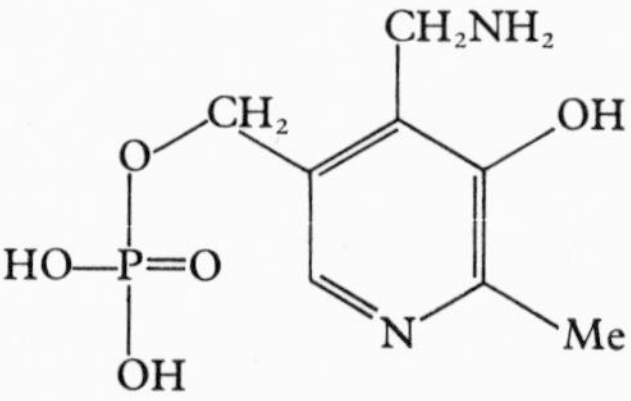

Amino acids are the substrates in practically all the enzymic reactions in which vitamin B_6 is concerned. An important reaction of this type is transamination,

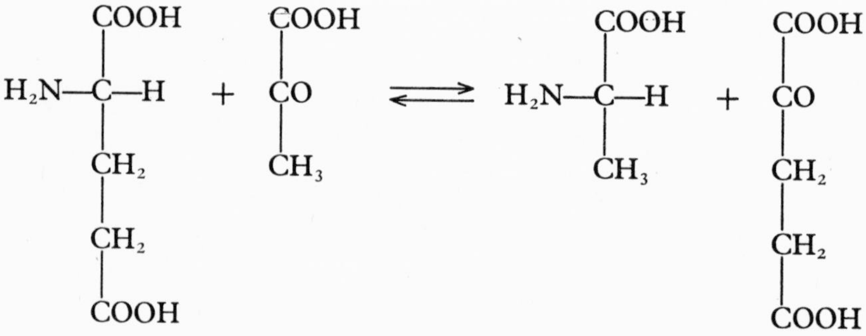

L-glutamic acid   pyruvic acid   L-alanine   2-oxo-glutaric acid

The overall reaction will be treated as the sum of two partial reactions, each of which consists of the interconversion of an amino acid and a keto acid.

The striking feature about the enzymic reactions involving vitamin B_6 is that they may all be carried out without the enzyme, but with pyridoxal and metal ions as catalysts.† These model reactions are not specific, so that several products are formed, but it seems probable that in the enzymic reactions the coenzyme here plays a major part in the activation process. The mechanism of the model reactions thus provides a working hypothesis for the enzymic reaction. Most of the rest of this section concerns the model reactions carried out with an amino acid, pyridoxal, and a metal ion.

Pyridoxal reacts with amino acids at room temperature in neutral solution; this reaction is an example of the condensation of carbonyl compounds with amines (§ 6).

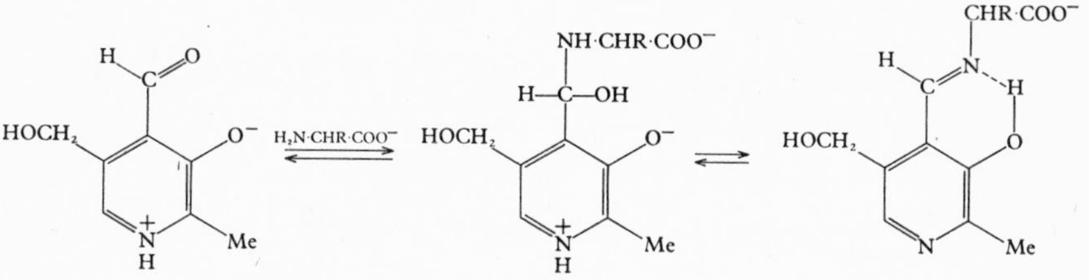

In the presence of metal ions (written as M^{++}; Cu^{++}, Fe^{+++}, and Al^{+++} are amongst those used) cyclic complexes (chelates) are formed. The simplest structure for such a chelate is (6), and so the reactions will be discussed in terms of this structure; there are several other possible structures.

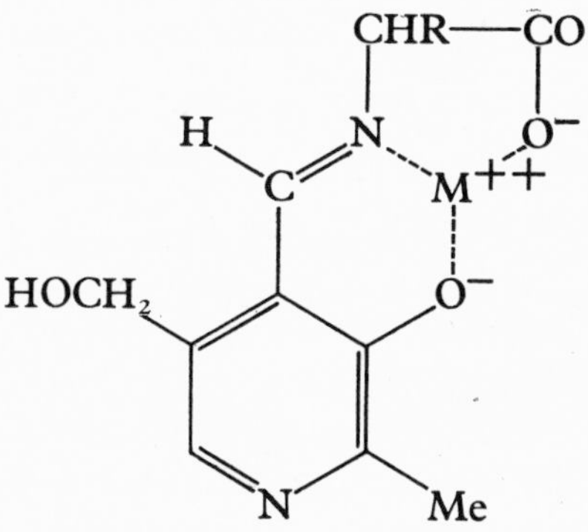

(6)

† Snell, *Vitamins and Hormones*, 1958, **16**, 78.

The nature of the catalysis in the model reaction is clarified by studies on analogues of pyridoxal. These compounds were tested for their activity in catalysing the formation of 2-oxoglutaric acid from glutamic acid and aluminium ions. Two active catalysts are 2-formyl-3-hydroxy-pyridine (7), and 4-nitrosalicylaldehyde (8), whereas 3,5-dinitrosalicyl-aldehyde (9) and 3-O-methylpyridoxal (10) are inactive. The inactivity

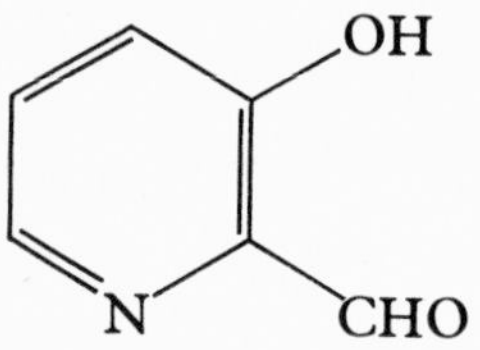

(7) 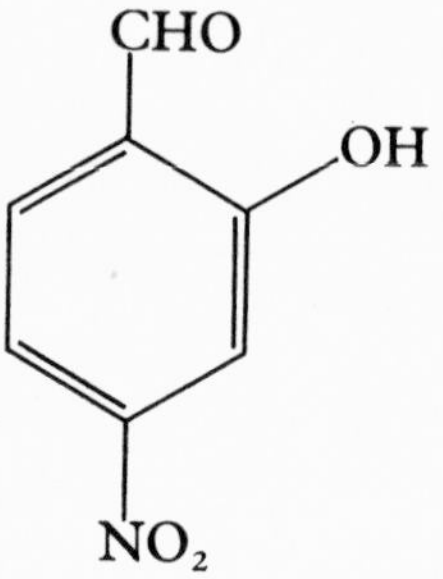   (8)

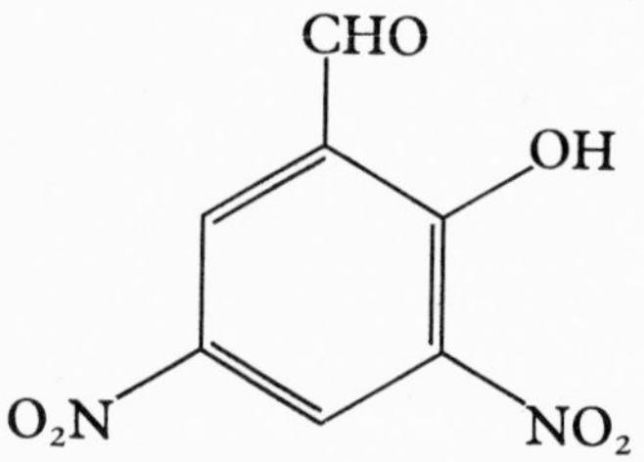

(9) 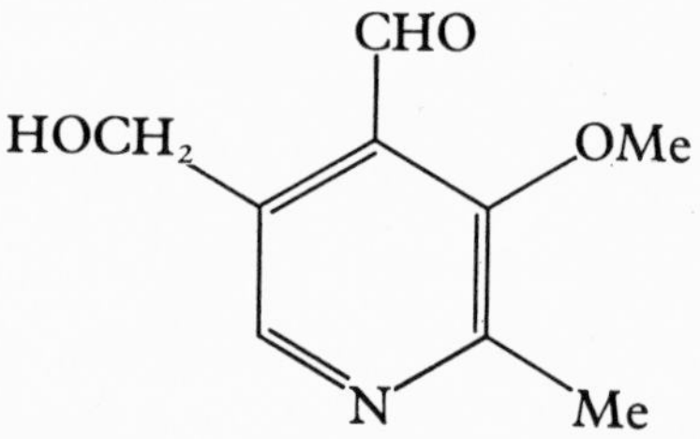   (10)

of (10) shows that the CHO group must be flanked by an OH group. The activity of (8) shows that the pyridine ring is not essential, but may be replaced by a *p*-nitrophenyl ring. The inactivity of (9) shows that *m*-nitro groups will not replace the *p*-nitro group in (8). The activity of (7) shows that the CHO group does not need to be *para* to the nitrogen (as it is in pyridoxal), but may instead be *ortho*.

The mechanism of the conversion of alanine into pyruvic acid may be written as:

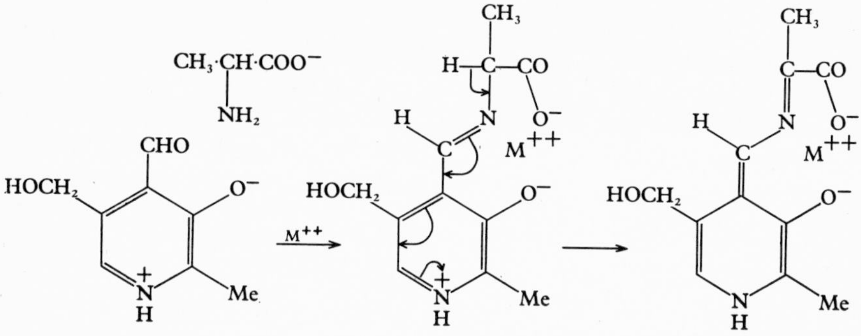

$$CH_3 \cdot CH \cdot COO^- \quad NH_2$$

(11)

$$CH_3 \cdot C \cdot COO^- \quad \underset{\parallel}{O}$$

$$CH_2NH_2 \qquad +M^{++}$$

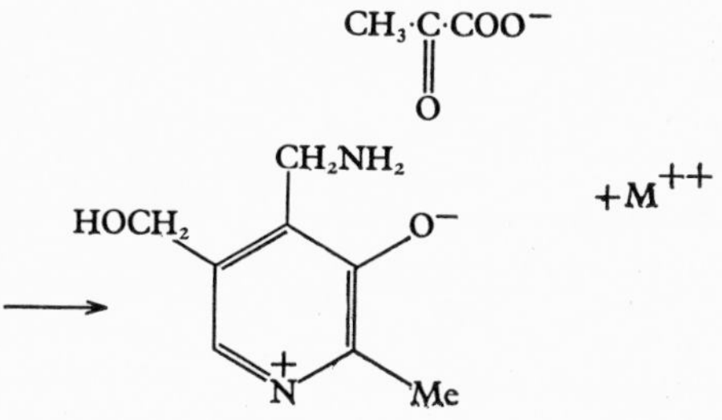

This sort of mechanism shows the function of the necessary groups in pyridoxal. The OH group, in its ionized form, helps to bind the metal atom. The function of the pyridine ring is to withdraw electrons, and the *para* nitro group in the benzene ring can also do this; thus (12) (p. 216) is analogous to (11). A nitro group in the *meta* position to the aldehyde group, however, could not function in the way shown in (12). *The essence of the catalytic activity in this reaction is the ability of the 'catalytic unit' to accommodate the extra pair of electrons which is driven into the system by the fission of the* C—H *bond.* The same feature arises in decarboxylation (Chapter VII, § 2), and this model system also catalyses the decarboxylations of amino acids, another reaction for which vitamin B_6 is the coenzyme.

We now turn to the enzymic reaction. The 'glutamic-aspartic' trans-aminase contains firmly-bound vitamin B_6, which may be liberated (by the addition of acid or alkali) as pyridoxal phosphate. After the enzyme has brought about the conversion of glutamic acid to 2-oxoglutaric acid, the vitamin B_6 may be liberated as pyridoxamine phosphate. This result† agrees with a mechanism of the type given above. The nitrogen

† Jenkins and Sizer, *J. Amer. Chem. Soc.* 1957, **79**, 2655; *J. Biol. Chem.* 1959, **234**, 1179.

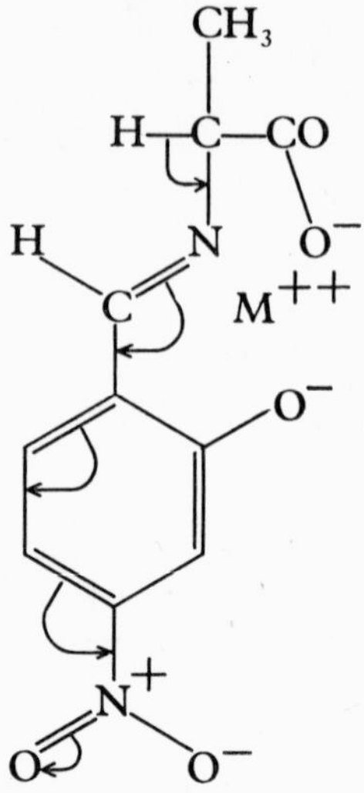

(12)

atom from the glutamic acid is received by the coenzyme; in a second step the nitrogen atom may be transferred to oxaloacetic acid (in the glutamic acid–aspartic acid transamination), or to pyruvic acid (in the glutamic acid–alanine transamination). Whether metal ions play a part in the enzymic reaction is not known.

ESTERIFICATION AND HYDROLYSIS

1. Carboxylic esters

THE formation and hydrolysis of carboxylic esters by the reaction

$$RCOOH + R'OH \rightleftharpoons RCOOR' + H_2O$$

is of general importance. Esters may also be prepared from derivatives of carboxylic acids, such as anhydrides or acid chlorides or, *in vivo*, thiol esters, rather than from the acids themselves. The other methods for the preparation of esters (e.g. from alkyl halides and a salt of the acid, or from acids and diazoalkanes) are not discussed here.

(*a*) *Acyl-oxygen fission.* Carboxylic esters are normally acylating agents, not alkylating agents: thus hydroxylamine is acylated, not alkylated:

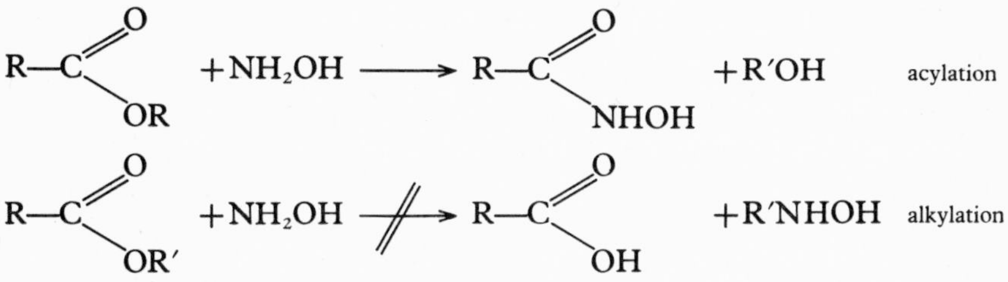

This reaction is often used analytically.† Here, the nature of the product shows that it is the acyl-oxygen bond in the carboxylic ester which is broken (1). In the hydrolysis of esters, however, the nature of the product does not normally differentiate between the alternatives (2) and (3):

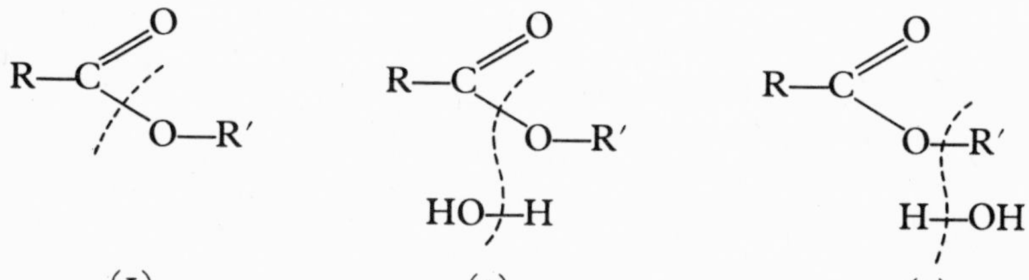

(1)	(2)	(3)
	acyl-oxygen fission	alkyl-oxygen fission

† Lipmann and Tuttle, *J. Biol. Chem.* 1945, **159**, 21; see also Jencks, *J. Amer. Chem. Soc.* 1958, **80**, 4581, 4585.

The first point, then, to consider in the mechanism of the hydrolysis of carboxylic esters is which bond in the ester is severed. Now alkyl-oxygen fission leads to an alcohol containing an oxygen atom derived from water, but acyl-oxygen fission does not. Thus if the hydrolysis is carried out in water containing $H_2^{18}O$ the alcohol formed will only be enriched in ^{18}O if alkyl-oxygen fission occurs. In fact, the hydrolysis of methyl hydrogen succinate in water containing $H_2^{18}O$ gave methanol which was not enriched with ^{18}O;[†] similarly, the alkaline hydrolysis of amyl acetate gave amyl alcohol not enriched in ^{18}O.[‡] Hence in these examples, acyl-oxygen fission occurs, as it did in the reaction with hydroxylamine. Other methods have also been used, and the conclusion is that acyl-oxygen fission occurs in general, except where the alkyl-oxygen bond is weakened by the special nature of the alkyl radical (§ 1 f).

(b) *Mechanism of alkaline hydrolysis.* The hydrolysis of carboxylic esters in alkaline solution ('saponification') is irreversible. The rate is proportional to the concentrations of hydroxide ion and of ester.

$$HO^- + RCO\cdot OR' \longrightarrow R\cdot COO^- + R'OH$$

The reaction is not a one-stage bimolecular substitution, however. If 'carbonyl-labelled' ethyl benzoate, $Ph\cdot C{=\!=}^{18}O$, is hydrolysed, it is found

$$\underset{\displaystyle OEt}{|}$$

that the label disappears from the unhydrolysed ester during the course of the reaction. Thus, there are two types of reaction going on, isotopic exchange and hydrolysis.[§]

These results can be interpreted by the mechanism at the top of the next page, which shows how isotopic exchange can proceed concurrently with hydrolysis.

The main feature of this mechanism is the addition of the nucleophilic hydroxide ion to the carbonyl group of the ester, a step which is similar to the additions of nucleophilic species to the carbonyl groups in aldehydes and ketones (Chapter V). Addition of alkoxide ions to the carbonyl groups of esters has been detected by a decrease in the intensity of the absorption of infra-red radiation by the carbonyl group.[||] There is a

[†] Datta, Day, and Ingold, *J. Chem. Soc.* 1939, p. 838.
[‡] Polanyi and Szabo, *Trans. Faraday Soc.* 1934, **30**, 508.
[§] Bender, *J. Amer. Chem. Soc.* 1951, **73**, 1626; Bender, Ginger, and Unik, ibid. 1958, **80**, 1044.
[||] Bender, ibid. 1953, **75**, 5986.

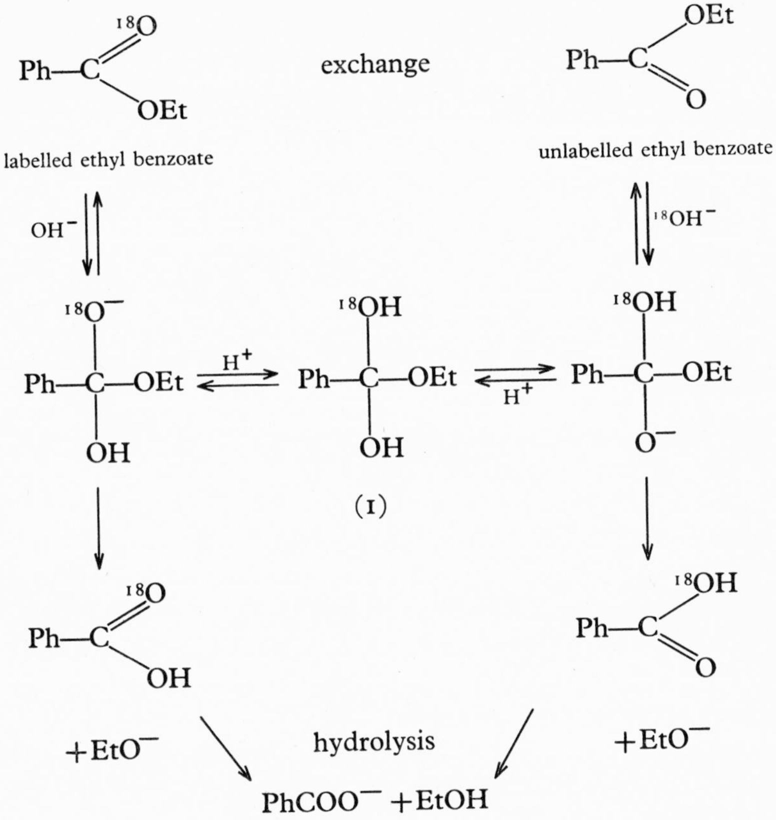

rapid, reversible reaction between sodium methoxide and ethyl tri-
fluoroacetate (in dibutyl ether):

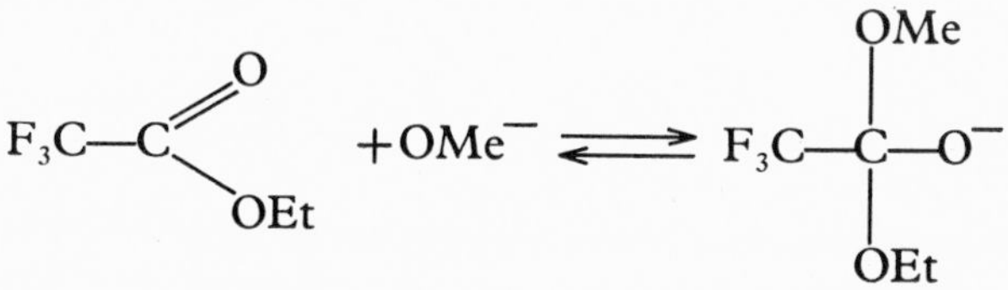

In this example, conversion into the adduct is essentially complete under
conditions which, with ethyl difluoroacetate, result in 77 per cent. conversion, and with ethyl monofluoroacetate, 26 per cent. conversion; with
ethyl acetate, no decrease in the intensity of the carbonyl band is detectable. Fluorine is considerably more electronegative than carbon, and so

the product (2) is stabilized by the attraction between the opposite charges on the carbon and oxygen atoms:

$$\overset{\delta-}{F} \quad OMe$$

$$\overset{\delta-}{F}-\overset{\delta+}{C}-\overset{}{C}-O^{-}$$

$$\underset{\delta-}{F} \quad OEt$$

(2)

The rates of hydrolysis (in alkaline solution) of the ethyl fluoroacetates follow the same order as the extent of reaction with methoxide ion.

The rates of isotopic exchange and hydrolysis in the reactions of ethyl benzoate described above are of the same order of magnitude, which suggests that the addition of the hydroxide ion is the rate-determining step. It is the symmetrical hydrate (1) which permits the isotopic exchange. There is no corresponding intermediate in the bimolecular nucleophilic substitutions which occur on saturated (sp^3) carbon atoms; the intermediate is possible here because the carbon atom is unsaturated (sp^2) in the ester and becomes saturated (sp^3) in the intermediate. This difference between the mechanisms of reactions at saturated and unsaturated centres runs all through organic chemistry.

(c) *Structure and reactivity in alkaline hydrolysis occurring by acyl-oxygen fission.* The rates of alkaline hydrolysis of ethyl benzoates substituted in the benzene ring depend on the substituent, as has been mentioned in Chapter II (§ 2 *e*). Electron-withdrawing substituents facilitate the reaction, and electron-repelling substituents retard it; the magnitudes of the effects, for *meta*- and *para*-substituents, are shown in Fig. 21 (p. 69) and are there compared with the effects of the same substituents on the ionization of benzoic acid. Now the rate-determining step in the alkaline hydrolysis is the attack of the hydroxide ion on the ester, and the main factor governing the rate of this step is the repulsive force between the electrons on the oxygen atom of the approaching hydroxide ion and the electrons on the carbon atom of the ester: thus electron-withdrawing substituents in the benzene ring, which lower the electron density at the carbon atom of the ester, facilitate the hydrolysis. These *meta*- and *para*-substituents affect the rate by altering the heat of activation, without causing much change in the entropy of activation. Substituents in the *ortho*-position, which is near to the reaction centre, affect both the heat and entropy of activation and normally retard the reaction more (or accelerate it less) than when they are in the *para*-position. Roughly speaking, *ortho*-substituents may be said to get in the way of the approaching hydroxyl ion (see § 1 e). The same sort of effect is also seen in the lowered rates of hydrolysis of esters of secondary and tertiary alcohols.

(d) *Mechanism of acid hydrolysis occurring by acyl-oxygen fission.* The acid-catalysed hydrolysis of esters is reversible; the hydrogen ion is a catalyst, in contrast to the hydroxide ion, which is a reactant. The equilibrium constant for most esters of primary and secondary alcohols is of the order of unity, and the mechanism of the acid-catalysed hydrolysis of an ester will be the same as that of the reverse reaction, the acid-catalysed esterification. In preparative work a large extent of reaction is required, and so esterifications are commonly conducted in the alcohol as solvent, and hydrolyses are carried out in water as solvent (or in aqueous acetic acid if the ester is insufficiently soluble in water).

The rate of hydrolysis is proportional to the hydrogen ion concentration, and (as in the alkaline hydrolysis) if the reaction is carried out with

$$\text{Ph—C} \overset{\text{}^{18}\text{O}}{\underset{\text{OEt}}{<}} \text{,}$$

isotopic exchange accompanies hydrolysis. Moreover, the rate of *exchange* is comparable with the rate of hydrolysis under both acidic and alkaline conditions, although the rate of acid *hydrolysis* is slower by a factor of about 10^4. So the exchange reaction must also be much slower in acid solution than in alkaline solution. The hydrate (1) has been suggested as an intermediate in the exchange reaction, and in the hydrolysis, in acid solution. The function of the acid is to increase the electrophilic character of the carbonyl group of the ester, as in the acid-catalysed additions to aldehydes and ketones described in the last chapter. The first step, then, is protonation of the ester, followed by addition of water and subsequent loss of a proton to give the hydrate (1). The hydrate may be regarded as intermediate between a carboxylic ester and a carboxylic acid, and so, as our mechanism is to apply to esterification as well as hydrolysis, the succeeding stages are simply the counterparts of what has gone before.

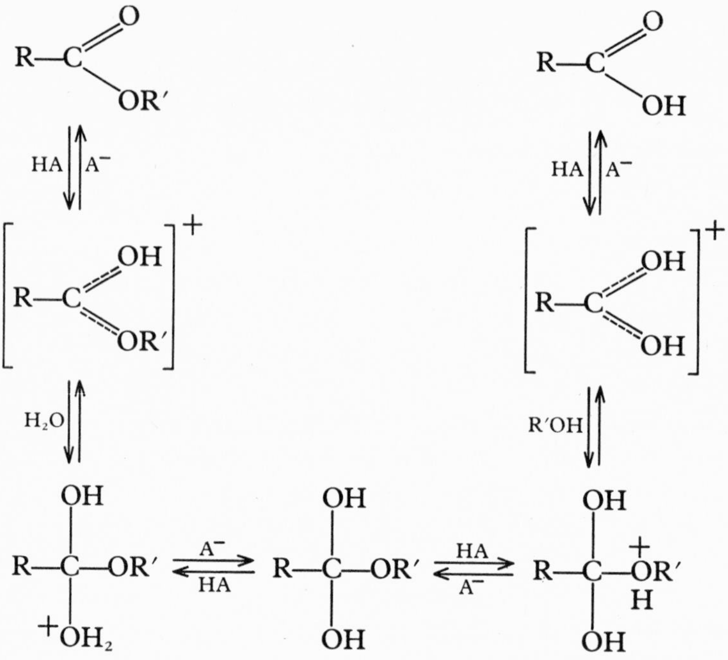

$$R-C{\overset{O}{\underset{OR'}{}}}$$

HA $\updownarrow$ A⁻

$$\left[R-C{\overset{OH}{\underset{OR'}{}}}\right]^+$$

H_2O $\updownarrow$

$$R-\underset{+OH_2}{\overset{OH}{C}}-OR' \underset{HA}{\overset{A^-}{\rightleftharpoons}} R-\underset{OH}{\overset{OH}{C}}-OR' \underset{A^-}{\overset{HA}{\rightleftharpoons}} R-\underset{OH}{\overset{OH}{C}}{\underset{H}{\overset{+}{-}}}OR'$$

$$R-C{\overset{O}{\underset{OH}{}}}$$

HA $\updownarrow$ A⁻

$$\left[R-C{\overset{OH}{\underset{OH}{}}}\right]^+$$

R'OH $\updownarrow$

(I)

The rate-determining step in the acid-catalysed hydrolysis of carb-oxylic esters is probably the one in which water is added; and other stages are proton transfers to or from an oxygen atom, which are usually fast. Thus, as in the alkaline hydrolysis, in the kinetically important step the carbon atom is changing from an sp^2 to an sp^3 hybridized state. However, in the acid-catalysed reaction, this is the second stage, and so the rate depends on the concentration of protonated ester. This results in a cancellation in the effect of substituents on the rate of reaction: electron-withdrawing substituents in the benzene ring of ethyl benzoate disfavour protonation but favour attack by the water molecule; the net effect turns out to be variable, and small compared with the effect of structure on reactivity observed in alkaline hydrolysis.

The rate constant for the attack of a neutral water molecule on the protonated ester is probably comparable with the rate constant for the attack of a hydroxyl ion on the neutral ester molecule. For the pK of the ester is probably in the neighbourhood of -6, so that in a solution which has a hydrogen ion concentration of unity only one part in a million of the ester is protonated. However, in a solution which has a hydroxyl ion concentration of unity the concentration of water is about

50, so that the ratio

$$\frac{\text{velocity of alkaline hydrolysis}}{\text{velocity of acid hydrolysis}} = \frac{k_{\text{alkaline}}[\text{OH}^-][\text{RCOOR}']}{k_{\text{acid}}[\text{H}_2\text{O}][\text{RCOOR}'\text{H}]^+}$$

$$\sim \frac{k_{\text{alkaline}}}{k_{\text{acid}}} \times \frac{10^6}{50} = 2 . 10^4,$$

if $k_{\text{alkaline}} = k_{\text{acid}}$.

The ratio of the rate of alkaline hydrolysis to that of acid hydrolysis for ethyl phenylacetate (in 56 per cent. acetone at 25° C) is about 8×10^3,[†] which is of the same order of magnitude as the figure obtained above. However, the rate of attack of hydroxyl ion on a neutral ester is probably about a million times as high as the rate of attack of a water molecule on neutral (not protonated) ester.[‡]

In the first stage of the mechanism given above, the protonated carboxylic acid is sometimes written as (2) rather than (3):

(2)   (3)

The distinction, although perhaps unimportant, is real, and has been the subject of experimental study in the case of amides (Chapter VII, § 1 b). Whereas (2) would lose the resonance energy of the carboxyl group, (3) would increase it, and so this symmetrical structure seems a more reasonable representation of the protonated form of a carboxylic acid, and is analogous to the structure established for alkylated amidines.

(e) *Steric hindrance; unimolecular mechanism of reaction occurring by acyl-oxygen fission.* The electronic effects of substituents on the rate of acid-catalysed hydrolysis and esterification may be gauged by their effect on the rate of hydrolysis of ethyl benzoates when the substituents are present in the *meta-* or *para-*position of the benzene ring, and, as mentioned, these effects are not large. But substituents in the *ortho-*position affect the rate of reaction markedly. Indeed, when two *ortho-*substituents are present, as in 2,6-dichlorobenzoic acid, the ester cannot be prepared by heating the acid with alcoholic hydrogen chloride. The effect is called steric, because it does not depend on whether the groups are electron-withdrawing or electron-repelling, but it does depend on their being close

† Tommila and Hinshelwood, *J. Chem. Soc.* 1938, p. 1801.
‡ Swain and Scott, *J. Amer. Chem. Soc.* 1953, **75**, 141.

to the reaction centre. This steric hindrance, which was studied by Meyer in the last century, shows up particularly clearly in the acid-catalysed reaction just because the electronic effects are relatively small. In the hydrolysis of ethyl benzoate the repulsive forces operate between the approaching water molecule and the carbon atom of the carbonyl group. When the *ortho*-hydrogen atoms of ethyl benzoate are replaced by the larger chlorine atoms, i.e. in the hydrolysis of ethyl 2,6-dichloro-benzoate, there are additional repulsive forces between the approaching water molecule and the chlorine atoms. The steric hindrance can also be described in terms of the transition state theory. In the transition state the carbon atom of the carbonyl group is between the initial sp^2 state and the sp^3 state; the change in bond angle (from $120°$ to $109°$) and the accommodation of another species (the water molecule) means that the transition state is more congested than the initial state. Hence the introduction of large groups near to the reaction centre affects the transition state more than the initial state, i.e. it preferentially renders the transition state unstable, and so retards the reaction. Steric hindrance is also observed with aliphatic acids; esters of triethylacetic acid, $Et_3C.COOH$, are hydrolysed more slowly than are esters of acetic acid, by a factor of about 10^4.

Under certain conditions, however, sterically hindered benzoic acids react readily, by a special mechanism. Mesitoic acid (1), which has two *ortho*-substituents, is not esterified under ordinary conditions, but if the acid is dissolved in concentrated sulphuric acid and the solution poured into alcohol, the ester is formed in good yield.†

(I)

Benzoic acid itself is not esterified under these conditions, so the success of the method with mesitoic acid is not simply due to the unusual conditions. The reason for the difference between benzoic acid and

† Newman, *J. Amer. Chem. Soc.* 1941, **63**, 2431.

mesitoic acid lies in their different behaviour when dissolved in concentrated sulphuric acid. Benzoic acid (like nearly all oxygen-containing organic compounds) functions as a base in sulphuric acid:

$$Ph \cdot C \overset{O}{\underset{OH}{\diagup}} \; + H_2SO_4 \rightleftharpoons Ph \cdot C \overset{\overset{+}{OH}}{\underset{OH}{\diagup}} \; + HSO_4^-$$

This ionization may be detected by measurements of the freezing-point of the solution, which show that one molecule of benzoic acid provides two molecular species. Mesitoic acid, however, gives four molecular species, not two, and this can be interpreted by the formation of an 'acylium ion':

$$Me_3C_6H_2 \cdot COOH + 2H_2SO_4 \rightleftharpoons Me_3C_6H_2 \cdot CO^+ + H_3O^+ + 2HSO_4^-$$

acylium ion

An acylium ion may be represented as mesomeric between a carbonium ion (2) and an oxonium ion (3):

$$\overset{+}{Ar-C}=O \qquad Ar-C\equiv\overset{+}{O} \qquad Ar-\overset{+}{C\equiv\!\!\equiv O}$$

$$(2) \qquad\qquad\qquad (3)$$

When the solution of mesitoic acid in sulphuric acid is poured into alcohol, the acylium ion reacts rapidly with the alcohol:

$$Me_3C_6H_2 \cdot CO^+ + EtOH \longrightarrow Me_3C_6H_2 \cdot COOEt + H^+$$

The necessary condition for this method of esterification is that the acid should ionize to give four particles, as mesitoic acid does. There is a hydrolytic counterpart to this method of esterification. Hydrolysis of esters of mesitoic acid can be effected by dissolving the ester in sulphuric acid and pouring the solution into water; here the acylium ion is formed from the ester, and finally reacts with the water.

Steric factors favour acylium ion formation. In mesitoic acid the ortho-methyl groups are uncomfortably close to the carboxyl group, but the acylium ion, having shed a hydroxyl group, is less congested. Acylium ion formation is the unimolecular counterpart to the more common bimolecular methods of hydrolysis and esterification, and the effect of steric factors described here is paralleled by their effect in unimolecular and bimolecular nucleophilic substitutions described in Chapter III.

Comparison of mesitoic acid and benzoic acid thus yields the interesting result that a substance which is sterically hindered to a reaction by a bimolecular mechanism may be sterically accelerated in reaction by a unimolecular mechanism.

(*f*) *Hydrolysis occurring by alkyl-oxygen fission.*† Alkyl-oxygen fission is only normally encountered in the hydrolysis of esters derived from alcohols possessing exceptional structural features. In an ester R . COOR′ it is the nature of the alkyl group, R′, which mainly governs the tendency to react by alkyl-oxygen fission.

When alcohols react with carboxylic esters the nature of the product reveals whether alkyl-oxygen fission has occurred. The reaction of ethanol with triphenylmethyl benzoate provides an example:‡

$$Ph_3C\!\!-\!\!O \cdot COPh + EtOH \longrightarrow Ph_3C\!\!-\!\!OEt + PhCOOH$$

The kinetics indicate a rate-determining unimolecular step, followed by a rapid product-forming step:

$$Ph_3C\!\!-\!\!O \cdot COPh \rightleftharpoons Ph_3C^+ + {}^-O \cdot COPh$$

$$Ph_3C^+ + EtOH \longrightarrow Ph_3C\!\!-\!\!OEt + H^+$$

Now the triphenylmethyl carbonium ion (Ph_3C^+) is stabilized by mesomerism: the positive charge is spread over the nine *ortho*- and *para*-positions of the three benzene rings (Chapter I, § 1 *q*; Chapter III, § 3 *b*). This, then, is why alkyl-oxygen fission occurs, and we may expect to observe it also in other cases where the carbonium ion derived from the alkyl group is stabilized by mesomerism.

Alkyl-oxygen fission in the hydrolysis of optically active esters may be detected by the production of racemic alcohols:

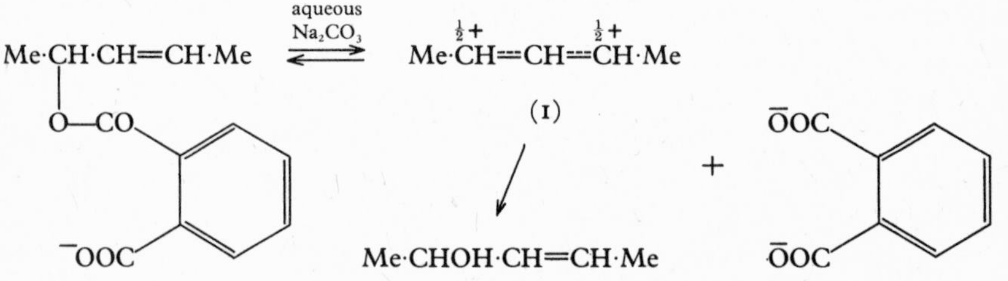

† Davies and Kenyon, *Quart. Rev.* 1955, **9**, 203.
‡ Hammond and Rudeshill, *J. Amer. Chem. Soc.* 1950, **72**, 2769.

The alkyl carbonium ion (1) is mesomeric, and so conditions are favour-able for alkyl-oxygen fission. The initial heterolysis is reversible, and so the unreacted ester is partially racemized during the course of the reaction. When the hydrolysis is carried out with 5N-sodium hydroxide, however, the alcohol which is obtained is not appreciably racemized. The interpretation of this result is that the increase in the concentration of hydroxide ions is sufficient to favour bimolecular acyl-oxygen fission, which takes place without racemization, as none of the bonds of the asymmetric carbon atom are severed. If one knew nothing of the mechanism of the reactions, one would have guessed that the 'milder' sodium carbonate was more likely to lead to retention of optical activity than the more 'drastic' 5N-sodium hydroxide.

Alkyl-oxygen fission is also encountered in the acid-catalysed hydro-lysis of esters derived from tertiary alcohols. Thus, *tert.*-butyl acetate, in an aqueous medium containing $H_2^{18}O$, gives *tert.*-butyl alcohol con-taining ^{18}O:[†]

$$Me_3C\text{—OCOMe} \underset{}{\overset{H^+}{\rightleftharpoons}} Me_3C^+ + \bar{O}COMe$$

$$\downarrow H_2^{18}O$$

$$Me_3C\text{—}^{18}OH$$

This is again consistent with the importance of the stability of the carbonium ion in favouring this mode of fission, as tertiary carbonium ions are particularly stable.

Lactones containing a four-membered ring can also undergo hydrolysis by alkyl-oxygen fission. Thus optically active β-lactones are hydrolysed in aqueous solution at pH values of from 3 to 8 (here called neutral solution) to give a hydroxy acid with the opposite configuration from that of the lactone:[‡]

$$\begin{array}{ccc} CH_2\text{—CO} & & CH_2\text{—COOH} \\ | \quad | & & | \\ H\text{—}C\text{——}O \quad +H_2O \longrightarrow & HO\text{—}C\text{—}H \\ | & & | \\ Me & & Me \end{array}$$

The fact that the configuration of the asymmetric carbon atom is affected entails alkyl-oxygen fission, and the fact that the product has the

[†] Bunton and Wood, *J. Chem. Soc.* 1955, p. 1522.
[‡] Cowdrey, Hughes, Ingold, Mastermann, and Scott, *J. Chem. Soc.* 1937, p. 1252; Olson and Miller, *J. Amer. Chem. Soc.* 1938, **60**, 2687.

opposite configuration, and is not just racemized, suggests that the reaction must be bimolecular. Thus this mechanism of alkyl-oxygen fission is different from those previously described. The reaction is peculiar to β-lactones: γ-lactones do not undergo a similar reaction.

The bond angles in a four-membered ring are 90°, less than the normal bond angle of 109° for a tetrahedral carbon atom, and so there is said to be ring-strain in a β-lactone. This strain is still present in the transition state for the attack by a water molecule which leads to acyl-oxygen fission (2), but is lessened in the transition state which leads to alkyl-oxygen fission (3):

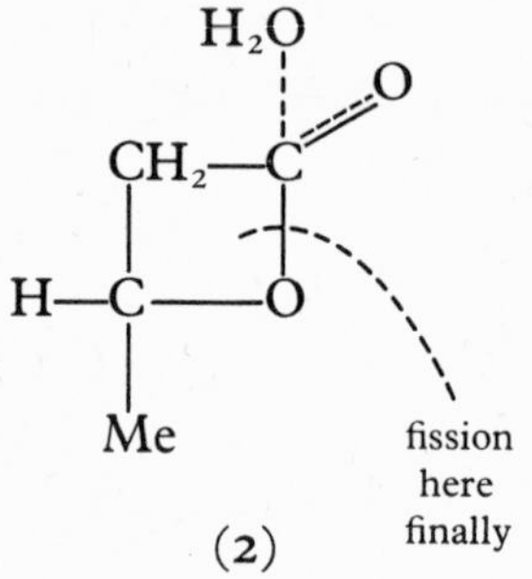

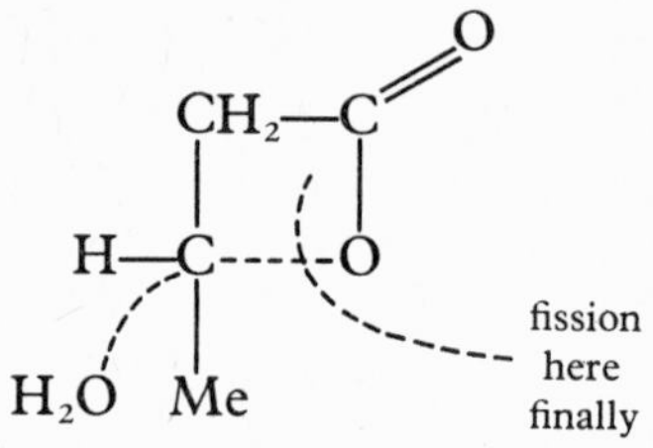

Thus this factor favours alkyl-oxygen fission. The rate of the hydrolysis is independent of the pH and so the reagent is taken to be a neutral water molecule. However, in acid and alkaline solutions, the rates of the hydrolyses by the usual acyl-oxygen fission routes are sufficiently high for these mechanisms to become dominant, and the product is the hydroxy acid with the same configuration as that of the lactone. The 'water-reaction' only takes over when the concentrations of hydrogen ion and hydroxide ion are both low.

That ordinary esters can, under special conditions, undergo alkyl-oxygen fission, is shown by the reaction of methyl benzoate with trimethylamine, in methanol solution;† here alkyl-oxygen fission is the only possibility:

$$PhCOOCH_3 + (CH_3)_3N \longrightarrow PhCOO^- + (CH_3)_4N^+$$

This reaction is, of course, simply a nucleophilic substitution at a saturated carbon atom, such as were described in Chapter III:

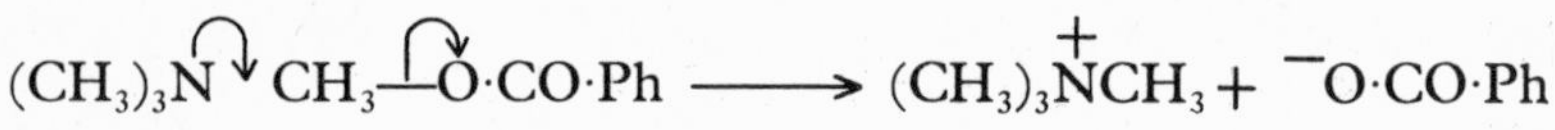

$$(CH_3)_3N \curvearrowright CH_3 \curvearrowright O \cdot CO \cdot Ph \longrightarrow (CH_3)_3\overset{+}{N}CH_3 + {}^-O \cdot CO \cdot Ph$$

† Hammett and Pfluger, *J. Amer. Chem. Soc.* 1933, **55**, 4079.

The mechanisms for the hydrolysis of carboxylic esters may be summarized as in Table 11.

TABLE 11

Mode of fission	Molecularity	Conditions	Example
Acyl-oxygen	Bimolecular	Alkaline	General
Acyl-oxygen	Bimolecular	Acid	General
Acyl-oxygen	Unimolecular	Acid	Methyl mesitoate
Alkyl-oxygen	Bimolecular	Neutral	β-Butyrolactone
Alkyl-oxygen	Unimolecular	Alkaline	1,3-Dimethylallyl hydrogen phthalate
Alkyl-oxygen	Unimolecular	Acid	t-Butyl acetate

(g) *Some enzyme 'models'.* We now turn to certain esters which have been studied in an effort to gain some idea how certain enzymes act. For some esterases (Chapter VI, § 1 h) the concept of an 'active centre' has been developed to the stage where the actual groups which play a major part in the enzymic reaction can be tentatively identified. There is, for example, evidence that a histidine residue (1) is important in some enzymes (e.g. chymotrypsin) which catalyse the hydrolysis of some esters, including p-nitrophenyl acetate (2).

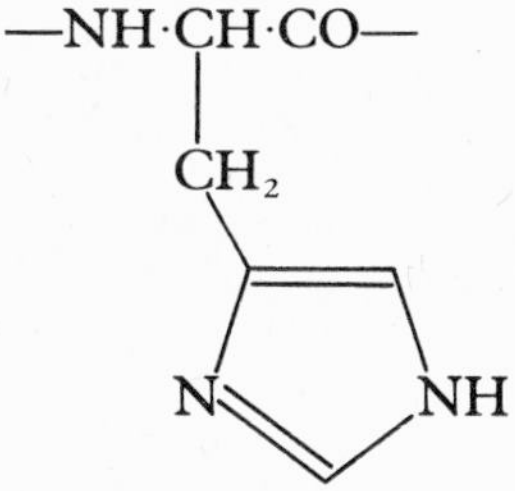

(1) 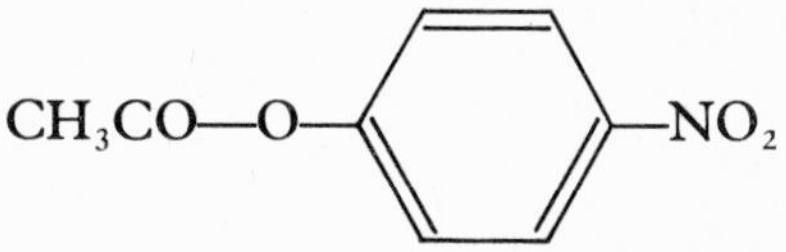   (2)

Histidine contains a glyoxaline (imidazole) ring. Glyoxaline is mesomeric between (3) and (4): it contains two nitrogen atoms, a tertiary

(3) 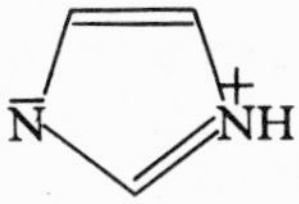   (4) 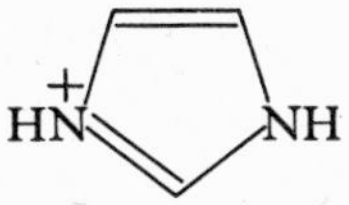   (5) 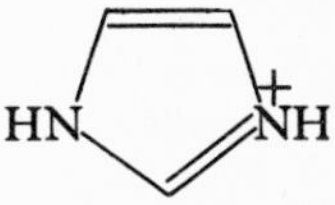   (6)

one and a secondary one. The assignment of the hydrogen atom to one particular nitrogen atom in the formulae for glyoxalines is arbitrary, but there are two nitrogen atoms with different characteristics. The tertiary nitrogen atom has a fractional negative charge, and it is due to this feature that glyoxaline is an especially reactive nucleophilic species. The glyoxaline ring is quite stable; it has the characteristics of an aromatic compound, and the lone-pair of electrons on the secondary nitrogen atom are conjugated with the four π-electrons to give a system with six π-electrons, as in benzene. Glyoxaline is a base (pK 7); the protonated form is mesomeric between (5) and (6); and is devoid of nucleophilic reactivity.[†]

Glyoxaline is one of several bases which catalyse the hydrolysis of *p*-nitrophenyl acetate (2);[‡] other bases include acetate ions, and phosphate ions. For a series of compounds of the same type the catalytic power is related to the basic strength; but the difference between structurally unrelated bases of the same strength may be quite large. Glyoxaline is a thousand times as effective a catalyst as the hydrogen phosphate anion, although they are both about equally strong as bases.[§] The mechanism of the hydrolysis of *p*-nitrophenyl acetate catalysed by glyoxaline must be based on the intervention of N-acetyl glyoxaline (7), because this compound can be detected by its characteristic absorption in the ultra-violet, and the kinetics indicate that it is an intermediate in the hydrolysis of both *p*-nitrophenyl acetate and phenyl acetate.[‖] An obvious mechanism for the hydrolysis of an acetate (ArOCOCH$_3$) catalysed by glyoxaline is somewhat analogous to that suggested for the alkaline hydrolysis of esters:

$$ArO \cdot CO \cdot CH_3 + HN \!\!-\!\!\langle \rangle\!\!-\!\! N \longrightarrow \left[HN\!\!-\!\!\langle \rangle\!\!-\!\!\overset{+}{N}\!\!-\!\!\underset{OAr}{\overset{O^-}{\underset{|}{\overset{|}{C}}}}\!\!-\!\!CH_3 \right]$$

$$\longrightarrow HN\!\!-\!\!\langle \rangle\!\!-\!\!\overset{+}{N}\!\!-\!\!C\!\!\underset{CH_3}{\overset{O}{\diagdown}} + \bar{O}Ar$$

$$(7)$$

$$\xrightarrow{H_2O}$$

$$HN\!\!-\!\!\langle \rangle\!\!-\!\!N + CH_3COOH + H^+$$

† See Barnard and Stein, *Adv. Enzymol.* 1958, **20**, 51, for an account of some biological roles of glyoxaline derivatives.

‡ Bender and Turnquest, *J. Amer. Chem. Soc.* 1957, **79**, 1652, 1656; Bruice and Schmir, ibid., p. 1663.

§ Bruice and Lapinski, ibid. 1958, **80**, 2265.

‖ Brouwar, Vlugt, and Havinga, *Kon. Ned. Akad. Wet. Proc.* 1957, B, **60**, 275.

Two features of the catalysis by glyoxaline are important. The protonated form (5, 6) of glyoxaline, which is not an active nucleophilic reagent, is ineffective. The rate of the reaction, then, depends on the pH, and as the pK of glyoxaline is 7, half the total amount of glyoxaline will be present in the reactive form at pH 7, and catalysis is possible in neutral solution: a stronger base would be at a disadvantage here.

The second feature is that there is no catalysis of the hydrolysis of esters of aliphatic alcohols (e.g. ethyl acetate). It is not simply that ethyl acetate is generally unreactive: the thiol ester (Me.CO.SEt) is hydrolysed by alkali at much the same rate as ethyl acetate, but only the thiol ester is catalytically hydrolysed in neutral solution by glyoxaline. There seems, in fact, to be some rudimentary specificity in glyoxaline catalysis. This point is discussed in more detail later (Chapter VII, § 6).

We now turn from intermolecular catalysis to intramolecular catalysis: in the latter instance, the glyoxaline ring and the phenyl ester are both present within the molecule. Two compounds with a 'built-in' catalytic site, (8) and (9), have been examined:†

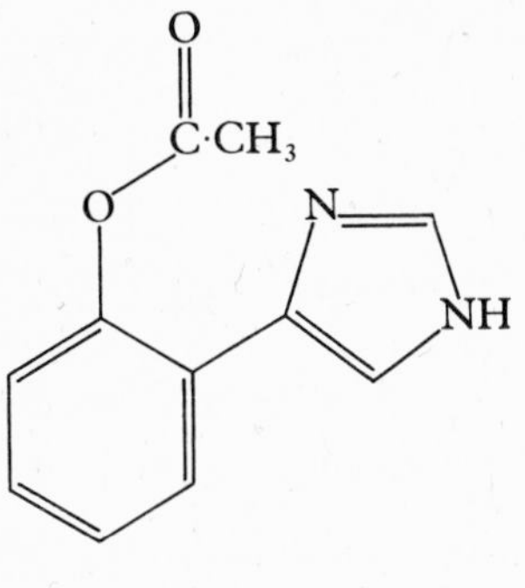

(8) 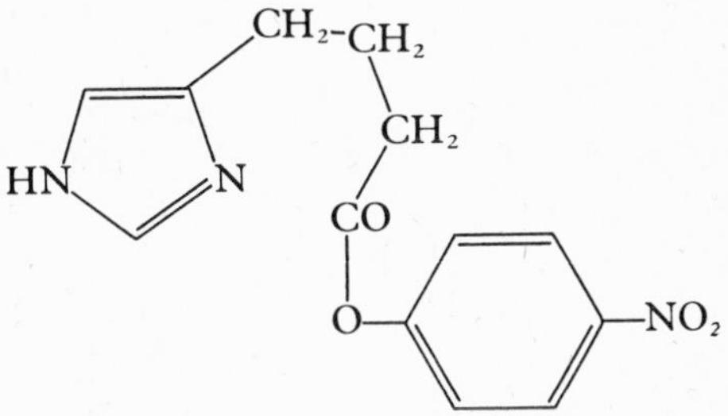   (9)

Both these compounds showed the expected characteristics of intramolecular catalysis: they decomposed in neutral solution by a first-order reaction, and the variation of the rate with pH showed that the protonated form was relatively unreactive. The value of the velocity constant for the liberation of *p*-nitrophenol from (9) was about 3 sec^{-1} which is comparable with the value obtained for the liberation of *p*-nitrophenol from *p*-nitrophenyl acetate by chymotrypsin.

† Schmir and Bruice, *J. Amer. Chem. Soc.* 1958, **80**, 1173; Bruice and Sturtevant, *Biochim. Biophys. Acta*, 1958, **30**, 208; *J. Amer. Chem. Soc.* 1959, **81**, 2860.

It should be noted that the status of the term 'catalysis' is not the same in intramolecular catalysis as it is in intermolecular catalysis. Intermolecular catalysis can be inferred from the stoicheiometric equation, and the kinetic equation, for a reaction: the concentration of a catalyst is raised to a higher power in the kinetic equation than in the stoicheiometric equation. Intramolecular catalysis is necessarily an inference about the mechanism of a reaction, and is thus at a further remove from observation.

Intramolecular catalysis of the hydrolysis of esters has also been demonstrated with the carboxyl ion as the nucleophilic catalyst. Methyl hydrogen phthalate (10) undergoes hydrolysis at a rate independent of the pH, in the region pH 4 to pH 7; this is consistent with the mechanism:†

(10)   (11)

The hydrolysis of phthalic anhydride (11) is known to be relatively rapid. It is a tribute to the efficiency of intramolecular catalysis that the intermolecular catalysis of the hydrolysis of a methyl ester by carboxyl ions is unknown.

As many reactions which may be catalysed by enzymes may also be catalysed by either acids or bases, part of the effectiveness of enzymes as catalysts may be due to their possession, and utilization, of both acidic and basic groups. This idea of bifunctional catalysis (cf. Chapter V, § 3 *b*) has been tested in the hydrolysis of certain esters. Thus the ester (12) has two carboxyl groups: one of them (chosen arbitrarily) is shown as the anion. This ester is rapidly hydrolysed (the half-life is a few seconds) at pH 4; this is the optimum pH, and the rate of hydrolysis is considerably less at pH 2 or pH 6.‡ This is just the expected result if the mono-anion is the reactive form (cf. § 2 *a*): at pH 2 neither carboxyl group will be appreciably ionized, and at pH 6 both of them will be largely ionized. The rapid reaction is then due to the ionized carboxyl group

† Bender, Chloupek, and Neveu, *J. Amer. Chem. Soc.* 1958, **80**, 5384; Bender and Neveu, ibid., p. 5388.

‡ Morawetz and Oreskes, ibid. p. 2591.

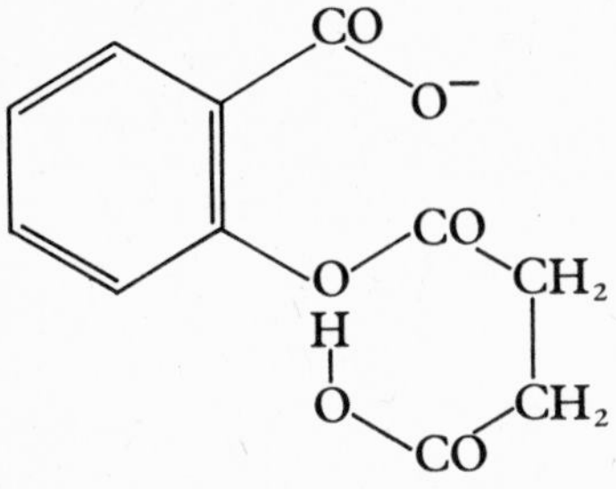

(12) 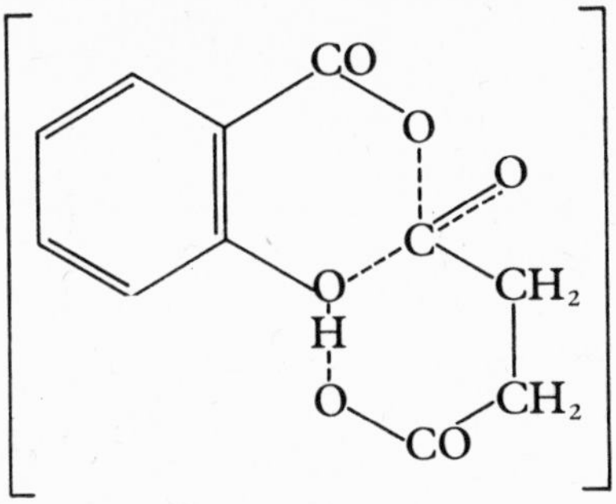   (13)

acting as a nucleophilic reagent and the unionized carboxyl group
simultaneously acting as an electrophilic reagent, leading to the transition state (13). Here, then, we have *intramolecular bifunctional catalysis*;
an example of intermolecular bifunctional catalysis was given on p. 162.
It seems probable that many enzymes will turn out to function along
these lines.

(*h*) *Esterases.* Although the reaction chiefly discussed in this section
is the hydrolysis of esters, the enzymes which we shall describe include
proteolytic enzymes (chymotrypsin, papain, ficin), as well as acetylcholine esterase. The proteolytic enzymes catalyse the hydrolysis of
both esters and amides, and indeed comparison of the rates of hydrolysis
of the two classes of compounds has proved informative.

There is probably more known about the hydrolyses catalysed by
chymotrypsin than about any other enzymic reaction, and only an
outline can be given here. Inhibitors have provided much information
about esterases. Thus di-isopropyl phosphorofluoridate (1) is one of a
number of highly toxic compounds which inhibit acetylcholine esterases,
chymotrypsin, and a number of other enzymes.

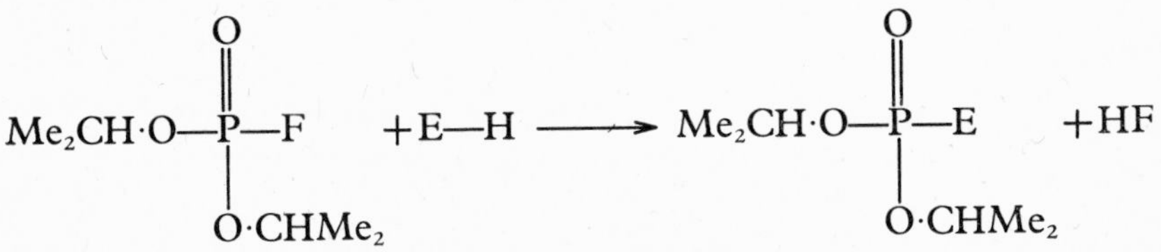

$$Me_2CH \cdot O - \overset{\overset{\text{O}}{\|}}{\underset{\underset{\text{O} \cdot CHMe_2}{|}}{P}} - F \quad + E - H \longrightarrow Me_2CH \cdot O - \overset{\overset{\text{O}}{\|}}{\underset{\underset{\text{O} \cdot CHMe_2}{|}}{P}} - E \quad + HF$$

(1)

The inhibitor (1) reacts with chymotrypsin (written as EH) in a
matter of minutes in neutral solution; the introduction of one molar
proportion of the phosphorus-containing moiety derived from the
inhibitor completely abolishes enzymic activity. Thus the chemical

modification of but one group on the enzyme suffices to inactivate it; such experiments form the basis for the idea of 'active sites' in enzymes. Moreover, none of the amino acids in chymotrypsin reacts under these conditions, neither does chymotrypsinogen, nor does denatured chymotrypsin.[†] Hence native chymotrypsin contains one group with enhanced reactivity towards the inhibitor. This group may be regarded as a nucleophilic reagent, as the P-F link breaks so that both of the formerly shared pairs of electrons depart with the fluorine atom. If no migration of the phosphoryl residue occurs, the reactive group may be identified by enzymic hydrolysis of the phosphorylated protein and detection of the phosphorylated amino acid: for this purpose the di-isopropyl phosphorofluoridate is isotopically labelled. Serine turns out to be the amino acid which is phosphorylated; the serine forms part of the sequence:[‡]

...glycyl–aspartyl–seryl–glycyl–glycyl–prolyl–leucyl...

Part of this sequence also forms some of the active site in trypsin, and in choline esterases. Moreover, a most remarkable finding is that an enzyme that plays a part in carbohydrate metabolism also belongs to this class. This enzyme, phosphoglucomutase, catalyses the interconversion of glucose-1-phosphate (G-1-P) and glucose-6-phosphate (G-6-P); the enzyme is a phosphoric ester, and is written EP, and the reaction is[§]

$$G-1-P + E-P \rightleftharpoons G-1,6-diP + E \rightleftharpoons G-6-P + E-P$$

where G-1,6-diP stands for glucose-1,6-diphosphate. Note that the enzyme is dephosphorylated, and then phosphorylated again, during the course of the reaction. Here a serine residue is again the site of phosphorylation, and this serine forms part of a sequence similar to that given above;[||] the same may apply to another enzyme, phosphoglyceromutase.[††] These results suggest an underlying unity in the mode of action of these enzymes.[‡‡]

We now turn from the inhibition of chymotrypsin to its action as an esterase. Chymotrypsin catalyses the hydrolysis of *p*-nitrophenyl

† Balls and Jansen, *Adv. Enzymol.* 1952, **13**, 321.

‡ Oosterbaan, Kunst, van Rotterdam, and Cohen, *Biochim. Biophys. Acta*, 1958, **27**, 423.

§ Kennedy and Koshland, *J. Biol Chem.* 1957, **228**, 419; McCoy and Najjar, ibid. 1959, **234**, 3017.

|| Koshland and Erwin, *J. Amer. Chem. Soc.* 1957, **79**, 2657; but see Milstein and Sanger, *Biochem. J.* 1961, **79**, 456.

†† Pizer, *J. Amer. Chem. Soc.* 1958, **80**, 4431.

‡‡ Koshland, Ray, and Erwin, *Fed. Proc.* 1958, **17**, 1145; see also Bernhard and Orgel, *Science*, 1959, **130**, 625.

acetate. Detailed study of this reaction† reveals three steps. The first step is a very rapid formation of an enzyme-substrate complex. The next step is formation of an acetylated enzyme and liberation of p-nitrophenol. The third step is hydrolysis of the acetylated enzyme; this step regenerates the enzyme and liberates acetate ions:

$$CH_3 \cdot CO \cdot O \cdot C_6H_4 \cdot NO_2 + EH \underset{\longleftarrow}{\overset{fast}{\longrightarrow}} complex \xrightarrow{k \sim 3 \ sec.^{-1}} CH_3 \cdot CO \cdot E + HO \cdot C_6H_4 \cdot NO_2$$

$$H_2O \Big\downarrow k \sim 0 \cdot 02 \ sec.^{-1}$$

$$CH_3 \cdot COOH + EH$$

The main feature of this mechanism is that an acylated enzyme (here acetyl chymotrypsin) is an intermediate, as in the 'models' described above. Although the acetylated enzyme decomposes quite rapidly at pH 7, it is stable enough to be isolated at pH 5.‡ The position of the acetyl group was determined by methods analogous to those described for the phosphoryl group, and the result was similar: the same serine residue appears to be acylated both in the phosphorylation by the inhibitor and the acetylation by the substrate.§ The connexion between inhibition and reaction is also shown by the preparation of other acyl chymotrypsins: trimethylacetyl chymotrypsin is sufficiently stable to be crystallized; like acetyl chymotrypsin it is itself inactive, but treatment with hydroxylamine, or increase in the pH of a solution to above 7, restores enzymic activity.‖

The regeneration of the (active) chymotrypsin from acetyl chymotrypsin, the second stage in the enzymic cycle, has been studied under various conditions. A particularly interesting result is that the high reactivity of acetyl chymotrypsin (towards hydroxylamine) disappears in urea solution, but is regained on removal of the urea.†† Now the highly coiled (tertiary) structure of proteins is partially disoriented in urea solution, and so the loss in reactivity of acetyl chymotrypsin in urea shows that the coiled structure is necessary for the functioning of the catalytic cycle. The 'active site' around serine is thus not the whole story; the critical placement of several groups in a readily deformed structure is essential for enzymic activity. This suggests that a group

---

† Hartley and Kilby, *Biochem. J.* 1954, **56**, 288; Gutfreund and Sturtevant, ibid. 1956, **63**, 656; *Proc. Nat. Acad. Sci.* 1956, **42**, 719; Spencer and Sturtevant, *J. Amer. Chem. Soc.* 1959, **81**, 1874.

‡ Balls and Wood, *J. Biol. Chem.* 1956, **219**, 245.

§ Oosterbaan and van Aldrichen, *Biochim. Biophys. Acta*, 1958, **27**, 423.

‖ McDonald and Balls, *J. Biol. Chem.* 1957, **227**, 727.

†† Dixon, Dreyer, and Neurath, *J. Amer. Chem. Soc.* 1956, **78**, 4810.

which is held near to the reactive serine in the coiled structure is more distant in the uncoiled structure. There is some evidence that this group is the glyoxaline ring of a histidine residue.

The rate of both the measurable steps in the hydrolysis of p-nitrophenyl acetate catalysed by chymotrypsin varies with the pH in a way that suggests that a group of pK about 7 plays a part: when this group is protonated, the activity disappears. The value of this pK is comparable with the values found for histidine and peptides of histidine. The importance of the glyoxaline residue is also suggested by the fact that on reaction of chymotrypsin with 1-fluoro-2,4-dinitrobenzene the rate of substitution on one glyoxaline parallels the loss in enzymic activity.†

We now have to consider how far these observations can be held to account for the action of chymotrypsin in catalysing the hydrolysis of p-nitrophenyl acetate. The main feature is the high nucleophilic reactivity of the hydroxyl group of the serine that is acylated. This was an unexpected result, since a hydroxyl group is not normally so reactive. Indeed, we might just as well speak of the enzyme being activated as the substrate. Now the reactivity of the hydroxyl group would be enhanced if hydrogen bonding operated to deprotonate the incoming group, and to protonate the outgoing one:

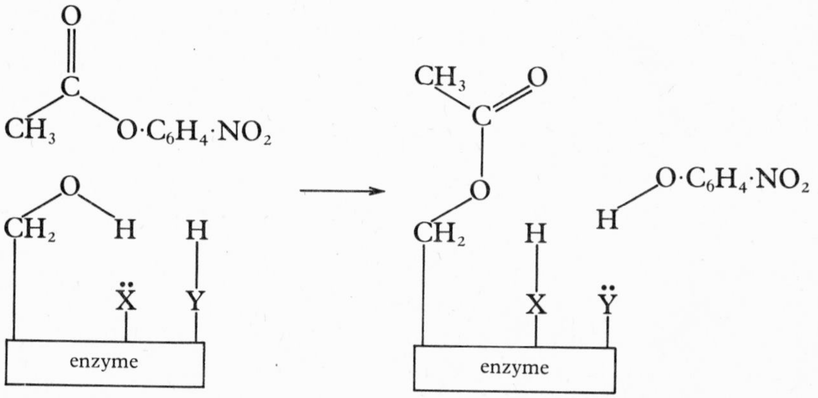

Thus, the hydrogen bonding would both increase the electron-donating tendency of the entering oxygen atom, and the electron-attracting tendency of the leaving oxygen atom; both effects aid reaction. The tertiary nitrogen of the glyoxaline ring could abstract the proton from the serine hydroxyl; activation would result from a hydrogen bond in

† Whitaker and Jandorf, *J. Biol. Chem.* 1956, **223**, 751.

the transition state which is appreciably stronger than in the enzyme-substrate complex. A similar cycle can be postulated for hydrolysis of the acylated enzyme: the leaving oxygen atom this time is the oxygen atom of the serine hydroxyl group and the entering oxygen atom that of water. As the transition states in both these reactions will contain a carbonyl group in some configuration between the trigonal and tetrahedral, preferential hydrogen bonding in the transition state may be possible in both the acylation and the hydrolysis step of the enzyme reaction. Similarly, when glyoxaline catalyses acyl transfer reactions, its action has been ascribed to a combination with a proton of the attacking reagent.†

It will be seen that our picture of the action of chymotrypsin on p-nitrophenyl acetate is incomplete and tentative. And so far we have not mentioned the substrates which are most readily attacked by chymotrypsin, such as N-acetyltyrosine ethyl ester (2), or the amide (3), which are cleaved to N-acetyltyrosine.‡ The ester (2) is hydrolysed in

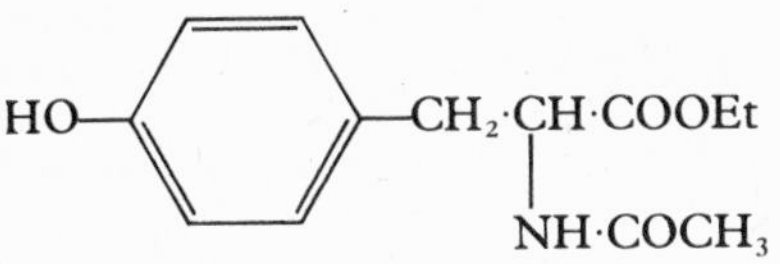

$$HO-\!\!\!\bigcirc\!\!\!-CH_2\cdot CH\cdot COOEt$$
$$|$$
$$NH\cdot COCH_3$$

(2)

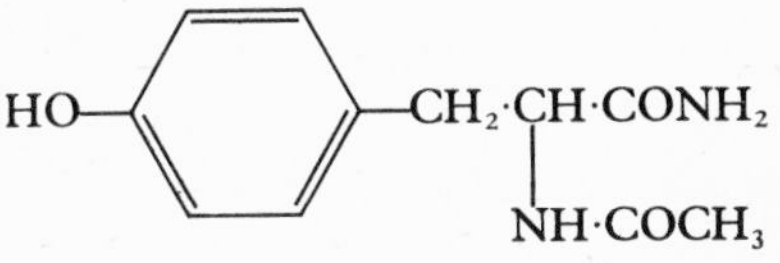

$$HO-\!\!\!\bigcirc\!\!\!-CH_2\cdot CH\cdot CONH_2$$
$$|$$
$$NH\cdot COCH_3$$

(3)

the presence of chymotrypsin much more rapidly than p-nitrophenyl acetate is; in fact, p-nitrophenyl acetate can be used as an inhibitor of the hydrolysis of (2), which suggests that we may carry over our knowledge of the active site to the reactive substrates.§ Moreover, it appears here that enzymic specificity is rather a result of the rates of the later steps in the reaction than of preferential formation of the initial enzyme-substrate complex. The amide (3) is hydrolysed about 1,000 times more slowly than the ester (2); the common intermediate, the N-acetyltyrosyl chymotrypsin, is formed relatively slowly from the amide.

One of the features which differentiates the proteolytic enzyme, ficin, from chymotrypsin is that structurally similar amides and esters (4) and (5) are hydrolysed at the same rate by ficin. Now esters are more easily hydrolysed non-enzymically than are amides and so the simplest interpretation is that, in the ficin-catalysed hydrolysis, esters and amides

† Jencks and Carriulo, J. Biol. Chem. 1959, 234, 1272, 1280.
‡ Foster and Niemann, J. Amer. Chem. Soc. 1955, 77, 1886.
§ Spencer and Sturtevant, ibid. 1959, 81, 1874; Gutfreund and Hammond, Biochem. J. 1959, 73, 526.

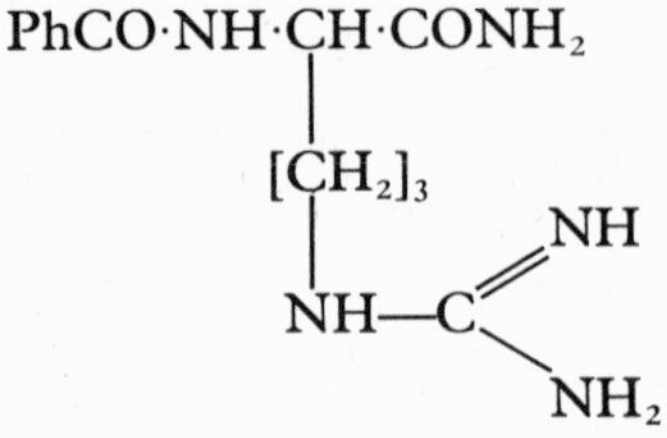

PhCO·NH·CH·CONH₂   PhCO·NH·CH·COOEt

$$PhCO\cdot NH\cdot CH\cdot CONH_2 \qquad\qquad PhCO\cdot NH\cdot CH\cdot COOEt$$
$$[CH_2]_3 \qquad\qquad\qquad\qquad\qquad [CH_2]_3$$

(4) 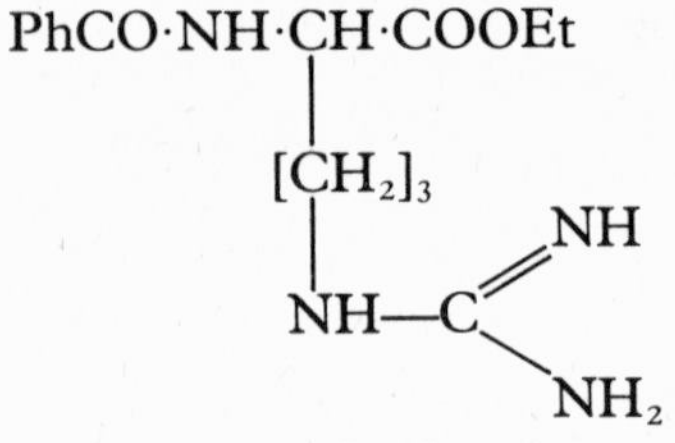   (5)

form a common intermediate whose hydrolysis is the rate-determining step.

Ficin is completely inhibited by one molar proportion of methyl-mercuric hydroxide, but the activity is restored by 2,3-dimercapto-propanol. These results suggest that a thiol group is necessary for enzymic activity. The common intermediate formed by esters and amides may thus be a thiol ester. The rate-determining step is then the hydrolysis of this thiol ester. Kinetic evidence suggests that an ionized carboxyl group, and an ionized amino group, play a part in the rate-determining step, which may thus be tentatively represented as:

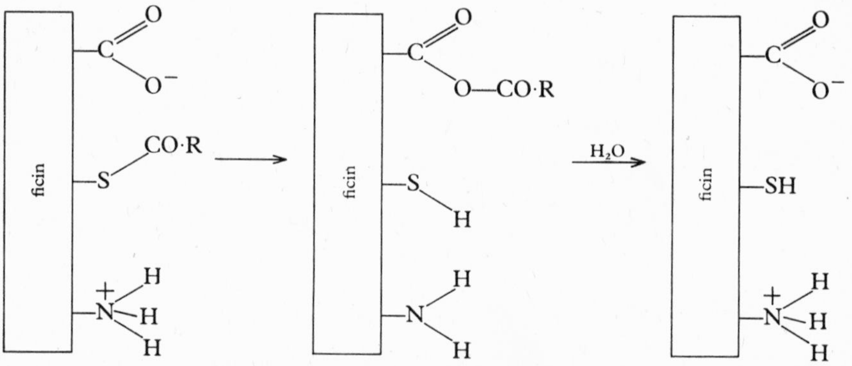

Here the carboxyl ion is shown as an intramolecular nucleophilic catalyst (as in the hydrolysis of methyl hydrogen phthalate, § 1 *g*). The fact that the acylated enzyme is relatively stable is consistent with the efficiency of ficin as a transfer enzyme.†

Another proteolytic enzyme, papain, closely resembles ficin, and has been extensively investigated. An interesting property of papain is that

† Bernhard and Gutfreund, *Biochem. J.* 1956, **63**, 61; Hammond and Gutfreund, ibid. 1959, **72**, 349.

proteolytic breakdown (about one-third of the molecule is removed) fails to destroy the enzymic activity.[†]

The main conclusion from the detailed studies on these proteolytic enzymes is that there is evidence for the intermediate formation of an acyl enzyme in a number of instances; the acyl enzyme is probably an ester (acylated serine, 6) in some cases and a thiol ester (acylated cysteine, 7) in others:

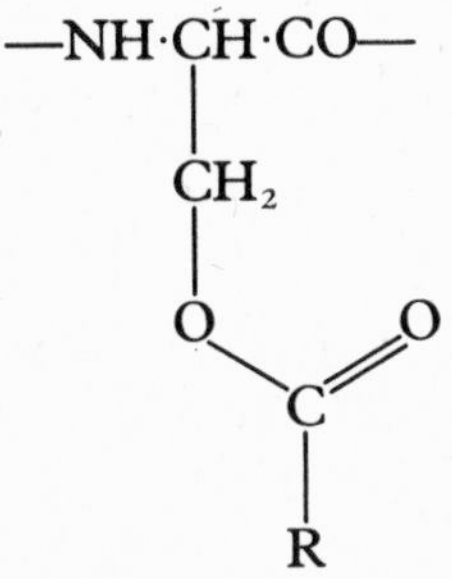

(6) 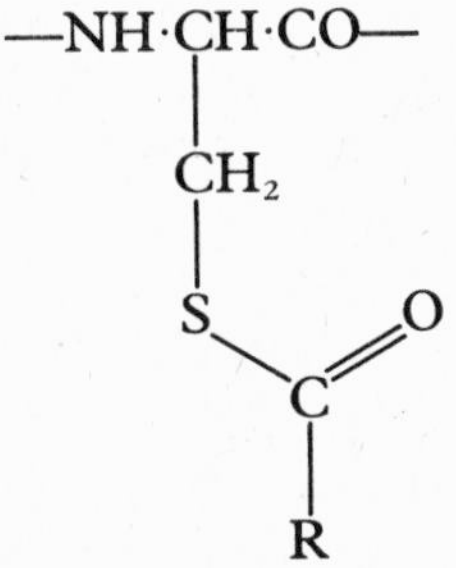   (7)

We now turn to acetylcholine esterases,[‡] which catalyse the reaction:

$$\overset{+}{Me_3N} \cdot CH_2 \cdot CH_2 \cdot O \cdot COMe + H_2O \longrightarrow \overset{+}{Me_3N} \cdot CH_2 \cdot CH_2OH + HO \cdot COMe$$

There are in fact several classes of enzyme which catalyse the hydrolysis of acetylcholine, but we shall only be concerned with the class which plays a part in conduction along nerve fibres.

Acetylcholine is not greatly different in reactivity from ordinary esters: it is hydrolysed more rapidly by alkali, but more slowly by acid, than ethyl acetate, as might be expected from the presence of the positively charged group in the molecule.[§] The same effect is observed, to a more marked extent, in other esters where a positive charge is nearer to the carbonyl carbon atom.[‖]

Much of what has been said about chymotrypsin applies also to acetylcholine esterase. Thus, acetylcholine esterase is inhibited by di-isopropyl phosphorofluoridate, and the inhibition results in the phosphorylation of the hydroxyl group of a serine residue. However,

---

[†] Smith, *J. Biol. Chem.* 1958, **233**, 1392; *Adv. Enzymol.* 1957, **19**, 267; Hill and Smith, *J. Biol. Chem.* 1958, **231**, 117.

[‡] Nachmansohn and Wilson, *Adv. Enzymol.* 1951, **12**, 259; Davies and Green, ibid. 1958, **20**, 283; Bergmann, *Adv. Catalysis*, 1958, **10**, 130.

[§] Butterworth, Eley, and Stone, *Biochem. J.* 1953, **53**, 30.

[‖] Bell and Lindars, *J. Chem. Soc.* 1954, p. 4601.

acetylcholine esterase differs from chymotrypsin in being (reversibly) inhibited by quaternary ammonium salts. Kinetic evidence suggests that these salts inhibit by competing with the substrate (which is, of course, also a quaternary ammonium salt) for a negatively charged 'site' on the enzyme. Furthermore, there is an optimum concentration of substrate, and the rate drops off at higher substrate concentrations, i.e. excess substrate also inhibits the enzyme.

The variation of the rate with pH can be interpreted on the basis that two groups play a part in the reaction; one has a pK of about 7, has to be deprotonated, and has been taken to be the glyoxaline ring of a histidine residue. The other group has a pK of about 9, and has to be protonated; this might be the hydroxyl group of a tyrosine residue.

Thiol esters, and phenyl esters, can also serve as substrates for the enzyme, and with these substrates the rate is constant in the range of pH 8 to pH 11, i.e. the group of pK 9 no longer plays a part in the reaction. If we assume that the role of this group is to donate a proton to the departing group, then it seems reasonable that the participation of the group with pK 9 should no longer be necessary with these substrates, as the anions corresponding to thiols and phenols are better leaving-groups than alkoxide ions.

2. (a) *Hydrolysis of esters of phosphoric acid*

The esters of phosphoric acid, like the esters of carboxylic acids, can undergo hydrolysis by acyl-oxygen, or alkyl-oxygen, fission (1):

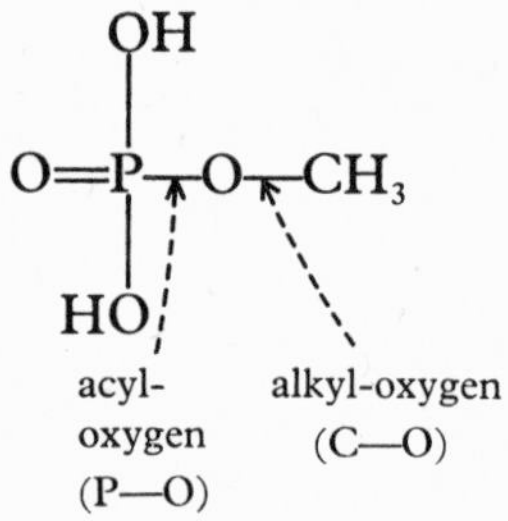

Here the two mechanisms are more simply described as phosphorus-oxygen (P—O), or carbon-oxygen (C—O), fission. Both mechanisms have been detected in a number of examples, including enzymic reactions. The relative rates turn out to be more delicately balanced than in the hydrolysis of carboxylic esters, so that P—O fission and C—O fission are both common reactions.

Some general remarks about phosphates may be useful at this stage.†
Triethyl phosphate (2) is considerably more stable towards alkali than
the analogous diethyl carbonate (3): another difference is that the
carbonate is not miscible with water, but the phosphate is. The P—O
group in (2) confers water-solubility on the molecule. The mono- and
di-esters of phosphoric acid are ionized and carry a negative charge in
alkaline solution and are not at all readily attacked by alkali. The
negative charge in (inorganic) pyrophosphate also confers stability on
the ion; tetra-alkyl pyrophosphates are also relatively stable in water,
but are readily hydrolysed by alkali.

The polar character of the P=O bond in, say, the methyl hydrogen
phosphate anion may be expressed by the formula (4). The molecule
may be considered to be mesomeric between this formula, and (5) and (6):

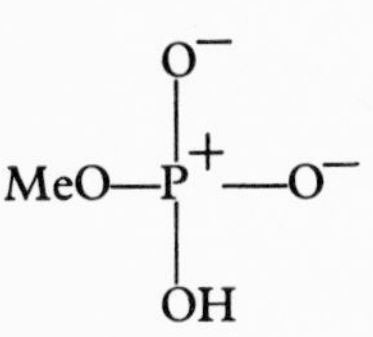

(4) 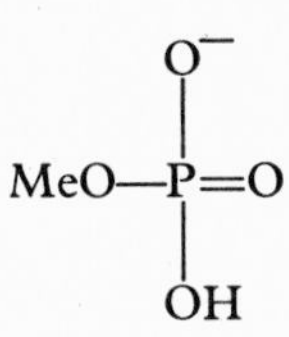   (5) 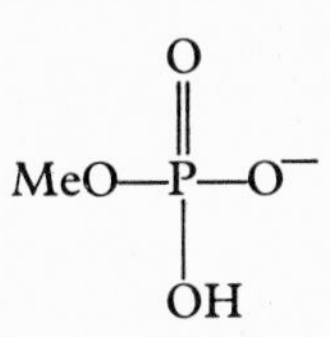   (6) 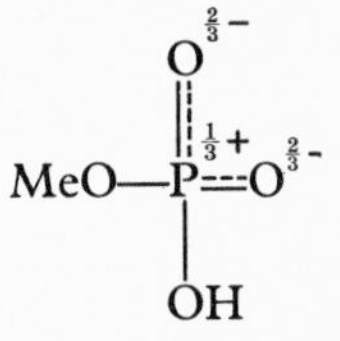   (7)

phosphorus is not restricted to a maximum covalency of 4 (Chapter I,
§ 1 e). If each of these formulae were equally satisfactory as a representation, then the final charge distribution would be as in (7), which
is nearly the same as that calculated by Grabe.‡ It should be noted that
the four oxygen atoms are tetrahedrally disposed about the phosphorus
atom.

The course of the hydrolysis of phosphate esters is characteristically
affected by the pH of the solution, because the substrate can ionize.
A mono-ester, such as methyl phosphate, is a dibasic acid, which can
ionize as shown:

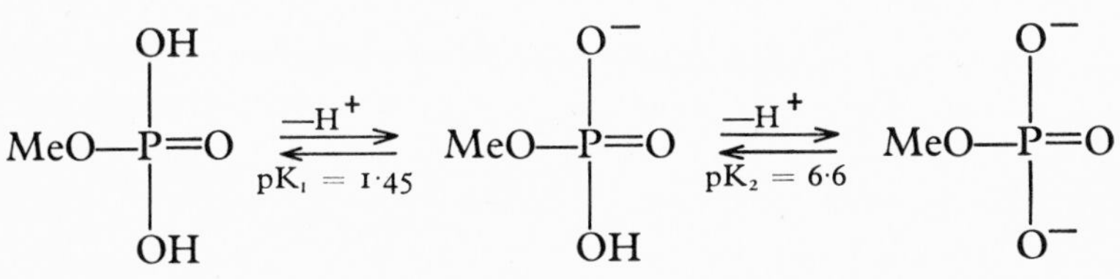

neutral form   mono-anion   di-anion

† Hartley, in *Phosphoric Esters*, Chemical Society Special Publication No. 8, p. 33,
Chemical Society, 1957; van Wazer, *Phosphorus and its Compounds*, Interscience, 1958.
‡ Grabe, *Biochim. Biophys. Acta*, 1958, **30**, 560.

Now the hydrolysis of methyl phosphate shows a well-marked pH optimum: the rate is over twice as great at pH 4 as it is at pH 1 or pH 7 (Fig. 27). This immediately suggests that in this range it is the mono-anion which is undergoing hydrolysis, for this species will predominate at pH 4; at a higher pH there will be more di-anion, and at a lower pH, more of the neutral form.†

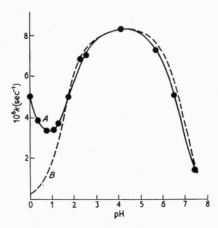

Fig. 27. The variation in the rate of hydrolysis of methyl phosphate with pH. A, experimental; B, calculated. (From Bunton, Llewellyn, Oldham, and Vernon, $J.\ Chem.\ Soc.$ 1958, p. 3574.)

The fraction of the total ester which is present as mono-anion at any pH is easily calculated as follows. The total concentration of ester is written as C, and the concentrations of neutral species, mono-anion and di-anion, as x, y, and z. Then if K_1 and K_2 are the ionization constants of the neutral species and mono-anion:

$$y[H^+]/x = K_1, \quad \text{or} \quad x = y[H^+]/K_1,$$
$$z[H^+]/y = K_2, \quad \text{or} \quad z = yK_2/[H^+].$$

Thus, since
$$x+y+z = C,$$
$$y(1+[H^+]/K_1+K_2/[H^+]) = C,$$

the fraction, y/C, present as mono-anion is given by
$$y/C = (1+[H^+]/K_1+K_2/[H^+])^{-1},$$
or
$$y/C = 1/\{1+10^{(pK_1-pH)}+10^{(pH-pK_2)}\}.$$

Differentiation shows that the maximum value of y/C is attained when the pH is equal to $(pK_1+pK_2)/2$, i.e. midway between the pK

† Bailly, $Bull.\ Soc.\ chim.\ France$, 1942, **9**, 405; Desjobert, ibid. 1947, 809.

values. At this pH, as pK_1 and pK_2 are widely separated, virtually all the ester is present as mono-anion. The equation can be used to calculate the relative rate at other pH values, on the assumption that the mono-anion is the only form undergoing hydrolysis. The agreement between the observed values and the theoretical curve in Fig. 27 confirms the idea that the reactive species between pH 1 and pH 7 is mainly the anion.

This analysis is based on reaction with a neutral water molecule. The alternative possibility is reaction between a hydroxide ion and the neutral form of methyl phosphate. This alternative entails an improbably high value for the velocity constant.[†]

The next question is whether C-O fission or P-O fission occurs during the hydrolysis of the mono-anion of methyl phosphate. This question was answered by carrying out the hydrolysis in water containing $H_2^{18}O$, when it was found that the methanol formed was not isotopically enriched, but that the (inorganic) phosphate was. Hence hydrolysis occurs by P-O fission. Similarly, the hydrolysis of the phosphate (8) of an optically active alcohol proceeds at pH 4 with retention of configuration, and the P-O fission suggested by this result has been confirmed by the use of isotopes.[‡] Other examples are known, and it seems likely that the hydrolysis of monophosphates at pH 4 generally proceeds by P-O fission.

$$\text{MeO·CH}_2\text{·}\overset{\overset{\displaystyle H}{|}}{\underset{\underset{\displaystyle Me}{|}}{C}}\text{-O-}\overset{\overset{\displaystyle OH}{|}}{\underset{\underset{\displaystyle OH}{|}}{P}}\text{=O}$$

(8)

As the mono-anion is so much more reactive than the other form, both an ionized and an unionized hydroxyl group must be playing an important part in the reaction with a water molecule. One possible formulation[§] suggests that the function of the unionized hydroxyl group is to supply a proton to the leaving group, which will aid heterolysis of the P—O bond, while the ionized hydroxyl group acquires a proton from the approaching water molecule (cf. p. 236). The different

† Bunton, Llewellyn, Oldham, and Vernon, *J. Chem. Soc.* 1958, p. 3574.
‡ Butcher and Westheimer, *J. Amer. Chem. Soc.* 1955, **77**, 2420.
§ Vernon, in *Phosphoric Esters*, Chemical Society Special Publication No. 8, p. 17, Chemical Society, 1957; cf. Herr and Koshland, *Biochim. Biophys. Acta*, 1957, **25**, 219.

formulae written below are merely to aid representation and are not meant to imply that the reaction takes place in several stages:

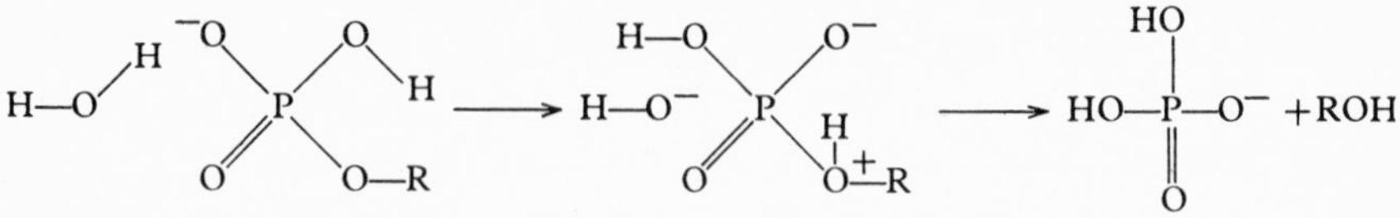

or, if we use bent arrows to symbolize the movements of pairs of electrons during the course of the reaction:

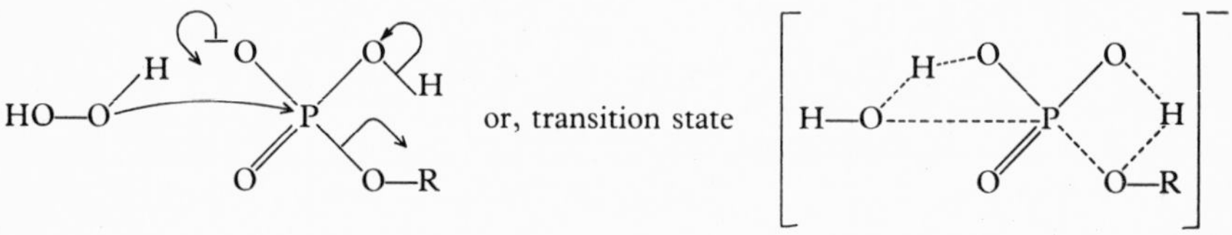

The discrepancy in Fig. 27 between the observed rate of hydrolysis of methyl phosphate and the rate calculated on the assumption that the mono-anion is the sole reactive species, shows that this assumption is not valid in strongly acidic solutions. Detailed investigations reveal, in fact, three other reactions.† One involves the unionized methyl phosphate and proceeds by C-O fission; this is presumably a nucleophilic substitution:

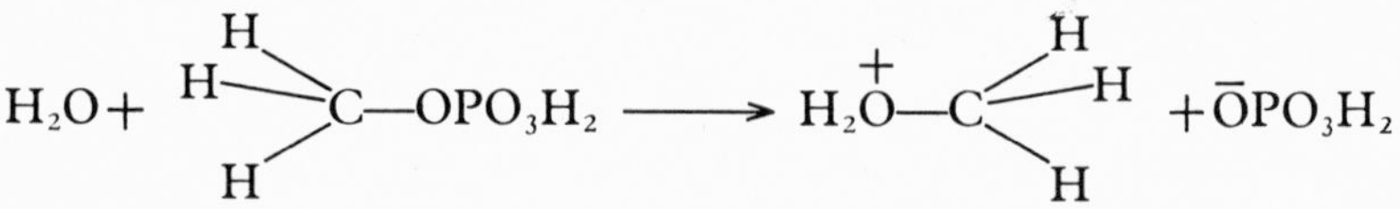

The other two reactions are acid-catalysed, and thus proceed via a protonated form of the substrate; the reactions are distinguished by the fact that one results in C-O fission, and the other in P-O fission. The former may be formulated as

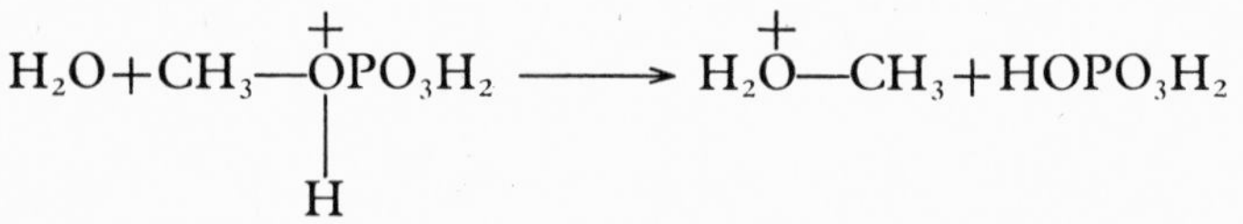

and the latter as

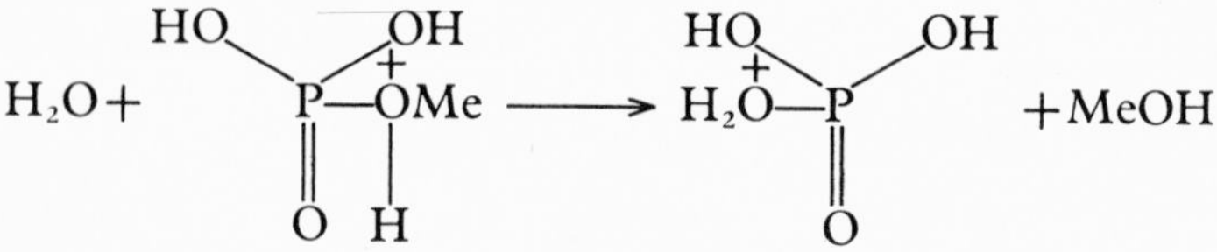

† Bunton, Llewellyn, Oldham, and Vernon, *J. Chem. Soc.* 1958, p. 3574.

These nucleophilic displacements on carbon and phosphorus here proceed at comparable rates.

Although ordinarily the rate of hydrolysis of monophosphates at pH 8 is very low (Fig. 27), metal ions catalyse the reaction. Thus 2-methoxy-1-methylethyl phosphate (8) is hydrolysed at pH 8·5 in the presence of lanthanum hydroxide gel.† In the hydrolysis of several other phosphates the rate depends on the extent of formation of a complex between the metal ion and the ester.‡ In these reactions the metal may play the same part as the proton does in the mono-anion.

The characteristic rate-pH profile shown in Fig. 27 is not seen in the hydrolysis of α-D-glucose-1-phosphate,§ where the rate of hydrolysis increases from pH 4 to pH 1. The decomposition of the neutral molecule is here so rapid (about 3,000 times as rapid as that of the mono-anion) that, as the pH is lowered from pH 5 to pH 1, the increased proportion of neutral molecules is the dominant factor in governing the shape of the pH-rate profile. As in the hydrolysis of methyl phosphate, the hydrolysis of the mono-anion proceeds by P-O fission, and of the neutral molecule by C-O fission. The rate of hydrolysis of the mono-anion is similar to the rate for the mono-anion of methyl phosphate, but the rate of hydrolysis of the neutral molecule of α-D-glucose-1-phosphate is about 10^5 as fast as the rate for the neutral molecule of methyl phosphate. Thus the special feature in the hydrolysis of glucose-1-phosphate is ready C-O fission.

The reaction is probably unimolecular:

$$R\!-\!OPO_3H_2 \longrightarrow R^+ + {}^-OPO_3H_2 \quad \text{rate-determining step}$$

$$R^+ + H_2O \longrightarrow R\overset{+}{O}H_2$$

$$R\overset{+}{O}H_2 + {}^-OPO_3H_2 \longrightarrow ROH + HOPO_3H_2$$

The ion, R^+, is mesomeric:

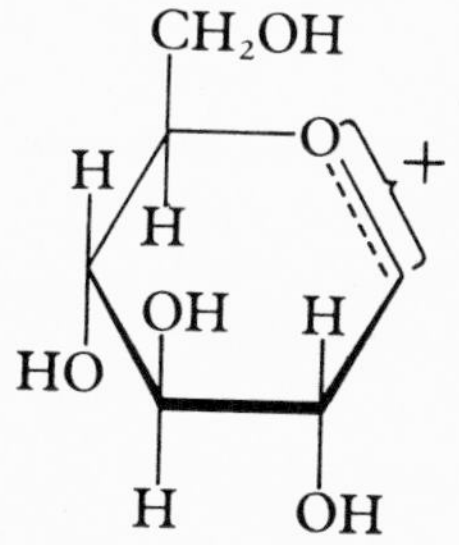

† Butcher and Westheimer, *J. Amer. Chem. Soc.* 1955, **77**, 2420.
‡ Bamann and Mütterlein, *Chem. Ber.* 1958, **91**, 1322.
§ Bunton, Llewellyn, Oldham, and Vernon, *J. Chem. Soc.* 1958, p. 3588.

The charge delocalization stabilizes the ion, and so may be held to account for the ready C-O fission, as in the high $S_N 1$ reactivity of chloromethyl ether (Chapter III, § 3 b).

As a mesomeric ion can only be formed from an aldose-1-phosphate, glucose-1-phosphate is much more labile in acid solution than is glucose-6-phosphate. However, the order of stability is reversed in alkaline solution.†

The rates of alkaline hydrolysis of cyclic phosphates containing a

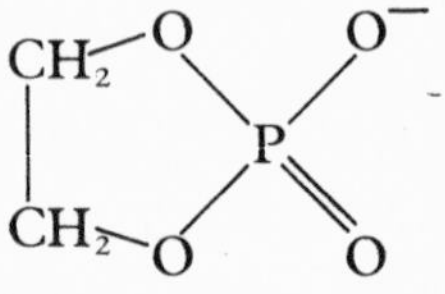

(9) 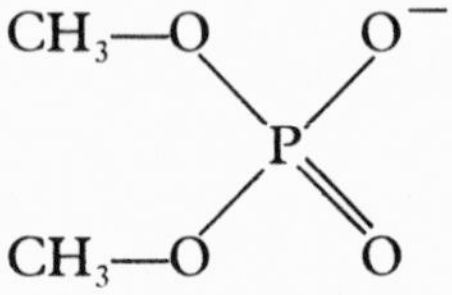   (10)

five-membered ring are surprisingly high. Thus ethylene phosphate (9) is hydrolysed about a million times as rapidly as dimethyl phosphate (10).‡ This high reactivity has yet to be accounted for. Cyclic phosphates may be readily formed from some phosphoric esters containing a hydroxyl group in the right position for forming a five-membered ring, by a reaction of the type

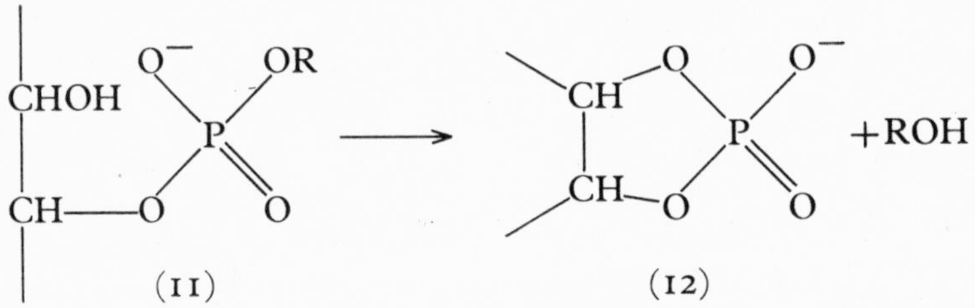

(11)   (12)

This is the reason for ribonucleic acids (but not deoxyribonucleic acids) being attacked by alkali.§ The nucleic acids are polynucleotides, and it is a phosphodiester group, as in (11), which provides the link between the nucleotide units; on formation of the cyclic phosphate (12), the internucleotide link is broken. The intervention of a cyclic intermediate

---

† Leloir, *Fortsch. chem. Org. Naturstoffe*, 1951, **8**, 47; Foster and Overend, *Quart. Rev.* 1957, **11**, 61.

‡ Westheimer, in *Phosphoric Esters*, Chemical Society Special Publication No. 8, p. 1, Chemical Society, 1957.

§ Brown and Todd, *J. Chem. Soc.* 1952, p. 52; Lipkin, Talbert, and Cohn, *J. Amer. Chem. Soc.* 1954, **76**, 2871; Markham and Smith, *Biochem. J.* 1952, **52**, 552.

probably occurs in the conversion of α- into β-glycerophosphate in acid
solution:[†]

(b) *Phosphatases.* There are many enzymes that catalyse the hydrolysis or transfer of phosphoric esters. Now, one of the main features of
the non-enzymic hydrolyses of phosphates that have just been described
was that these esters might undergo either P-O or C-O fission. This
feature is exploited in enzymic reactions and leads, for example, to
glucose-1-phosphate being utilized either for phosphoryl or for glucosyl
transfer. In the non-enzymic reactions the two mechanisms (P-O and
C-O fission) often proceed concurrently. In the enzymic reactions the
nature of the enzyme decides which mode of fission is selected. One of
the virtues of phosphates, then, is to present to an enzyme two bonds
of comparable strength: the enzyme then discriminates.

The hydrolysis of α-D-glucose-1-phosphate in water enriched with
$H_2{}^{18}O$, catalysed by either 'acid' or 'alkaline' phosphatase, leads to
orthophosphate enriched with ${}^{18}O$: the reactions thus proceed by P-O
fission.[‡] The same mode of fission is also found for enzymes which
hydrolyse adenosine triphosphate, and for those ('kinases') which catalyse its transfer reactions (Chapter III, § 7).[§] These are all, in a sense,
phosphate-transferring enzymes; a phosphoryl group is transferred to
a second substrate (sometimes water). The reactions may thus be
regarded as acylations.

The same substrates (e.g. glucose-1-phosphate) may take part in
reactions of a different kind, such as reactions catalysed by phosphorylases, e.g.

α-D-glucose-1-phosphate+fructose → sucrose+orthophosphate.

Here C-O fission was demonstrated, and this glucosyl transfer may be
regarded as an alkylation.

Sucrose transglucosylase (sucrose phosphorylase), which catalyses

† Bailly, *Bull. Soc. chim. France*, 1942, **9**, 314.
‡ Cohn, *J. Biol. Chem.* 1949, **180**, 771; Bunton, Silver, and Vernon, *Proc. Chem. Soc.*
1957, 348.
§ Cohn, *Biochim. Biophys. Acta*, 1956, **20**, 92.

the reaction written above, was the enzyme for which isotope incorporation from labelled orthophosphate, in the absence of 'acceptor', was
first demonstrated.[†] This method has since been widely used in studying
enzymic reactions,[‡] and the results have led to the idea that many
enzymes form new covalent bonds during the course of the reactions
they catalyse. In the original experiment the enzyme (sucrose transglucosylase), glucose-1-phosphate, and radioactive orthophosphate
$(KH_2{}^{32}PO_4)$ were incubated together, in the absence of the 'acceptor',
fructose; the glucose-1-phosphate then became radioactive. This indi-
cates an exchange reaction:

$$\text{glucose-1-phosphate} + H\,{}^{32}PO_4^{--} \rightleftarrows \text{glucose-1-}{}^{32}PO_4 + HPO_4^{--}.$$

The exchange reaction was interpreted on the assumption that the
enzyme became glucosylated:

$$\text{glucose-1-phosphate} + \text{enzyme} \rightleftarrows \text{glucosyl-enzyme} + HPO_4^{--}$$

and

$$\text{glucosyl-enzyme} + H\,{}^{32}PO_4^{--} \rightleftarrows \text{glucose-1-}{}^{32}PO_4 + \text{enzyme}.$$

In chemical terms, the enzyme is functioning as a nucleophilic reagent,
and becoming alkylated; we say this because C-O fission of glucose-1-
phosphate occurs and as oxygen is more electronegative than carbon
the oxygen will depart with the electrons which previously bound the
carbon and oxygen atoms, and so the enzyme which promotes this
fission must supply electrons to the C-1 of the sugar phosphate.

In the presence of fructose the second stage is then another glucosyl
transfer:

$$\text{glucosyl-enzyme} + \text{fructose} \rightleftarrows \text{sucrose} + \text{enzyme}.$$

If we assume that each nucleophilic substitution inverts the configuration of C-1 of the glucose, then the overall result would be retention of
configuration, as is observed (cf. Chapter V, § 4).

It may be noted that sucrose transglucosylase does not catalyse the
hydrolysis of glucose-1-phosphate. Fructose is an acceptor, but water
is not. Water is a nucleophilic reagent of comparable reactivity to
fructose, and present at a high 'concentration', but it fails to react.
This type of result has led to the 'induced fit' theory of enzyme specificity.[§] Briefly, this theory stresses the point that the formation of an

[†] Doudoroff, Barker, and Hassid, *J. Biol. Chem.* 1947, **168**, 725.

[‡] Koshland, *Disc. Faraday Soc.* 1955, **20**, 142; Axelrod, *Adv. Enzymol.* 1956, **17**, 159;
Boyer, *Arch. Biochem. Biophys.* 1959, **82**, 387.

[§] Koshland, in *The Enzymes*, edited by Boyer, Lardy, and Myrbäck, vol. **1**, p. 305,
Academic Press, New York, 1959; *J. Cell. Comp. Physiol.* 1959, **54**, suppl. 1, 245.

enzyme-substrate complex will be attended by some reorganization of the mode of folding of the polypeptide chain of the enzyme. Since proteins are known to have easily deformable ('motile') structures in aqueous solution,† it seems very likely that the substrate should 'distort' the enzyme.

† Linderstrøm-Lang and Schellman, in *The Enzymes*, edited by Boyer, Lardy, and Myrbäck, vol. **1**, p. 443, Academic Press, New York, 1959.

FURTHER REACTIONS OF ACIDS AND THEIR DERIVATIVES

1. Amides

(a) *Formation of amides from esters.* Esters react with ammonia, or amines, a procedure often used to prepare amides, e.g.

$$\text{Me.COOMe} + \text{NH}_3 \rightleftarrows \text{Me.CO.NH}_2 + \text{MeOH}.$$

Although the reaction is reversible, a 90 per cent. yield of acetamide is obtained at room temperature, even in methanolic solution;† since the reaction is exothermic, amide formation is favoured by low temperatures.

Carboxylic acids, however, do not readily react with ammonia or amines to form amides, unless the water formed is removed by distillation. Amide formation might be expected, because in reaction (i) (esterification) the equilibrium is not unfavourable, and in reaction (ii) the equilibrium is on the side of the amide:

$$\text{RCOOH} + \text{MeOH} \rightleftarrows \text{RCOOMe} + \text{H}_2\text{O} \qquad \Delta G \sim 0 \qquad \text{(i)}$$

$$\text{RCOOMe} + \text{NH}_3 \rightleftarrows \text{RCONH}_2 + \text{MeOH} \qquad \Delta G < 0 \qquad \text{(ii)}$$

Sum: $\quad \text{RCOOH} + \text{NH}_3 \rightleftarrows \text{RCONH}_2 + \text{H}_2\text{O} \qquad \Delta G < 0$

The sum of reactions (i) and (ii) represents the formation of an amide from a carboxylic acid and ammonia. These two reactions are chosen so as to get an idea of the apparent thermodynamic feasibility of forming an amide, starting from an acid and ammonia.‡ The reaction would be feasible were it not for ionization. Even at the most favourable pH

$$\text{RCOOH} + \text{NH}_3 \rightleftarrows \text{RCOO}^- + \text{NH}_4^+$$

(about 7) only about 1 per cent. of each species is in the unionized form, and the equilibrium constant for amide formation becomes unfavourable.

The reaction of methyl phenylacetate with ammonia is accelerated by the addition of methoxide ions, and retarded by the addition of ammonium ions.§ Similarly, in the reaction of ethyl formate with butylamine,

---

† Baltzly, Berger, and Rothstein, *J. Amer. Chem. Soc.* 1950, **72**, 4149.

‡ Compare Brenner, Muller, and Pfister, *Helv. Chim. Acta*, 1950, **33**, 568; Linderstrøm-Lang, *Lane Medical Lectures*, p. 97, Oxford University Press, 1952.

§ Betts and Hammett, *J. Amer. Chem. Soc.* 1937, **59**, 1568.

the main term in the kinetic equation† is of the form [ester][amine]$^{\frac{3}{2}}$. Thus these reactions are base-catalysed. A probable mechanism,‡ which accounts for these findings, involves an intermediate which may decompose either by a unimolecular reaction or a bimolecular reaction with a base (B):

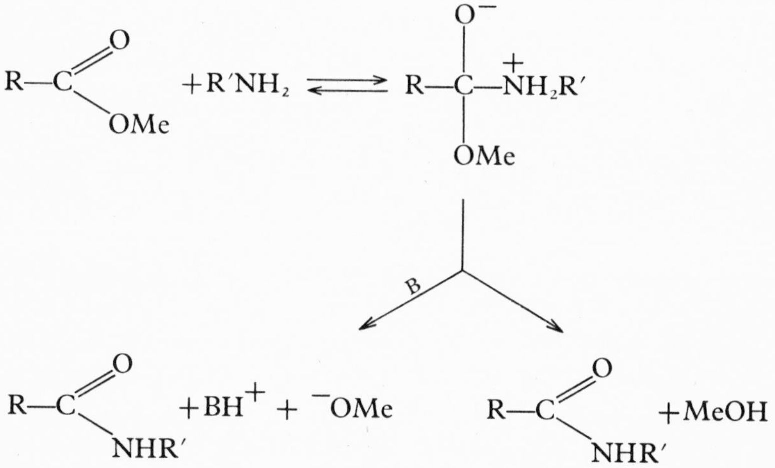

$$
R-C\underset{OMe}{\overset{O}{\big<}} \ +R'NH_2 \ \rightleftharpoons \ R-\underset{OMe}{\overset{O^-}{\underset{|}{\overset{|}{C}}}}-\overset{+}{N}H_2R'
$$

$$
\xrightarrow{\quad B \quad}
$$

$$
R-C\underset{NHR'}{\overset{O}{\big<}} \ +BH^+ + \ ^-OMe \qquad R-C\underset{NHR'}{\overset{O}{\big<}} \ +MeOH
$$

This mechanism is similar to that put forward for the reaction of esters with hydroxide ions, except that there the decomposition of the intermediate was not base-catalysed.

(b) *Hydrolysis of amides.* Amides resemble esters in being hydrolysed more readily by bases than by acids. The mechanism of the hydrolysis of amides and esters is probably similar; thus in the hydrolysis of carbonyl-labelled benzamide (Ph.C^{18}O.NH$_2$) in alkaline solution, isotopic exchange accompanies hydrolysis,§ which suggests that there is an intermediate (1) containing two hydroxyl groups:

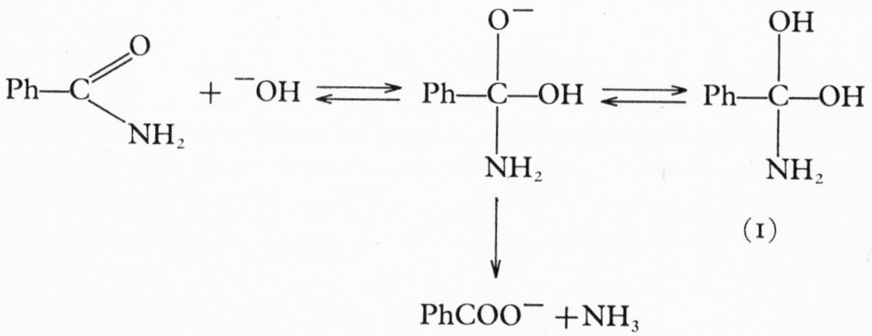

$$
Ph-C\underset{NH_2}{\overset{O}{\big<}} \ + \ ^-OH \ \rightleftharpoons \ Ph-\underset{NH_2}{\overset{O^-}{\underset{|}{\overset{|}{C}}}}-OH \ \rightleftharpoons \ Ph-\underset{NH_2}{\overset{OH}{\underset{|}{\overset{|}{C}}}}-OH
$$

(1)

$$
\downarrow
$$

$$
PhCOO^- + NH_3
$$

† Watanabe and Defonso, ibid. 1956, **78**, 4542.
‡ Bunnett, in *Theoretical Organic Chemistry*, p. 144, Butterworths, 1959.
§ Bender and Ginger, *J. Amer. Chem. Soc.* 1955, **77**, 348.

In acid solution, however, the hydrolysis of amides is no longer accompanied by isotopic exchange. The mechanism may still be analogous to that put forward for the acid-catalysed hydrolysis of esters:

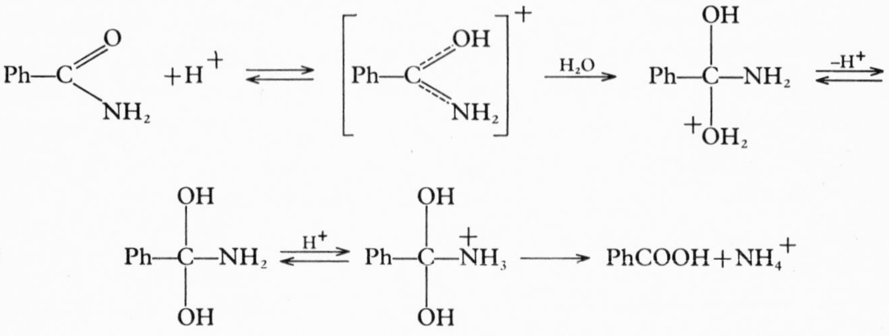

(I)

Isotopic exchange can only take place if the top hydroxyl group in (1) (corresponding to the carbonyl group of the amide) is protonated; but as amines are much more basic than alcohols, it will be the amino group which is protonated (as shown), and this results in hydrolysis without exchange. Some details of the mechanism are, however, uncertain.

Thus, the protonated form of benzamide has been written with the newly acquired proton on the oxygen atom, and not on the nitrogen atom. This form would be expected to be more stable (Chapter VI, § 1 d), but the experimental evidence is conflicting;[†] indeed, both forms may be present.[‡]

The rate of the acid-catalysed hydrolysis of substituted benzamides in dilute acid is little affected by the nature of the substituent. The same result was obtained in the acid-catalysed hydrolysis of esters (Chapter VI, § 1 d). In both cases this is a consequence of the fact that electron-withdrawing substituents in the benzene ring will disfavour protonation, but favour attack by the water molecule. However, in strongly acid solution, amides, which are appreciably basic, are almost completely protonated. Hence, in strongly acid solution, the only effect of the substituents in substituted benzamides is upon the ease of attack by the water molecule, and so electron-withdrawing substituents increase the rate ($\rho = +1$).[§]

[†] Frankel and Niemann, Proc. Nat. Acad. Sci. 1958, 44, 688; Huisgen and Brade, Chem. Ber. 1957, 90, 1432; Spinner, Spectrochim. Acta, 1959, p. 95.

[‡] Klages and Zange, Annalen, 1957, 607, 35; Berger, Loewenstein, and Meiboom, J. Amer. Chem. Soc. 1959, 81, 62.

[§] Leisten, J. Chem. Soc. 1959, p. 765; Duffy and Leisten, ibid. 1960, p. 853.

An interesting effect of the basicity of amides on the rate of acid hydrolysis is that there is an optimum acidity for the medium: thus acetamide is hydrolysed more rapidly in 4N-HCl than in 3N- or 5N-HCl. Below 4N-HCl acetamide is incompletely protonated; above 4N-HCl the effective concentration of water apparently diminishes.†

The hydrolysis of phthalamic acid (2) shows a number of differences from the hydrolysis of benzamide (cf. Chapter VI, § 1 g). The rate of hydrolysis of phthalamic acid is independent of the pH between pH 1 and pH 3, and is about a million times larger than the rate of hydrolysis of the *para*-isomer (3), at pH 3.‡ Thus there is a special mechanism permitting ready hydrolysis of the *ortho*-isomer (2) which is independent of the supply of hydrogen ions. Now the special structural feature in phthalamic acid is that there is a carboxyl group near to the amide group, and this carboxyl group can supply a proton to the amide group: the protonated amide can then be attacked by the nucleophilic carboxyl anion:

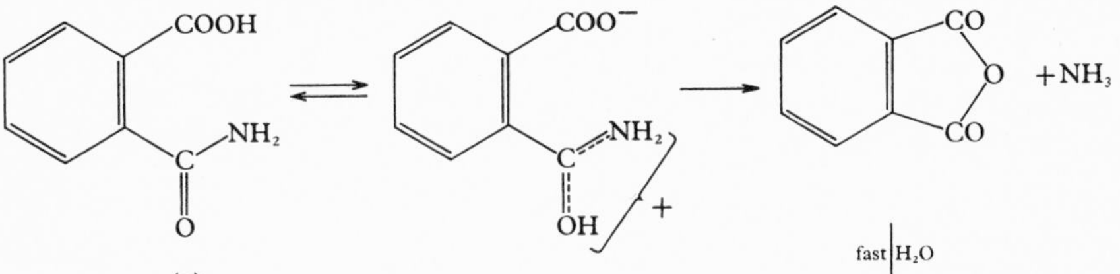

(2)

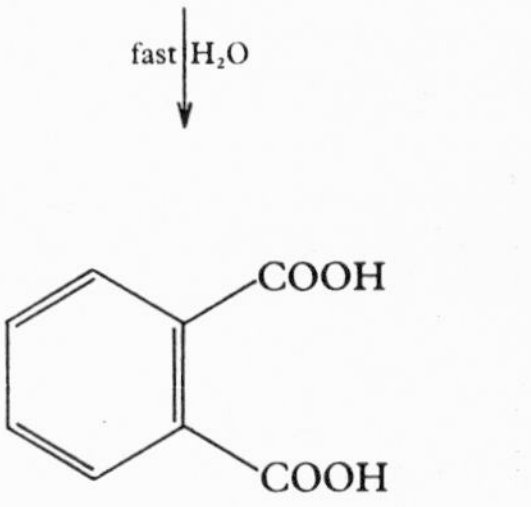

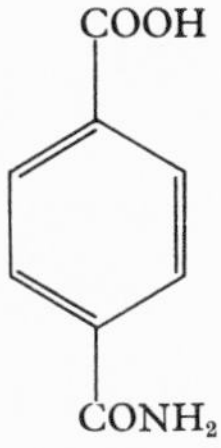

(3)

This type of mechanism may also apply to the hydrolysis of N-butylacetamide catalysed by acetic acid:§

$$CH_3 \cdot COOH \rightleftharpoons CH_3 \cdot COO^- + H^+$$

$$H^+ + CH_3 \cdot CO \cdot NHBu \rightleftharpoons CH_3 \cdot C(\overset{+}{O}H) \cdot NHBu \xrightarrow{CH_3 \cdot COO^-} CH_3 \cdot CO \cdot O \cdot CO \cdot CH_3 + BuNH_2$$

$$2CH_3 \cdot COOH$$

† Edward and Meacock, ibid. 1957, pp. 2000, 2007, 2009.
‡ Bender, Chow, and Chloupek, *J. Amer. Chem. Soc.* 1958, **80**, 5380.
§ Wyness, *J. Chem. Soc.* 1958, p. 2934.

On this basis the acetic acid has a twofold function: it supplies a proton to the amide group, and then the nucleophilic acetate ion combines with the electrophilic protonated amide.

(c) *Hydrolysis of peptides.* This is a field that has been explored in width rather than in depth: there are many comparative studies of the hydrolysis of various peptides, but few detailed investigations of the mechanism. One point of difference from simpler amides is that with peptides the rate of hydrolysis is not maximum at a given acidity, but increases steadily as the acid concentration is raised. This has been observed for piperazine-2,5-dione (1) (the simplest cyclic peptide), and for gelatin.† The presence of several amide groups has the effect of weakening the basicity of any one of them, so that even at high acidities the amide group is not completely protonated.

$$
\begin{array}{ccc}
 & \diagup \text{CO} \diagdown & \\
\text{NH} & & \text{CH}_2 \\
| & & | \\
\text{CH}_2 & & \text{NH} \\
 & \diagdown \text{CO} \diagup & \\
\end{array}
$$

(1)

The effect of the structure of a peptide on the rate of its hydrolysis can only be touched on.‡ One general point is that dipeptides (e.g. glycylglycine, 2) tend to be less readily hydrolysed than higher peptides; this can be attributed to the fact that the peptide bond is nearer to the positively charged amino group in dipeptides, and this proximity is unfavourable to proton uptake by the peptide:

$$
\overset{+}{\text{NH}_3}\cdot\text{CH}_2\cdot\text{CO}\cdot\text{NH}\cdot\text{CH}_2\cdot\text{COOH} \qquad \overset{+}{\text{NH}_3}\cdot\underset{|}{\text{CH}}\cdot\text{CO}\cdot\text{NH}\cdot\text{CH}_2\cdot\text{COOH} \qquad \overset{+}{\text{NH}_3}\cdot\text{CH}_2\cdot\text{CO}\cdot\text{NH}\cdot\underset{|}{\text{CH}}\cdot\text{COOH}
$$

$$
\qquad\qquad\qquad\qquad\qquad\qquad\qquad \text{CHMe}_2 \qquad\qquad\qquad\qquad\qquad\qquad\qquad \text{CHMe}_2
$$

(2)   (3)   (4)

(these formulae show the predominant forms in acid solution).

Amongst dipeptides, those containing valine are hydrolysed relatively slowly, and this effect is more marked with valylglycine (3) than glycyl-valine (4). The difference here is due to steric hindrance. The rate-determining step is presumably the attack of a water molecule on the

---

† Edward and Meacock, *J. Chem. Soc.* 1957, pp. 2007, 2009.

‡ Harris, Cole, and Pon, *Biochem. J.* 1956, **62**, 154, and references quoted there; Sanger, *Adv. Protein Chem.* 1952, **7**, 1; Leach, *Rev. Pure Appl. Chem.* (*Australia*), 1953, **3**, 25.

carbonyl carbon atom of the protonated peptide, and the bulky iso-propyl group is nearer to this carbon atom in (3) than in (4).

Another well-marked effect is the relative lability of peptide bonds in which the amino acids serine or threonine contribute the nitrogen atom; thus glycylserine (5) is five times as reactive as glycylalanine (6).

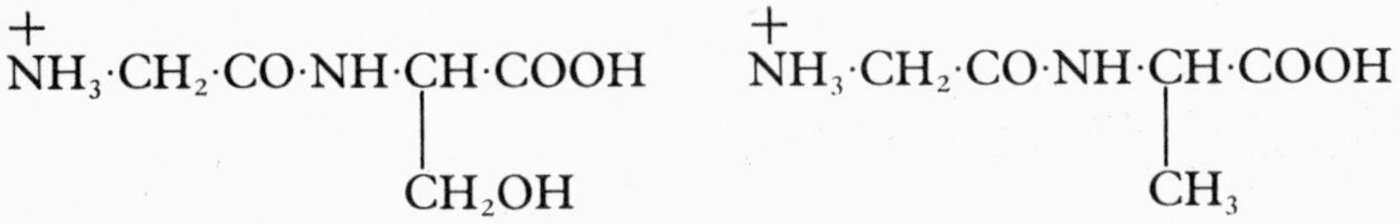

$$\overset{+}{NH_3}\cdot CH_2\cdot CO\cdot NH\cdot \underset{\underset{\displaystyle CH_2OH}{|}}{CH}\cdot COOH \qquad \overset{+}{NH_3}\cdot CH_2\cdot CO\cdot NH\cdot \underset{\underset{\displaystyle CH_3}{|}}{CH}\cdot COOH$$

$$(5) \hspace{4cm} (6)$$

This effect persists in proteins,† and is due to a rearrangement (Chapter VIII, § 5) in which the acyl group shifts from the nitrogen atom to the nearby oxygen (of the hydroxyl group of serine or threonine) to give an ester (7) which is then hydrolysed relatively readily:

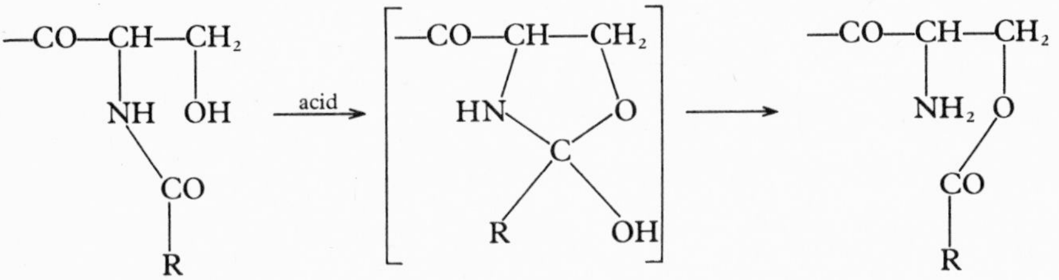

$$(7)$$

2. Decarboxylation and carboxylation

(a) *Decarboxylation of β-keto acids.* A decarboxylation is simply a reaction in which one of the products is carbon dioxide,

$$CH_3\cdot CO\cdot CH_2\cdot COOH \longrightarrow CH_3\cdot CO\cdot CH_3 + CO_2$$

$$(1)$$

and, conversely, in a carboxylation one of the reactants is carbon dioxide; the examples discussed here are those in which a carbon-carbon bond is broken. These reactions have been much studied‡ and they are important biologically since the carbon dioxide of the atmo-sphere is taken up by carboxylations and returned by decarboxylations. We shall discuss the mechanism of a few decarboxylations and then

† Elliott, *Biochem. J.* 1952, **50**, 542.
‡ Brown, *Quart. Rev.* 1951, **5**, 131.

comment on the structural features which are present in some bio-chemically important examples. β-Keto acids are probably the most important carboxylic acids which decarboxylate readily.

The first question concerning the decarboxylation of acetoacetic acid (1) is which form is the most reactive. There are, in fact, four possibilities: the unionized or anionic forms, and the keto (1) or enol forms (2).

$$CH_3 \cdot C{=}CH \cdot COOH \qquad\qquad CH_3 \cdot \underset{\underset{\displaystyle CH_3}{|}}{\overset{\overset{\displaystyle CH_3}{|}}{C}}{-}\underset{}{C} \cdot COOH$$

OH   O   CH₃

(2)   (3)

Argument by analogy helps us to make a choice. α,α-Dimethylaceto-acetic acid (3) cannot exist in an enolic form corresponding to (2), and it is decarboxylated rather more rapidly than acetoacetic acid,† and so it is probably the keto form which is reactive in acetoacetic acid itself. For both acids the unionized form is more reactive than the anion. For acetoacetic acid the unionized form is about fifty times as reactive as the anion,‡ so that in acid solution it will be mainly the unionized form which is undergoing reaction, but in neutral solution there is so little of the unionized form present that most of the reaction will proceed via the anion.

We now come to some experiments which throw light on the nature of the product first formed. When the decarboxylation of α,α-dimethyl-acetoacetic acid (3) is carried out in the presence of iodine, the rate of uptake of iodine is the same as the rate of carbon dioxide evolution.§ Neither the starting material (3) nor the final product (4) reacts with iodine under these conditions at an appreciable rate. Hence it must be

(4)   (5)

---

† Pedersen, *J. Amer. Chem. Soc.* 1929, **51**, 2098.
‡ Widmark, *Acta Med. Scand.* 1920, **53**, 393.
§ Pedersen, *J. Amer. Chem. Soc.* 1936, **58**, 240.

an intermediate which is reacting with iodine. This intermediate is probably the enol (5) (enols react rapidly with halogens, Chapter V, § 7 a). So the keto form of the β-keto acid reacts to give the enol form of the ketone, and the mechanism may be written†

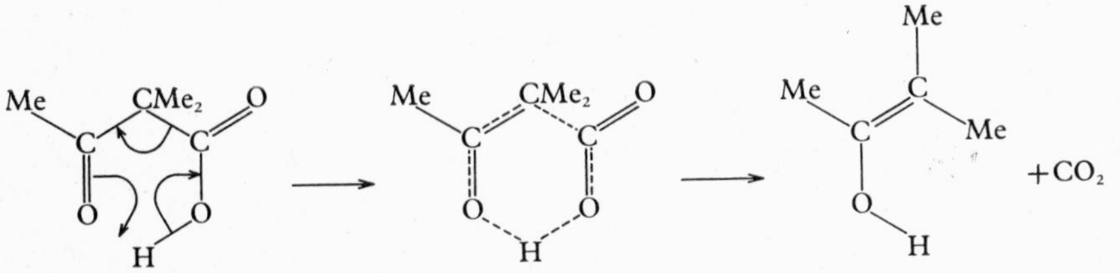

(3)   transition state   (5)

The same pattern holds for the decarboxylation of a β-keto-*di*-carboxylic acid. During the course of the decarboxylation of dimethyl-oxaloacetic acid (6) (at pH 5) an intermediate (7) is formed which absorbs strongly in the ultra-violet: the strong absorption is associated with the conjugated system

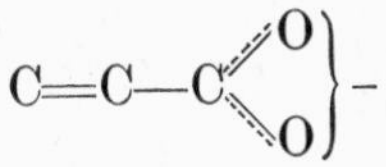

$$C=C-C\underset{\diagdown O}{\overset{\diagup O}{\Big\}} -$$

in the enol (7):‡

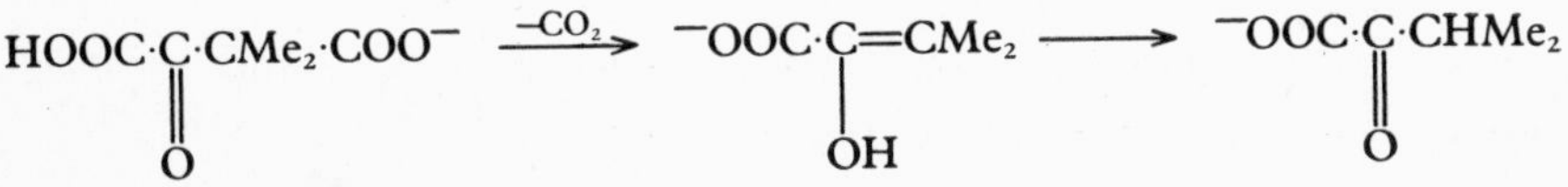

(6)   (7)

Catalysis by metal ions is a characteristic feature of the decarboxylation of dimethyloxaloacetic acid and also of oxaloacetic acid.§ These are dicarboxylic acids. The decarboxylation of β-keto acids containing only *one* carboxyl group, however, is not catalysed by metal ions. This difference is explained if the metal is bound both to the oxygen atom of the ketone group and the oxygen atom of the stable carboxyl group in the decarboxylic acids (e.g. (8)); binding of the metal to the would-be labile carboxyl group (as has to happen with β-keto-monocarboxylic acids) stabilizes the carboxyl group. The main route in the metal-ion catalysed decarboxylation of β-ketodicarboxylic acids is shown for the

† Westheimer and Jones, ibid. 1941, **63**, 3283.
‡ Steinberger and Westheimer, ibid. 1951, **73**, 429.
§ Pedersen, *Acta Chem. Scand.* 1952, **6**, 285; Gelles and Hay, *J. Chem. Soc.* 1958, p. 3673; Gelles and Salama, ibid., pp. 3683, 3689.

manganous-ion catalysed decarboxylation of oxaloacetic acid:

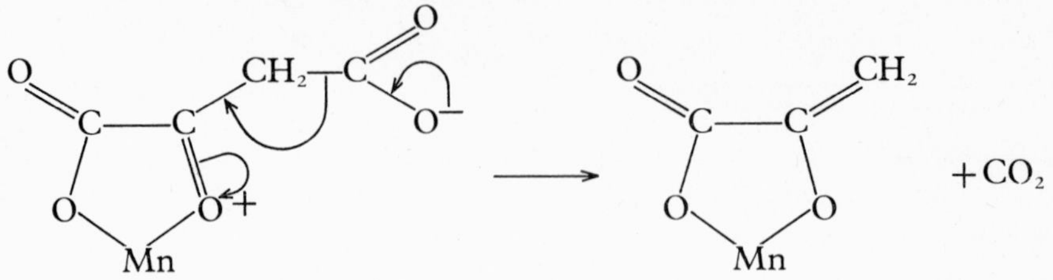

$$\text{(structure: oxaloacetate–Mn complex)} \longrightarrow \text{(structure: enolate–Mn complex)} + CO_2$$

(8)

In the ferric-ion catalysed decarboxylation of dimethyloxaloacetate the colour of the solution changes from yellow to blue, and then finally returns to yellow:

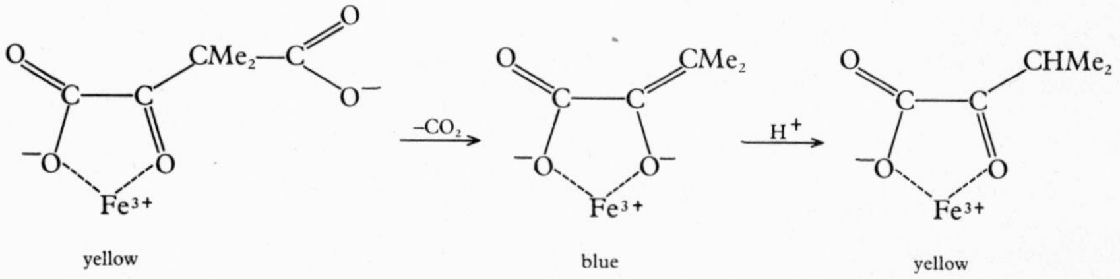

$$\text{(structure, } Fe^{3+}\text{)} \xrightarrow{-CO_2} \text{(structure, } Fe^{3+}\text{)} \xrightarrow{H^+} \text{(structure, } Fe^{3+}\text{)}$$

　　　yellow　　　　　　　　blue　　　　　　　　yellow

In these catalysed reactions the metal ion will attract electrons, and thus promote the carbon-carbon bond cleavage which takes place in such a way that an 'extra' pair of electrons has to find a region of low potential energy somewhere in the decarboxylated fragment, as shown by the bent arrows in (8).

　　Unlike metal ions, primary amines catalyse the decarboxylation of both mono- and dicarboxylic β-keto acids. It seems probable that the keto acid forms an imine (e.g. (9) from acetoacetic acid and aniline) which decarboxylates as shown.

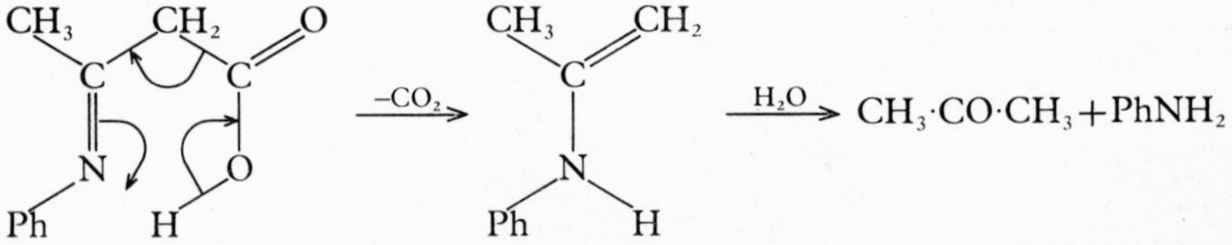

$$\text{(imine structure)} \xrightarrow{-CO_2} \text{(structure)} \xrightarrow{H_2O} CH_3 \cdot CO \cdot CH_3 + PhNH_2$$

(9)

　　Certain β-keto acids, e.g. ketopinic acid (10), do not decarboxylate readily. Now if the enol has to be formed on decarboxylation of a β-keto acid, here the enol (11) would be exceedingly unstable, as the four numbered atoms joined to the C=C system have to be coplanar. In other words, the C=C bond here would be very weak, as the stereo-chemistry of the 'caged' structure prevents the p-orbitals on the carbon atoms from overlapping adequately. In practice, molecules with double bonds in this sort of (bridgehead) position are not known, unless the rings are larger than they are here (Bredt's rule). Thus, we attribute the reluctance of the acid (10) to decarboxylate to the instability of the enol (11) which, hypothetically, would be formed.†

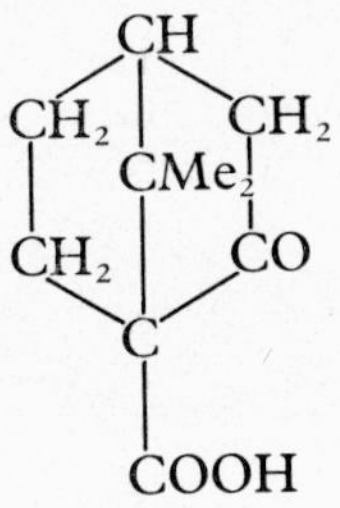

(10) 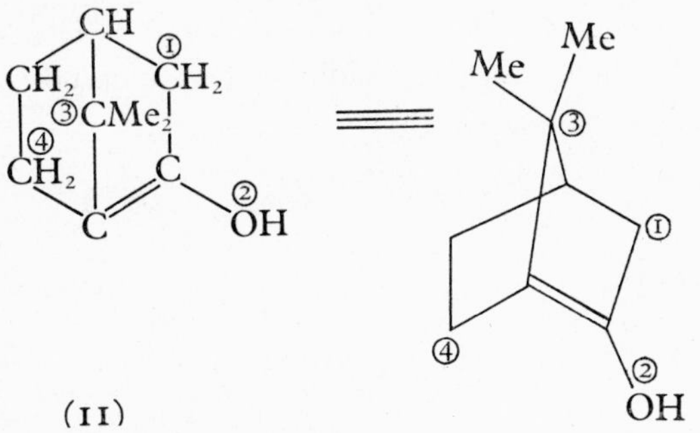   (11)

(b) *Decarboxylation of other acids.* The mechanism for the ready decarboxylation of β-keto acids containing the system (1) may be applied to other acids containing the more general system (2):

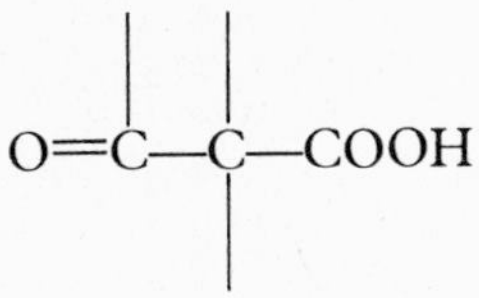

(1) 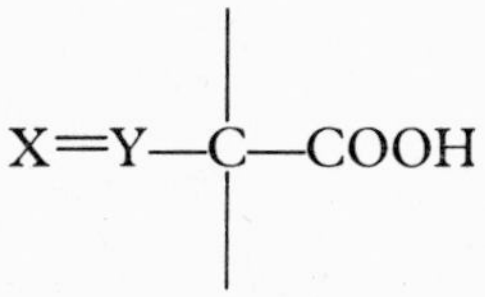   (2)

Of the two atoms symbolized by X, Y in (2), one may be carbon, as in (1), or both may be, as in (3), or neither may be, as in (4).

$$CH_2{=}CH{-}CMe_2{-}COOH$$

(3)   (4)

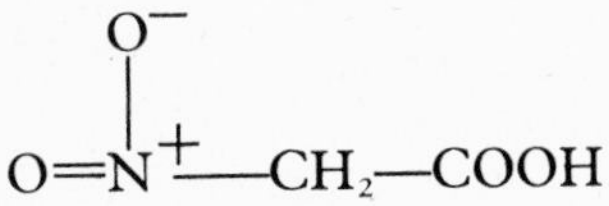

The decarboxylation of β,γ-unsaturated acids, e.g. (3), proceeds relatively easily, and is accompanied by a shift of the double bond.

† Wassermann, in Newman, *Steric Effects in Organic Chemistry*, p. 349, New York, Wiley, 1956. See also Bartlett and Knox, *J. Amer. Chem. Soc.* 1939, **61**, 3184.

In this example this shift cannot *precede* the loss of carbon dioxide. By analogy with β-keto acids the mechanism may be expressed:†

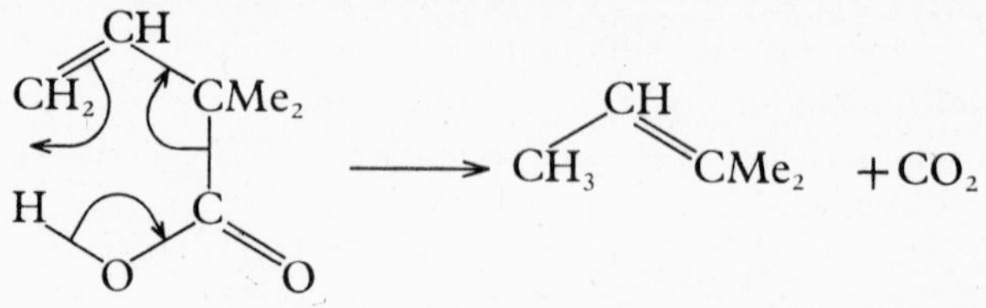

Another acid which contains the system (2) is the acid (5). This acid is stable in strongly acidic or alkaline solution, but loses carbon dioxide in neutral solution to give the base (6); furthermore the optically active acid gives racemic base.

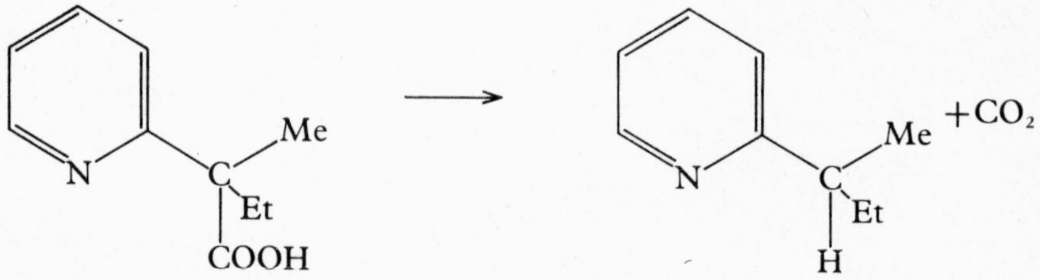

These observations are accounted for by the mechanism:

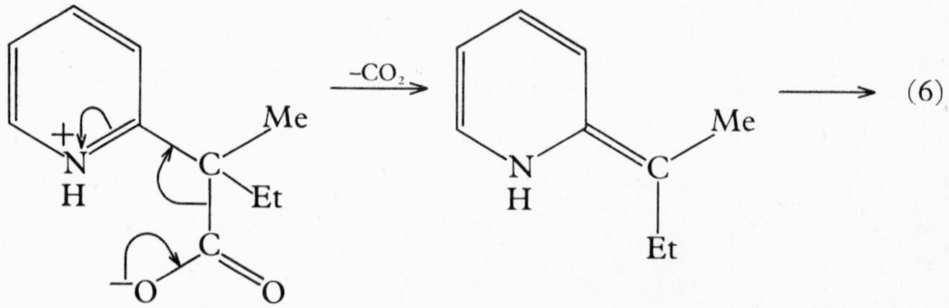

The dipolar form (7) will predominate only in neutral solution, and the asymmetric carbon atom in (7) loses its asymmetry in the intermediate (8).‡

† Arnold, Elmer, and Dodson, *J. Amer. Chem. Soc.* 1950, **72**, 4359.
‡ Doering and Pasternak, ibid., p. 143.

The carbanion transitorily formed on decarboxylation of certain pyridine and quinoline carboxylic acids can be trapped with an aldehyde, just as the enol from the decarboxylation of β-keto acids can be trapped with iodine. When quinaldinic acid (9) is heated with benzaldehyde, decarboxylation occurs, and some of the alcohol (10) is formed.†

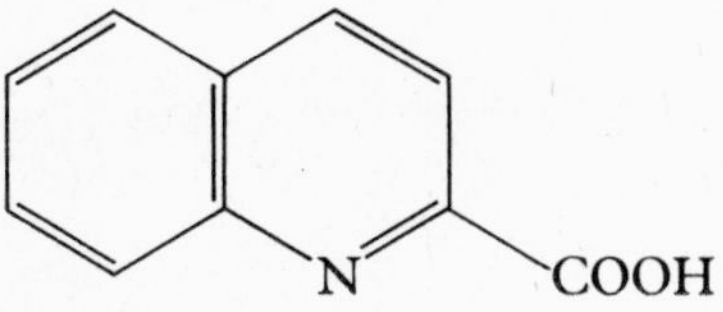

(9) 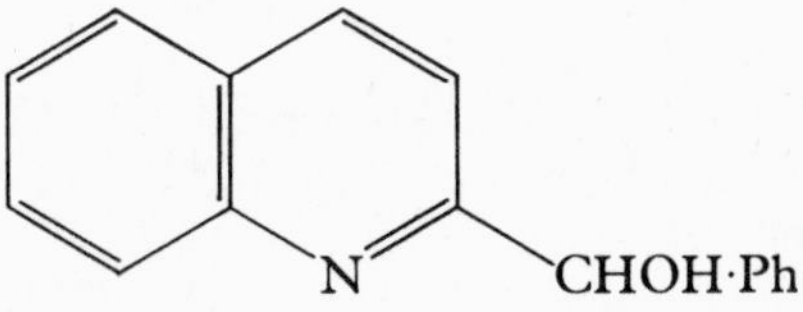   (10)

This result suggests that the carbanion (11) is first formed, and then adds to the carbonyl group of benzaldehyde; the dipolar form of (9) is taken to be the form undergoing decarboxylation:

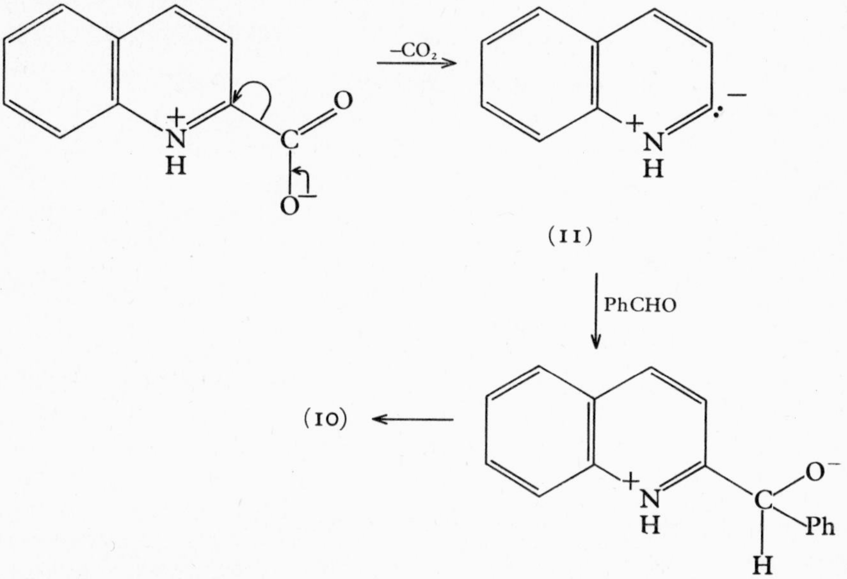

(11)

PhCHO

(10) ←

The ion (11) has been written with a negatively charged carbon atom with an unshared pair of electrons and a positively charged nitrogen atom, but the molecule will be mesomeric between this formula and one (12) containing divalent carbon. The same state of affairs is present

† Dyson and Hammick, *J. Chem. Soc.* 1937, p. 1724; Ashworth, Daffern, and Hammick, ibid. 1939, p. 809; Brown and Hammick, ibid. 1949, pp. 173, 659.

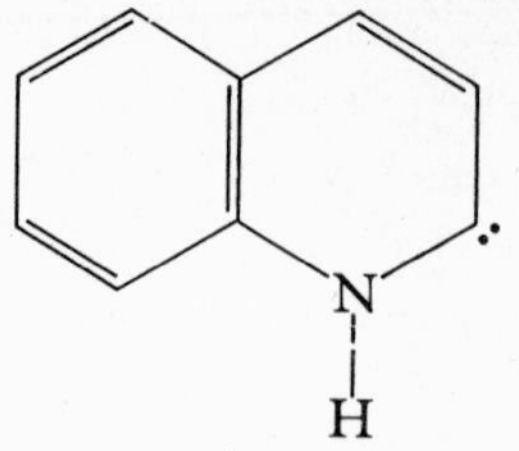

$$R\overset{+}{-}N\equiv\overline{C}\colon$$

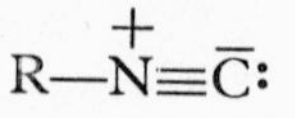

$$(13)$$

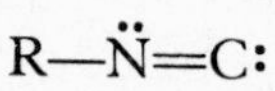

$$R-\overset{\cdot\cdot}{N}=C\colon$$

$$(14)$$

(12)

in alkyl isocyanides, mesomeric between (13) and (14). In both (13) and (14) the carbon has an unshared pair of electrons, but in (14) the nitrogen also has an unshared pair. Several of the properties (e.g. the bond dipole moment, Chapter I, § 2 a) of isocyanides indicate that (13) is the better representation: in other words, the system has a lower potential energy when as many electrons as possible (i.e. six) move for most of the time in the field of force of both nuclei.

The carbanion (11) is similar to the carbanion derived from thiazoles which was discussed in connexion with the reactions of thiamine in Chapter V (§ 11).

A quite different class of carboxylic acids, which decarboxylate readily, comprises the trihalogenoacetic acids (15)†

$$X_3C-COOH, \qquad X = F, \; Cl, \; or \; Br.$$

$$(15)$$

Here it is the anion which loses carbon dioxide as, under various conditions, the rate of decarboxylation parallels the extent of ionization. The halogen atoms are more electronegative than carbon, and the dipole favours the electron-recession accompanying decarboxylation.

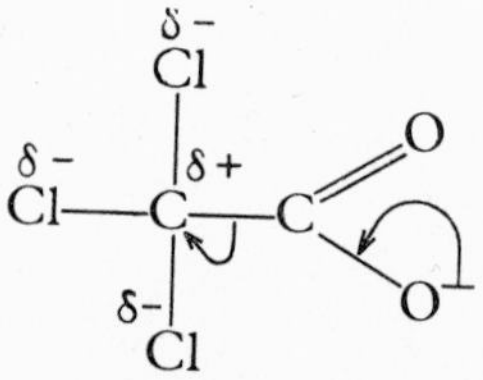

The decarboxylation of certain *ortho*-substituted benzoic acids (16) in strongly acid solution provides an example of 'steric acceleration'.‡

† Muus, *J. Phys. Chem.* 1935, **39**, 343; 1936, **40**, 121; Fairclough, *J. Chem. Soc.* 1938, p. 1186; Johnson and Moelwyn-Hughes, *Proc. Roy. Soc.* A, 1940, **175**, 118; Auerbach, Verhoek, and Henne, *J. Amer. Chem. Soc.* 1950, **72**, 299, and earlier papers.

‡ Schubert, Donohue, and Gardner, *J. Amer. Chem. Soc.* 1954, **76**, 9.

The rates of decarboxylation are in the order

$$R = \text{isopropyl} > R = \text{ethyl} > R = \text{methyl},$$

and it seems that the bulky *ortho*-groups weaken the bond between the (protonated) carboxyl group and the aromatic ring.

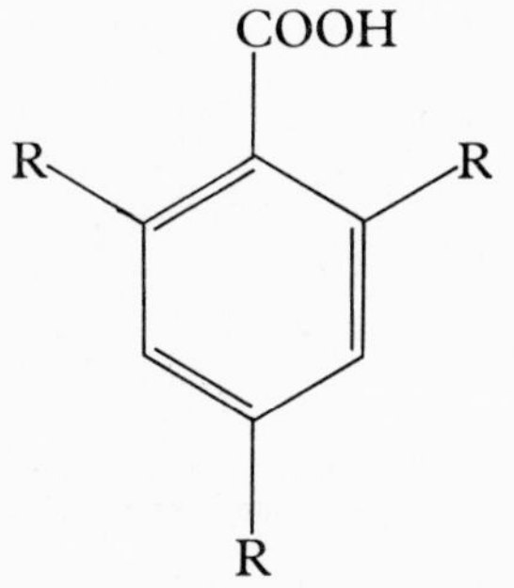

COOH

R⟍ ⟋R

R

(16)

(c) *Carboxylation.* The usual method of carboxylation is by way of an organometallic compound and carbon dioxide. In an organometallic compound containing an alkyl-metal bond the carbon is more electronegative than the metal, and so the alkyl group functions as a nucleophilic reagent. Thus, the reaction is formally similar to decarboxylation: in both the carbon atom of the alkyl group furnishes, or takes possession of, both the electrons which bind this carbon atom to the carboxyl group. The metal salts of phenols may also be carboxylated; thus sodium phenoxide reacts with carbon dioxide to give sodium salicylate.

(d) *Enzymic decarboxylation and carboxylation.* There are many enzymic reactions in which carbon dioxide is a reactant or a product.†
In most cases there is little knowledge of the mechanism of the enzymic reaction, but there are some interesting similarities between the enzymic and non-enzymic reactions. The main point concerns the nature of the substrates. The carboxylic acids which are the substrates for the enzymic decarboxylations usually contain a double bond β,γ to the carboxyl group, i.e. they contain the system (2) (p. 259). This double bond is between carbon and oxygen for a β-keto acid, or for malonyl-coenzyme A, or between two carbon atoms (e.g. in β-methylglutaconyl-coenzyme A), or between a nitrogen and a carbon atom in the anils from pyridoxal phosphate and amino acids which, for the purpose of this 'rule', are considered as the substrates for amino acid decarboxylases.

† Calvin and Pon, *J. Cell. Comp. Physiol.* 1959, **54**, suppl. 1, 51.

Now these are the types of compound which are prone to undergo non-enzymic decarboxylation, so that apparently the enzyme can only help to break a bond which was relatively easy to break in any case.

In two enzyme systems that are concerned with the decarboxylation of oxaloacetic acid, one aspect of the mechanism of enzymic reactions closely resembles the non-enzymic reaction. The non-enzymic reaction converts the keto form of the acid to the enol form of the ketone. An enzyme (from chicken liver) displays the same preference but here the enol is phosphorylated, and the nucleotides inosine triphosphate (ITP) and diphosphate (IDP) are also involved:

$$
\begin{array}{c}
\text{COOH} \\
| \\
\text{CO} \\
| \\
\text{CH}_2 \\
| \\
\text{COOH}
\end{array}
\quad +\text{ITP} \rightleftharpoons \quad
\begin{array}{c}
\text{COOH} \\
| \\
\text{C}-\text{OPO}_3\text{H}_2 \\
\| \\
\text{CH}_2
\end{array}
\quad +\text{CO}_2+\text{IDP}
$$

$$(\text{I})$$

Another enzyme (a wheat-germ extract) catalyses the reaction between phosphoenol pyruvic acid (1) and carbon dioxide to give oxaloacetic acid: nucleotides are not required for this carboxylation, and the equilibrium is over to the side of carboxylation.

The evidence that it is the keto form of oxaloacetic acid which loses carbon dioxide comes from experiments with isotopes.[†] In practice, the reaction is studied in reverse, and so the problem amounts to whether the keto or enol form of oxaloacetic acid is formed by the carboxylation of phosphoenolpyruvic acid. This problem is settled by enzymic reduction of the oxaloacetic acid in D_2O with reduced diphosphopyridine nucleotide (written as DPNH) as hydrogen donor (see Chapter V, § 18). If the enol form (2) of oxaloacetic acid were formed on carboxylation, then the subsequent reduction would give (3), and the keto form would give (4):

$$
\text{carboxylation to} \quad \text{HOOC·C}=\text{CH·COOH} \quad \xrightarrow[\text{in } D_2O]{\text{DPNH}} \quad \text{HOOC·C}-\text{CH·COOH}
$$

with OH below the first structure and $\text{H}\ \text{D}$ above, OD below the second structure.

$$\text{enol} \quad (2) \qquad\qquad\qquad\qquad\qquad (3)$$

† Vennesland, *Disc. Faraday Soc.* 1955, **20**, 240.

carboxylation to $\quad$ HOOC·C·CH$_2$·COOH $\quad \xrightarrow[\text{in D}_2\text{O}]{\text{DPNH}} \quad$ HOOC·C—CH$_2$·COOH
(with C=O, labelled keto) and (with C bearing H and OD)

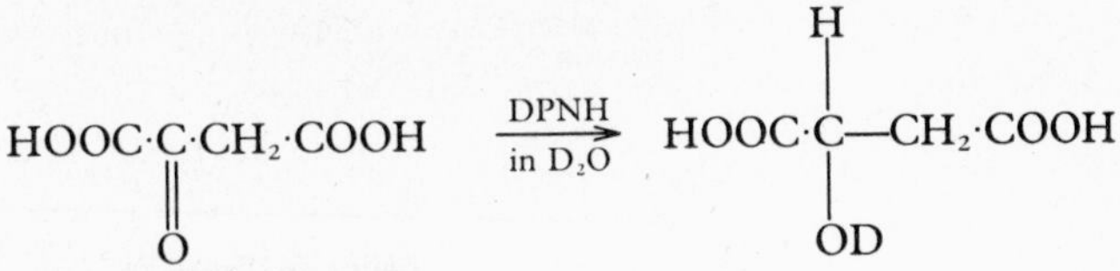

keto $\qquad\qquad\qquad\qquad\qquad$ (4)

Now in (4) the deuterium atom is on an oxygen atom, and so exchanges readily with the medium and is lost on brief exposure to H$_2$O; but in (3) there is stable, carbon-bound, deuterium. The experimental result was that the malic acid did not contain appreciable amounts of carbon-bound deuterium; hence the keto form of oxaloacetic acid is the product of the enzymic carboxylation. And so the reaction pattern

$$\text{keto form of keto-acid} \rightleftharpoons \text{enol form of ketone} + CO_2$$

seems to be common to both the enzymic and non-enzymic reactions.

Two further enzymes may be classed amongst those liberating carbon dioxide from β-keto acids: the 'malic' enzyme, and the 'isocitric' enzyme; both require triphosphopyridine nucleotide (TPN$^+$) and manganous ions.

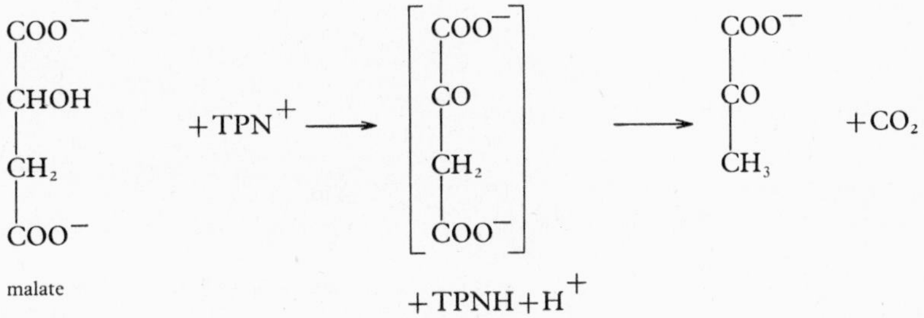

COO$^-$ / CHOH / CH$_2$ / COO$^-$ (malate) $+$ TPN$^+$ $\longrightarrow$ [COO$^-$ / CO / CH$_2$ / COO$^-$] $\longrightarrow$ COO$^-$ / CO / CH$_3$ $+CO_2$

$+$ TPNH $+$ H$^+$

and

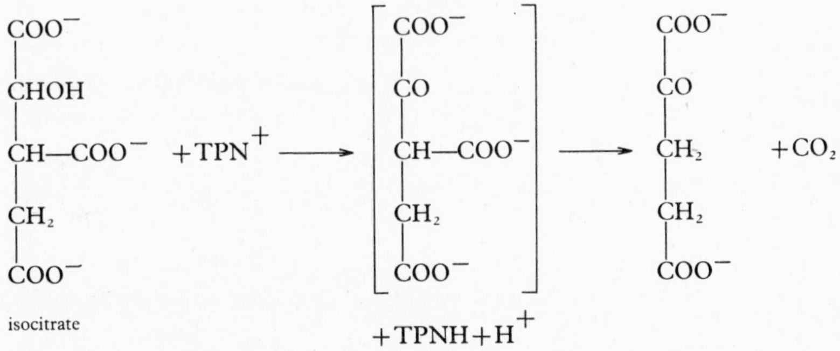

COO$^-$ / CHOH / CH—COO$^-$ / CH$_2$ / COO$^-$ (isocitrate) $+$ TPN$^+$ $\longrightarrow$ [COO$^-$ / CO / CH—COO$^-$ / CH$_2$ / COO$^-$] $\longrightarrow$ COO$^-$ / CO / CH$_2$ / CH$_2$ / COO$^-$ $+CO_2$

$+$ TPNH $+$ H$^+$

We shall discuss only the latter of these two enzymes, which has been purified and studied in detail,[†] but the main conclusions about the mechanism are probably applicable also to the 'malic' enzyme.

The reaction proceeds in two stages: the first, oxidation by TPN^+, is the slower; the second stage is decarboxylation of oxalosuccinate and it is only for this stage that manganous ions are necessary.

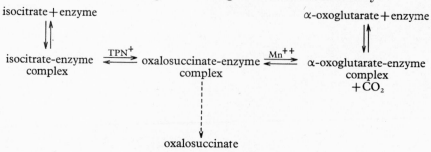

Free oxalosuccinate is only slowly liberated from the complex, so this slow side reaction is shown by a dotted line in the scheme set out above. Thus the intermediate, oxalosuccinate, in effect remains bound to the enzyme. We may surmise that there is a strong attraction between the labile carboxyl group in oxalosuccinate and the enzyme, so that only when the carboxylate ion is lost as carbon dioxide can the molecule become detached from the enzyme at all easily. It should be noted that this is one of the few examples where a single enzyme catalyses two quite separate types of reaction.

There are several other enzyme systems which catalyse the decarboxylation of oxaloacetic acid (5). The enzyme from *Micrococcus lysodeikticus*

$$HOOC \cdot CO \cdot CH_2 \cdot COOH \longrightarrow HOOC \cdot CO \cdot CH_3 + CO_2$$

$$(5)$$

requires divalent metal ions (preferably manganous or cadmium ions) for activity;[‡] metal ions also catalyse the non-enzymic reaction (§ 2 a), but the order of effectiveness of various metal ions differs in the enzymic and non-enzymic reactions. This does not necessarily indicate a difference in mechanism, as the relative activities of metal ions in enzymic reactions depend partly upon how tightly the metal ions are bound to different groups on the enzyme.[§] However, another enzyme (from rat

† Moyle and Dixon, *Biochem. J.* 1956, **63**, 548; Moyle, ibid., p. 552.

‡ Herbert, in *Methods of Enzymology*, edited by Colowick and Kaplan, vol. **1**, p. 753, Academic Press, New York, 1955.

§ Williams, in *The Enzymes*, edited by Boyer, Lardy, and Myrbäck, vol. **1**, p. 391, Academic Press, New York, 1959.

liver mitochondria), which catalyses the same reaction, is apparently inhibited by manganous ions.†

Finally, we may mention the enzymic reaction in photosynthesis whereby atmospheric carbon dioxide is incorporated.‡

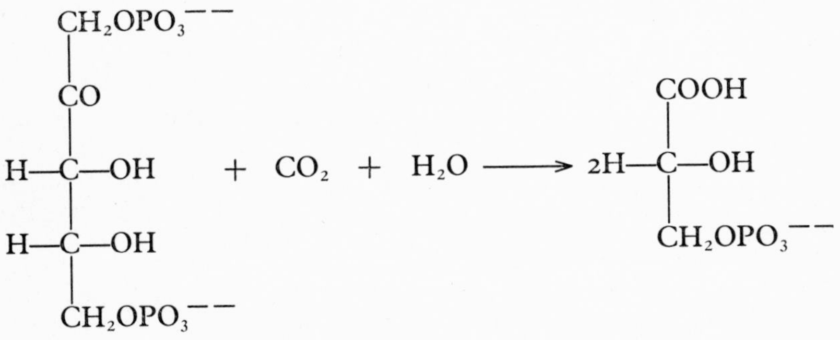

$$
\begin{array}{c}
CH_2OPO_3^{--} \\
| \\
CO \\
| \\
H-C-OH \\
| \\
H-C-OH \\
| \\
CH_2OPO_3^{--}
\end{array}
\quad + \ CO_2 \ + \ H_2O \ \longrightarrow \
2\,\begin{array}{c}
COOH \\
| \\
H-C-OH \\
| \\
CH_2OPO_3^{--}
\end{array}
$$

ribulose-1,5-diphosphate   3-phosphoglyceric acid

The mechanism may be similar to those discussed above if, as Calvin has suggested, an enol is carboxylated; the resulting β-keto acid would then suffer hydrolytic fission (see § 4 b):

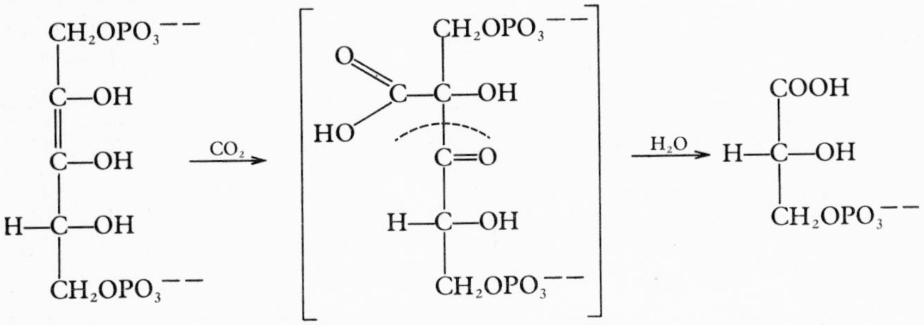

$$
\begin{array}{c}
CH_2OPO_3^{--} \\
| \\
C-OH \\
\| \\
C-OH \\
| \\
H-C-OH \\
| \\
CH_2OPO_3^{--}
\end{array}
\xrightarrow{\ CO_2\ }
\left[
\begin{array}{c}
CH_2OPO_3^{--} \\
| \\
\underset{HO}{\overset{O}{\diagdown\!\!C}}-C-OH \\
| \\
C=O \\
| \\
H-C-OH \\
| \\
CH_2OPO_3^{--}
\end{array}
\right]
\xrightarrow{\ H_2O\ }
\begin{array}{c}
COOH \\
| \\
H-C-OH \\
| \\
CH_2OPO_3^{--}
\end{array}
$$

3. Decarbonylation

A decarbonylation is a reaction in which one of the products is carbon monoxide. α-Keto esters, for example, on heating lose carbon monoxide; the use of isotopically-labelled carbon shows that the carbon monoxide is derived from the ester group in ethyl pyruvate.§ This pyrolysis is often a heterogeneous reaction, and necessarily involves the breaking

$$ CH_3-{}^{14}CO-COOEt \ \longrightarrow \ CH_3-{}^{14}COOEt \ + \ CO $$

† Corwin, *J. Biol. Chem.* 1959, **234**, 1338.
‡ Vishniac, Horecker, and Ochoa, *Adv. Enzymol.* 1957, **19**, 1.
§ Calvin and Lemmon, *J. Amer. Chem. Soc.* 1947, **69**, 1232.

of carbon-carbon and carbon-oxygen bonds and the formation of a new carbon-oxygen bond in the ester. The reaction may be pictured

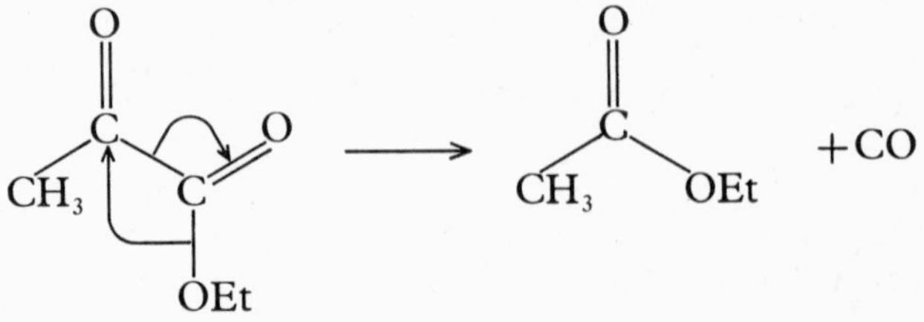

but in a process of this kind the mechanism cannot usefully be classified.

In sulphuric acid both α-hydroxy acids and α-keto acids undergo decarbonylation; aldehydes or ketones are formed from α-hydroxy acids,

$$RCHOH \cdot COOH \longrightarrow RCHO + CO + H_2O,$$

and carboxylic acids from α-keto acids

$$RCO \cdot COOH \longrightarrow RCOOH + CO.$$

Thus, citric acid (1) gives acetone dicarboxylic acid (2):

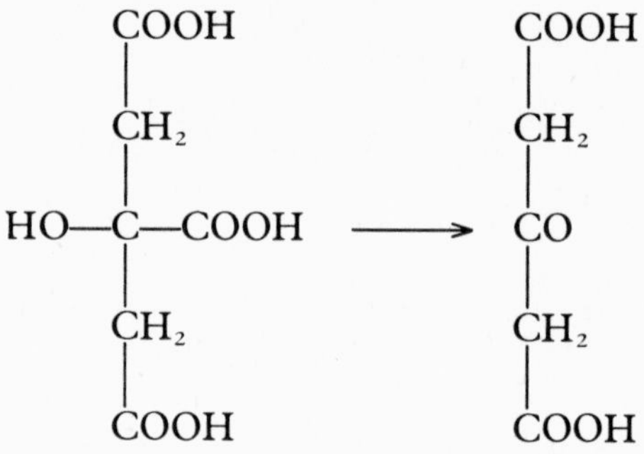

The reaction proceeds through positively charged intermediates, and the products are also protonated in the strongly acidic sulphuric acid.†

4. Formation and hydrolysis of β-keto acids and β-keto esters

(a) *Reactions of esters with carbanions.* The most important reaction of this type is the Claisen acetoacetic ester condensation, exemplified by the formation of ethyl acetoacetate (1) itself:

† Elliott and Hammick, *J. Chem. Soc.* 1951, p. 3402; Schubert *et al., J. Amer. Chem. Soc.* 1959, **81**, 3923, and earlier papers.

$$2CH_3 \cdot COOEt \underset{\longleftarrow}{\overset{base}{\longrightarrow}} CH_3 \cdot CO \cdot CH_2 \cdot COOEt + EtOH$$

(1)

The essence of the reaction is that one molecule of ethyl acetate acylates the other, and so the product is formed by a 'head to tail' union. The biological counterpart plays a part in the metabolism of fatty acids:

$$2CH_3 \cdot CO \cdot SCoA \underset{\longleftarrow}{\overset{thiolase}{\longrightarrow}} CH_3 \cdot CO \cdot CH_2 \cdot CO \cdot SCoA + CoASH$$

Here coenzyme A (written as CoA—SH) is the formal equivalent of ethanol in the Claisen condensation, and the enzymic reaction involves thiol esters (§ 6).

The mechanism of the Claisen condensation has been discussed for over seventy years;† the accepted mechanism for the reaction catalysed by sodium ethoxide (largely due to Lapworth) is set out below:

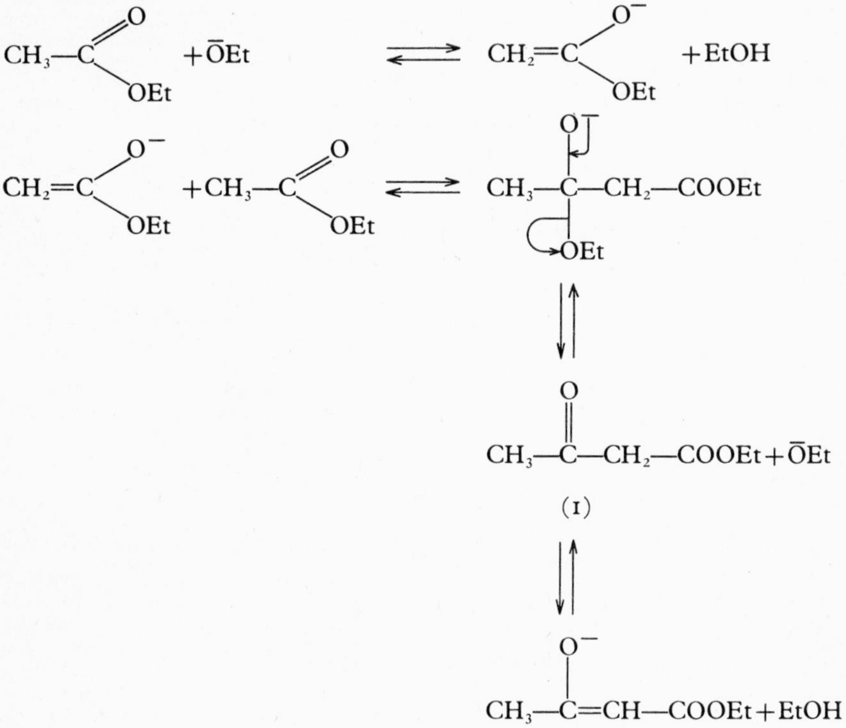

(1)

(2)

† References to earlier work, and a fuller discussion, will be found in Ingold, *Structure and Mechanism in Organic Chemistry*, Cornell University Press, 1953.

This mechanism is essentially similar to that put forward for the aldol reaction (Chapter V, § 7 c). The first step here is the ionization of ethyl acetate brought about by the ethoxide ion; this ionization can be directly detected by the exchange of the hydrogen atoms (of the acetyl group) in ethyl acetate for deuterium, in EtOD. The enolate, a nucleophilic reagent, then attacks the electrophilic carbon atom of the carbonyl group of the second molecule of ethyl acetate, and the product (the ion from a hemiketal) expels ethoxide ion to give the ethyl acetoacetate (1); this last step has no counterpart in the aldol reaction.

The overall reaction is found to be reversible, and so each step in the mechanism must be reversible. Now ethyl acetoacetate (pK 10·7), which forms an enolate ion (Chapter V, § 7 a), is a stronger acid than ethanol (pK 18), and so the β-keto ester will be present mainly as anion (2). This favours condensation, because the anion (2) is unreactive towards the ethoxide ion and so does not enter into reaction in the reverse direction. Thus the effect of the acidity of the β-keto ester is that the concentration of the unionized form is maintained at a low level, just as if it were precipitated out of solution. Ethyl acetate, however, is a weaker acid than ethanol, and so the equilibrium in the first stage will be unfavourable towards condensation. The pK values quoted are for water as solvent; the reaction is, of course, carried out under anhydrous conditions, often without any added solvent, but the same order of acidities should hold.

The overall reaction proceeds with ethyl acetate, but not with ethyl isobutyrate (3), in the presence of sodium ethoxide. Here the β-keto ester (4) lacks the hydrogen atom between the carbonyl group and the ester group which is readily ionized, and so the energetically favourable last stage is absent.

$$Me_2CH \cdot COOEt \qquad\qquad Me_2CH \cdot CO \cdot \overset{\displaystyle Me}{\underset{\displaystyle Me}{\overset{|}{\underset{|}{C}}}} \cdot COOEt$$

(3)   (4)

This line of reasoning leads to the idea that a stronger base than ethoxide ion might bring about condensation of ethyl isobutyrate; a strong enough base should convert the ester into the anion, and the energetically favourable last stage referred to above can be dispensed with if the first stage is rendered energetically favourable. In practice, sodium triphenylmethyl can be used successfully;† the first stage is now:

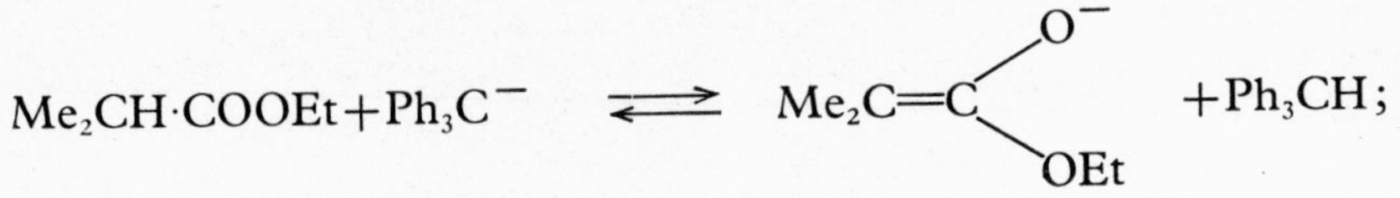

$$\text{Me}_2\text{CH·COOEt} + \text{Ph}_3\text{C}^- \rightleftharpoons \text{Me}_2\text{C}{=}\text{C}\overset{\displaystyle \text{O}^-}{\underset{\displaystyle \text{OEt}}{\big\langle}} + \text{Ph}_3\text{CH};$$

the equilibrium here is over to the right-hand side, as is shown by the disappearance of the red colour of the triphenylmethyl anion, Ph_3C^-.

The enolate in the Claisen condensation may be derived from a ketone: the product is then a β-diketone instead of a β-keto ester,

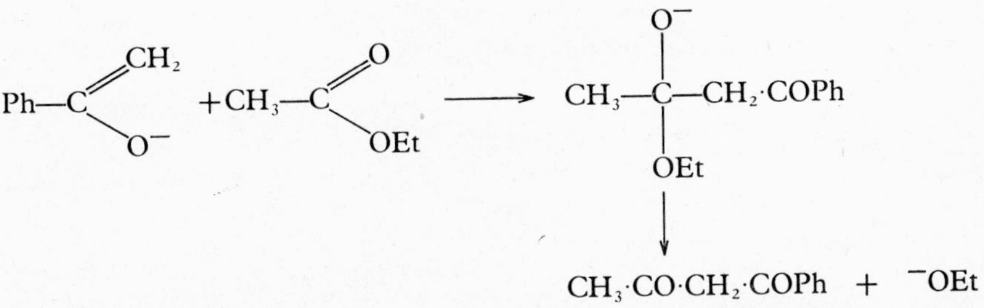

$$\text{Ph}{-}\text{C}\overset{\displaystyle \text{CH}_2}{\underset{\displaystyle \text{O}^-}{\big\langle}} + \text{CH}_3{-}\text{C}\overset{\displaystyle \text{O}}{\underset{\displaystyle \text{OEt}}{\big\langle}} \longrightarrow \text{CH}_3{-}\underset{\displaystyle \text{OEt}}{\overset{\displaystyle \text{O}^-}{\text{C}}}{-}\text{CH}_2\text{·COPh}$$

$$\downarrow$$

$$\text{CH}_3\text{·CO·CH}_2\text{·COPh} + {}^-\text{OEt}$$

In dilute ethereal solution the reaction is second-order,‡ and so the rate-determining step is the attack of the enolate ion on the carbonyl group of the ester.

This type of reaction is also reversible, i.e. β-diketones are cleaved by bases. In the attack of sodium ethoxide on acetylacetone (5) (in ethanol) the kinetics suggest that the first step shown below is rate-determining.§

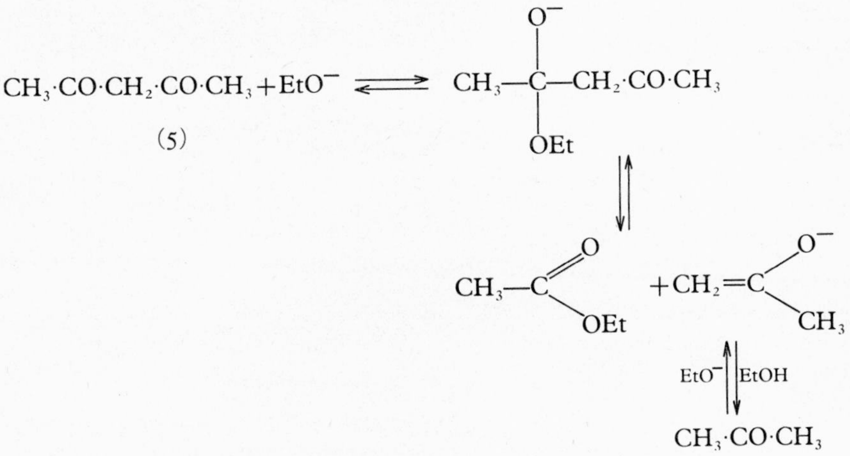

$$\underset{(5)}{\text{CH}_3\text{·CO·CH}_2\text{·CO·CH}_3} + \text{EtO}^- \rightleftharpoons \text{CH}_3{-}\underset{\displaystyle \text{OEt}}{\overset{\displaystyle \text{O}^-}{\text{C}}}{-}\text{CH}_2\text{·CO·CH}_3$$

$$\updownarrow$$

$$\text{CH}_3{-}\text{C}\overset{\displaystyle \text{O}}{\underset{\displaystyle \text{OEt}}{\big\langle}} + \text{CH}_2{=}\text{C}\overset{\displaystyle \text{O}^-}{\underset{\displaystyle \text{CH}_3}{\big\langle}}$$

$$\text{EtO}^- \updownarrow \text{EtOH}$$

$$\text{CH}_3\text{·CO·CH}_3$$

† Hauser and Renfrow, *J. Amer. Chem. Soc.* 1937, **59**, 1823.
‡ Hill, Burkus, and Hauser, ibid. 1959, **81**, 602.
§ Pearson and Sandy, ibid. 1951, **73**, 931.

The pK values of acetylacetone (5) and acetone are 9 and 20, and the pK of ethanol about 18. Thus the equilibrium

$$CH_3 \cdot CO \cdot CH_2 \cdot CO \cdot CH_3 + EtO^- \rightleftharpoons CH_3 \cdot \overset{\overset{\displaystyle O^-}{|}}{C}{=}CH \cdot CO \cdot CH_3 + EtOH$$

is far over to the right, and the cleavage of acetylacetone is restrained by the fact that so much of the β-diketone is 'protected' by being in the unreactive, ionized, form. This situation is rather reminiscent of that in the reaction of amines with carboxylic acids (§ 1 a): the ionized β-diketone, an enolate, resembles the carboxylate ion where carbonyl group reactivity is also diminished.

Trihalogenoketones are also cleaved by bases; thus the iodoform test includes a step which may be expressed (X = halogen) as:

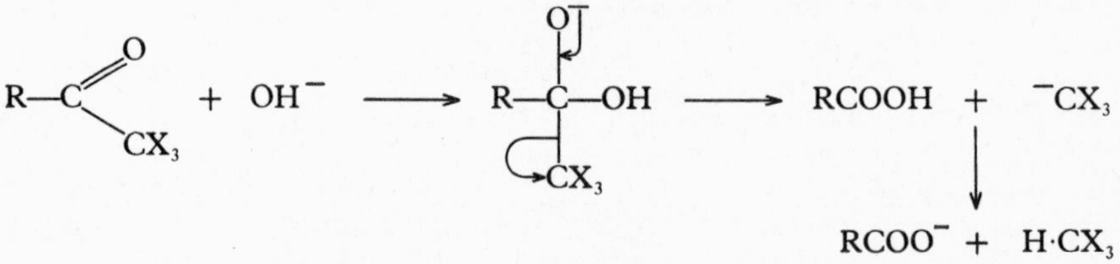

It is no coincidence that trihalogenoketones are cleaved by alkali and trihalogenoacetic acids readily decarboxylated, or that β-diketones are cleaved by alkali and β-keto acids readily decarboxylated. A general formulation of these reactions is

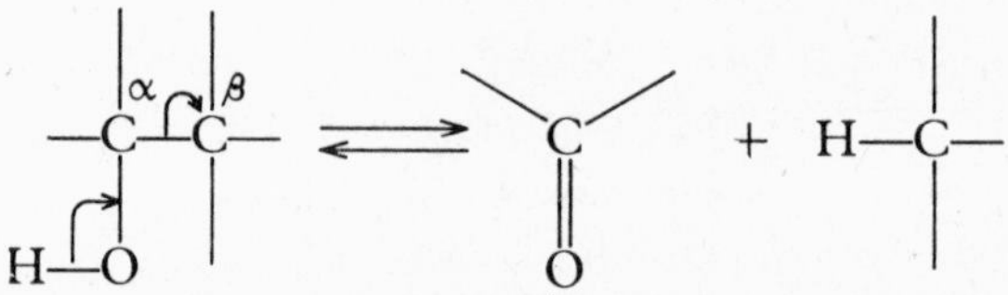

The essence of this method of description† is that it stresses the need for polarization of the C—C bond; the reaction is thus facilitated by electron-donating groups on C-α and electron-withdrawing groups on C-β. The electron-donating group on C-α may, for example, be an ionized hydroxyl group and the electron-withdrawing group on C-β may be a trichloromethyl or acetyl group.

This relation between the two modes of carbon-carbon cleavage means

† Shemyakin and Shchukina, *Quart. Rev.* 1956, **10**, 261; Grob, in *Theoretical Organic Chemistry*, p. 114, London, Butterworths, 1959.

that acetoacetic ester (and its substitution products) can undergo fission in either of two ways:

(i) $HO^- + CH_3 \cdot CO \cdot CHR \cdot COOEt \xrightarrow{\text{in EtOH}} CH_3 \cdot COO^- + RCH_2 \cdot COOEt$

or   (ii) $HO^- + CH_3 \cdot CO \cdot CHR \cdot COOEt \longrightarrow CH_3 \cdot CO \cdot CHR \cdot COO^- + EtOH$

$$\downarrow H^+$$

$$CH_3 \cdot CO \cdot CH_2 R + CO_2$$

The two reactions are carried out, of course, under different conditions; the former is favoured by a high concentration of hydroxide ions,† and is similar to the reverse of the Claisen condensation.

Both these reactions have their enzymic counterparts; enzymic decarboxylation has been discussed, and we now turn to the enzymic cleavage of β-keto acids.

(b) *Enzymic cleavage of β-keto acids.* Oxaloacetic acid undergoes enzymic hydrolysis to give oxalic and acetic acids:‡

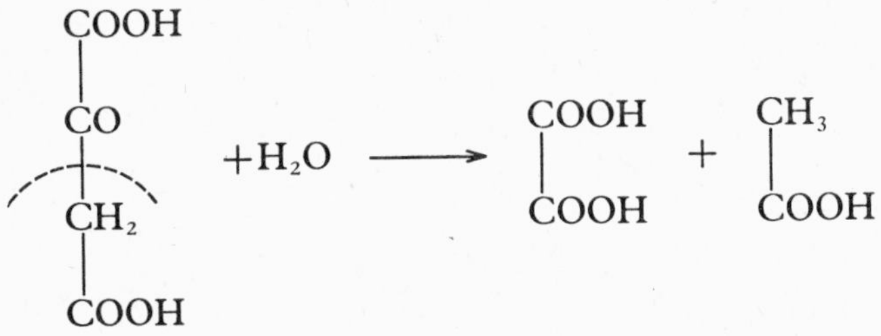

This reaction is analogous to the 'reverse Claisen' fission of acetoacetic ester. Thus enzymes exploit the potentiality of β-keto acids to be split in two ways (hydrolysis and decarboxylation).

Similarly, an enzyme from liver catalyses the hydrolysis of fumaryl acetoacetic acid to fumaric and acetic acids.§

$$HOOC \cdot CH{=}CH \cdot CO \cdot CH_2 \cdot CO \cdot CH_2 \cdot COOH + H_2O \longrightarrow HOOC \cdot CH{=}CH \cdot COOH$$

$$+ CH_3 \cdot CO \cdot CH_2 \cdot COOH$$

5. Acid anhydrides and acid chlorides

(a) *Acid anhydrides.* Acid anhydrides are common acylating agents; although they react with water, they react more rapidly with many

---

† Pearson and Mayerle, *J. Amer. Chem. Soc.* 1951, **73**, 926.
‡ Hayaishi, Shimazono, Katagiri, and Saito, ibid. 1956, **78**, 5126.
§ Edwards and Knox, *J. Biol. Chem.* 1956, **220**, 79.

amines and thiols, and so can be used in aqueous solution, e.g.

$$(CH_3 \cdot CO)_2 O + NH_2 \cdot CH_2 \cdot COO^- \xrightarrow{\ OH^-\ } CH_3 \cdot CO \cdot NH \cdot COO^- + {}^-O \cdot CO \cdot CH_3 + H_2O.$$

The hydrolysis of acetic anhydride is a bimolecular reaction,† which is catalysed by tertiary bases, such as pyridine. The reaction may proceed via an intermediate, such as (1):

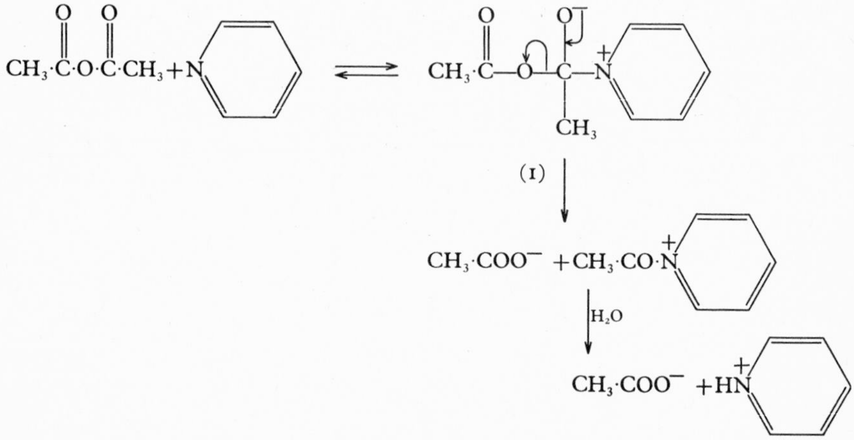

The hydrolysis of acetic anhydride is also acid-catalysed, and here a probable mechanism is:‡

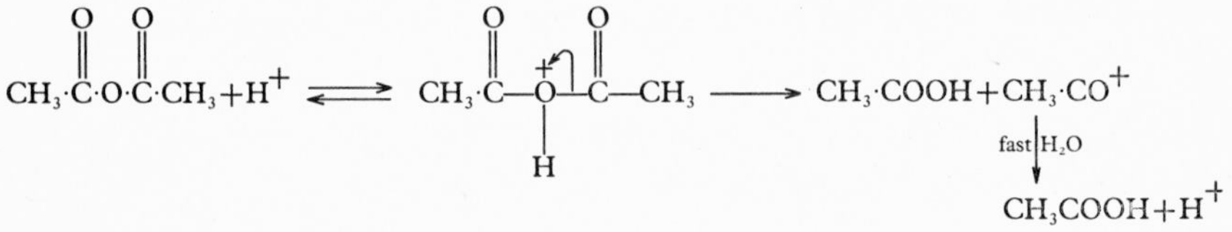

The rate of attack of a nucleophilic water molecule on the carbonyl group of an anhydride should increase with decreasing electron density at the carbon atom of the carbonyl group, and, in fact, electron-withdrawing groups in the benzene ring of substituted benzoic anhydrides cause an increase in the rate of hydrolysis,§ as in the alkaline hydrolysis of benzoic esters. These considerations help in considering the products expected from a mixed anhydride, such as formic acetic anhydride (2). Mixed anhydrides are potentially capable of reacting in two ways, and

† Gold, *Trans. Faraday Soc.* 1948, **44**, 506; Bafna and Gold, *J. Chem. Soc.* 1953, p. 1406; Gold and Jefferson, ibid., p. 1409.
‡ Gold and Hilton, *J. Chem. Soc.* 1955, p. 843.
§ Berliner and Altschul, *J. Amer. Chem. Soc.* 1952, **74**, 4110.

formic acetic anhydride could be a formylating or an acetylating agent; in fact, it is a formylating agent.

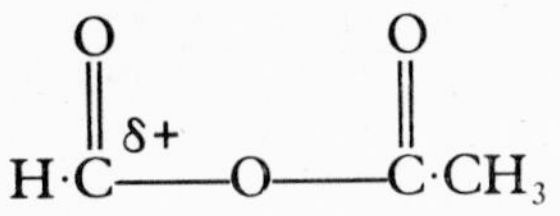

(2) 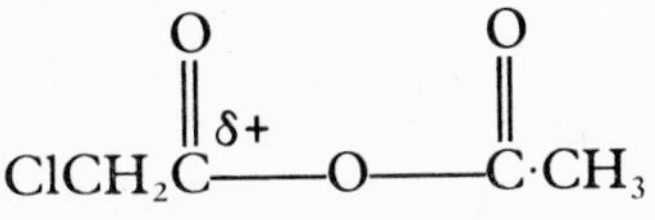   (3)

A methyl group is electron-repelling compared with a hydrogen atom, and so there is a greater fractional positive charge on the left-hand carbon atom in the formula (2). Hence a nucleophilic amino group, for example, attacks this carbon atom, and so the anhydride functions as a formylating agent. Similarly, the electronegativity of chlorine results in the left-hand carbon in the formula (3) having a greater fractional positive charge, and acetic chloroacetic anhydride (3) is a chloro-acetylating agent, at least under most conditions.†

(b) *Acid chlorides.* Acid chlorides, even more than acid anhydrides, are vigorous acetylating agents. Isotopic exchange experiments, of the kind already discussed in connexion with the hydrolysis of esters and amides, suggest a carbonyl-addition type of mechanism for the hydrolysis of benzoyl chloride:‡

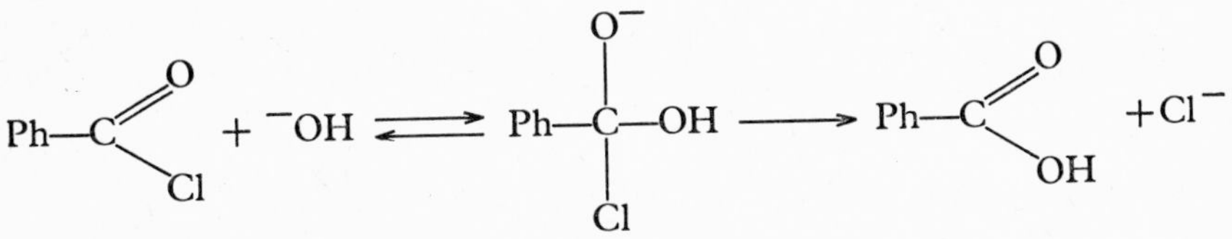

However, as chlorine is considerably more electronegative than carbon, the C—Cl bond is quite prone to heterolysis in the sense C—Cl, and so a unimolecular (ionization) mechanism (cf. $S_N 1$, Chapter III) is quite feasible:

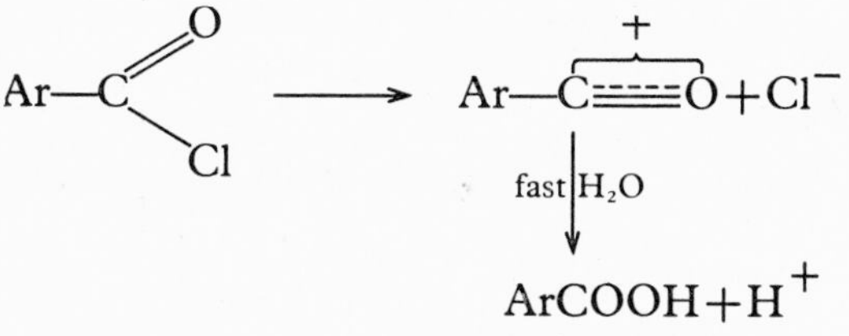

† Emery and Gold, *J. Chem. Soc.* 1950, pp. 1443, 1447, 1455; Gold and Jefferson, ibid. 1953, p. 1416.
‡ Bunton, Lewis, and Llewellyn, *Chem. and Ind.* 1954, p. 1154.

There is, in fact, considerable evidence for this mechanism, as well as the bimolecular mechanism, in a number of instances.[†]

6. Thiol esters

Thiol esters are important biologically because 'activated acetic acid'[‡] is a thiol ester, S-acetyl-coenzyme A. Simple thiol esters, such as ethyl thiol acetate (1), mostly undergo the same reactions as the corresponding oxygen compounds (2), and so only a few topics will be touched on here.

$$CH_3-C\overset{O}{\underset{SEt}{\big<}} \qquad\qquad CH_3-C\overset{O}{\underset{OEt}{\big<}}$$

$$(1) \qquad\qquad\qquad (2)$$

The equilibria, and rates, in the hydrolysis of thiol esters will be discussed first. The equilibrium in the reaction

$$CH_3-C\overset{O}{\underset{OH}{\big<}} +EtSH \rightleftharpoons CH_3-C\overset{O}{\underset{SEt}{\big<}} +H_2O$$

lies farther over to the left than in the corresponding reaction

$$CH_3-C\overset{O}{\underset{OH}{\big<}} +EtOH \rightleftharpoons CH_3-C\overset{O}{\underset{OEt}{\big<}} +H_2O$$

The difference in the standard free energy changes is about 3 to 5 kcal/mol.[§] The hydrolysis of ethyl thiol acetate in aqueous solution is more exothermic than the hydrolysis of ethyl acetate by about 6 kcal/mol;[||] the difference is mainly due to the higher heat of solution of the thiol. In certain cases, esters are formed spontaneously in aqueous solution, and the same applies to thiol esters. Just as γ-lactones are formed spontaneously, so are γ-thiolactones:

$$\begin{array}{cc} CH_2\text{---}CH_2 & CH_2\text{--}CH_2 \\ | \qquad\quad | & \diagup \qquad \diagdown \\ CH_2 \quad COOH & CH_2 \qquad CO \quad +H_2O \\ \diagdown \qquad\qquad & \diagdown \quad \diagup \\ SH & S \end{array} \longrightarrow$$

---

† Crunden and Hudson, *J. Chem. Soc.* 1956, p. 501; Brown and Hudson, ibid. 1953, p. 3352, and earlier papers.

‡ Decker, *Die aktivierte Essigsäure*, Chem. & Chem. Tech. Beiträge, Sammlung Enke, Stuttgart, 1959.

§ Faber and Reid, *J. Amer. Chem. Soc.* 1917, **39**, 1930; Decker, op. cit., p. 91; Jencks et al., *J. Biol. Chem.* 1960, **235**, 3608.

|| Wadsö, *Acta chem. Scand.* 1957, **11**, 1745; 1958, **12**, 630.

Thus if the spatial factors (see below) are favourable, the equilibrium is on the side of formation of the thiol ester. However, the difference between thiol esters and the corresponding oxygen compounds is seen in that δ-hydroxyvaleric acid cyclizes in aqueous solution to give about 30 per cent. of the lactone at equilibrium, whereas δ-mercaptovaleric acid does not give detectable amounts of the thiolactone.†

We shall digress here to comment on the useful generalization that compounds containing 5- or 6-membered rings are 'favoured', both thermodynamically and kinetically, when compared with their open-chain counterparts. In the example quoted above a cyclic thiol ester was formed under conditions where an open-chain thiol ester would not be formed. Both open-chain and cyclic compounds contain the same kind of bonds, and the difference arises mainly from the fact that the open-chain reaction is of the type

$$A+B \rightleftarrows C+D,$$

and the cyclization of the type

$$A' \rightleftarrows C'+D.$$

Now the free energy change, which determines the position of the equilibrium, is composed of an energy term and an entropy term (Chapter II, § 1 a), and it is the entropy term which favours the second case, as here there is one more molecule on the right-hand side of the stoicheiometric equation. In the simplest case the contribution of the entropy term to the free energy change in aqueous solution when D is a water molecule is about 4·5 kcal/mol. The same sort of considerations apply also to the kinetics of cyclization, where the entropy of activation may be considerably greater than for an analogous intermolecular reaction.

We now return to the hydrolysis of thiol esters. The alkaline hydrolysis proceeds at a rate comparable to that of ordinary esters: in both cases, the bimolecular rate constants are of the order of unity (in units of l. mol^{-1}min^{-1}, at 10° C in aqueous solution). In acid solution, thiol esters are less readily hydrolysed than ordinary esters.‡ The position of bond fission is shown by the nature of the products: the mercaptan

† Schjänberg, *Ber.* 1942, **75**, 468.
‡ Tarbell and Harnish, *Chem. Rev.* 1951, **49**, 1; Noda, Kuby, and Lardy, *J. Amer. Chem. Soc.* 1953, **75**, 913; Tarbell and Cameron, ibid. 1956, **78**, 2731.

and the acid are formed, rather than the alcohol and the thiol acid. This corresponds to the usual acyl-oxygen fission in the case of ordinary esters, and the mechanisms of hydrolysis of ordinary esters and thiol esters are probably quite closely similar.

An interesting difference between thiol esters and ordinary esters is that thiol esters react much more readily with amines, and similarly, the hydrolysis of thiol esters is catalysed by glyoxaline (Chapter VI, § 1 g). Thiol esters may thus be considered as good acylating agents and they are exploited as such in the enzymic synthesis of fats. An example of a thiol ester acting as an acylating agent in aqueous solution is the reaction of ethyl thiol acetate with butylamine:

$$CH_3 \cdot CO \cdot SEt + BuNH_2 \longrightarrow CH_3 \cdot CO \cdot NHBu + EtSH$$

The reaction is base-catalysed, and the kinetics fit a mechanism of the following type:†

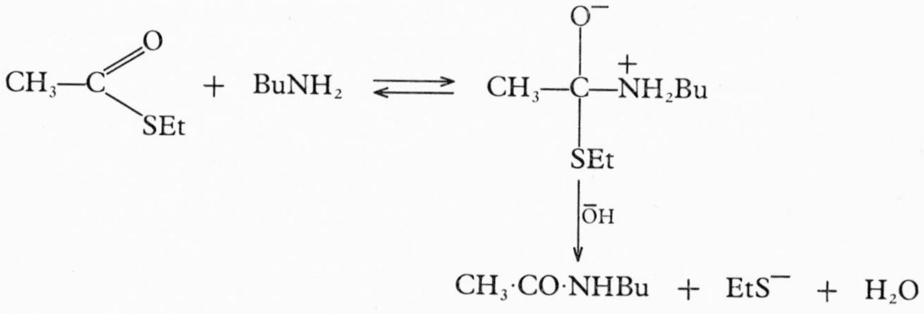

Thiols are considerably more acidic (pK in the region of 10) than alcohols (pK in the region of 18). Conversely, the anion EtS⁻ is much less basic than EtO⁻. This may be the reason why thiol esters can react readily with relatively weak bases, such as amines, since the mercaptide ion is, in effect, a better leaving group than the alkoxide ion. In terms of the general scheme:

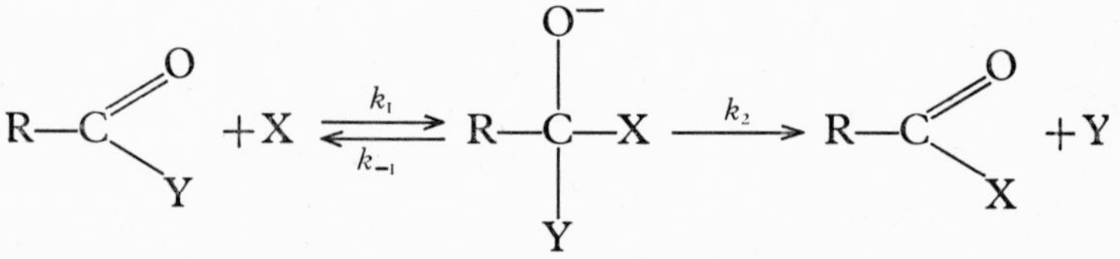

If Y is a good leaving group the value of the ratio k_{-1}/k_2 will be small

† Hawkins and Tarbell, J. Amer. Chem. Soc. 1953, **75**, 2982.

compared with one; the success of the reaction depends both on this ratio and the absolute value of k_1.[†]

So far we have been discussing the carbonyl-group reactivity of thiol esters. In such reactions as the Claisen condensation of ethyl thiol acetate

$$2CH_3 \cdot CO \cdot SEt \longrightarrow CH_3 \cdot CO \cdot CH_2 \cdot CO \cdot SEt$$

the extent to which the thiol ester forms an anion is important (cf. § 4 a), and here, too, thiol esters are quite reactive.[‡]

[†] Wiberg, *J. Amer. Chem. Soc.* 1955, **77**, 2519.
[‡] Cronyn, Chang, and Wall, ibid., p. 3031.

VIII

SATURATED REARRANGEMENTS

1. Introduction

SUBSTITUTIONS, additions, and eliminations have been discussed in earlier chapters, and now we come to rearrangements. One way of dividing rearrangements is into those which are peculiar to aromatic systems,† and those (here called saturated rearrangements) which are not. Only the latter are discussed here. It is particularly important to know when rearrangements do occur, since in the deduction of the structure of a compound from its reactions it is normally assumed that no rearrangement has taken place.

Formally, rearrangements have been represented (Chapter II, §3b) simply as

$$A \to B,$$

but additional reagents are normally required, and these intramolecular reactions are often intramolecular only as regards the organic species. The term rearrangement is used here in a somewhat restricted sense, as isomerizations and tautomerizations are excluded.

The rearrangements described in §§ 1 to 4 are sometimes referred to as 1,2-shifts, as they are reactions in which one group 'moves' from one atom to the adjacent one, e.g.

$$\underset{\overset{|}{OH} \quad \overset{|}{OH}}{Me_2C\!\!-\!\!-\!\!-\!\!CMe_2} \longrightarrow Me_3C\!\!-\!\!-\!\!-\!\!COMe$$

$$(1) \hspace{6cm} (2)$$

In the alcohol (1) each carbon atom has two methyl groups, and in the product (2) one carbon atom has three methyl groups and the other but one, so a methyl group has migrated. Most of these rearrangements can be described in the following way.‡ A group departs with both of the electrons formerly shared with another atom (a carbon, nitrogen, or oxygen atom). This atom now has only a sextet of electrons round it, instead of the normal octet, i.e. it is electron-deficient. The rearrange-

---

† Ingold, *Structure and Mechanism in Organic Chemistry*, chap. xi, Cornell University Press, 1953; Hughes and Ingold, *Quart. Rev.* 1952, **6**, 34; Dewar, in *Theoretical Organic Chemistry* (Kekulé Symposium), p. 179, London: Butterworths, 1959.

‡ Whitmore, *J. Amer. Chem. Soc.* 1932, **54**, 3274.

ment then consists in the migration of another group (with its pair of bonding electrons) on the electron-deficient atom. The evidence for this description, which forms the basis for most of the subdivision of this chapter, will be given later.

2. Rearrangements of compounds containing an electron-deficient carbon atom

(a) *Pinacol-pinacone rearrangement*. This reaction, which has been known for about a hundred years, takes place in acid solution; a 1,2-diol (e.g. pinacol (1)) is converted into a ketone (e.g. pinacone, or pinacolone (2)); the reaction is quite general for compounds of this type. The rate is first-order in pinacol, and is also proportional to the acidity of the solution.† Now the only groups with any basic properties in pinacol are the hydroxyl groups, and so the function of the acid must be to protonate one of the hydroxyl groups. This will greatly aid the heterolysis of the C—O bond, for the departing species can now be H_2O rather than OH^-. An electron-deficient carbonium ion is then formed, and it is in this species (3) that a methyl group migrates:

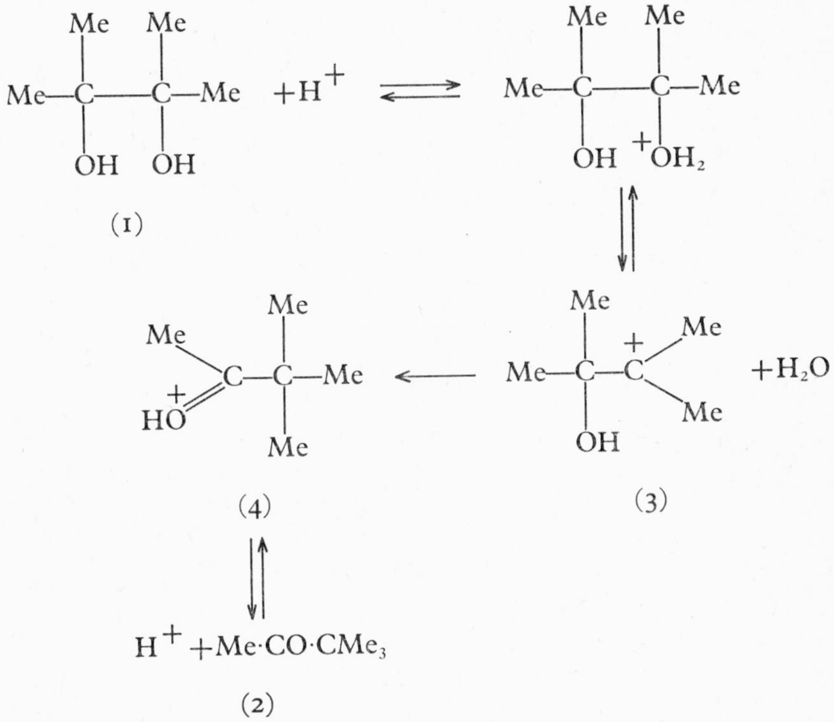

† Duncan and Lynn, *J. Chem. Soc.* 1956, pp. 3512, 3519.

The immediate product of the migration is the protonated ketone (4), which is, of course, in equilibrium with the ketone, pinacone. We may now inquire whether there is any evidence that the carbonium ion (3) exists, or whether the methyl group moves over as the C—O bond splits. In fact, the 'choice of reaction' criterion (Chapter II, § 1 b) provides evidence for the existence of the carbonium ion. If the rearrangement is carried out in water containing $H_2^{18}O$ it is found that, during the course of the reaction, the remaining pinacol acquires a labelled hydroxyl group (^{18}OH). This exchange reaction is also acid-catalysed, and its rate varies with the acidity of the medium in much the same way as does the rate of rearrangement. This finding fits the postulated mechanism, since the isotopic exchange results from the reaction of the carbonium ion (3) with water: in other words, the carbonium ion either reacts with water and reverts to the (protonated) pinacol, or rearranges to the (protonated) ketone.[†]

The reaction proceeds over a thousand times more rapidly when one of the methyl groups in pinacol is replaced by a tertiary butyl group, and it is mainly the tertiary butyl group which shifts.[‡]

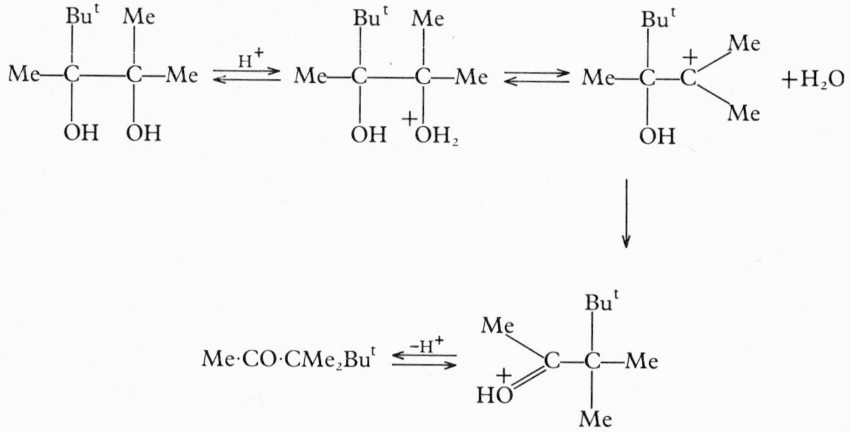

It is possible that the fact that a tertiary butyl group can accommodate a positive charge better than can a methyl group may be a factor in the more rapid rearrangement of the tertiary butyl compound.

In some cases the pinacol rearrangement can proceed partly via the cyclic epoxide (5):[§]

† Bunton, Hadwick, Llewellyn, and Pocker, J. Chem. Soc. 1958, p. 403.
‡ Stiles and Mayer, J. Amer. Chem. Soc. 1959, 81, 1497.
§ Gebhart and Adams, ibid. 1954, 76, 3925.

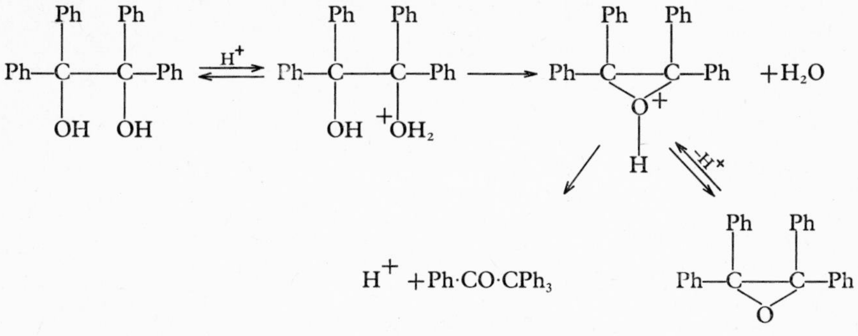

(5)

The reaction is carried out with perchloric acid in acetic acid. This route is probably restricted to aromatic pinacols in non-aqueous systems, when the epoxides are more stable. In the example shown, the epoxide is relatively stable, so that the rate of formation of the ketone is less than the rate of disappearance of the pinacol.

A pinacol (6) (the term is often used generically) with four different groups could in principle give four different products. The nature of the predominating reaction depends both on which hydroxyl group is lost, and which group actually migrates. If there are only two different groups the problem is somewhat simpler. Thus, in an 'unsymmetrical' pinacol (8) the nature of the product is determined solely by which

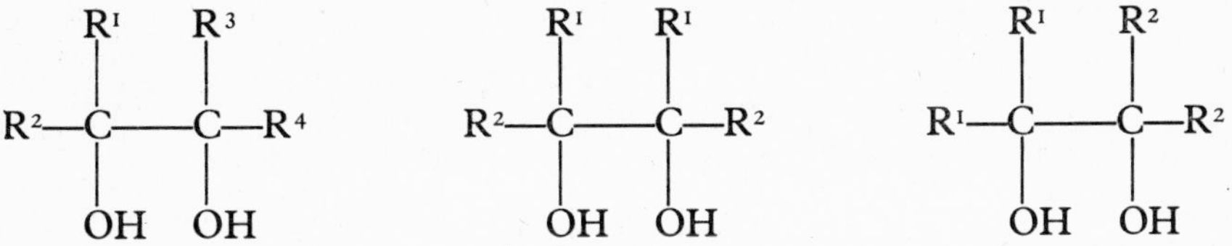

(6)   (7)   (8)

hydroxyl group is lost. A result such as

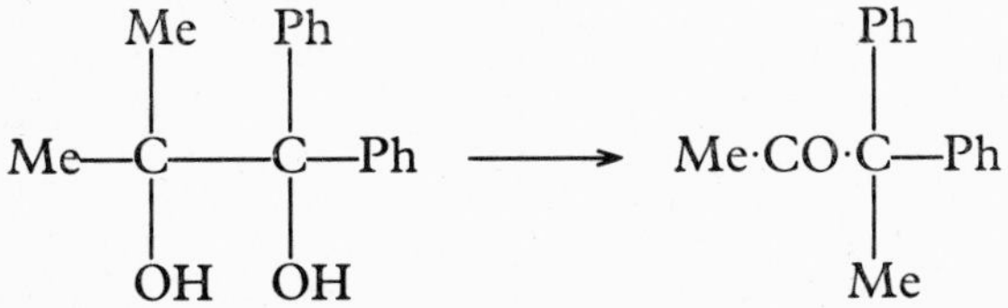

is explicable; the carbonium ion (9) would be expected to be more stable than the alternative (10), because the positive charge can be spread over the *ortho-* and *para*-positions of the benzene rings (cf. stability of Ph_3C^+, Chapter III, § 3 *b*).

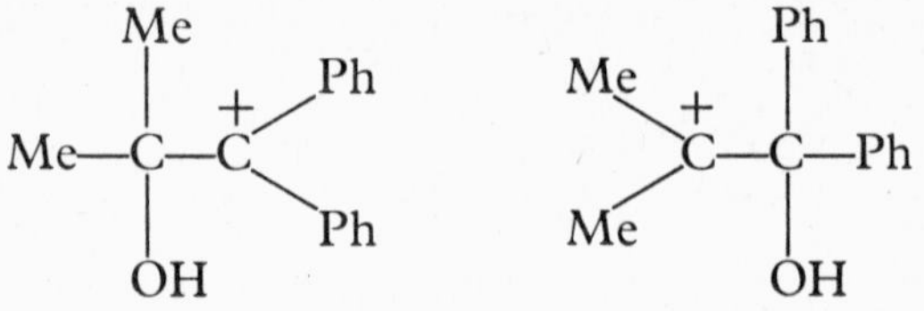

$$(9) \qquad\qquad (10)$$

On the other hand, in a 'symmetrical' pinacol (7), the nature of the products is determined by which group migrates, e.g.

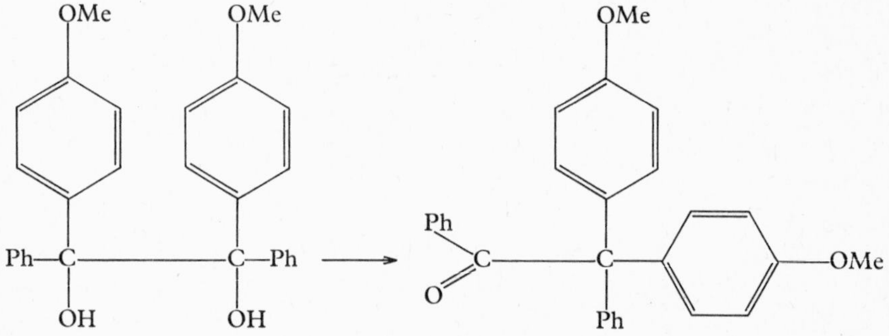

Here the general rule is that the so-called migratory aptitude of an aryl group can be gauged by the reactivity of the corresponding compound towards electrophilic reagents. Thus, in the example shown, anisole (methoxybenzene) is more readily nitrated than benzene (Chapter IX), and the anisyl group is the one which migrates. In the pinacol rearrangement the migrating group interacts with an electrophilic carbonium ion, and so the parallel between migratory aptitude and reactivity in electrophilic aromatic substitution is quite reasonable.

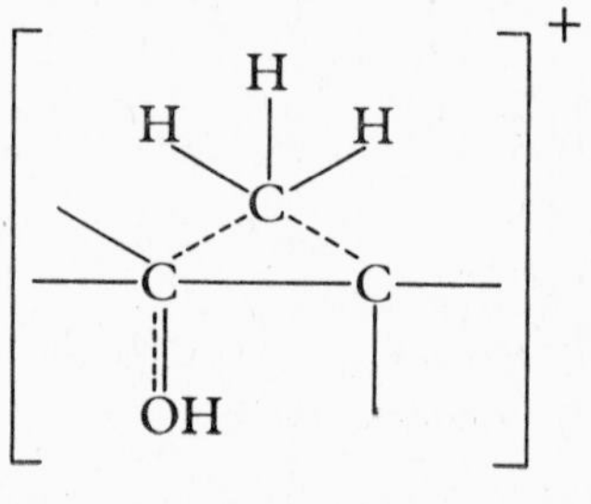

In general, the transition state of the migration of a group (e.g. methyl) from one carbon atom to the other in these reactions may be represented as and is an electron-deficient species containing a three-centre bond formed by the triple overlap of three orbitals, one from each of the carbon atoms shown at the bottom of the preceding page.

The pinacol rearrangement is not restricted to di-tertiary alcohols, but is more general:

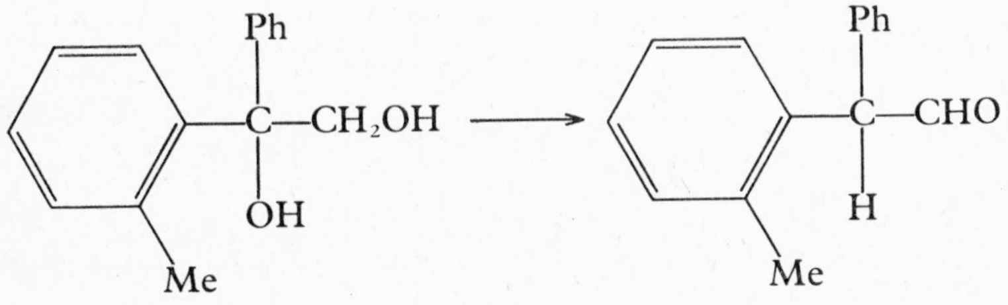

$$(\text{II}) \qquad\qquad\qquad\qquad (\text{12})$$

As this reaction, when carried out with the optically active alcohol (11), yields optically active aldehyde (12), the hydrogen atom seems to shift intramolecularly and synchronously with the expulsion of the hydroxyl group as water.†

Similarly, there is evidence for an intramolecular hydrogen shift in the conversion of 2-methylpropan-1,2-diol (13) into isobutyraldehyde (14) by the mechanism‡

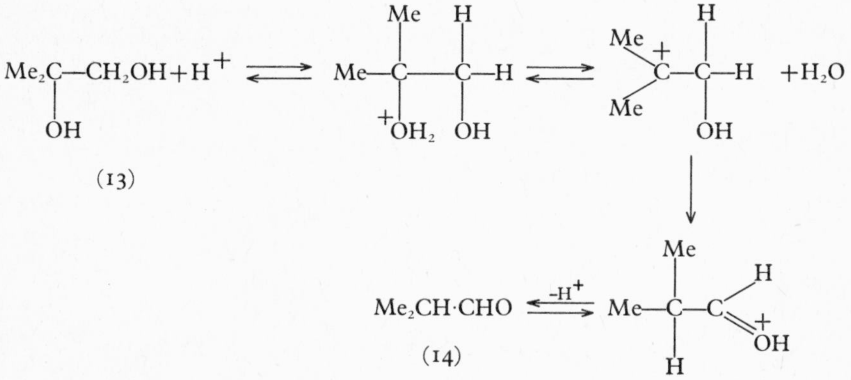

(b) *Rearrangements related to the pinacol rearrangement.* There are several other rearrangements which are similar to the pinacol one and also take place in acid solution. In one of these an aldehyde is converted into a ketone:§

† Mislow and Siegel, *J. Amer. Chem. Soc.* 1952, **74**, 1060.

‡ Ley and Vernon, *J. Chem. Soc.* 1957, p. 2987.

§ Danilov and Venus-Danilova, *Ber.* 1926, **59**, 377.

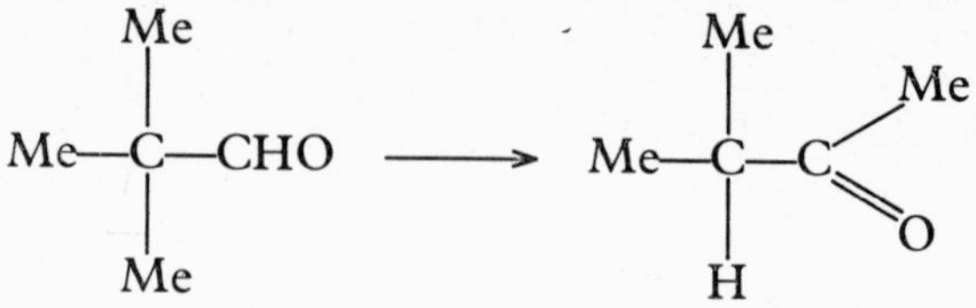

$$\underset{\underset{Me}{|}}{\overset{\overset{Me}{|}}{Me-C-CHO}} \longrightarrow \underset{\underset{H}{|}}{\overset{\overset{Me}{|}}{Me-C-C}}\overset{Me}{\underset{O}{\diagdown}}$$

Another rearrangement occurs with acyloins:†

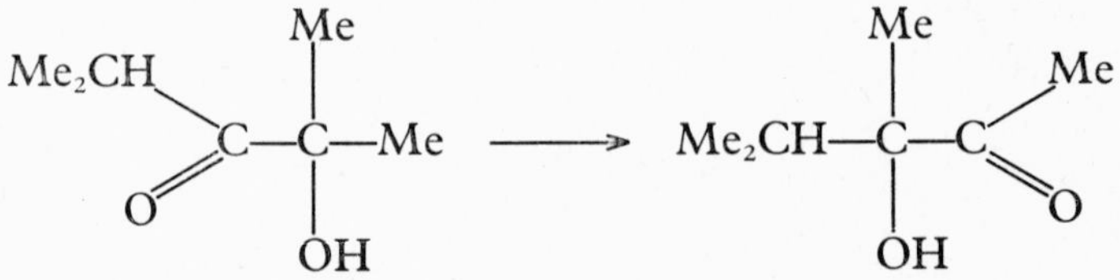

$$Me_2CH\diagdown\underset{O}{\overset{\overset{Me}{|}}{C-C-Me}}\underset{OH}{|} \longrightarrow Me_2CH-\underset{OH}{\overset{\overset{Me}{|}}{C-C}}\overset{Me}{\underset{O}{\diagdown}}$$

In another example, hydrogen may be considered to migrate:‡

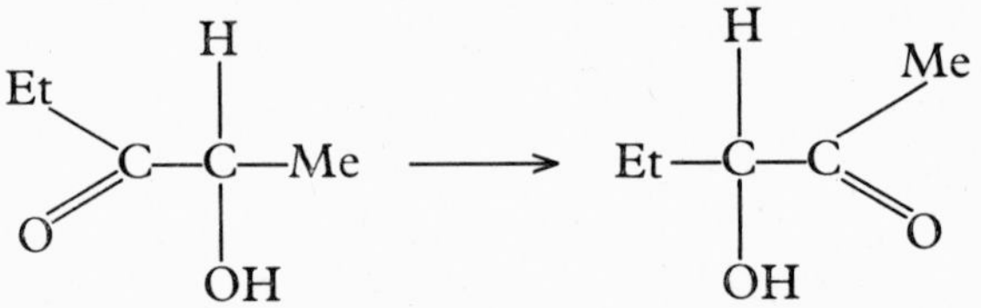

$$Et\diagdown\underset{O}{\overset{\overset{H}{|}}{C-C-Me}}\underset{OH}{|} \longrightarrow Et-\underset{OH}{\overset{\overset{H}{|}}{C-C}}\overset{Me}{\underset{O}{\diagdown}}$$

A similar rearrangement is postulated in the pathway of biosynthesis of isoleucine (and valine):§

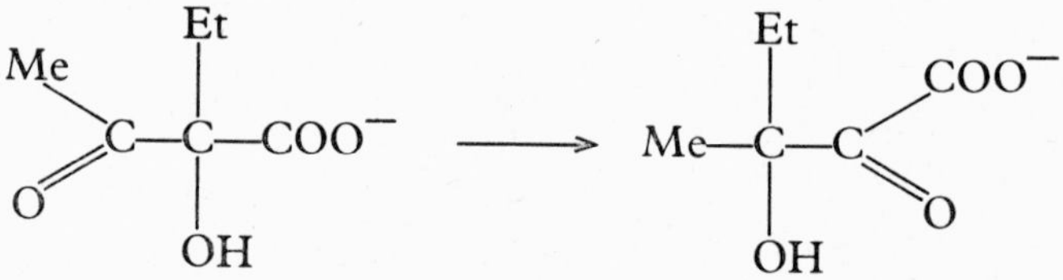

$$Me\diagdown\underset{O}{\overset{\overset{Et}{|}}{C-C-COO^-}}\underset{OH}{|} \longrightarrow Me-\underset{OH}{\overset{\overset{Et}{|}}{C-C}}\overset{COO^-}{\underset{O}{\diagdown}}$$

Finally, two other related rearrangements may be mentioned; hitherto the departing atom has been oxygen, here it is halogen or nitrogen:

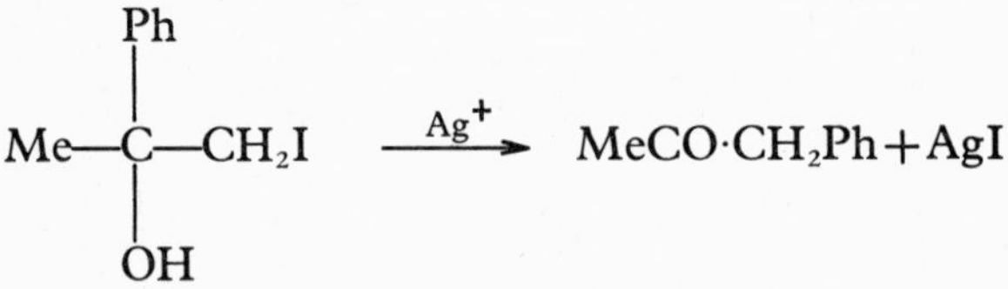

$$\underset{OH}{\overset{\overset{Ph}{|}}{Me-C-CH_2I}} \xrightarrow{Ag^+} MeCO\cdot CH_2Ph+AgI \qquad \text{iodohydrin rearrangement}$$

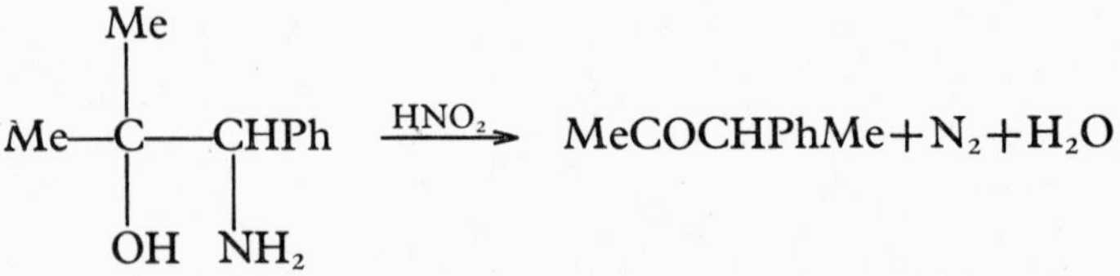

$$\underset{OH\ \ NH_2}{\overset{\overset{Me}{|}}{Me-C-CHPh}} \xrightarrow{HNO_2} MeCOCHPhMe+N_2+H_2O \qquad \text{pinacolic deamination}$$

† Oumnov, *Bull. Soc. chim. France*, 1928, **43**, 568.   ‡ Venus-Danilova, ibid., p. 582.
§ Wagner, Bergquist, and Forrest, *J. Biol. Chem.* 1959, **234**, 99.

The main stage in the last example may be represented as

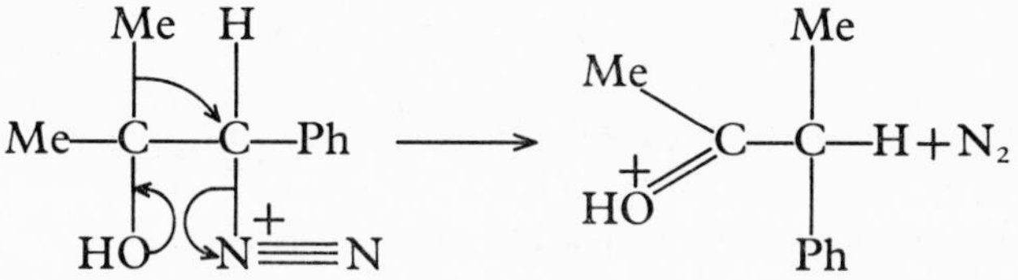

$$\underset{\overset{|}{HO}\;\; \overset{|}{\overset{+}{N}\equiv N}}{\overset{\overset{Me\;\; H}{|\quad\;|}}{Me\!-\!C\!-\!C\!-\!Ph}} \longrightarrow \underset{HO}{\overset{Me}{>}}C\!-\!\underset{\overset{|}{Ph}}{\overset{\overset{Me}{|}}{C}}\!-\!H + N_2$$

and there is evidence that the configuration of the carbon atom carrying the (leaving) diazonium group is inverted during the reaction,† which would be expected if the migrating methyl group attacked the carbon atom from the side opposite to that of the leaving group, as in an $S_N 2$ displacement (Chapter III).

(c) *Wagner–Meerwein rearrangement*. Rearrangements similar to those we have already described occur in compounds containing only one oxygen, nitrogen, or halogen atom:

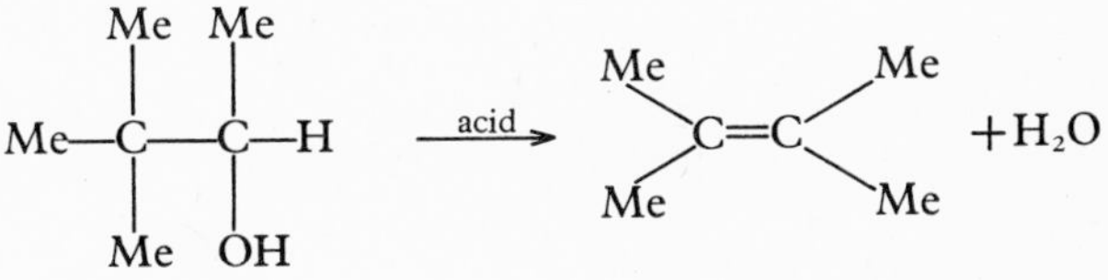

$$\underset{\overset{|}{Me}\;\;\overset{|}{OH}}{\overset{\overset{Me\;\;Me}{|\quad\;|}}{Me\!-\!C\!-\!C\!-\!H}} \xrightarrow{\;acid\;} \underset{Me}{\overset{Me}{>}}C\!=\!C\underset{Me}{\overset{Me}{<}} + H_2O$$

and

$$\underset{\overset{|}{Me}}{\overset{\overset{Me}{|}}{Me\!-\!C\!-\!CH_2NH_2}} \xrightarrow{\;HNO_2\;} \underset{\overset{|}{OH}}{\overset{\overset{Me}{|}}{Me\!-\!C\!-\!CH_2Me}} + H_2O + N_2$$

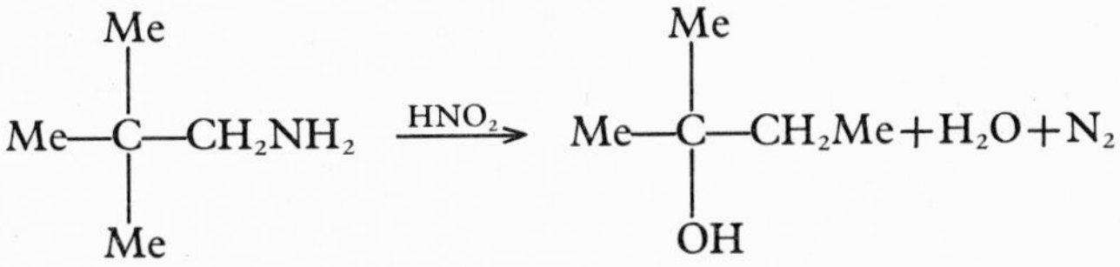

In both these examples the reactions can be understood if we assume that a carbonium ion is formed as an intermediate. Thus in the first example the mechanism may be formulated by analogy with the pinacol rearrangement as

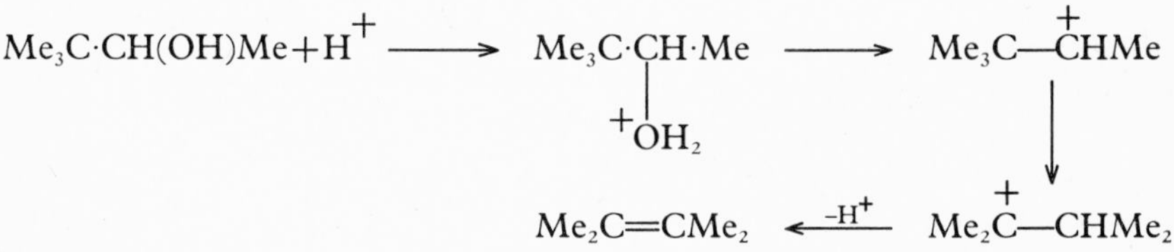

$$Me_3C\cdot CH(OH)Me + H^+ \longrightarrow \underset{\overset{+}{OH_2}}{Me_3C\cdot\overset{|}{CH}\cdot Me} \longrightarrow Me_3C\!-\!\overset{+}{CH}Me$$

$$Me_2C\!=\!CMe_2 \xleftarrow{\;-H^+\;} Me_2\overset{+}{C}\!-\!CHMe_2$$

The formation of an olefine by the β-elimination of a proton from a

† Ingold, *Structure and Mechanism in Organic Chemistry*, p. 504, Cornell University Press, 1953.

carbonium ion has been described in Chapter IV. A similar mechanism in the second example is

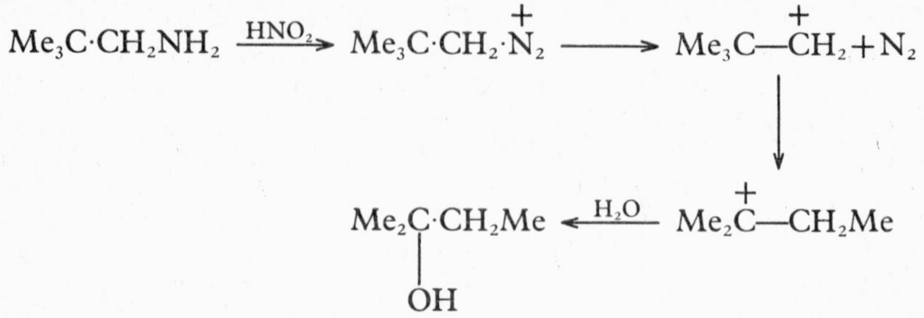

$$Me_3C \cdot CH_2NH_2 \xrightarrow{\text{HNO}_2} Me_3C \cdot CH_2 \cdot \overset{+}{N}_2 \longrightarrow Me_3C \overset{+}{-} CH_2 + N_2$$

$$Me_2\underset{|}{C} \cdot CH_2Me \xleftarrow{\text{H}_2\text{O}} Me_2\overset{+}{C} - CH_2Me$$
$$OH$$

In the first example, the rearrangement step converts a secondary carbonium ion into a tertiary one, and in the second example, a primary carbonium ion into a tertiary one. Now the order of stability of carbonium ions is, in general, tertiary > secondary > primary (Chapter III, § 3 b), and the general principle underlying most of these rearrangements is that the 1,2-shift is in the direction leading to a more stable carbonium ion. A carbonium ion is stabilized by conjugation with a phenyl group, so that the substitution

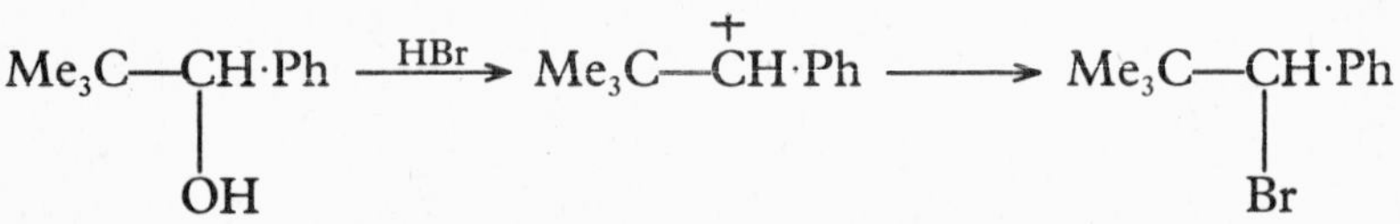

$$Me_3C \underset{|}{-} CH \cdot Ph \xrightarrow{\text{HBr}} Me_3C \overset{+}{-} CH \cdot Ph \longrightarrow Me_3C \underset{|}{-} CH \cdot Ph$$
$$OH \qquad\qquad\qquad\qquad\qquad\qquad\qquad\qquad Br$$

takes place without rearrangement. But rearrangement occurs if it enables the positive charge to be conjugated with more phenyl groups.[†]

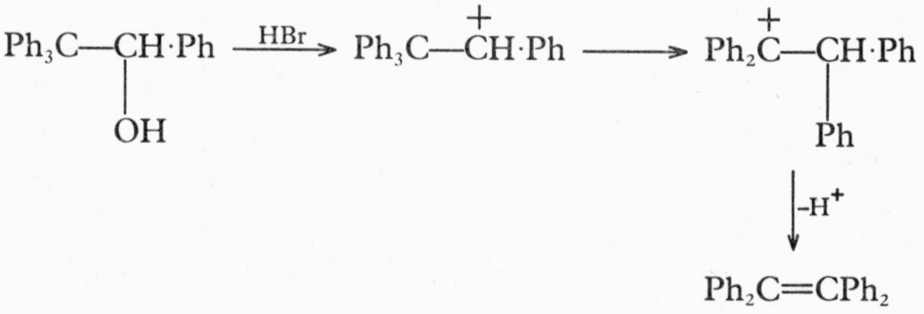

$$Ph_3C \underset{|}{-} CH \cdot Ph \xrightarrow{\text{HBr}} Ph_3C \overset{+}{-} CH \cdot Ph \longrightarrow Ph_2\overset{+}{C} \underset{|}{-} CH \cdot Ph$$
$$OH \qquad\qquad\qquad\qquad\qquad\qquad\qquad\qquad Ph$$

$$\downarrow -H^+$$

$$Ph_2C = CPh_2$$

Comparison of the rates of related rearrangements reveals something about the timing of the events. When one group leaves, and another group migrates, there are obviously two extreme possibilities. A relatively long-lived carbonium ion might be formed, the migrating group moving over sometime after the leaving group has gone. Or the migrating

† Skell and Hauser, J. Amer. Chem. Soc. 1942, **64**, 2633.

group might provide nucleophilic assistance and move over synchronously ('speeding the parting guest' as it were). An example of the latter process is the formation of triphenylethylene from triphenylethyl chloride,

$$Ph_3C—CH_2Cl \longrightarrow Ph_2C{=}CH{\cdot}Ph,$$

which proceeds more rapidly than the reaction of neopentyl chloride, $Me_3C—CH_2Cl$, by a factor of about 10^4.[†] Here the phenyl group which migrates is helping the chlorine atom to depart as an ion, and this can only happen if there is some kind of bonding between the phenyl group and the 'terminus' carbon atom to which the phenyl group is moving. A 'bridged ion' structure may be written to show this bonding:

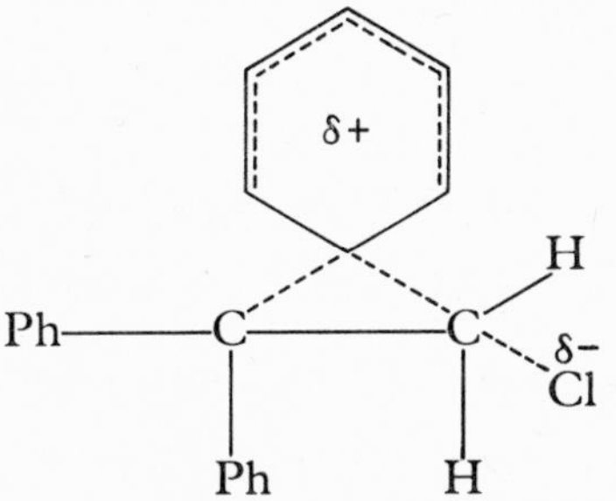

There is stereochemical evidence for the existence of such bridged ions; the argument is similar to that applied to bromonium ions in Chapter III (§ 4).[‡]

We now come to Wagner–Meerwein rearrangements in cyclic systems. Here the size of the ring is often altered, e.g.

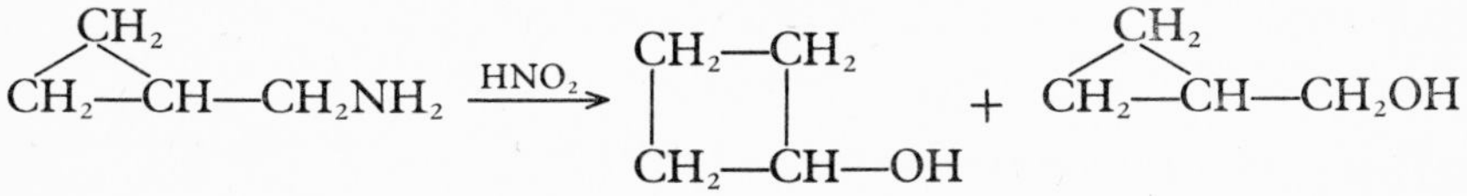

If a carbonium ion is formed, the rearrangement shifts the charge from a primary to a secondary carbon atom:

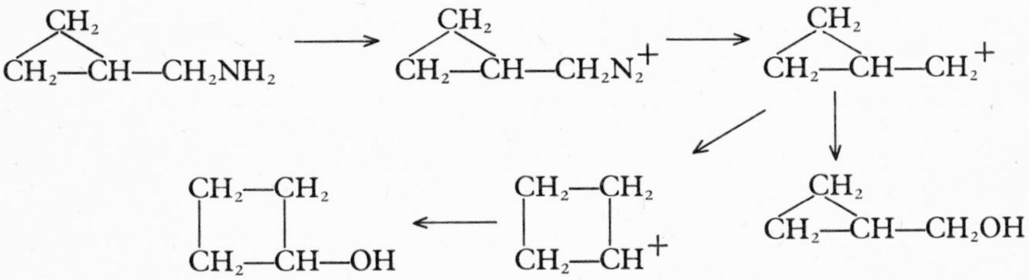

---

† Hughes, *Bull. Soc. chim.* 1951, **18**, p. C39; Winstein, ibid., p. C55.
‡ Cram, in Newman, *Steric Effects in Organic Chemistry*, chap. 5, New York: Wiley, 1956.

However, this mechanism entails that the labelled cyclopropyl methyl-amine (1) should yield the cyclopropyl methyl alcohol (2) exclusively labelled in the position shown, whereas actually only about half the isotopic carbon was in this position and the rest distributed amongst the other methylene groups. The isotope was similarly 'shuffled' in the cyclobutanol formed.

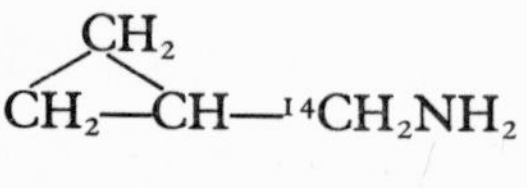

$$
\begin{array}{ccc}
\text{(1)} & \text{(2)} & \text{(3)}
\end{array}
$$

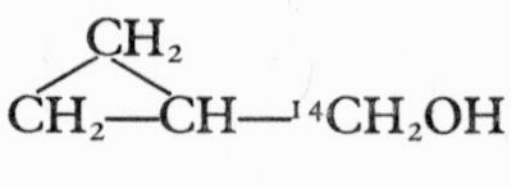

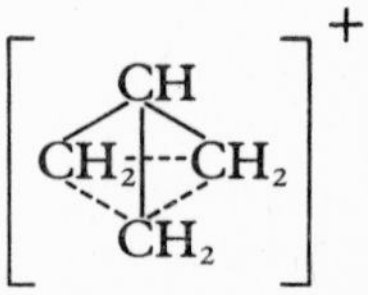

These results have led to the suggestion that a 'non-classical' carbonium ion (3) is formed as an intermediate; here the distinction between the three methylene groups has disappeared, and the dotted lines represent bonding arising from the triple overlap of the three sp^3 orbitals of the methylene carbon atoms.[†]

Wagner–Meerwein rearrangements occupy an important place in the chemistry of terpenes; these cyclic systems are also helpful in giving information about the steric course of the reactions. An example is the conversion of camphene hydrochloride (4) (the chlorine is covalently linked, in spite of the name) into isobornyl chloride (5).

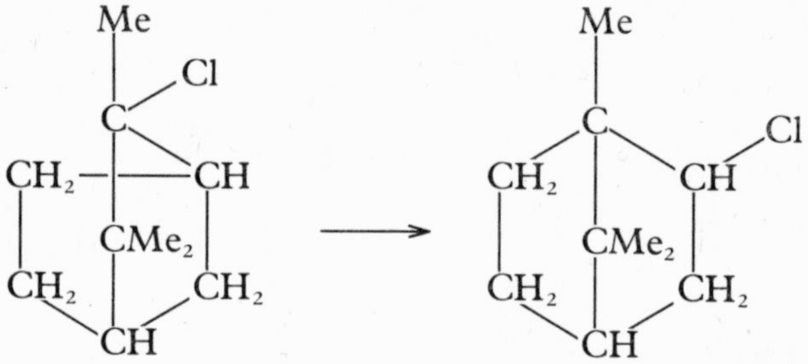

$$
\begin{array}{ccc}
\text{(4)} & & \text{(5)}
\end{array}
$$

The reaction proceeds more rapidly in solvents which aid ionization, and is accelerated by electrophilic substances such as $FeCl_3$ and $HgCl_2$ which have an affinity for chloride ion. Hence it is the cation which rearranges,[‡] i.e. this is another carbonium ion rearrangement; when suitably stabilized, the carbonium ion may be directly observed.[§]

[†] Roberts and Mazur, *J. Amer. Chem. Soc.* 1951, **73**, 3542.
[‡] Meerwein and van Emster, *Ber.* 1922, **55**, 2500.
[§] Bartlett, Webster, Dills, and Richey, *Annalen*, 1959, **623**, 217.

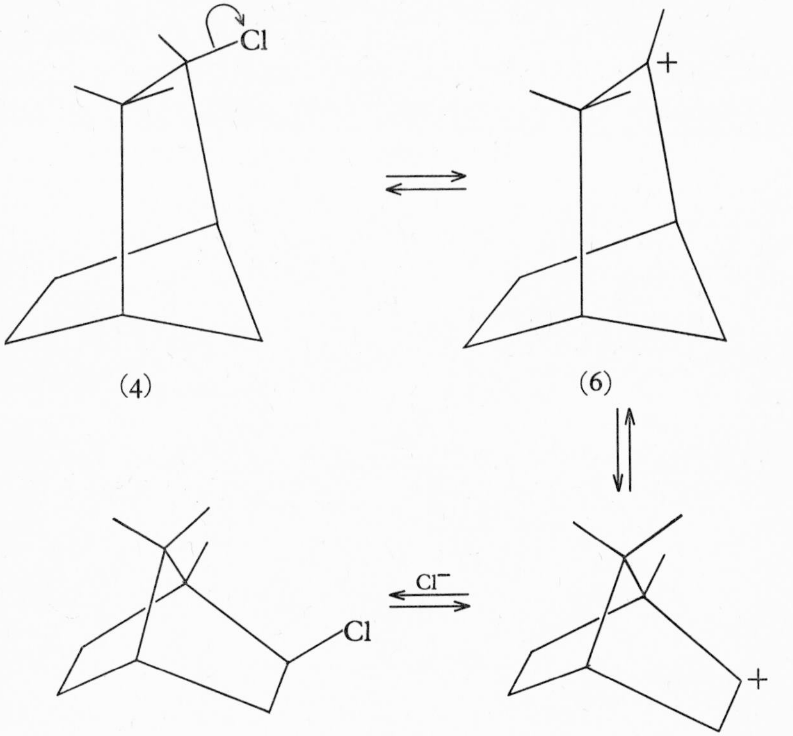

The structure sketched for the intermediates in the camphene hydro-chloride-isobornyl chloride rearrangement show that the carbon atom in (4) from which the chlorine atom departs forms its new bond on the side opposite from that which the chlorine left. There is, then, inversion of configuration at this carbon atom, which is the 'origin' of the migra-tion. The reaction is reversible, and the formulae show that this entails inversion of configuration also at the migration origin of the reverse reaction, which is the migration terminus of the forward reaction.

(d) *Benzilic acid rearrangement.* Benzil (1) is converted into benzilic acid (2) in alkaline solution; the rate is proportional to the concentra-tions of benzil and of hydroxide ion.

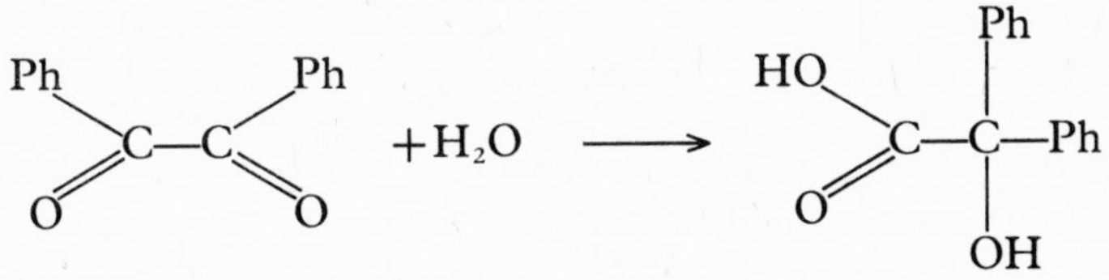

The benzilic acid rearrangement is somewhat like the pinacol rearrangement in reverse, in as far as the product contains two hydroxyl groups (although one of them is part of the carboxyl group), and a molecule of water is taken up during the reaction.

The nucleophilic hydroxide ion will attack the electrophilic carbon atom of a carbonyl group, and the high electron density due to the negative charge in the ion (3) will help to push the migrating phenyl group on to the electrophilic carbon atom of the other carbonyl group:

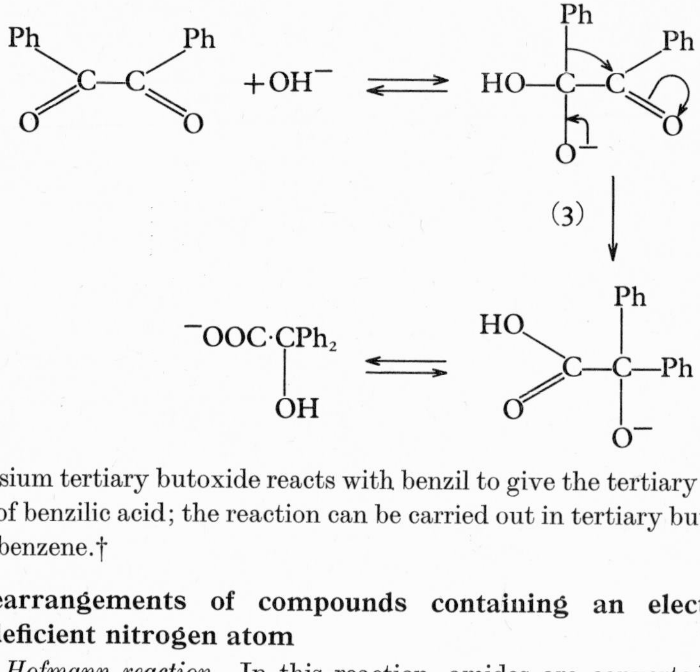

Potassium tertiary butoxide reacts with benzil to give the tertiary butyl ester of benzilic acid; the reaction can be carried out in tertiary butanol, or in benzene.†

3. Rearrangements of compounds containing an electron-deficient nitrogen atom

(a) *Hofmann reaction.* In this reaction, amides are converted into amines containing one carbon atom less.

$$RCONH_2 \longrightarrow RNH_2$$

The usual reagent is bromine, in alkaline solution, and the stoicheiometric equation then is

$$RCONH_2 + Br_2 + 2OH^- \longrightarrow RNH_2 + 2Br^- + CO_2 + H_2O$$

The Hofmann reaction proceeds via several intermediates, and so the first step in discussing the mechanism of the overall reaction is to

† Doering and Urban, *J. Amer. Chem. Soc.* 1956, **78**, 5939.

describe these intermediates, which, as they are relatively stable, can be identified by isolation.

The first stage is simply bromination of the amide:

$$RCONH_2 + Br_2 + OH^- \longrightarrow RCONH\cdot Br + H_2O + Br^-$$

The N-bromo-amide is ionized in alkaline solution: the anion will be mesomeric between (1) and (2).

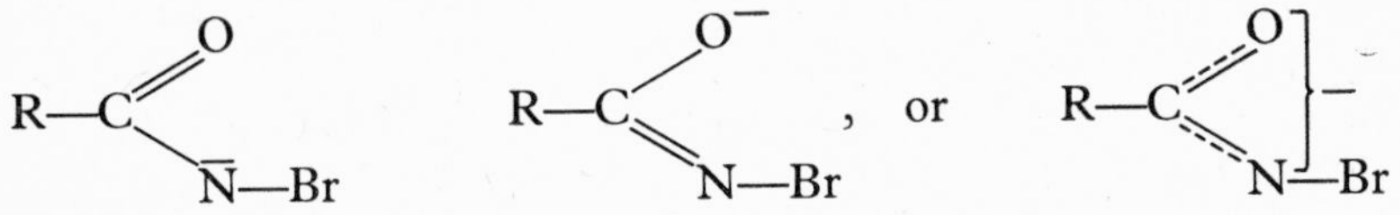

(1)   (2)   (3)

The next product which can be isolated is the isocyanate (4); with excess alkali in aqueous solution, this is hydrolysed to the amine.

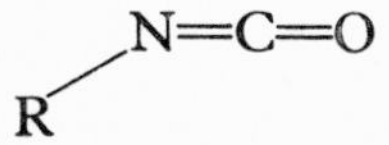

(4)

The rearrangement, then, is of the N-bromo-amide anion (3) to the isocyanate (4), and takes place with simultaneous expulsion of the bromide ion. The process may be illustrated with formula (2) for the anion:

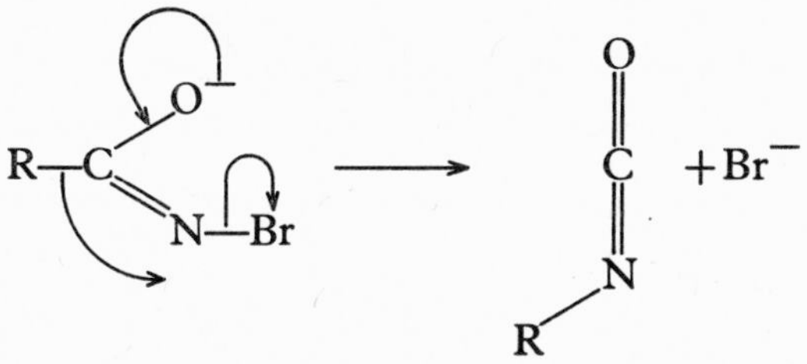

In a series of *meta*- and *para*-substituted bromo-benzamides, the rate of reaction (as measured by the rate of disappearance of the bromo-amide) is decreased by electron-attracting groups (e.g. nitro group) in the benzene ring, and increased by electron-repelling ones (e.g. methoxy group);† in Hammett's equation, $\rho = -2.5$. This is consistent with the picture we have drawn, since the migrating aryl group has to act as a nucleophile, and the sharp dependence of the rate on the structure

† Hauser and Renfrow, *J. Amer. Chem. Soc.* 1937, **59**, 121.

of the migrating group suggests that participation of this group is necessary for the reaction to take place. Hence strongly electron-attracting R groups are not favourable for the Hofmann reaction, and under the usual conditions perfluoro compounds give the perfluoro alkyl bromide and sodium cyanate.

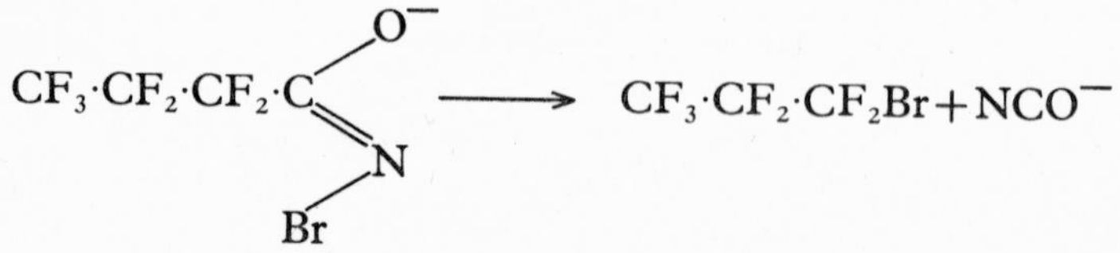

$$CF_3 \cdot CF_2 \cdot CF_2 \cdot C \overset{O^-}{\underset{N}{\diagdown}} \quad \longrightarrow \quad CF_3 \cdot CF_2 \cdot CF_2 Br + NCO^-$$
Br

Only under anhydrous conditions is the organic isocyanate (C_3F_7—NCO) formed. The formation of the perfluoro alkyl bromide has been ascribed to a 1,3-shift† (instead of the usual 1,2-shift) and could be formulated

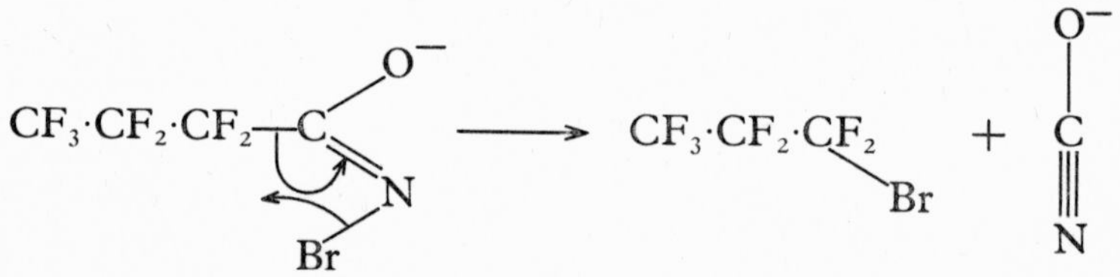

$$CF_3 \cdot CF_2 \cdot CF_2 \overset{O^-}{\underset{\underset{Br}{}}{C \diagdown N}} \quad \longrightarrow \quad CF_3 \cdot CF_2 \cdot CF_2 \underset{Br}{} \quad + \quad \overset{O^-}{\underset{N}{\overset{|}{\underset{\|}{C}}}}$$

A similar mechanism might apply to the Hofmann reaction with α-hydroxy acids (Weerman reaction), which gives aldehydes and sodium cyanate, and is used (preparatively and analytically) in the chemistry of carbohydrates.

The mechanism described above for the Hofmann reaction can be tested with regard to its stereochemical implications. If the shift of the alkyl group is synchronous with the expulsion of the bromide ion, the configuration of the carbon atom in the migrating group should be retained. This has been shown to be so, in the example given below.‡

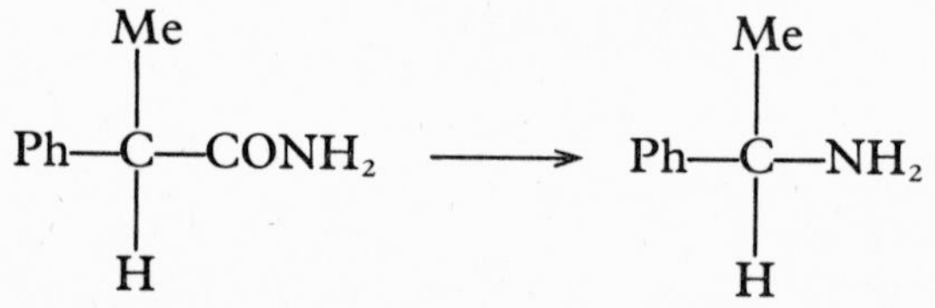

$$\underset{H}{\overset{Me}{Ph-\overset{|}{\underset{|}{C}}-CONH_2}} \quad \longrightarrow \quad \underset{H}{\overset{Me}{Ph-\overset{|}{\underset{|}{C}}-NH_2}}$$

Moreover, the optically active amide (5) gives the active amine (6).§

† Barr and Hazeldine, *J. Chem. Soc.* 1957, p. 30.
‡ Campbell and Kenyon, ibid. 1946, p. 25.
§ Bell, ibid. 1934, p. 835.

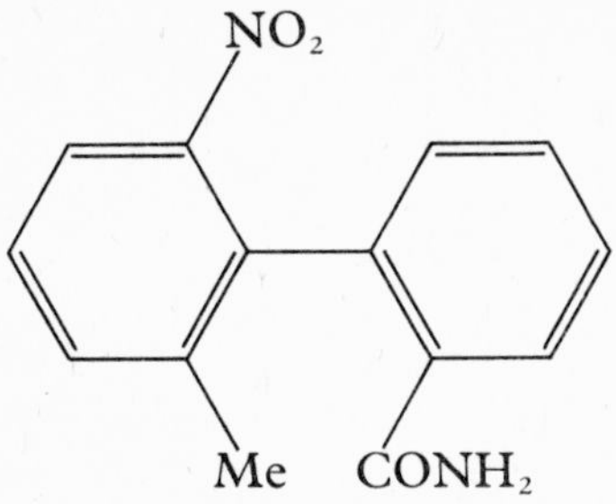

$$(5) \qquad\qquad\qquad\qquad (6)$$

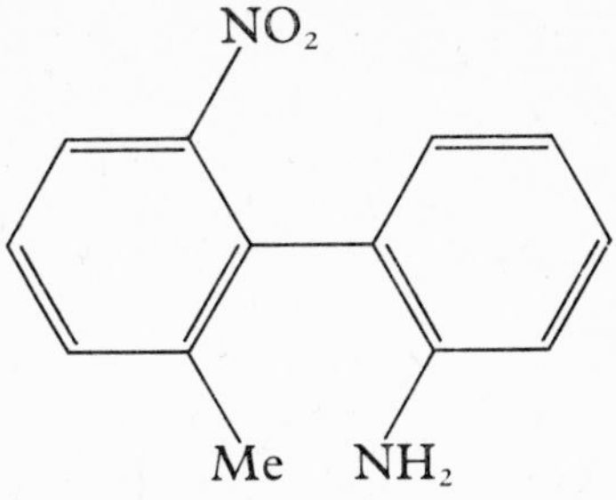

The optical activity of these diphenyls depends on the two benzene rings lying in different planes; if the rings can become co-planar the common plane is a plane of symmetry for the molecule as a whole, and consequently racemization ensues. Thus the preservation of optical activity means that here the R group in the Hofmann reaction of $RCONH_2$ never cuts loose from the rest of the molecule during the reaction. This suggests, although it does not demand, a synchronous shift.

(b) *Curtius reaction of acid azides.* This reaction takes place on warming an acyl azide in an inert solvent (e.g. benzene):

$$RCON_3 \longrightarrow RNCO + N_2$$

The azides are mesomeric between

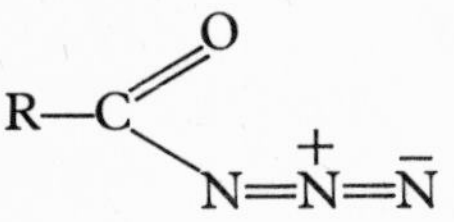

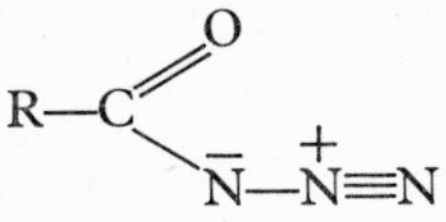

$$(1) \qquad\qquad\qquad (2) \qquad\qquad\qquad (3)$$

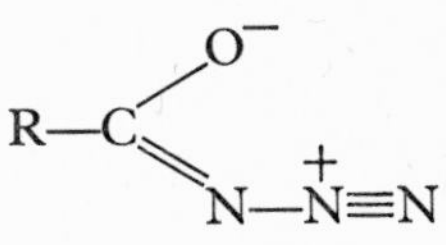

The rearrangement may be depicted, by analogy with the Hofmann reaction of amides (formula (3) is chosen), as

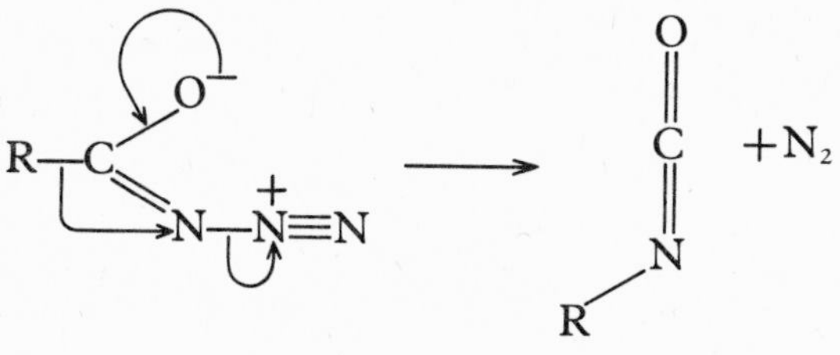

The bond $N{-}N_2^+$ in azides, like the bond $C{-}N_2^+$ in diazonium salts, is

readily broken, as the high bond energy in molecular nitrogen (226 kcal/mol) makes a contribution towards lowering the energy of the transition state. Effectively, molecular nitrogen is a particularly good leaving group, and does not require much help from the migrating group. Thus even the strongly electron-attracting perfluoro alkyl groups behave normally in the Curtius reaction.

The migrating group has been shown to preserve its configuration, and remain bound to the rest of the molecule during rearrangement, by the same methods as were illustrated for the Hofmann reaction. The Curtius reaction is catalysed by acids;† a protonated form of the azide would be expected to lose nitrogen even more readily than the neutral form.

The Schmidt reaction is similar to the Curtius reaction, but broader in scope. The reagents in the Schmidt reaction are hydrazoic acid (HN_3) and another acid; as well as the reaction with carboxylic acids,

$$PhCOOH + HN_3 \xrightarrow{\ H_2SO_4\ } PhNH_2 + CO_2 + N_2,$$

there is a reaction with ketones to give amides,

$$R \cdot CO \cdot R + HN_3 \xrightarrow{\ H_2SO_4\ } R \cdot CO \cdot NH \cdot R + N_2.$$

Unsymmetrical ketones (R_1—CO—R_2) can give two amides

$$(R_1—CONHR_2 \text{ and } R_2—CONHR_1),$$

the result depending on which group migrates. A ketone with two different aryl groups usually gives a nearly 1:1 mixture of products, even when one aryl group has an electron-withdrawing substituent and the other an electron-repelling one:‡ hence the migrating group is again not called upon to help off the leaving group (molecular nitrogen).

When two groups are very different in size, then the bulkier group tends to migrate,§ which may be a consequence of the preferred conformation of the intermediate (5): the —N^+≡N group will be directed away from the bulkier of the two R groups, and the bulkier group will then migrate.

† Coleman, Newman, and Garett, *J. Amer. Chem. Soc.* 1954, **76**, 4534.
‡ Smith and Ashby, ibid. 1950, **72**, 2503; Smith and Horwitz, ibid., p. 3718.
§ Badger, Howard, and Simons, *J. Chem. Soc.* 1952, p. 2849.

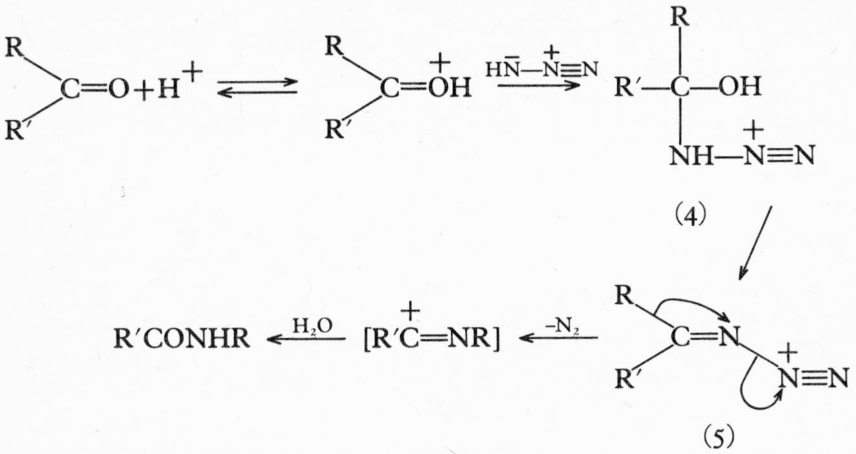

(4)

$$R'CONHR \xleftarrow{H_2O} [R'\overset{+}{C}{=}NR] \xleftarrow{-N_2}$$

(5)

This mechanism assumes that the function of the acid is to convert the carbonyl compound into the protonated form, which then reacts with hydrazoic acid to give, after dehydration, (5), which then undergoes rearrangement:† there is no direct evidence for (4) and (5). A similar sort of mechanism can be written down for the Schmidt reaction with carboxylic acids.

(c) *Beckmann rearrangement.* This is also a 1,2-shift from carbon to nitrogen: oximes are converted into amides under acidic conditions.

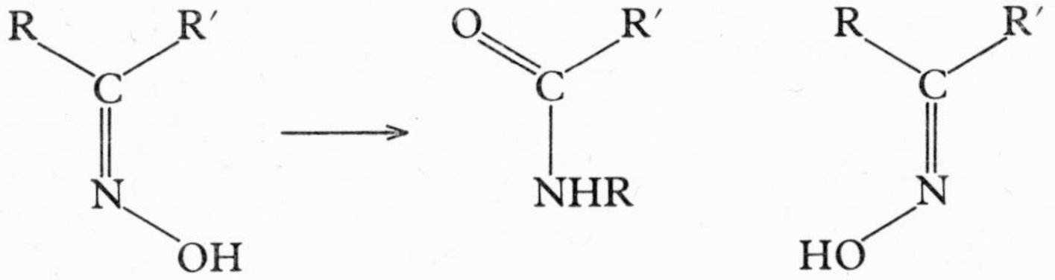

(1)   (2)

The reaction has been written so as to show that the group *trans* with respect to the hydroxyl group is the one that migrates and becomes bound to the nitrogen atom. This conclusion can only be reached if it is known that the oxime has the configuration (1) and not that of its geometrical isomer (2). In several cases both isomeric oximes, and their configurations, are known, and the migration of the *trans* group is invariably observed.‡ Often the oxime appears to consist entirely of

† Smith, *J. Amer. Chem. Soc.* 1948, **70**, 320.
‡ Taylor and Baker, *Sidgwick's Organic Chemistry of Nitrogen*, chap. 6, Oxford: Clarendon Press, 1937.

one isomer, e.g. (3), a configuration based on the *trans* migration to give (4). The configuration of (3) is such that the hydroxyl group points away from the bulkier R group.

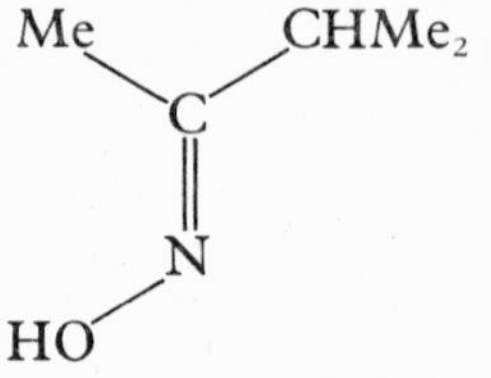

$$
\begin{array}{c}
\text{Me} \qquad \text{CHMe}_2 \\
\diagdown \diagup \\
\text{C} \\
\| \\
\text{N} \\
\diagup \\
\text{HO}
\end{array}
\qquad\qquad
\text{MeCO·NH·CHMe}_2
$$

(3)   (4)

The *trans* migration entails inversion of the configuration of the nitrogen atom; the migrating group itself, however, retains its configuration. This was established with the analogues of the compounds used to settle this point in the Hofmann reaction.

The Beckmann rearrangement can be carried out in sulphuric acid; the function of the acid is to convert the oxime ($R_2C{=}NOH$) into the protonated form ($R_2C{=}N\overset{+}{O}H_2$) so that H_2O rather than $\overset{-}{O}H$ can be lost:

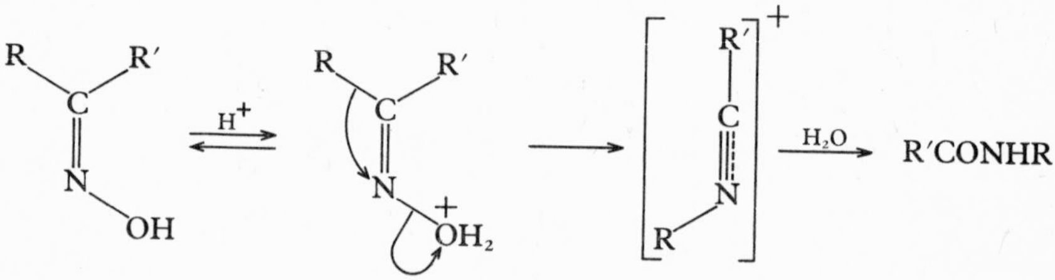

4. Rearrangements of compounds containing an electron-deficient oxygen atom

Ketones react with per-acids to give esters (Baeyer–Villiger reaction); per-trifluoro-acetic acid has been recommended as the per-acid to use:†

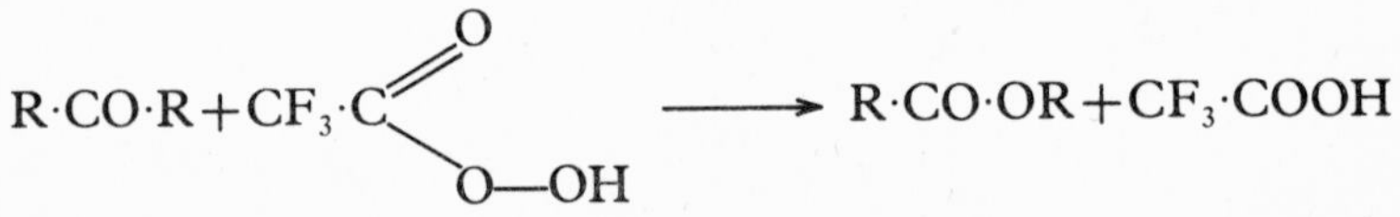

$$
\text{R·CO·R} + \text{CF}_3\text{·C}\underset{\text{O—OH}}{\overset{\text{O}}{\diagup\diagdown}} \longrightarrow \text{R·CO·OR} + \text{CF}_3\text{·COOH}
$$

The formula of the product differs from that of the starting material by one oxygen atom, which appears to have been 'inserted' (cf. the Schmidt reaction). An unsymmetrical ketone can give two different

† Sager and Duckworth, *J. Amer. Chem. Soc.* 1955, **77**, 188; Emmons and Lucas, ibid., p. 2287.

esters, and there is a parallelism between the positions of fission of the carbon chain in the Beckmann rearrangement and in the per-acid one. This suggests a similar mechanism. Two other observations which have a bearing on the mechanism are that the carbonyl group of the ketone becomes the carbonyl group of the ester[†]

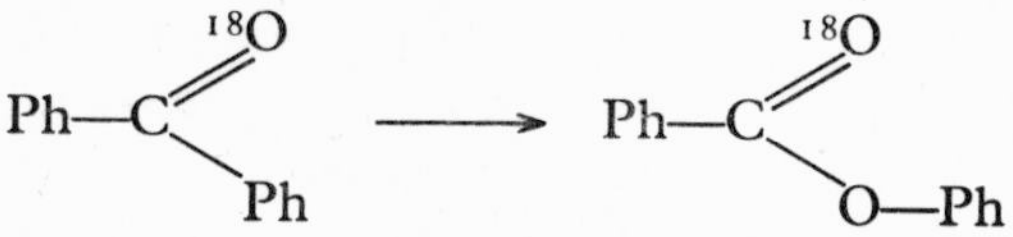

$$\text{Ph—C}\Big(\!\begin{array}{c}^{18}\text{O}\\\text{Ph}\end{array} \quad\longrightarrow\quad \text{Ph—C}\Big(\!\begin{array}{c}^{18}\text{O}\\\text{O—Ph}\end{array}$$

and that the migrating group retains its configuration.[‡]

The following mechanism interprets these results:[§]

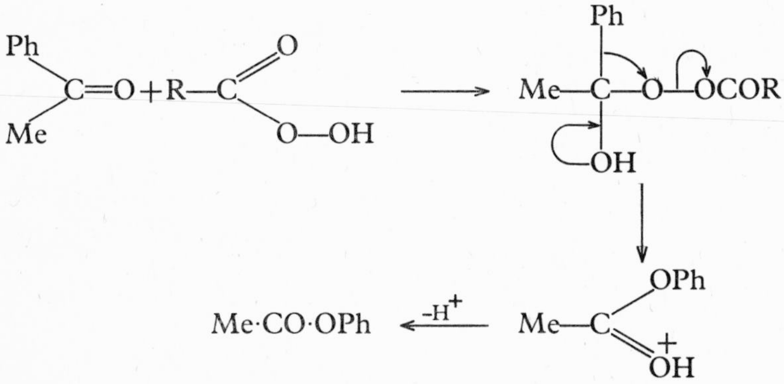

$$\begin{array}{c}\text{Ph}\\\text{C}=\text{O}\\\text{Me}\end{array} + \text{R—C}\Big(\!\begin{array}{c}\text{O}\\\text{O—OH}\end{array} \quad\longrightarrow\quad \begin{array}{c}\text{Ph}\\\text{Me—C—O—OCOR}\\\text{OH}\end{array}$$

$$\text{Me·CO·OPh} \quad\xleftarrow{-\text{H}^+}\quad \text{Me—C}\Big(\!\begin{array}{c}\text{OPh}\\\overset{+}{\text{OH}}\end{array}$$

The first stage is an addition to the carbonyl group, and then, as the acyl residue from the per-acid moves away, the oxygen atom becomes electron-deficient and the phenyl group migrates on to the oxygen atom.

Summary

In the rearrangements so far described the main features are:

(i) A 1,2-shift of a migrating group on to an atom which is (or is becoming) electron-deficient because the leaving group is taking both of the formerly shared pair of electrons with it.

(ii) The group which migrates retains its configuration and never becomes free from the rest of the molecule.

(iii) The configurations of the atoms from which the migrating group departs, and to which it goes, both become inverted, in the cases where the type of reaction lends itself to such scrutiny.

† Doering and Dorfmann, *J. Amer. Chem. Soc.* 1953, **75**, 5595.
‡ Turner, ibid. 1950, **72**, 878.
§ Robertson and Waters, *J. Chem. Soc.* 1948, 1574.

5. Rearrangements involving shift of an acyl group

There are several reactions which may be assigned to this category, but only a few examples will be discussed here. Since amines react with esters to give amides, if an amino group and an ester, or thiol ester, group are present in the same molecule, the ester may rearrange to give an amide. Thus O-benzoylthreonine (1) is promptly converted in alkaline solution into N-benzoylthreonine (2):†

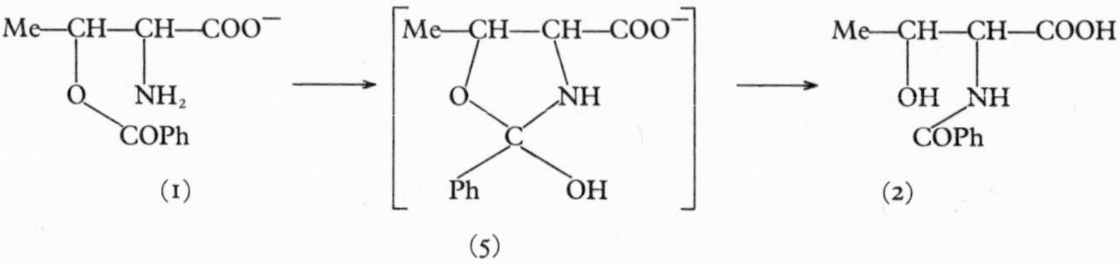

(1)   (5)   (2)

Similarly, S-glycylcysteamine (3) rearranges to N-glycylcysteamine (4):‡

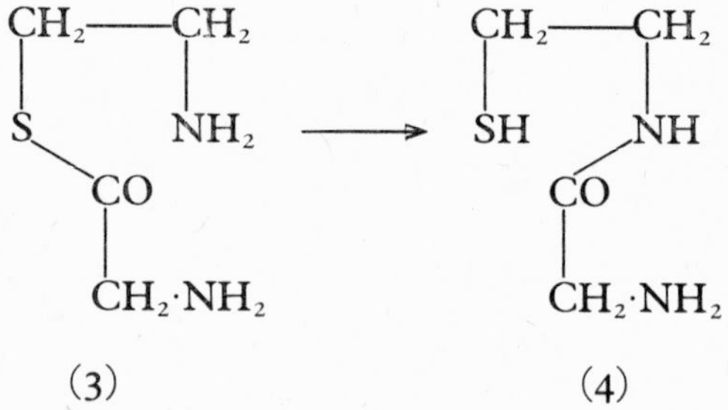

(3)   (4)

If the sulphur and nitrogen atoms are separated by more than two carbon atoms, this acyl shift proceeds much less readily. This is consistent with the view that these rearrangements proceed via (unstable) cyclic intermediates, e.g. (5), which are analogous to the intermediates formulated for the reactions of esters with amines in Chapter VII (§ 1 a).

The reverse sequence (amide to ester, acyl shift from nitrogen to oxygen) can also be effected, although not so directly. Here the cyclic intermediates (6) and (7) are stable and can be isolated.§

There is an interesting stereochemical feature in these reactions. The amino acid, threonine, contains two dissimilar asymmetric carbon atoms,

† Elliott, *J. Chem. Soc.* 1949, 589.
‡ Wieland and Pfleiderer, *Adv. Enzymol.* 1957, **19**, 235.
§ Attenburrow, Elliott, and Penny, *J. Chem. Soc.* 1948, p. 310.

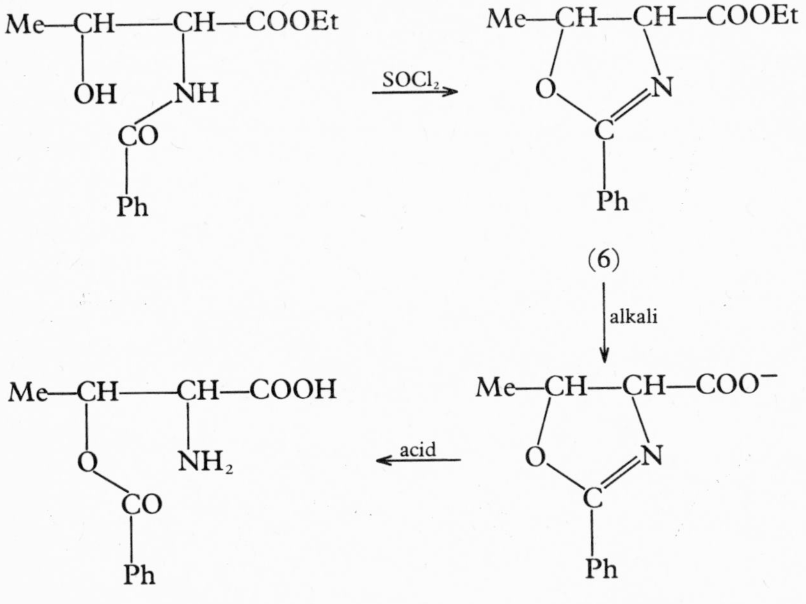

Me—CH———CH—COOEt $\xrightarrow{\text{SOCl}_2}$ Me—CH——CH—COOEt

(with OH and NH—CO—Ph substituents on left structure; O and N=C—Ph ring on right structure)

(6)

↓ alkali

Me—CH———CH—COOH $\xleftarrow{\text{acid}}$ Me—CH——CH—COO⁻

(7)

so there are four stereoisomers; the absolute configurations are shown below, in Fischer projections:

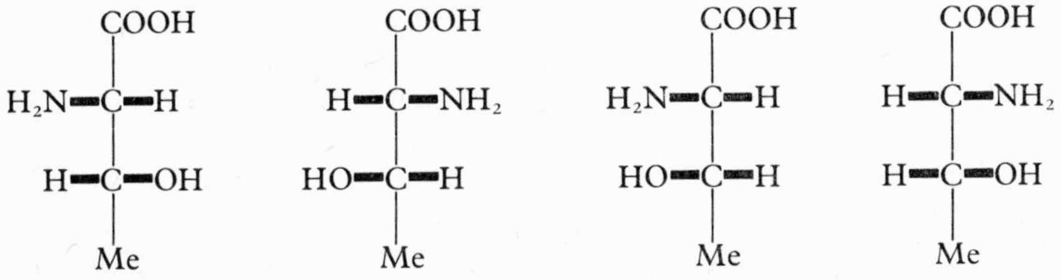

	COOH	COOH	COOH	COOH
	H_2N—C—H	H—C—NH_2	H_2N—C—H	H—C—NH_2
	H—C—OH	HO—C—H	HO—C—H	H—C—OH
	Me	Me	Me	Me
	L-threonine	D-threonine	L-*allo*threonine	D-*allo*threonine

The terms L and D refer to the configuration of the upper carbon atom to which the amino group is linked, and the term *allo* refers to the relationship between the configurations of the two asymmetrical atoms and signifies that the amino and hydroxyl groups are *cis* in the projection formula. The cyclization with thionyl chloride causes inversion of the configuration of the carbon atom carrying a hydroxyl group, and in the reactive conformation there is a *trans* relation between the nitrogen and oxygen atoms linked to the asymmetric carbon atoms.† This means

† Johnson and Schubert, *J. Amer. Chem. Soc.* 1950, **72**, 2187.

that derivatives of *allo*threonine can be converted into threonine. Thus N-benzoyl-DL-*allo*threonine ethyl ester is converted by thionyl chloride into the oxazoline (8) configurationally related to (and hydrolytically convertible into) threonine rather than *allo*threonine (for simplicity, the formulae show only one enantiomer):

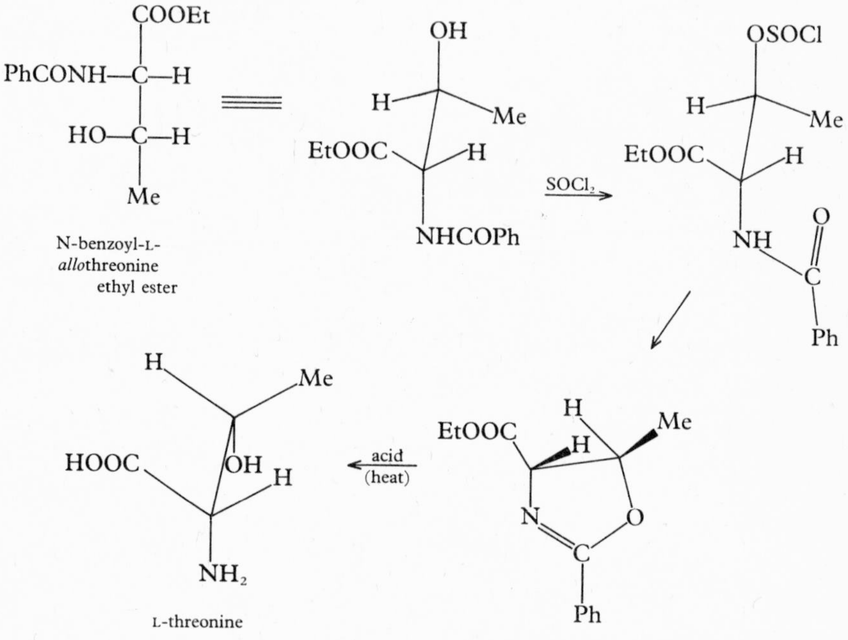

(8)

The cyclization to (8), as a nucleophilic substitution, causes inversion. Since several preparative methods give mostly *allo*threonine derivatives,† and since threonine is the naturally occurring stereoisomer, the inversion sequence is useful.

† Elliott, *J. Chem. Soc.* 1949, p. 589; Pfister, Robinson, Shabica, and Tishler, *J. Amer. Chem. Soc.* 1949, **71**, 1101.

AROMATIC SUBSTITUTIONS

1. Aromatic character

AROMATIC rings are present in proteins and in nucleic acids, and in most coenzymes and prosthetic groups. Aromatic character is thus a subject of general interest. Although we are only concerned with reactions, the structure and reactivity of aromatic compounds are closely connected, and so our account of aromatic substitution reactions is preceded by a brief description of aromatic character.

The term aromatic character summarizes certain aspects of the chemical behaviour of a compound, and (as suggested by the everyday usage of the word character) aromatic character is more readily recognized than defined. Aromatic compounds are generally thermally stable and can often be formed by reactions carried out at relatively high temperatures (e.g. the formation of some benzene from acetylene at 500° C, and of toluene from heptane). The special stability of aromatic systems is shown most markedly in the nature of the unsaturation of aromatic compounds. Although aromatic compounds resemble other unsaturated compounds in being reduced by hydrogen, it is characteristic of aromatic compounds to react by substitution rather than by addition. Thus olefines commonly react with (decolourize) bromine water, and with alkaline potassium permanganate, but benzene does not affect these reagents. Similarly, olefines add hydrogen bromide (Chapter IV), and sulphuric acid, but benzene does not react with the first, and is substituted by the second. These are the types of experimental criteria which are used in judging aromatic character.

It is not only the reactions of benzene which are at variance with the conventional structures (1) and (2). All the carbon-carbon distances are

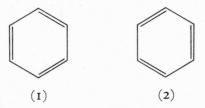

(1)   (2)

the same, and the molecule is a regular hexagon, so that there are no ordinary single and double carbon-carbon bonds. This situation was discussed in Chapter I (§ 1 *o*) and was ascribed to mesomerism between (1) and (2). The mesomerism was also correlated with the high stability of benzene, as reflected in the discrepancy between the observed heat of formation and that calculated from the average bond energies (Chapter I, § 2 *c*). Before discussing this point in more detail, we shall extend our range and note a few other aromatic systems, without citing the evidence for their being aromatic.

The aromatic ring need not be six-membered, nor need it be uncharged, nor need it be carbocyclic. Thus, the tropylium cation (3) is a stable aromatic species. It is a regular plane heptagon mesomeric between the seven formulae of the same type as (3) with the positive charge located on a different carbon atom in each formula; hence formulae such as (4) are often used.

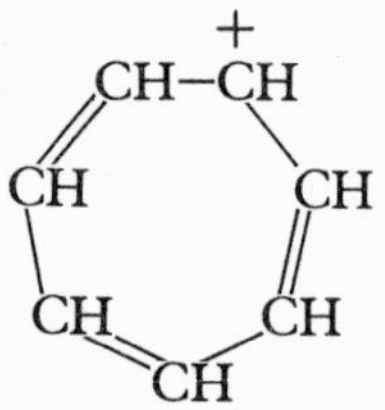

(3) 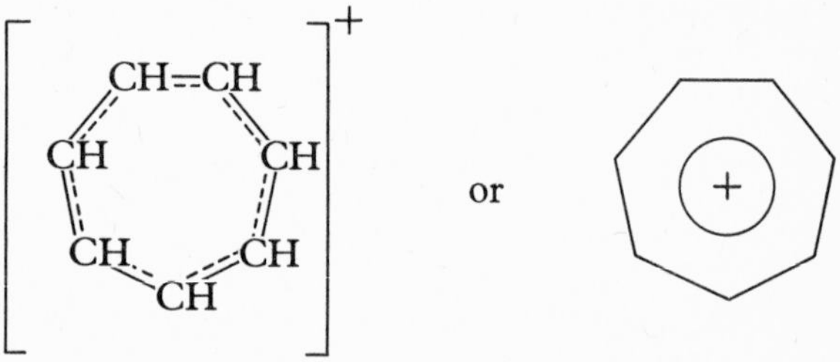   (4)

Similarly, the anion (6) derived from cyclopentadiene (5) is aromatic.

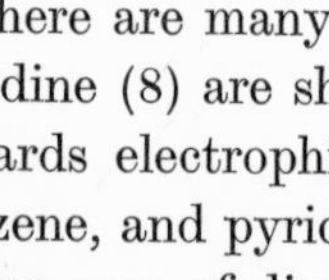

(5) 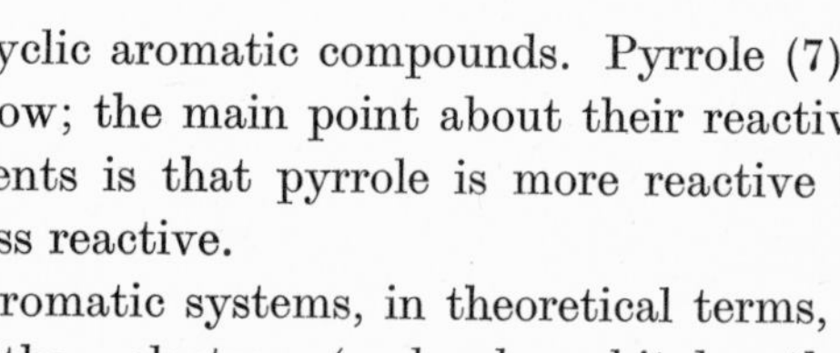   (6)

There are many heterocyclic aromatic compounds. Pyrrole (7) and pyridine (8) are shown below; the main point about their reactivities towards electrophilic reagents is that pyrrole is more reactive than benzene, and pyridine is less reactive.

One way of discussing aromatic systems, in theoretical terms, concentrates on the orbitals of the π-electrons (molecular orbital method).†

† Coulson, *Valence*, Oxford: Clarendon Press, 1952; Dewar, in *Progress in Organic Chemistry*, edited by Cook, vol. **2**, London: Butterworths, 1953; Longuet-Higgins, *Proc. Chem. Soc.* 1957, 157.

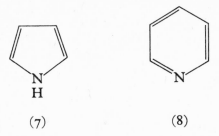

(7)   (8)

The six π-electrons in benzene (Chapter I, § 1 o) are allotted in pairs to the three orbitals which are of lowest energy. Now it turns out that there are just three stable ('bonding') orbitals to be filled, in all the aromatic systems we have cited. The arrangement, as in benzene, of six π-electrons in three stable orbitals, can be described as a 'closed shell' arrangement. The tropylium ion (4) also has six π-electrons, and also has a closed shell and the same applies to the anion (6) from cyclopentadiene.

Pyridine (8) is similar to benzene, in that the replacement of CH by N is an iso-electronic replacement; however, as nitrogen is more electro-negative than carbon, the mobile π-electrons will be drawn towards the nitrogen atom and the carbon atoms of the ring will be correspondingly depleted of electrons. These features are also brought out by repre-senting pyridine as mesomeric between (8), (9), (10), and (11).

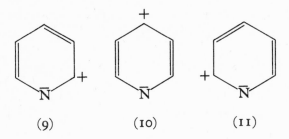

(9)   (10)   (11)

The signs of the charges on the ring carbon atoms can be correlated with the relative unreactivity of pyridine towards electrophilic reagents. Conversely, pyridine is reactive towards nucleophilic reagents; thus it reacts with NH_2^- to give 2-aminopyridine.

For pyrrole (7) to be aromatic, the ring nitrogen atom must contribute its unshared pair of electrons to make up the total of six π-electrons to fill the three orbitals. There is then a fractional positive charge on the nitrogen atom, and fractional negative charges on the carbon atoms, which can again be correlated with the enhanced reactivity of pyrrole towards electrophilic reagents. In terms of mesomerism pyrrole is described as being mesomeric between (7), (12), (13), (14), and (15).

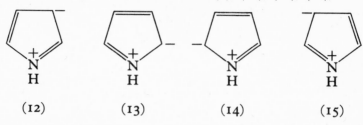

(12)   (13)   (14)   (15)

The resonance or mesomerism does not 'explain' the behaviour of pyridine or pyrrole, but the formulae show the signs of the charges. Furthermore, pyrrole is devoid of basic properties; the unshared pair of electrons of the nitrogen atom are not available for bonding a proton as they have been pooled with the electrons of the ring carbon atoms to form the aromatic sextet.

Aromaticity, then, in a monocyclic system demands the presence of six π-electrons, and also demands uninterrupted conjugation of all the annular atoms. Thus cyclopentadiene and cycloheptatriene are not themselves aromatic (although the latter contains six π-electrons), as the methylene (CH_2) groups interrupt the conjugation.

The same principles apply to heterocyclic rings containing more than one hetero atom. Pyridine can be regarded as derived from benzene by the replacement of one CH group by a nitrogen atom, and this process can be repeated: there are three six-membered aromatic rings containing two nitrogen atoms, of which one is pyrimidine (16). Similarly, a CH group in pyrrole can be replaced by a nitrogen atom to give glyoxaline (iminazole) (17). Glyoxaline, as was pointed out in Chapter VI, contains both a secondary nitrogen atom, bearing a partial positive charge (as in pyrrole) and a tertiary nitrogen atom bearing a partial negative charge (as in pyridine). There are several other heterocyclic systems containing one ring. An oxygen atom, or a sulphur atom, may, like the NH group, supply two electrons to make up the complement of six, as in thiophen (18) and thiazole (19). All these monocyclic aromatic systems contain

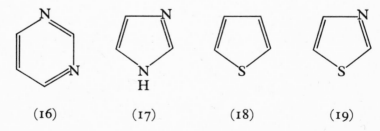

(16)   (17)   (18)   (19)

six π-electrons: either there are six annular atoms which can each provide one electron, or there are five annular atoms of which one can
provide two electrons. In this way, each annular atom takes part in
the conjugated system.

So far, only monocyclic systems have been mentioned, but there are,
of course, many polycyclic aromatic systems. The simplest are fused
bicyclic molecules, such as naphthalene (20) and purine (21), which

(20)   (21)

contain ten π-electrons instead of the six π-electrons in the monocyclic
compounds. Several aromatic systems, in fact, have altogether $(4n+2)$
π-electrons, where n is an integer ($n = 1$ for benzene, $n = 2$ for naphthalene, $n = 3$ for anthracene, etc.). This is a consequence of there being,
for example, three stable orbitals available in a monocyclic system.[†]
It should, perhaps, be stressed that although theoretical treatments
have progressed farther in the field of aromatic structure than elsewhere
in organic chemistry, whether a compound is deemed aromatic has to
be decided from experimental observations.

A brief outline of the structure of some aromatic systems has now
been given, and we can turn to our real subject-matter of substitutions
in aromatic compounds. The π-electrons play the main part in these
reactions, and aromatic compounds, like olefines, are characteristically
nucleophilic species, so that the most important type of reaction is with
electrophilic reagents. An example from free-radical substitutions will
also be discussed; some nucleophilic substitutions were described in
Chapter III (§ 5 b).

2. Nitration of aromatic compounds[‡]

(a) *The nature of the reagent.* The reactivities of aromatic compounds
towards substitutions in general, and towards nitration in particular,
have been studied for many years. The general nature of the active

---

† Longuet-Higgins, in *Theoretical Organic Chemistry* (The Kekulé Symposium), p. 9,
London: Butterworths, 1959; Craig, ibid., p. 20. For the application of these ideas to
coenzymes, see Pullmann and Pullmann, *Proc. Nat. Acad. Sci. Wash.* 1959, **45**, 136.

‡ De la Mare and Ridd, *Aromatic Substitution*, London: Butterworths, 1959.

species in nitration has also long been familiar. The evidence from measurements of dipole moments (Chapter I, § 2 a) shows that there is a general correlation between ease of nitration and electron density; compounds such as nitrobenzene, in which the ring is (relative to benzene) depleted of electrons, are nitrated much less readily than benzene. Hence the reagent seems to prefer rings of high electron density, i.e. it is an electrophilic reagent. Before discussing any further the nature of the reactive species in nitration we must specify the conditions which bring about the reaction.

Nitrations (of all but the most reactive compounds) are commonly carried out in sulphuric acid solution. So the first step is to consider the nature of the reagent (nitric acid) and the reactant (the aromatic compound) in this strongly acidic medium. Now the Raman spectrum of nitric acid in sulphuric acid does not show the lines characteristic of molecular nitric acid, but instead shows one line which is also observed in nitronium perchlorate (1); the structure of this salt is known from crystallographic measurements.

$$O\!=\!\overset{+}{N}\!=\!O \quad ClO_4^- \qquad\qquad HNO_3 \xrightarrow{\ H_2SO_4\ } NO_2^+$$

$$(\mathbf{1})$$

This (and other evidence) shows that nitric acid is ionized in sulphuric acid, and that nitronium ions (NO_2^+) are formed, as shown above. The complete equation

$$HNO_3 + 2H_2SO_4 \rightleftharpoons NO_2^+ + H_3O^+ + 2HSO_4^-$$

may be regarded as the sum of three processes: protonation of nitric acid

$$HNO_3 + H_2SO_4 \rightleftharpoons H_2NO_3^+ + HSO_4^-,$$

dehydration $$H_2NO_3^+ \rightleftharpoons NO_2^+ + H_2O,$$

and protonation of the water so formed

$$H_2O + H_2SO_4 \rightleftharpoons H_3O^+ + HSO_4^-.$$

The predominating species in a solution of nitric acid in sulphuric acid is then the nitronium ion. This is also a species suitable for effecting nitration: it is positively charged, and the third nitrogen-oxygen bond of molecular nitric acid has already been severed. After the nitronium ion has combined with the aromatic ring, only the loss of a proton is required to give the nitro compound. The organic compound may be partially protonated in sulphuric acid; this will greatly decrease its reactivity, and is probably why nitration of, for example, anthraquinone, proceeds less rapidly in 100 per cent. than in 90 per cent. sulphuric acid. Nitration in sulphuric acid, then, proceeds by way of the nitronium ion; the reaction is usually first-order in reactant, and first-order in (total) nitric acid.

In pure nitric acid (i.e. in the absence of sulphuric acid) there is evidence for the equilibrium (i)

$$2HNO_3 \rightleftharpoons NO_2^+ + H_2O + NO_3^- \tag{i}$$

The rate of nitration of several compounds (including nitrobenzene) is decreased by the addition of nitrate ion, which displaces the equilibrium (i) to the left, and increased by the addition of sulphuric acid, which removes the nitrate ion by the reaction

$$NO_3^- + H_2SO_4 \rightleftharpoons HNO_3 + HSO_4^-,$$

and so displaces the equilibrium (i) to the right. This evidence suggests that the nitronium ion is also the reactive nitrating agent in pure nitric acid.

Kinetic studies on nitration in sulphuric acid, or in nitric acid, as solvents are restricted to relatively unreactive compounds, which do not react at a rate too great to measure. In organic solvents, however, more reactive compounds can be studied. Several different compounds (including toluene, and ethylbenzene) are nitrated at the same rate in nitromethane as solvent. The rate-determining step, therefore, cannot involve the aromatic compound at all, but must be the formation of a reactive species from molecular nitric acid. In these reactions, the nitric acid is present in excess, and so the reaction is zero-order, i.e. the rate is constant throughout the course of a single run. Moreover, the addition of nitrate ions decreases the rate, but does not prevent the reaction from being zero-order. Hence the rate-determining step is still formation of the active nitrating species, but the rate of formation of this species is lessened when nitrate ions are added. These results can be interpreted by the following mechanism:

$$2HNO_3 \underset{\longleftarrow}{\overset{fast}{\longrightarrow}} H_2NO_3^+ + NO_3^- \tag{ii}$$

$$H_2NO_3^+ \overset{slow}{\longrightarrow} NO_2^+ + H_2O \tag{iii}$$

$$NO_2^+ + ArH \overset{fast}{\longrightarrow} ArNO_2 + H^+ \tag{iv}$$

Here again the reactive species is the nitronium ion, and, provided that the aromatic compound (ArH) is sufficiently reactive, the rate-determining step in these nitrations is the formation of the nitronium ion (reaction iii). Hence, as there is excess of nitric acid, the reaction is zero-order. The addition of nitrate ions displaces equilibrium (ii) to the left, and so cuts down the *rate* of formation of nitronium ions by decreasing the *extent* of formation of $H_2NO_3^+$. However, with less reactive aromatic compounds the reaction becomes first-order in the reactant, as the nitration proper (reaction iv) is now no longer rapid compared with formation of the nitronium ion.

Although the nitronium ion is the reactive species in these nitrations, the nitration of phenols and amines may proceed by a different mechanism. These compounds are particularly reactive (and are also readily oxidized) and so the reaction is carried out in dilute aqueous solution; here the concentration of nitronium ions is very low. Nitrous acid (present in the nitric acid, and formed from it by reduction) can furnish nitrosating agents, and the aromatic nitroso compounds are then oxidized by nitric acid to give the nitro compounds.†

(*b*) *Mechanism of nitration by the nitronium ion.* Substitutions at an unsaturated carbon atom seem usually to proceed via an intermediate, as we have noted in earlier chapters, and so the question arises whether aromatic substitutions constitute an exception or not. In certain instances ionic complexes can be detected, or even isolated. When an olefinic double bond is conjugated with aromatic rings, substitution rather than addition may occur:

$$Ar_2C{=}CH_2 + Br_2 \longrightarrow Ar_2C{=}CHBr + HBr$$

Salts of the carbonium ion (1) were, in fact, isolated and this led to the

---

† Most of the work on the mechanism of nitration has been carried out by Ingold and Hughes, and their collaborators; it is described in Ingold, *Structure and Mechanism in Organic Chemistry*, Cornell University Press, 1953; Gillespie and Millen, *Quart. Rev.* 1948, **2**, 277; Hughes, in *Theoretical Organic Chemistry* (Kekulé Symposium), p. 209, London: Butterworths, 1959; De la Mare and Ridd, *Aromatic Substitution*, London: Butterworths, 1959.

suggestion that such carbonium ions might be intermediates in aromatic substitution.† Thus, in a nitration, the salt would be formed by the

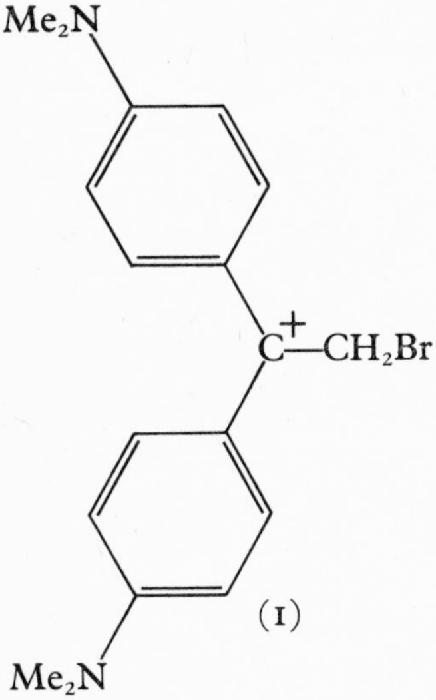

addition of the nitronium ion to the aromatic ring. Similarly, ionic complexes can be formed from alkyl benzenes, aluminium chloride, and hydrogen chloride; thus (2) (which is one of several mesomeric formulae) is obtained from toluene.

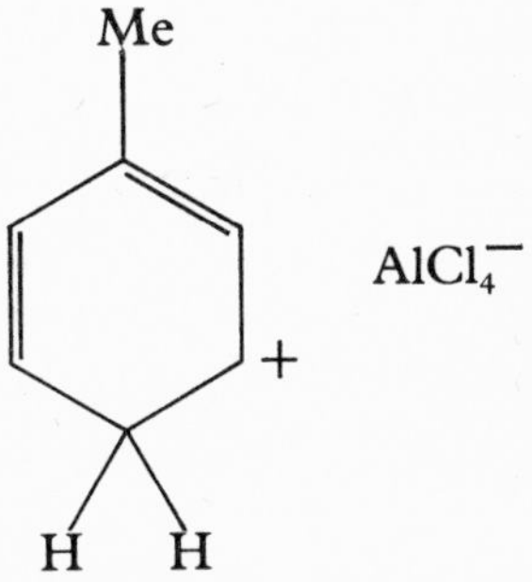

This kind of evidence shows that ionic complexes can be formed in some substitutions, but it does not directly point to the existence of charged intermediates in aromatic nitration. The most clear-cut evidence comes from a study of the kinetic isotope effect (Chapter II, § 2 f). How this evidence is supplied can be seen from a description of one example.

Naphthalene, in which one hydrogen atom has been replaced by tritium, can be prepared by the reactions:

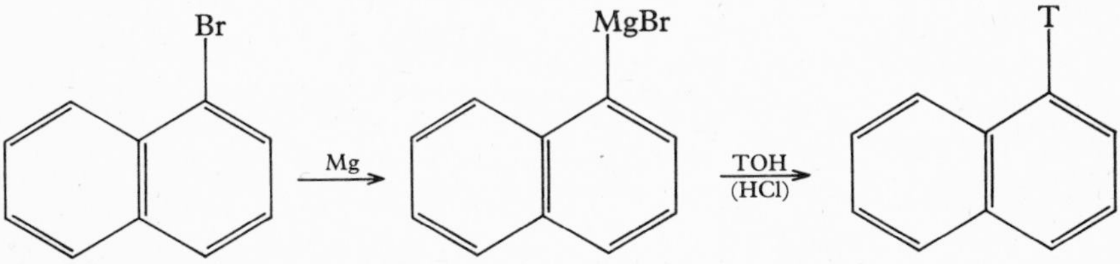

Only tracer quantities of tritium are used, so that the product is a mixture of naphthalene and naphthalene-1-T. Now the nitration of

† Pfeiffer and Wizinger, *Annalen*, 1928, **461**, 132.

naphthalene (in nitric acid as solvent) gives α-nitronaphthalene. There are four α positions in naphthalene. Nitration of naphthalene-1-T gave α-nitronaphthalene, whose specific activity was three-quarters of that of the starting material. Thus the nitronium ion displaced the tritium from one α position just as readily as it displaced hydrogen from any of the three other α positions. But a carbon-tritium bond may be expected to break at only one-twentieth the rate of a carbon-hydrogen bond. This result shows that the carbon-tritium bond is not broken in the rate-determining step.† There must be then at least two steps in the nitration of naphthalene: the rate-determining step and the hydrogen-losing step. So the process might be formulated

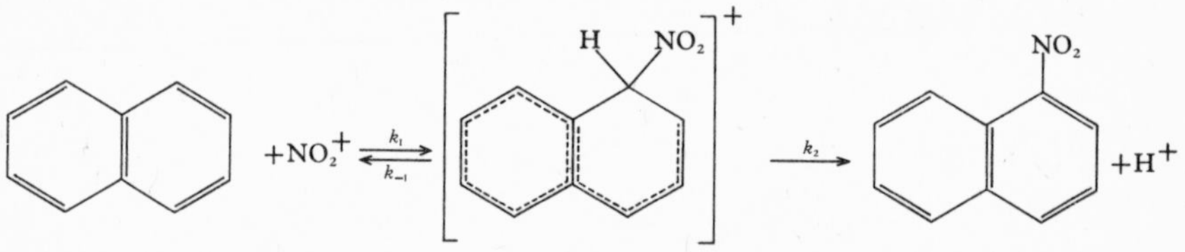

If $k_2 \gg k_{-1}$, the first step will be rate-determining, and the carbon-hydrogen bond is not broken in this step. Thus the absence of a kinetic isotope effect in nitration (which has been shown to be quite general) is accounted for by this mechanism.

The intermediate in the nitration of benzene, to take the simplest example, may be represented as mesomeric between (3), (4), and (5), and is often shown as (6). This last formula does not bring out the

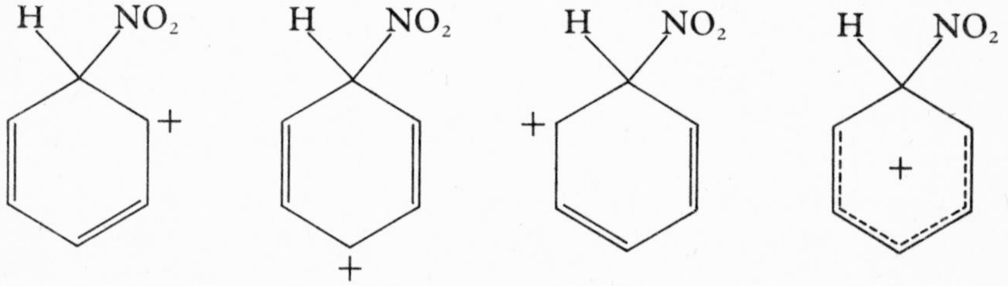

(3)   (4)   (5)   (6)

point that the positive charge is essentially distributed over the carbon atoms *ortho* and *para* to the substitution centre; a classical structure with the positive charge on the *meta* position cannot be written.

In the attack of a nitronium ion on benzene the reagent will approach the planar ring from above or below, so that the positively charged ion interacts with the π-electrons, which are above and below the plane of

† Melander, *Arkiv Kemi*, 1951, **2**, 211.

the ring. In the transition state there will be some overlap of the $2p$ orbital of the carbon atom on which substitution is taking place and a vacant orbital of the nitronium ion, and the resulting binding energy will help to compensate for the loss in freedom of movement of the aromatic π-electrons, one of which is partially localized in the region of space near the nitrogen atom. These are the factors which govern the readiness with which an aromatic compound is nitrated.

The complex formed in the rate-determining step in nitration may be a charge-transfer complex,† in which something less than a full covalent bond is formed between the nitrogen and carbon atoms; however, the extent of charge transfer is probably still large, i.e. the charge on the aromatic ring is almost unity, and for our purposes it is simpler to continue to represent the complexes by classical formulae.

(c) *Orientation in aromatic nitration.* A monosubstituted benzene has five positions, of three kinds, available for further substitution. If the substituent already present had no effect, the distribution of isomers would be: *ortho*, 40 per cent.; *meta* 40 per cent.; *para*, 20 per cent. However, in general, nitration of a monosubstituted benzene gives either mainly the *meta* nitro compound, or the *ortho* and *para* nitro compounds: the nature of the substituent governs the nature of the products, and substituents are called *meta*-directing, or *ortho-para*-directing. The basis for this classification can be seen from the figures in Table 12.

TABLE 12. *Nitration of monosubstituted benzenes*

No.	Substituent	Ortho	Meta	Para	$\frac{1}{2}$ Meta: para	Comments
1	$\overset{+}{\text{NMe}}_3$		100		(∞)	cf. nos. 5 and 9
2	CF_3		100		(∞)	cf. no. 6
3	NO_2	6·4	93·2	0·3	155	
4	COOEt	28·3	68·4	3·3	10·3	
5	$CH_2\overset{+}{\text{NMe}}_3$	2	88	10	4·4	
6	CCl_3	6·8	64·5	28·7	1·1	
7	$CHCl_2$	23·3	33·8	42·9	0·39	cf. nos. 6 and 8
8	CH_2Cl	32	15·5	52·5	0·15	
9	$CH_2CH_2\overset{+}{\text{NMe}}_3$	13	17	70	0·12	
10	CH_2COOEt	42	10·6	47·4	0·11	cf. no. 4
11	CH_3	58·5	4·4	37·1	0·059	
12	$C(CH_3)_3$	12	8·5	79·5	0·053	
13	$CH=CHNO_2$	31	2	67	0·015	cf. no. 3
14	Cl	29·6	0·9	69·5	0·0065	
15	NHCOMe	∼ 20		∼ 80	0	
16	OMe	∼ 30		∼ 70	0	

Figures from De la Mare and Ridd, *Aromatic Substitution*, London: Butterworths, 1959.

† Brown, *J. Chem. Soc.* 1959, p. 2224.

These figures refer to nitrations under a variety of conditions, but the type of orientation is generally independent of the conditions. The classification into *meta*-directing groups (the first six) and *ortho-para* (the rest) is here based on whether the $\frac{1}{2}$ *meta*:*para* ratio is greater or less than unity, but most substituents give some of all three isomers.

The sign of the mesomeric dipole moment of the monosubstituted benzene (Chapter I, § 2 a) can be correlated with the type of orientation: if the aromatic compound has a negative mesomeric dipole moment, the substituent (e.g. NO_2, CCl_3) is *meta*-directing; if positive, the substituent (e.g. OMe, Cl, Me) is *ortho-para*-directing. Now the mesomeric dipole moments give information directly about the effect of a substituent on the mobile π-electrons which interact with the nitronium ion. This is because the mesomeric dipole moments are given by the difference between aliphatic and aromatic compounds, and it is the π-electrons of the aromatic ring which give rise to this difference. Most of the substituents with positive mesomeric dipole moments have atoms with unshared p electrons (e.g. Cl, OMe), which can interact with the π-electrons of the aromatic ring. When this happens, the ring will be more ready to give up a pair of π-electrons to bind the nitronium ion because the deficit can be made good by the substituent, but this can only happen if the nitronium ion is becoming bound to a carbon atom which is in a position *ortho* or *para* to the substituent. This can be seen if the complex formed in the *ortho* nitration of anisole is represented as mesomeric between (1), (2), (3), and (4); the complex in the *para* nitration

(1)   (2)   (3)   (4)

as mesomeric between (5), (6), (7), and (8); and the complex in the *meta* nitration as mesomeric between (9), (10), and (11). Formulae (1) and (5), in which the substituent bears the positive charge, and in which there are three double bonds (because the p electrons of the oxygen atom have formed a double bond with a ring carbon atom), can be written for *ortho* and *para* substitution, but not for *meta* substitution. It is this 'geometrical' factor which dominates the issue in orientation.

Of course, it is really the transition state, rather than the complex,

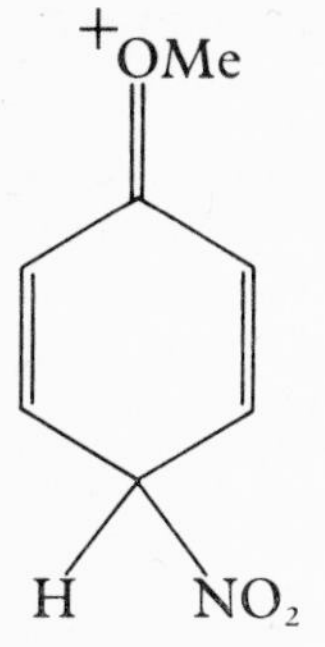

$^+$OMe   OMe   OMe   OMe

H   NO$_2$ H   NO$_2$ H   NO$_2$ H   NO$_2$

(5) 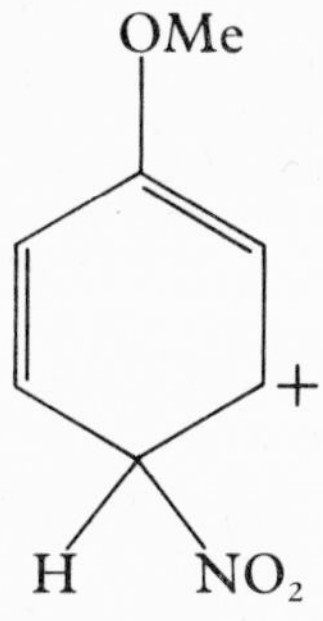   (6) 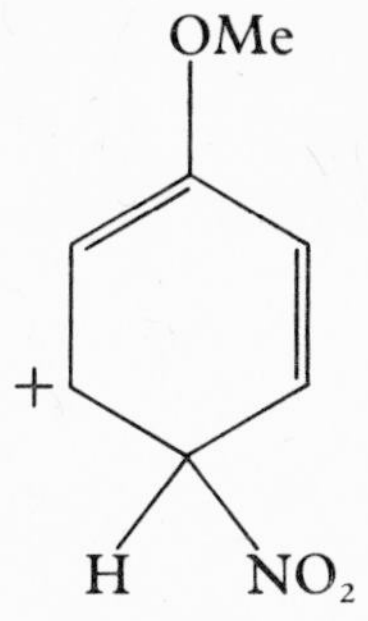   (7) 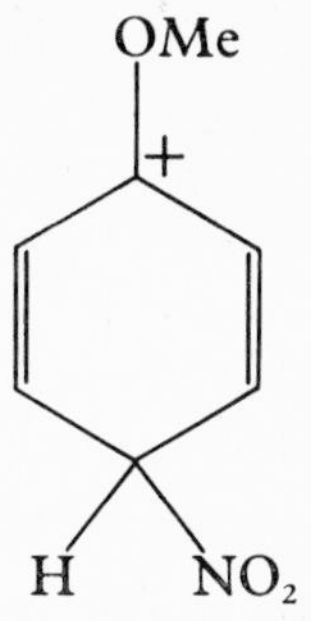   (8)

OMe   OMe   OMe

—NO$_2$ —NO$_2$ —NO$_2$

H   H   H

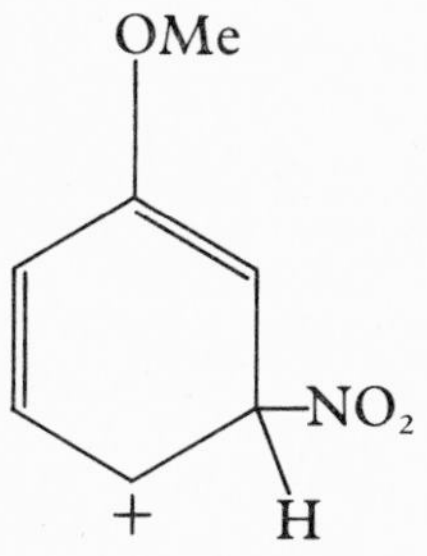

(9) 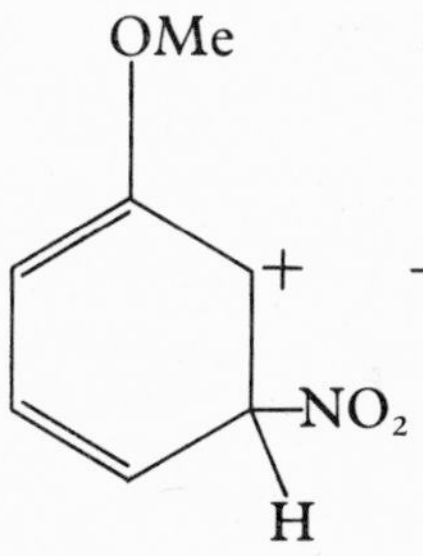   (10) 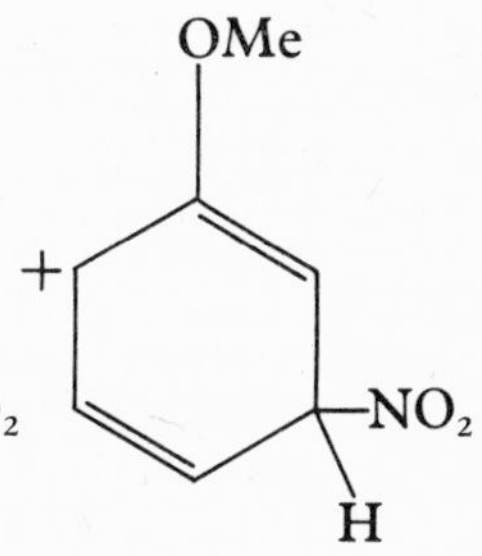   (11)

that we are concerned with in assessing reactivity, but these formulae show what happens when one carbon atom is entirely removed from the conjugated system, and thus bring out the factors operative in the transition state, when the carbon atom is only partially removed from the conjugated system.

Alkyl groups (methyl and tertiary butyl are the examples given) also have positive mesomeric dipole moments and are *ortho-para*-directing. We may regard this as analogous to the stabilization of carbonium ions by attached alkyl groups, since the ring carbon bearing the alkyl group will have a partial positive charge in the transition state leading to *ortho* and *para* substitution. This stabilization must be absent in *meta* substitution. Formulae for the intermediate may be written again, and (12) and (13) show a positive charge on the carbon atom carrying a methyl group (nitration of toluene).

If we wish to take this explanation a stage farther and inquire why alkyl groups stabilize carbonium ions, then a formula (14) which shows hyperconjugation of the methyl group can be written (Chapter I, § 1 *r*).

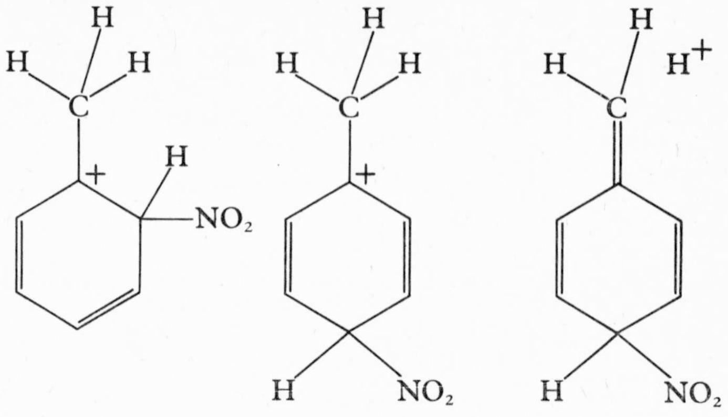

(12)   (13)   (14)

To what extent the formula constitutes an explanation of the stabilization is an open question; moreover, it should be noted that tertiary-
butyl benzene, $PhCMe_3$, gives a $\frac{1}{2}$ *meta*:*para* ratio similar to that of
toluene. It is also possible (and perhaps not very different) to discuss
the effect in terms of the differing electronegativities of trigonal (sp^2
hybridized) and tetrahedral (sp^3 hybridized) carbon atoms (Chapter I).

The general approach that we have adopted is thus that the correlation
between the mesomeric dipole moments and the orientation tells us that
the orientation must depend on the interaction between the substituent
and the π-electrons, and our knowledge of the mechanism of the reaction
tells us that a pair of π-electrons is being removed from the pool and
allocated to the nitronium ion during the reaction, and we can see by
writing formulae for the complex how to connect the phenomena.

The *ortho-para*-directing groups listed are, with one exception, either
alkyl or substituted alkyl groups, or groups joined to the ring by oxygen
or nitrogen atoms. The exception is the group —CH=CH—NO_2; here
presumably the π-electrons of the double bond play the same part as
the *p* electrons of the oxygen atom in anisole (see '*p*-π' analogy,
p. 102).

Although alkyl groups are *ortho-para*-directing, their orientation can
be modified by substituents. Thus if the hydrogen atoms of the methyl
group in toluene are successively replaced by chlorine atoms the tendency towards the *ortho-para* type of orientation diminishes, and the
effect is quite regular (Fig. 28). Each replacement increases the electronegativity of the group, and when all the hydrogen atoms are replaced
(i.e. in $PhCCl_3$) the group is weakly *meta*-directing. However, with

the more electronegative fluorine atom, the group CF_3 is strongly *meta*-directing.

Positively charged groups are also strongly *meta*-directing. The high electronegativity of the positively charged nitrogen atom results in the electrons of the bond linking the substituent with the ring being drawn

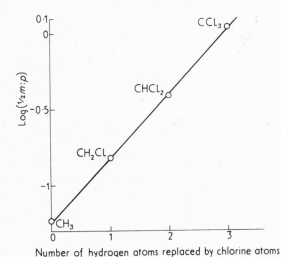

Fig. 28. Orientation in the nitration of $PhCCl_3$, $PhCHCl_2$, $PhCH_2Cl$, and $PhCH_3$.

towards the nitrogen atom. Here apparently a pair of π-electrons can be provided to bind the nitronium ion more readily at the *meta* carbon atom, which must therefore be less affected by the substituent. We may try to understand this as before by writing formulae for the mesomeric intermediate, e.g. in the nitration of $Ph\!-\!\overset{+}{N}Me_3$:

para substitution

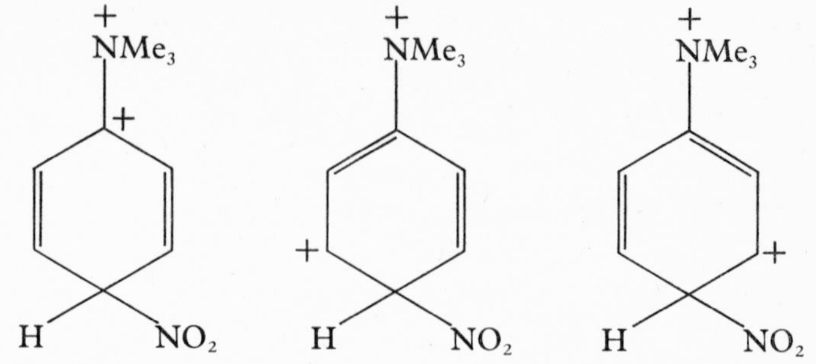

unfavourable

meta substitution

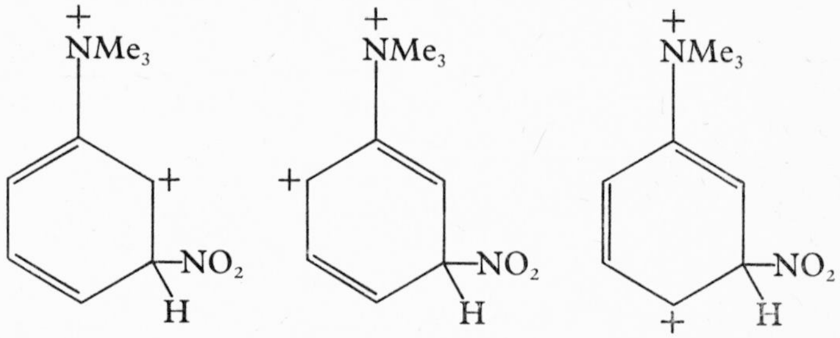

The two formulae marked 'unfavourable' may be discounted, as two neighbouring atoms are both positively charged. This guide is often referred to as the adjacent charge rule, and was put forward by Pauling. The consequence here is that there is a greater extent of charge delocalization in the intermediate in *meta* substitution than there is in *ortho* or *para* substitution.

Similar factors are operative in the other *meta*-directing groups. These groups are not charged, but are dipolar (e.g. NO_2 group) and have the positive end of the dipole linked to the aromatic ring. The orientation in the nitration of, for example, nitrobenzene, or ethyl benzoate, is thus similar to that for $Ph\overset{+}{N}Me_3$, although the effects are often not so marked.

The *meta*-directing effects of a charged group ($\overset{+}{N}Me_3$) or of a polar one (COOEt) become markedly diminished by intervening methylene groups, as the figures in Table 12 show. When sufficient methylene groups are interposed, then the *ortho-para* orientation of alkyl groups takes over.

The ratio $\frac{1}{2}$ *meta:para* has been used in discussing the effects of substituents because of the possibility that *ortho* substitution will be affected by steric hindrance. One of the clearest cases of a steric effect is shown by the value of the *ortho:meta* ratio in the nitration of tertiary butyl benzene, which is only about one-tenth the value of the ratio for toluene, although the $\frac{1}{2}$ meta:para ratios are nearly the same. Similarly, in the series Ph.CH_3, Ph.CH_2Cl, Ph.$CHCl_2$, and Ph.CCl_3, the meta:ortho ratios rise more sharply than the $\frac{1}{2}$ meta:para ratios by about a factor of 10, and this also suggests that substitution in the ortho position is being affected by steric hindrance. However, in general, there is not much evidence for such steric hindrance. The nitration of acetanilide and anisole usually gives more para than ortho substitution, although the results are particularly dependent on the conditions of nitration. The transition state for para substitution is thus favoured over that for ortho substitution, which is perhaps analogous to the greater stability of para quinones as compared with ortho quinones.†

Orientation has so far been the topic in this account of nitrations; we must now turn to a comparison of the reactivities of two different aromatic compounds. The study of the relative reactivity of two compounds, say benzene and toluene, can be effected by the 'competitive' method.‡ In this method, the two aromatic compounds are allowed to react with a relatively small amount of nitric acid, i.e. they compete for the reagent.

The reactive species will be assumed to be the nitronium ion, although, as can be seen from the expressions given below, the success of the method does not depend on this assumption. The rates do not have to be measured to obtain the ratio of the velocity constants. If the concentrations of benzene and toluene are x and y, and the initial and final concentrations are denoted by the subscripts zero, infinity, then

$$-dx/dt = k[NO_2]^+x, \qquad -dy/dt = k'[NO_2]^+y,$$

$$dx/dy = kx/k'y, \quad \text{or} \quad \log(x_0/x_\infty)/\log(y_0/y_\infty) = k/k'.$$

The initial and final amounts (as the volume is constant) thus give the ratio k/k'. The rate of reaction of a given position in toluene relative to one of the positions in benzene is called the partial rate factor for that position. The partial rate factors are found from k/k' and the product proportions (orientation) previously given. Thus, for toluene, the partial rate factors for ortho, meta, and para nitrations are: $6/2 \times 0.585 \times k'/k$, $6/2 \times 0.044 \times k'/k$, and $6 \times 0.371 \times k'/k$.

The partial rate factors for the ortho, meta, and para positions in toluene, ethyl benzoate, and chlorobenzene are shown below:

† Waters, J. Chem. Soc. 1948, p. 727.
‡ Ingold and Shaw, ibid. 1927, p. 2918; 1949, p. 575.

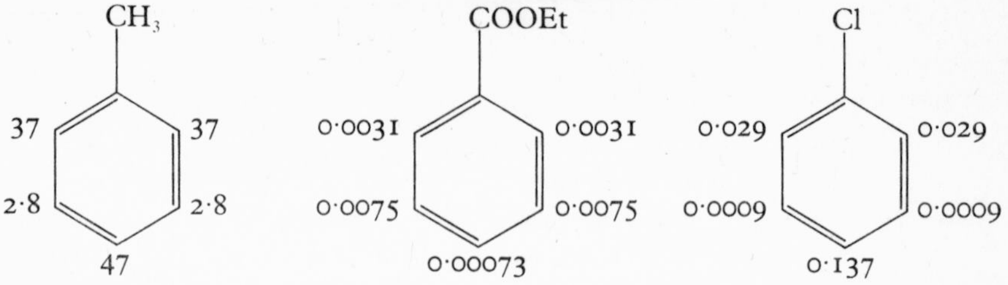

CH₃

37   37

2·8   2·8

47

COOEt

0·0031   0·0031

0·0075   0·0075

0·00073

Cl

0·029   0·029

0·0009   0·0009

0·137

Of these compounds, ethyl benzoate contains a *meta*-directing substituent, and toluene and chlorobenzene contain *ortho-para*-directing ones. The partial rate factors for the nitration of ethyl benzoate are seen to be much less than unity. It turns out that all compounds containing a *meta*-directing substituent are nitrated less rapidly than benzene, i.e. that *meta*-directing substituents are deactivating. However, *ortho-para*-directing substituents may be either activating or deactivating (see the figures for toluene and chlorobenzene, given above). In a sense, the difference between *ortho-para*-directing and *meta*-directing substituents is less marked than the effect of the substituents on the overall reactivity. All the positions in toluene are nitrated more rapidly than one position in benzene, and none of the positions in ethyl benzoate as rapidly.

The interpretation of orientation is particularly straightforward because there is only one ground state to consider: any effect of a substituent which is exerted solely on the ground state cancels, and so the only feature is the effect of a substituent on the transition state. But in the interpretation of a partial rate factor, where two compounds are being compared, there are four energy levels to consider: two ground states and two transition states. The relation between these four levels can be brought out in a simple diagram.

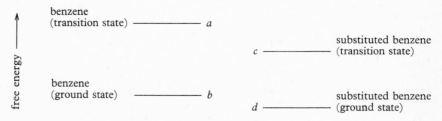

The rate of nitration of benzene is governed by the difference in free energy levels, which is (in the diagram) $a-b$, and the rate of nitration of the substituted benzene is governed by $c-d$. Whether the substituent activates is then given by the sign of F, where $F = (c-d)-(a-b)$.

This may also be written as $F = (b-d)-(a-c)$; here the first term represents the stabilization of the ground state by the substituent, and the second term the stabilization of the transition state by the substituent. It is the difference between the terms which determines whether or not the substituent activates the benzene ring; in the diagram this difference is negative, and the substituent activates.

The figures given above show that the carbethoxy (COOEt) and chloro groups stabilize the ground state more than the transition state, but that the methyl group preferentially stabilizes the transition state. The typical *ortho-para*-directing groups (e.g. OMe) stabilize the transition states leading to *ortho* and *para* substitution very effectively, and so they are strongly activating. *Meta*-directing groups have no effective way of stabilizing the transition state, and are deactivating.

3. Halogenation of aromatic compounds

The halogenation of aromatic compounds is a more complex subject than the nitration, and only a brief outline is given here.† The cause of this complexity is the number of different mechanisms operative under different conditions; whereas nitration is nearly always effected by the nitronium ion, several different species can effect halogenation. In the first place, both homolytic and heterolytic halogenations are possible.

The homolytic reaction is sometimes not a substitution but an addition; thus, if chlorine is passed into benzene in sunlight hexachlorocyclohexane is formed. This is a homolytic addition, effected by chlorine atoms. Aromatic compounds with alkyl side chains may be halogenated in the side chain by halogen atoms; this is a homolytic substitution. However, substitution in the aromatic ring is normally a heterolytic reaction.

Heterolytic substitution is favoured by the addition of catalysts, if molecular chlorine or bromine are being used, or by the use of hypohalous acids as reagents. The function of a catalyst such as ferric bromide in a bromination is to facilitate the heterolysis of the Br—Br bond by combining with incipient bromide ion:

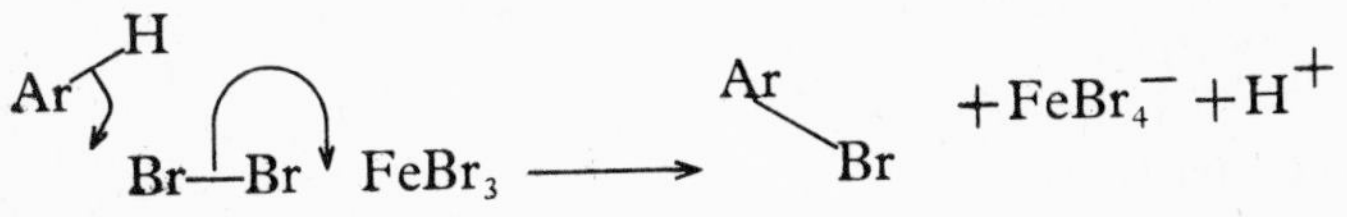

† See De la Mare and Ridd, *Aromatic Substitution*, London: Butterworths, 1959, for a detailed account.

This process is shown schematically; there are several stages, which are here telescoped into one. Another molecule of bromine can apparently take the place of the ferric bromide; the bromination of anisole in acetic acid is first-order in anisole but second-order in bromine, and here the anion Br_3^- is probably being formed. These reactions, in which molecular chlorine, or bromine, are the reactive entities, differ from nitrations effected by the nitronium ion where the reactive species is a cation. However, halogenations may also be effected by cations, and we now come to the evidence for this type of mechanism.

The reaction of either hypochlorous acid or hypobromous acid with sodium toluene-ω-sulphonate ($PhCH_2$—SO_3Na) is acid-catalysed; at a given acidity the rate is first-order in hypohalous acid and in the aromatic compound, and the rate is also proportional to the acidity.[†] The hypohalous acid is thus being converted into a more reactive species by the added acid, and the simplest interpretation is that this reactive species is the protonated hypohalous acid.

$$HOCl \;+\; H^+ \;\rightleftharpoons\; H_2\overset{+}{O}Cl$$

or
$$HOBr \;+\; H^+ \;\rightleftharpoons\; H_2\overset{+}{O}Br$$

These cations will be more reactive electrophilic reagents than the neutral hypohalous acids from which they are derived. There is also the possibility that these cations will decompose into water and the still more reactive chlorinium ion (Cl^+) or brominium ion (Br^+).

$$H_2\overset{+}{O}Cl \;\rightleftharpoons\; H_2O \;+\; Cl^+$$

or
$$H_2\overset{+}{O}Br \;\rightleftharpoons\; H_2O \;+\; Br^+$$

The form of the kinetic equation for the chlorination of anisole suggests that both $H_2\overset{+}{O}Cl$ and Cl^+ are reacting with the aromatic compound.[‡]

Further evidence for positively charged chlorinating agents has come from an investigation of the reaction of diethylchloroamine (1) with phenols.[§] The reagent (1) is prepared from hypochlorous acid and diethylamine:

---

† Derbyshire and Waters, *J. Chem. Soc.* 1950, p. 564; 1951, p. 73.

‡ De la Mare, Ketley, and Vernon, ibid. 1954, p. 1290; Swain and Ketley, *J. Amer. Chem. Soc.* 1955, **77**, 3410.

§ Brown and Soper, *J. Chem. Soc.* 1953, p. 3576.

$$Et_2NH + HOCl \longrightarrow Et_2NCl + H_2O$$

(1)

When the rate of reaction of phenols with diethylchloramine was measured at various pH values, it was found that it did not increase over a range where the phenol is being converted into the more reactive phenoxide ion. This suggests that the reactants are, in fact, the proto-nated diethylchloramine and the phenoxide ion; this mechanism leads to the kinetic equation given below (here K_p and K_c are the ionization constants of the phenol and of $Et_2\overset{+}{N}HCl$):

$$v = \frac{k\{[Et_2\overset{+}{N}HCl] + [Et_2NCl]\}\{[ArOH] + [ArO^-]\}K_p[H^+]}{\{K_p + [H^+]\}\{K_c + [H^+]\}}$$

and this was found to tally with the results obtained.

Iodination may also involve a positively charged species. Thus in the reaction of phenol with iodine there is a term in the kinetic equation proportional to the concentrations of HOI and of phenol. This could also result from an attack of the cation, I^+, on the anion, PhO^-. Similarly, in the reaction of aniline with iodine, the alternative terms are

$$[PhNH_3^+][IOH] \quad \text{or} \quad [PhNH_2][I^+].$$

But the reaction of $PhNH_3^+$ would lead to *meta* substitution, whereas the main product is *p*-iodo-aniline. So it must be the free base, $PhNH_2$, which is reacting, either with I^+ or $H_2\overset{+}{O}I$. Similarly, in the iodination of phenol, the active species are the less abundant but much more reactive, I^+ (or $I\overset{+}{O}H_2$) and PhO^-.†

The effect of structure upon reactivity follows the same general lines noted in nitration. There is, however, a much greater spread in the rates of halogenation by molecular bromine or chlorine than in the rates of nitration. This may be expressed quantitatively in terms of the reaction constant, ρ, of Hammett's equation, which has been applied (in a modified form) to aromatic substitutions;‡ for halogenation (by Br_2 or Cl_2, in acetic acid), $\rho = -11$, but for nitration, $\rho = -6.5$. Thus, for investigating the effect of structure upon reactivity, halogena-tion is a more sensitive probe than nitration. The relative rates of

† Berliner, *J. Amer. Chem. Soc.* 1950, **72**, 4003; 1951, **73**, 4307.
‡ Okamoto and Brown, *J. Org. Chem.* 1957, **22**, 485.

halogenation of a number of monosubstituted benzenes are given in Table 13.†

TABLE 13. *Logarithms of rates of halogenation of monosubstituted benzenes* (PhX) *relative to benzene*

X	Logarithm of relative rate	X	Logarithm of relative rate
NMe$_2$	19	OCOPh	1·3
OH	11	CH$_2$COOEt	0·36
OMe	9	F	0·08
NHCOMe	8·3	H	0
OPh	7·2	Cl	−0·96
Me	2·5	COOEt	−3·3
		NO$_2$	−5·74

4. Enzymic halogenation

The conversion of tyrosine into mono-iodotyrosine is catalysed by an enzyme from the thyroid gland.‡

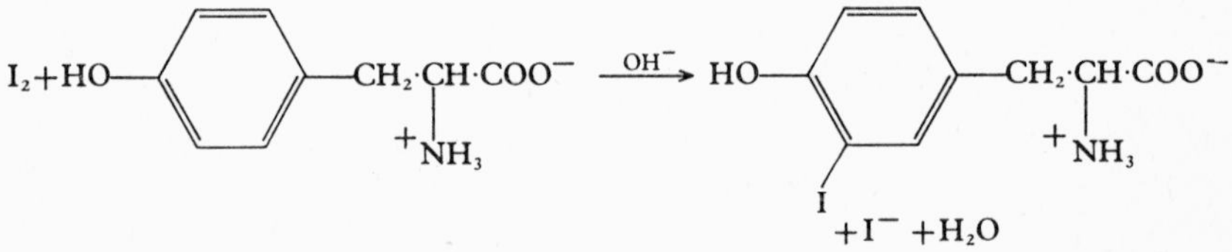

Although the reverse of the reaction can be demonstrated, the equilibrium (in neutral solution) is over to the right-hand side. When the reagent is iodide ion the enzyme system requires oxygen (and cupric ions) to generate iodine.

It is uncertain whether nitration of the aromatic ring is a step in the formation of the aromatic nitro compounds which occur naturally. Two aromatic nitro compounds which have been isolated from micro-organisms are chloramphenicol and 2-nitroglyoxaline,§ and a nitrophenanthrene has been obtained from plants.‖

5. Reactions of diazonium ions with aromatic compounds

The main characteristic of this reaction (often referred to as diazocoupling) is that it is only encountered with particularly reactive aromatic systems, usually amines or phenols. In this restricted scope, diazo-coupling differs from nitration and halogenation, which are general

† Robertson, De la Mare, and Swedlund, *J. Chem. Soc.* 1953, p. 782.
‡ Fawcett and Kirkwood, *J. Biol. Chem.* 1954, **209**, 249; Serif and Kirkwood, ibid. 1958, **233**, 109; Cunningham and Kirkwood, ibid. 1961, **236**, 485.
§ Nakamura, *Pharm. Bull.* (*Japan*), 1955, **3**, 379.
‖ Pailer and Schleppnik, *Monatsh.* 1958, **89**, 175.

reactions. An example of a diazo-coupling with a phenol is

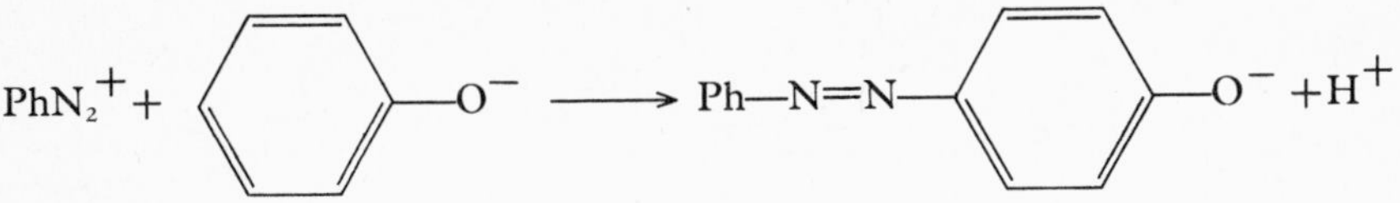

$$PhN_2^+ + \text{[benzene ring]}-O^- \longrightarrow Ph-N{=}N-\text{[benzene ring]}-O^- + H^+$$

In the reaction of certain diazonium salts with aromatic amines, the variation in rate with the pH of the solution showed that the kinetic equation was either

$$v = k[ArN_2^+][Ar'NH_2]$$

or
$$v = k[ArN_2OH][Ar'NH_3^+].$$

The former may be chosen as the correct alternative because the protonated amine ($Ar'NH_3^+$) would have a deactivated aromatic nucleus (as in $Ph-\overset{+}{N}Me_3$).†

These results suggest that the electrophilic species in diazo-coupling is the positively charged diazonium ion, which may be represented as mesomeric between (1) and (2);‡ it resembles the nitronium ion in carrying unit positive charge. However, the diazonium ion, unlike the nitronium ion, has only a fractional positive charge on the atom which

$$\overset{+}{Ar-N}{\equiv}N\colon \qquad\qquad Ar-\overset{..}{\overset{+}{N}}{=}N\colon$$

(1)　　　　　　　　　　　　(2)

becomes bound to the aromatic carbon atom, and this is a factor which contributes to the lesser reactivity of the diazonium ion.

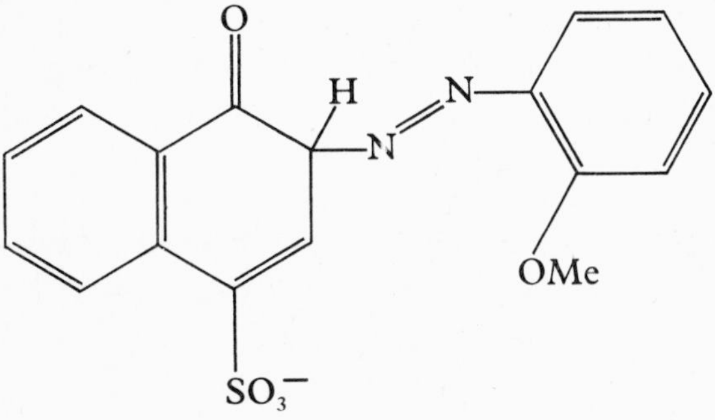

(3)

† Wistar and Bartlett, *J. Amer. Chem. Soc.* 1941, **63**, 413.
‡ Hauser and Breslow, ibid., p. 418.

Normally, there is no kinetic isotope effect in diazo-coupling, e.g. the two reactions

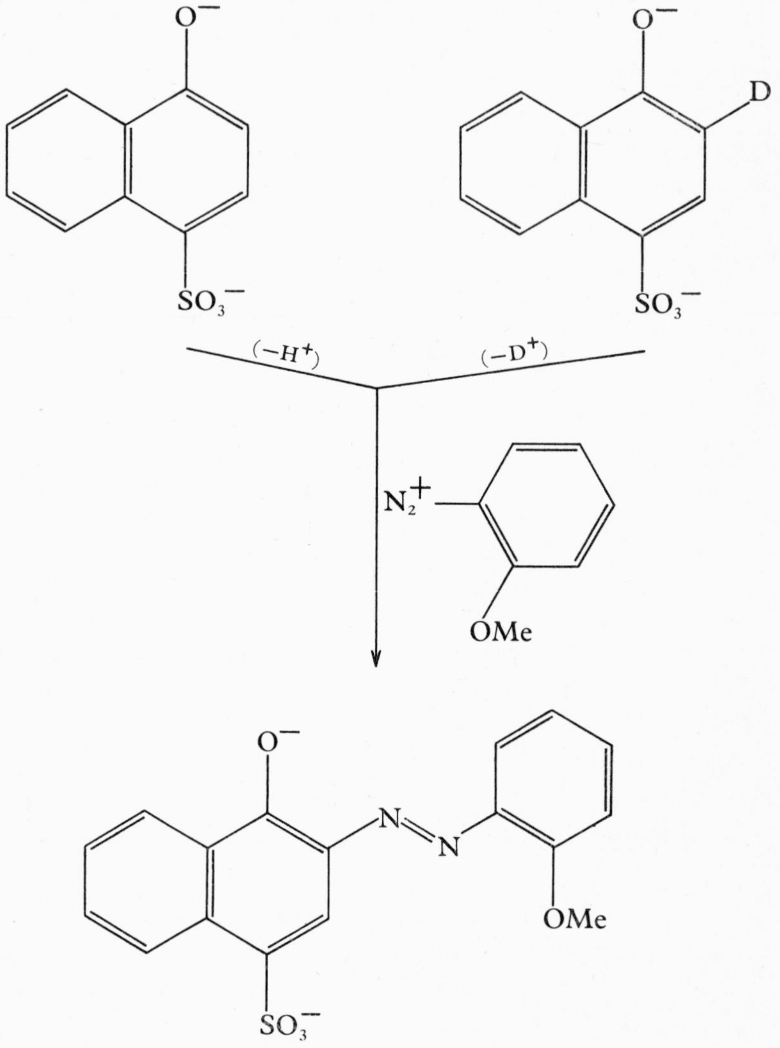

proceed at the same rate. Thus we may formulate a mechanism, analogous to that of nitration, in which there is an intermediate, e.g. (3) on p. 325 for the reaction shown above.

The diazo-coupling is not base-catalysed; this observation, and the lack of a kinetic isotope effect, show that the rate-determining step is the formation of the intermediate (3). But in another example,

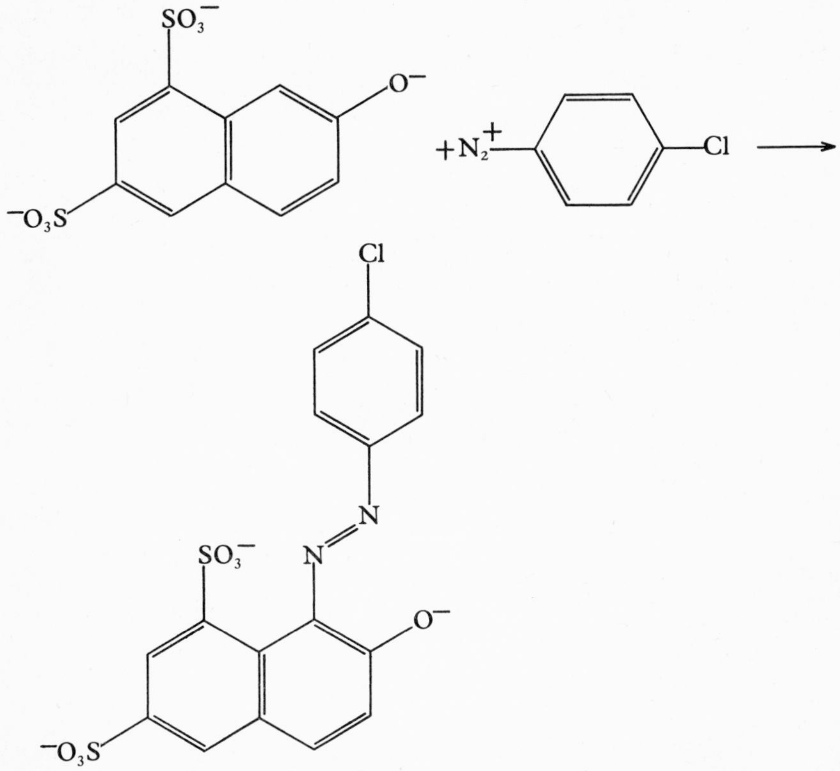

the reaction *is* base-catalysed, and furthermore shows a large kinetic isotope effect ($k_{\mathrm{H}}/k_{\mathrm{D}} = 6{\cdot}55$). This reaction cannot proceed by a one-step mechanism, as the rate is not a linear function of the concentration of base, and moreover the magnitude of the isotope effect depends on the concentration of base.

The results can be quantitatively accounted for by the same mechanism,

$$\mathrm{ArN_2^+ + Ar'H} \underset{k_{-1}}{\overset{k_1}{\rightleftharpoons}} \text{intermediate}$$

$$\text{intermediate} \xrightarrow{k_2} \text{products.}$$

The difference here is that k_{-1} and k_2 are comparable. This mechanism (for an unstable intermediate) leads to the kinetic equation

$$\text{rate} = \frac{k_1(k_2/k_{-1})[\text{base}]}{1+(k_2/k_{-1})[\text{base}]}[\mathrm{ArN_2^+}][\mathrm{Ar'H}].$$

Formation of the intermediate is no longer rate-determining when k_{-1} and k_2 are of the same order of magnitude. The step in which the carbon-hydrogen bond is broken is the one whose rate constant is k_2, i.e. the kinetic isotope effect makes a difference to the value of k_2. The observed result of displacing deuterium instead of hydrogen depends, however, on the relative magnitude of the two terms in the denominator of the equation, and thus depends on the concentration of the base. Now the intermediate in this reaction is (4), and apparently the main way in which this differs from the previous intermediate (3) is that in (4) the steric congestion facilitates the loss of the diazonium group, i.e. k_{-1} is raised by steric acceleration.

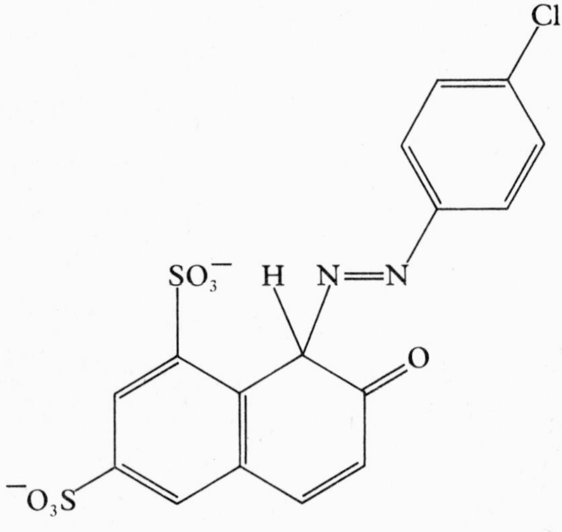

(4)

Another consequence of the congested nature of (4) is that the effectiveness of the base depends on its size. Thus, the effectiveness of pyridine (5), β-picoline (6), and γ-picoline (7) is governed simply by the basicity: this is reasonable, as the basicity measures the tendency to acquire a proton, and this is what the bases are doing in this reaction. But α-picoline (8) and 2,6-lutidine (9) are much less effective; here the methyl groups are close to the basic nitrogen atom, and interfere with the approach of the base to the intermediate (4).†

† Zollinger, *Experientia*, 1956, **12** 165.

(5)   (6)   (7)   (8)   (9)

In diazo-coupling with phenols, the reaction is carried out in weakly alkaline solution, as the phenolate ion (ArO⁻) is more reactive than the unionized phenol (ArOH) towards the electrophilic diazonium ion. At too high a pH value, however, the diazonium ion is converted into the unreactive diazoate (the diazo hydroxide and the diazoate ion can also exist in stereoisomeric form):†

$$\text{HO}^- + \text{ArN} \overset{+}{\equiv} \text{N} \longrightarrow \text{ArN}=\text{N}-\text{OH} \longrightarrow \text{ArN}=\text{N}-\text{O}^-$$

The effect of structural variation on the reactivity of diazonium ions may be summarized briefly. Electron-withdrawing groups increase the reactivity, and electron-repelling groups decrease it: the p-nitrobenzene diazonium cation is over 10,000 times as reactive as the corresponding para-methoxy-compound under comparable conditions.‡ The 2,4,6-trinitrobenzene diazonium ion is even sufficiently reactive to couple with a hydrocarbon, mesitylene. This is the expected effect of structure upon reactivity for an electrophilic reagent.

Certain heterocyclic compounds have activated aromatic nuclei, notably those with a five-membered ring containing an NH group (§ 1), and these activated rings can couple with diazonium ions. Glyoxaline reacts as its anion (10), with the diazonium ion (11) from sulphanilic acid. This conclusion is based on the variation of rate with pH.§ Glyoxaline is only very weakly acidic (pK 14·5) so the anion (which is, of course, symmetrical, as shown by the representation (12)) must be very much more reactive than the unionized compound. This diazo-coupling of glyoxaline is widely used in the detection (Pauly test) and estimation of histidine.

The reaction of indole (13) with the p-nitrobenzene diazonium ion (14) is a second-order reaction, and the rate constant is independent of pH

† Le Fèvre, Roper, and Reece, *J. Chem. Soc.* 1959, p. 4104.
‡ Conant and Peterson, *J. Amer. Chem. Soc.* 1930, **52**, 1220.
§ Brown, Duffin, Maynard, and Ridd, *J. Chem. Soc.* 1953, p. 3937.

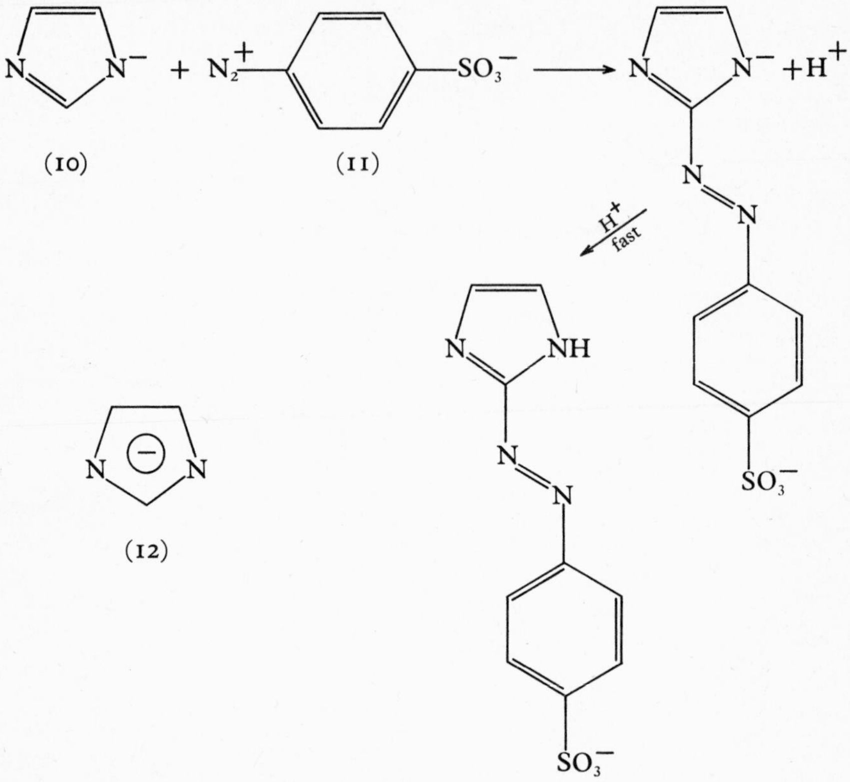

(10)   (11)

(12)

(in the region, pH 4–6), so that here the unionized heterocyclic compound is the reactant.†

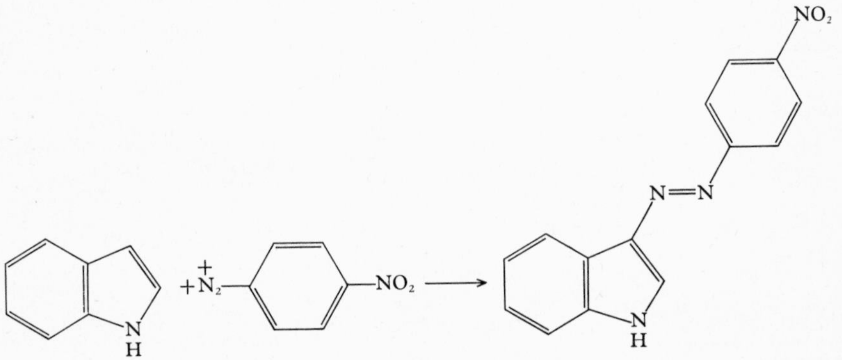

(13)   (14)

There is no kinetic isotope effect in either of these last two examples, so

† Binks and Ridd, *J. Chem. Soc.* 1957, p. 2398.

that the mechanisms involve an intermediate which loses a proton much more rapidly than it reverts to starting materials.

6. Hydroxylation of aromatic compounds

This topic is introduced as an example of an aromatic substitution generally proceeding by a free radical (homolytic) mechanism.† Moreover, enzymic hydroxylation has attracted considerable attention, and may also be a homolytic reaction.

One way in which hydroxylation of aromatic compounds has been effected is by reaction with hydrogen peroxide and ferrous salts (Fenton's reagent). The reactive species are hydroxyl radicals; Fenton's reagent initiates vinyl polymerizations (Chapter X), and this is part of the evidence that free radicals are being generated.

$$Fe^{2+} \ + \ HO\text{---}OH \ \longrightarrow \ Fe^{3+} \ + \ HO^- \ + \ \bullet OH$$

(The unshared electron is, as usual, symbolized by a dot.) The hydroxyl radicals then react with the aromatic compound; thus benzene gives phenyl radicals:

$$HO\bullet \ + \ Ar\text{---}H \ \longrightarrow \ Ar\bullet \ + \ H_2O$$

This reaction is exothermic since the O—H bond being formed is stronger than the C—H one being broken. It is possible that the formation of phenyl radicals proceeds via an intermediate mesomeric between (1), (2), and (3), which is formulated by analogy with the intermediate in electrophilic substitution:

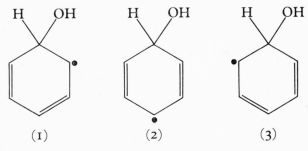

(1)   (2)   (3)

There are several possibilities for further reactions of the phenyl radicals. One possibility is combination of the phenyl and hydroxyl radicals:‡

$$HO\bullet \ + \ Ph\bullet \ \longrightarrow \ PhOH$$

† Dermer and Edmison, *Chem. Rev.* 1957, **57**, 77.
‡ Merz and Waters, *J. Chem. Soc.* 1949, p. 2427.

However, in the presence of a high concentration of ferric ions, this reaction is supplanted by[†]

$$Fe^{3+} + H_2O + Ph\bullet \longrightarrow PhOH + Fe^{2+} + H^+$$

The other main way in which the phenyl radicals react is with each other, to give diphenyl (4):

$$2Ph\bullet \longrightarrow Ph-Ph$$

(4)

Nitrobenzene, it will be recalled, is relatively unreactive towards electrophilic reagents, and is substituted mainly in the *meta* position. The reaction of Fenton's reagent with nitrobenzene, however, proceeds readily, and gives *ortho, meta*, and *para* nitrophenols in the proportions: *ortho*, 28 per cent.; *meta*, 22 per cent.; *para*, 50 per cent.[‡] Here, therefore, the nitro group is functioning as an *ortho-para*-directing substituent ($\frac{1}{2}$ *meta*:*para* = 0·22). In electrophilic substitution the hydroxyl group is *ortho-para*-directing, and phenol reacts with hydroxyl radicals to give the *ortho* and *para* dihydroxybenzenes (catechol and quinol), but no *meta* compound (resorcinol) is formed.[§] So here the orientation in electrophilic and homolytic substitutions is similar. In other words, both types of group (in the classification derived from electrophilic substitution) are *ortho-para*-directing here.

The orientation in these homolytic substitutions can be accounted for if we suppose that intermediates, such as the species represented

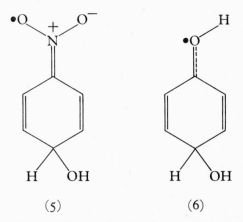

(5)   (6)

† Baxendale and Magee, *Disc. Faraday Soc.* 1953, **14**, 160.
‡ Loebl, Stein, and Weiss, *J. Chem. Soc.* 1949, p. 2074.
§ Stein and Weiss, ibid. 1951, p. 3265.

by (1) to (3), are formed (together with the usual ancillary assumptions about the resemblance between the structures of the transition state and the intermediate). *Para* substitution is facilitated because the unshared electron in the intermediate is distributed over several positions, including the substituent. The nitro group can participate as shown in (5), and the hydroxy group as in (6) (here a three-electron bond is supposed to be formed). Both substituents can thus favour homolytic substitution, although they have opposite effects in heterolytic substitution.

Hydroxyl radicals can also be produced by the action of ionizing radiations on water:

$$H_2O \longrightarrow H\bullet + \bullet OH$$

The orientation in the hydroxylations of nitrobenzene is similar to that already described,[†] and this seems to be fairly general. Benzene gives phenol, by the reaction:

$$Ph\bullet + \bullet OH \longrightarrow PhOH$$

The yield of phenol is increased in the presence of oxygen, which reacts with the hydrogen atoms and so cuts down the incidence of the reaction:

$$Ph\bullet + \bullet H \longrightarrow PhH$$

The hydroxylation of aromatic compounds proceeds particularly smoothly by the use of a rather complex mixture, which contains ferrous ions, ethylene diamine tetra-acetic acid, and ascorbic acid. The reaction is carried out aerobically, and atmospheric oxygen is introduced into the aromatic ring as a hydroxyl group.[‡] The main interest in this procedure for effecting hydroxylation is that the same products (and in comparable proportions) seem to be formed as in enzymic hydroxylation; the reactive species is probably a hydroxyl radical.[§]

7. Enzymic hydroxylation of aromatic compounds

Enzymic hydroxylations may be divided into two classes; those that are concerned with the metabolism of some specific substrate, and those

† Loebl, Stein, and Weiss, *J. Chem. Soc.* 1950, p. 2704.

‡ Udenfriend, Clark, Axelrod, and Brodie, *J. Biol. Chem.* 1954, **208**, 731; Brodie, Axelrod, Shore, and Udenfriend, ibid., p. 741; Dalgliesh, *Arch. Biophys. Biochem.* 1955, **58**, 214; Mason, *Adv. Enzymol.* 1957, **19**, 79.

§ Breslow and Lukens, *J. Biol. Chem.* 1960, **235**, 292.

that are not. It is this latter group, the non-specific hydroxylations of aromatic compounds, with which we are now concerned. There are probably several enzymes which catalyse these reactions, but as they share some common characteristics they can be dealt with as a group. These enzymes are concerned with the metabolism of foreign compounds ('detoxication') rather than normal metabolites, and are localized in the microsomal fraction from liver cells. By the use of isotopically labelled molecular oxygen it has been shown that one atom of atmospheric oxygen finds its way into the hydroxyl group which is introduced into the aromatic molecule; the other atom is reduced to water (the enzymes are mixed function oxidases in the classification of Mason).[†] This accounts for the requirement for a reducing agent, here reduced triphospho-pyridine nucleotide (TPNH), and the overall reaction may be written:

$$Ar{-}H + O_2 + TPNH + H^+ \longrightarrow Ar{-}OH + TPN^+ + H_2O$$

The orientation in the hydroxylation of monosubstituted benzenes generally follows the pattern observed in homolytic substitution. Most of the results are obtained after the aromatic compound has been metabolized by an animal, and thus has had every chance to be subjected to several transformations,[‡] but there is also some information obtained with an enzyme system from liver microsomes.[§] Hydroxylation of phenol takes place in the *ortho* and *para* positions exclusively. Either an electrophilic or free-radical reagent would give this result. But benzonitrile and nitrobenzene are both hydroxylated in the *para* position, and this is consistent with a free-radical attack; the difficulty of accounting for all the material metabolized, however, renders this conclusion tentative.

[†] Mason, *Adv. Enzymol.* 1957, **19**, 79.
[‡] Mason, loc. cit.; Smith, *Biochem. Soc. Symposium* No. 5, 1950, p. 15.
[§] Booth and Boyland, *Biochem. J.* 1957, **66**, 73.

X

MECHANISMS OF SOME POLYMERIZATIONS

1. Vinyl polymerization

(*a*) *Free-radical mechanism.* A number of olefines (called, in the present context, monomers) undergo a characteristic type of reaction to give a product which has the physical properties of a macromolecule.† Such addition polymerizations may be represented as

$$n\mathrm{CH_2{=}CHR} \longrightarrow -(\mathrm{CH_2{-}CHR})_n- \qquad \text{(i)}$$

Here the nature of the end groups is (for the moment) left unspecified. Typical monomers are styrene (1), vinyl acetate (2), and methyl methacrylate (3): the polymers are named simply by adding the prefix 'poly', and polymethyl methacrylate is also referred to by trade names (e.g. Perspex or Lucite).

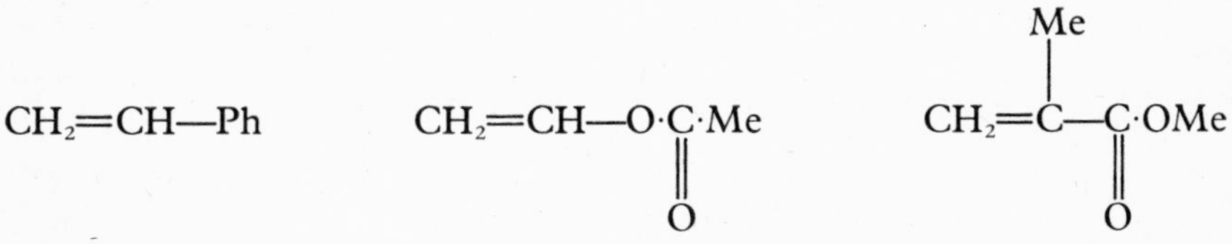

(1) (2) (3)

An important characteristic of all polymerizations is that the product is not, strictly speaking, homogeneous. For one thing, the value of n in equation (i) is an average value; thus n (the degree of polymerization) may have the average value of 1,000, but the product will be a mixture of polymers of varying degrees of polymerization. There is also the possibility of structural variation, but in fact nearly all the units are arranged in the head-to-tail fashion (4), rather than as in (5).

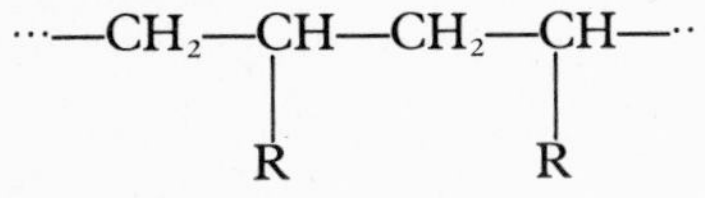

not

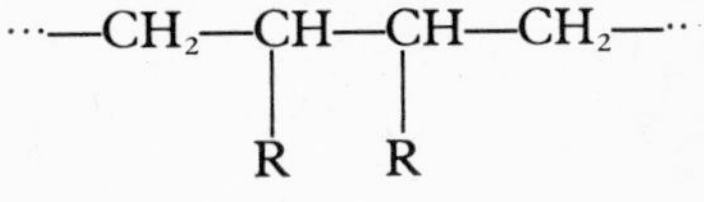

(4) (5)

† For a general account of polymers, see Flory, *Principles of Polymer Chemistry*, Cornell University Press, 1953.

Finally, there is the question of the disposition of the R groups, which are usually not regularly directed (see § 1 c).

We can now turn our attention to the course of the polymerization. The rate of the reaction is greatly influenced by the presence of small quantities of various compounds. These may either accelerate the reaction (initiators) or retard it (inhibitors). Practical work is made more difficult by the fact that two ubiquitous environmental factors also affect these reactions, and in opposite directions: light acts as an initiator and oxygen as an inhibitor.

The most direct way to try to gain some information about the course of a vinyl polymerization is to stop the reaction after various times and see if any intermediates are detectable. When this is done, the mixture is found to consist only of monomer and polymer; moreover, the degree of polymerization of the polymer that is formed does not increase during the course of the reaction. No intermediates between monomer and full-grown polymer are detectable. This negative result is, in fact, quite helpful. It shows that two very different time scales are operative. The time taken for a polymer chain to grow must be much shorter than the time taken for the complete conversion of monomer into polymer. Indeed, the average lifetime of a growing chain is usually less than a second, and for an average degree of polymerization of 1,000, this means that the individual reactions (leading to chain growth) must follow each other at intervals of less than one-thousandth of a second. And the concentration of actively growing chains is low, around 10^{-8} molar, so that the main components during reaction are monomer and polymer.

Vinyl polymerizations are usually free-radical (homolytic) reactions. The evidence for this conclusion comes from a number of sources. One point is that the polymerizations can be initiated by light, and experience shows that when a molecule undergoes fission after absorbing a quantum of light, the fission is homolytic. The reason for this is that the bond-breaking in the photochemically excited molecule takes place before solvent molecules can arrange themselves in a suitable orientation to solvate the ions, and the production of unsolvated ions is energetically less favourable than fission to free radicals. Perhaps the most direct evidence for the presence of free radicals during a polymerization is that they have been detected by paramagnetic resonance absorption spectroscopy.† This method depends on the behaviour of the unpaired electron (characteristic of free radicals) in a magnetic field.

† Fraenkel, Hirshon, and Walling, *J. Amer. Chem. Soc.* 1954, **76**, 3606; Bamford, Jenkins, Ingram, and Symons, *Nature*, 1955, **175**, 894.

The simplest mechanism for a reaction of this type consists of three stages: chain initiation, chain propagation, and chain termination. These may be illustrated by the polymerization of styrene, initiated by (decomposing) benzoyl peroxide. The reaction might, for example, be carried out by the addition of 1 gramme of the peroxide to 1 litre of (purified) styrene at 60° C, in the absence of oxygen and ultra-violet light. The chain initiation is the formation of styrene radicals (as usual, the unpaired electron is indicated by a dot):

$$PhCO—O—O—COPh \longrightarrow 2PhCO—O\bullet$$

$$PhCO—O\bullet + CH_2{=}CHPh \longrightarrow PhCO—O—CH_2—\overset{\bullet}{C}HPh$$

In the chain propagations, the styrene radicals react with more monomer:

$$PhCO—O—CH_2—\overset{\bullet}{C}HPh + CH_2{=}CHPh \xrightarrow{k_p} PhCOOCH_2—CHPh—CH_2\overset{\bullet}{C}HPh$$

$$PhCOOCH_2CHPhCH_2\overset{\bullet}{C}HPh + CH_2{=}CHPh \xrightarrow{k_p} PhCOO[CH_2CHPh]_2CH_2\overset{\bullet}{C}HPh, \text{ and so on.}$$

One method of chain termination is by combination of the radicals:

$$PhCOO[CH_2CHPh]_x\,CH_2\overset{\bullet}{C}HPh + Ph\overset{\bullet}{C}HCH_2[PhCHCH_2]_y OCOPh$$

$$\downarrow k_t$$

$$PhCOO[CH_2CHPh]_x—CH_2CHPh—CHPh—CH_2[PhCHCH_2]_y OCOPh$$

The kinetics are simplified by the assumption that the reactivity of the terminal radical does not depend on the chain length. The kinetic scheme only applies to the early stages of a reaction leading to long chains; the solution of polymer in monomer becomes viscous as the reaction proceeds, and this affects the course of the reaction. The monomer is written as M, a growing chain as X, and the rate of initiation as v_i; the steady-state approximation may be applied to a growing chain:

$$d[X]/dt = v_i - 2k_t[X]^2 = 0,$$

$$[X] = (v_i/2k_t)^{\frac{1}{2}}.$$

As the reaction is to lead to long chains, the monomer must be reacting mainly with the growing chains rather than with the radicals formed by the fission of benzoyl peroxide, so that

$$-d[M]/dt = k_p[M][X] = k_p[M](v_i/2k_t)^{\frac{1}{2}}.$$

The rate of initiation (v_i) is proportional to the concentration of initiator (benzoyl peroxide). So this equation can be tested by seeing if, in a number of runs, the rate of polymerization is proportional to the square root of the initiator concentration. This relationship does, in fact, hold quite generally.

The average number of monomer units added to a growing chain before the termination reaction is the average degree of polymerization $(\bar{P})$, and is given by the ratio of the rate of propagation to the rate of termination:

$$\bar{P} = \frac{-d[M]/dt}{2k_t[X]^2} = \frac{k_p[M][X]}{2k_t[X]^2},$$

thus

$$\bar{P} = \frac{k_p[M]}{2k_t[X]} = \frac{k_p[M]^2}{2k_t[M][X]},$$

i.e.

$$\bar{P} = \frac{k_p^2[M]^2}{-2k_t.d[M]/dt}.$$

The degree of polymerization is thus inversely proportional to the rate of chain propagation, and this also has been confirmed.

The absolute values of the rate constants, k_p and k_t, cannot be found from these equations, but have been determined by special methods.[†] The values of k_p are commonly in the range of 10–100 l. mol^{-1} sec^{-1}, and the values for k_t are even larger, usually about 10^7 l. mol^{-1} sec^{-1}. The combination of two radicals needs little in the way of activation energy (about 2 kcal/mol) and is a very fast reaction. For a polymerization to lead to long chains the propagation step must also be fast.

When two monomers are undergoing polymerization together, it is commonly found that there is an intermingling of monomer units in the chains being formed: this reaction is known as copolymerization. If a mixture of styrene and methyl methacrylate is caused to polymerize there are four different propagation reactions:

$$\sim CH_2-\overset{\bullet}{C}HPh + CH_2{=}CHPh \xrightarrow{k_1} \sim CH_2-CHPh-CH_2-\overset{\bullet}{C}HPh$$

chain ending   styrene
in radical derived
from styrene

$$\sim CH_2-\overset{\bullet}{C}HPh + CH_2{=}CMeCOOMe \xrightarrow{k_2} \sim CH_2-CHPh-CH_2-\overset{\bullet}{C}(Me)COOMe$$

methyl methacrylate

$$\sim CH_2-\overset{\bullet}{C}(Me)COOMe + CH_2{=}CHPh \xrightarrow{k_3} \sim CH_2-\underset{\underset{COOMe}{|}}{C}(Me)CH_2\overset{\bullet}{C}HPh$$

chain ending in
radical derived from
methyl methacrylate

$$\sim CH_2-\overset{\bullet}{C}(Me)COOMe + CH_2{=}CMeCOOMe \xrightarrow{k_4} \sim CH_2-\underset{\underset{COOMe}{|}}{C}(Me)CH_2-\overset{\bullet}{C}(Me)COOMe$$

† Bamford, Barb, Jenkins, and Onyon, *Kinetics of Vinyl Polymerization by Radical Mechanisms*, Butterworths, 1958; Burnett, *Mechanism of Polymer Reactions*, Interscience, 1954; Walling, *Free Radicals in Solution*, Wiley, 1957.

Of these four propagation steps, the first and last are between like radical and monomer, and the other two reactions are the 'cross' reactions leading to the copolymer. Hence the values of the ratios k_1/k_2 and k_4/k_3 are a measure of the tendency of the system to give copolymers. In the example given, both these ratios are about $\frac{1}{2}$. In other words, a chain ending in a styrene radical is twice as likely to react with methyl methacrylate as with styrene, and the same applies to the other pair. Thus, the 'cross' reactions are favoured. This is often referred to as the alternating effect, as it favours the sequence in which residues derived from different monomers are juxtaposed in the polymer.

Two monomers, both undergoing polymerization, may not copolymerize; on the other hand, there are several examples of monomers which do not polymerize on their own but readily enter into copolymerizations. Maleic anhydride is one such monomer, and even benzene can copolymerize to a limited extent with vinyl acetate. Many of the technically important compounds are copolymers, as a wider range of properties is thus available.

A few of the main points of vinyl polymerizations have now been described, and we can try to interpret them in structural terms. The first question is why polymerization should occur at all. In this context, the question is taken to mean: is there a general reason why the polymer should be thermodynamically favoured? Now in the formation of a vinyl polymer, two carbon-carbon single bonds in the polymer replace one carbon-carbon double bond in the monomer. This corresponds to a difference in bond energies of about 20 kcal/mol and it is, in fact, found that the polymerizations are exothermic to the extent of 10 to 20 kcal/mol. However, the entropy change will be unfavourable, as the translational entropy of the monomers is lost; the experimental values are in the range -25 to -35 entropy units. The free energy change may therefore be unfavourable above a certain temperature.† Some polymers, e.g. polymethyl methacrylate, do give the monomer on heating strongly.

The second question is why head-to-tail addition should occur. This question can be answered by considering the stability of the radical (cf. Chapter IV, § 3 b). A radical R· could add to styrene to give either (6) or (7). Only in the former is the radical stabilized by mesomerism. The unshared electron in (6) can interact with the benzene ring so that, in effect, the electron is delocalized, which can be expressed by writing formulae such as (8). Steric factors operate towards giving the same

† Dainton and Ivin, *Quart. Rev.* 1958, **12**, 61.

R—CH₂—ĊH—Ph   ĊH₂—CH—Ph   R—CH₂—CH=⟨benzene ring⟩•
                              |
                              R

(6)   (7)   (8)

orientation, and with some monomers, such as vinyl acetate, it may well be mainly the fact that the unsubstituted CH_2 group is more accessible to attack by the radical that leads to the head-to-tail orientation as the chief (but not the sole) arrangement.

The rate of a propagation step naturally depends on both the monomer and the radical. Some values of the rate constants (in l. mol^{-1} sec^{-1}) at 60° C are given below.

Monomer	Radical derived from:		
	Styrene	Methyl methacrylate	Vinyl acetate
Styrene . . .	145	1,520	> 100,000
Methyl methacrylate	278	705	> 100,000
Vinyl acetate . .	3	35	2,300

From Walling, *Free Radicals in Solution*, Wiley, 1957.

These figures can be compared in several ways. The order of reactivity of the radicals (with any of the monomers) is vinyl acetate > methyl methacrylate > styrene, i.e. along any row the values increase from left to right. The order of reactivity of the monomers, however, is quite different, and vinyl acetate is the least reactive monomer. A more reactive monomer, styrene, reacts to give a radical derived from styrene which is stabilized by mesomerism. Conversely, a radical derived from vinyl acetate, which is not so stabilized, is more reactive (by a factor of about 1,000) than the radical derived from styrene. Thus, the effects of stabilization of the radical on the reactivities of monomer and radical are opposed.

The figures given above also illustrate the alternating effect. The radical derived from methyl methacrylate reacts more rapidly with styrene than with its own monomer, and the radical derived from styrene reacts more rapidly with methyl methacrylate than with its own monomer. The alternating effect has been ascribed to the complementary character of the two species; the carbonyl group of the methyl ester can interact with the double bond of the styrene, so that there can be some charge-transfer in the transition states of the 'cross' reactions.

(b) *Ionic mechanisms.* Vinyl compounds can polymerize by ionic mechanisms,† as well as by the free-radical mechanism just described. Cationic polymerization may be represented as proceeding via carbonium ions (which are usually present as one partner of a closely clustering ion pair). Hydrogen bromide initiates the polymerization of styrene, in nitromethane solution, and the simplest mechanism is:

$$CH_2{=}CHPh + HBr \longrightarrow CH_3{-}\overset{+}{C}HPhBr^- \qquad \text{initiation}$$

$$Br^- \, CH_3{-}\overset{+}{C}HPh + CH_2{=}CHPh \longrightarrow Br^- \, CH_3{-}CHPh{-}CH_2{-}\overset{+}{C}HPh \qquad \text{propagation}$$

$$Br^- \, CH_3{-}CHPh[CH_2CHPh]_n CH_2{-}\overset{+}{C}HPh \longrightarrow CH_3{-}CHPh[CH_2CHPh]_n CH_2CHBrPh \quad \text{termination}$$

Long chains can only be formed if the carbonium ion reacts much more rapidly with the monomer than it does with bromide ion.

This scheme illustrates the cationic nature of the intermediates, but the process is, in general, more complex than is indicated by the simple mechanism given above. Aluminium halides may be used to initiate these polymerizations and here a trace of water is often required; the initiation can then proceed by the stages:

$$H_2O + AlCl_3 \longrightarrow H_2\overset{+}{O}{-}\overset{-}{A}lCl_3$$

$$H_2\overset{+}{O}{-}\overset{-}{A}lCl_3 + CH_2{=}CHR \longrightarrow CH_3{-}\overset{+}{C}HR + HO\overset{-}{A}lCl_3$$

A striking difference between the cationic and free-radical mechanisms is brought out in the polymerization of an equimolar mixture of styrene and methyl methacrylate. The polymer initially formed by a free-radical mechanism (benzoyl peroxide at 60° C) contains 51 per cent. styrene. But with cationic reagents (stannic chloride, or boron trifluoride and ether) almost pure polystyrene is formed initially. There is a third mechanism by which some vinyl compounds can polymerize, and this is the anionic mechanism. The same mixture of styrene and methyl methacrylate gives initially, with metallic sodium or potassium, almost pure polymethyl methacrylate.‡ Both the ionic mechanisms of polymerization are more restricted in scope than the free-radical mechanism.

The most active monomers in anionic polymerizations contain the olefinic double bond conjugated with a C=O or C≡N group (e.g. methyl methacrylate, acrylonitrile); these are the olefines which add anions (Chapter IV, § 3 e). An example of a polymerization proceeding by the

---

† Pepper, *Quart. Rev.* 1954, **8**, 88; Burnett, *Mechanism of Polymer Reactions*, Interscience, 1954.

‡ Walling, Briggs, Cummings, and Mayo, *J. Amer. Chem. Soc.* 1950, **72**, 48.

anionic mechanism which has been studied in some detail is the polymerization of styrene by potassium amide in liquid ammonia solution:[†]

$$H_2N^- + CH_2{=}CHPh \longrightarrow H_2N{\cdot}CH_2{-}\overline{C}HPh \qquad \text{initiation}$$

$$H_2N{\cdot}CH_2{-}\overline{C}HPh + CH_2{=}CHPh \longrightarrow H_2N{\cdot}CH_2{-}CHPh{-}CH_2{-}\overline{C}HPh \quad \text{propagation}$$

$$H_2N[CH_2{-}CHPh]_n CH_2{-}\overline{C}HPh + NH_3 \longrightarrow H_2N[CH_2{-}CHPh]_n CH_2{-}CH_2Ph \quad \text{termination}$$
$$+ H_2N^-$$

As required by this mechanism, there is one nitrogen atom per polymer chain.

(c) *Stereoselective polymerization.* The polymerization of a vinyl compound of the type $CH_2{=}CHR$ (e.g. styrene) leads to a polymer in which each unit contains a carbon atom which may have one of two configurations. Under some circumstances, certain configurations are formed exclusively. The causes and consequences of this situation are outlined in this section.[‡]

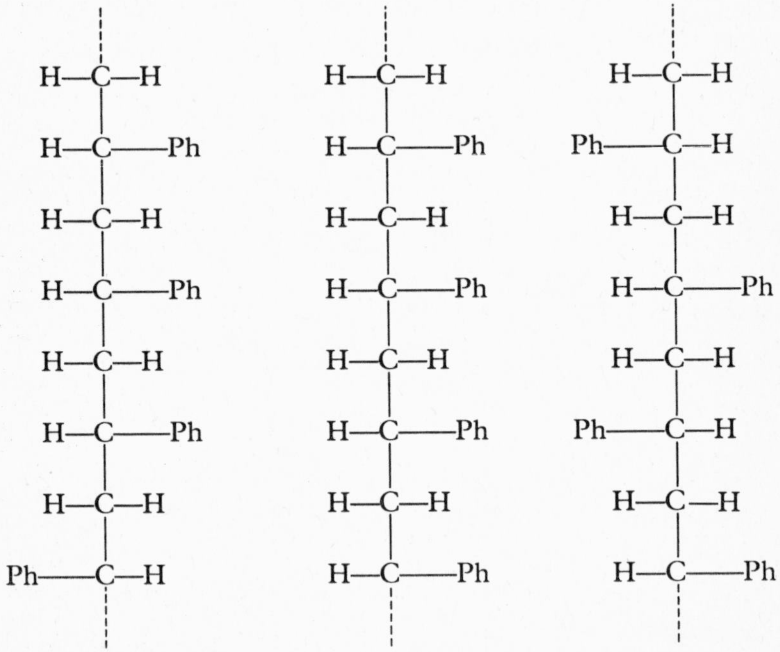

atactic	isotactic	syndyotactic
(1)	(2)	(3)

† Higginson and Wooding, *J. Chem. Soc.* 1952, p. 760.

‡ For references, and a detailed discussion, see Gaylord and Mark, *Linear and Stereo-regular Addition Polymers*, Interscience, New York, 1959; Stille, *Chem. Rev* 1958, **58**, 541; Natta, *Adv. Catalysis*, 1959, **11**, 1.

Rotation about the carbon-carbon bonds leads to there being many possible conformations of long-chain polymers, such as polystyrene. If we choose the most extended conformation, and write this in a Fischer projection with the backbone carbon atoms in a vertical plane, then there are several possible ways of disposing of the phenyl groups. They may be distributed at random as in (1), or they may all be on the same side of the backbone as in (2), or they may alternate as in (3). In a long chain, none of these structures will be capable of optical activity, but the differences between them are shown by other physical properties, which arise because the ordered arrangements (2) and (3) can pack more closely in the solid than the irregular arrangement (1) can.

Ordinarily, the irregular atactic structure (1) is formed. This can be appreciated if the monomer, styrene, is shown as (4); then the attacking radical (or carbanion, or carbonium ion, depending on the mechanism) is just as likely to attack the monomer from above (5) as from below (6), and these lead to opposite configurations of the newly formed CHPh

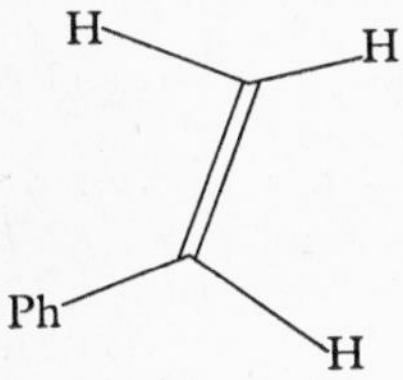

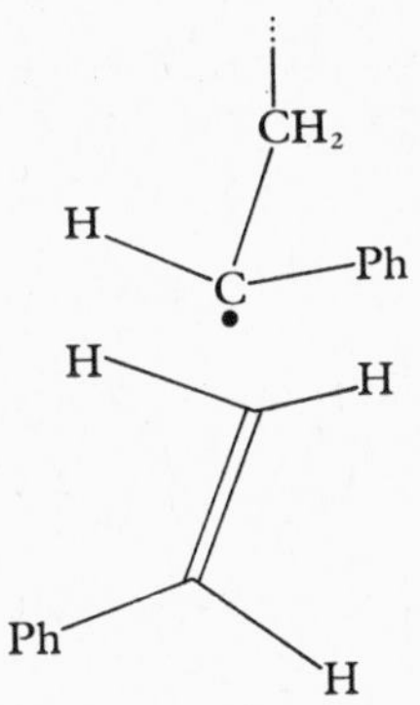

group. Natta† found that polystyrene formed in the presence of certain initiators (TiCl$_4$ and AlEt$_3$) had unusual physical properties; thus the polymer softened at 240° C whereas 'ordinary' (atactic) polystyrene softens at about 80° C. Moreover, this new polystyrene could be 'crystallized', i.e. drawn and orientated fibres gave sharp and intense X-ray diffraction diagrams, and it was from these that the isotactic structure was established. The polymerization is thus a highly stereoselective reaction; the initiators used must control, in particular, the propagation step. The reaction is heterogeneous, and chain growth takes place on a surface.

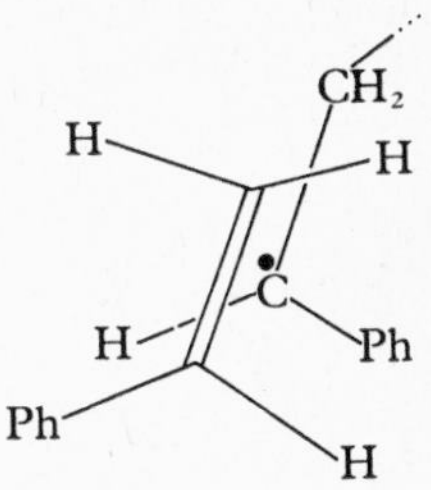

† Natta, *Angew. Chem.* 1956, **68**, 393.

More polar olefines can be stereoselectively polymerized in homogeneous solution, and polymethyl methacrylate has been obtained in
regular (isotactic and syndyotactic) forms. The polymerization can
proceed by a free-radical mechanism (initiation by ultra-violet light) or
a carbanion mechanism (initiation by sodamide in liquid ammonia).
The detailed mechanisms of these remarkable reactions have yet to be
worked out. An isotactic structure would be obtained if the growing
chain were in the most extended conformation, and if also the monomer
units of say, styrene, were added so that the distance between the phenyl
groups was as great as possible; however, there is no evidence to suggest
that these conditions are the relevant ones.† There are certain formal
similarities with enzymic reactions, and the question of a 'three-point
contact' between the reactants has been discussed for stereoselective
polymerizations, just as it has for enzymic reactions (Chapter IV).

(d) *Enzymic synthesis of rubber and of geranyl pyrophosphate.* Natural
rubber (from *Hevea brasiliensis*) may be represented as derived from
isoprene (1) units, joined together by 1,4-addition, with a head-to-tail
arrangement of the units, and is the *cis* isomer (2).

The polymerization of isoprene gives material in which some of the units
are linked as in (2). The biological monomer is mevalonic acid (3), which
can be converted into rubber by the latex from the tree, without the
addition of any co-factors.‡ The detailed mechanism is not yet known.

Many compounds (terpenes, steroids, carotenoids, etc.) may be regarded as derived from isoprene units.§ The enzymic reaction by which
the C—C bond is formed in one such compound will now be described.

† Cf. Cram and Kopecky, *J. Amer. Chem. Soc.* 1959, **81**, 2748.
‡ Park and Bonner, *J. Biol. Chem.* 1958, **233**, 340; Kekwick, Archer, Barnard, Higgins,
McSweeney, and Moore, *Nature*, 1959, **184**, 268.
§ See, for example, Ruzicka, *Proc. Chem. Soc.* 1959, p. 341.

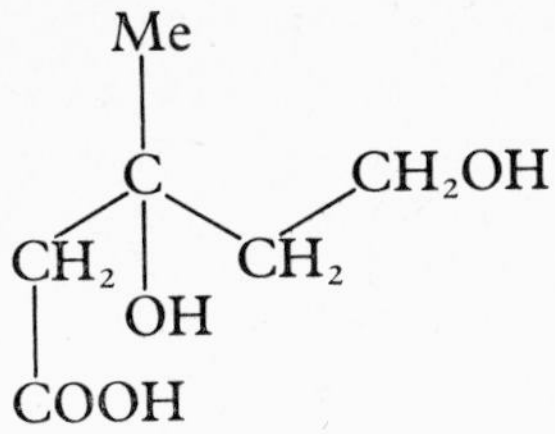

Me
|
C————CH₂OH
CH₂ | CH₂
OH
|
COOH

(3)

Isopentenyl pyrophosphate (4) (see Chapter IV, § 2) isomerizes, in the presence of an enzyme from yeast, to dimethylallyl pyrophosphate (5):†

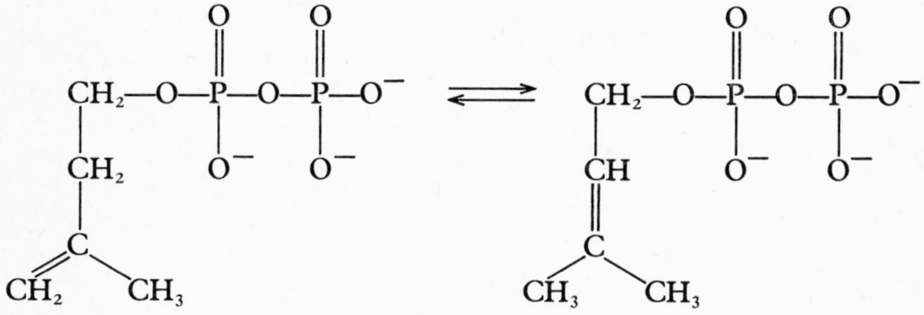

isopentenyl
pyrophosphate

(4)

dimethylallyl
pyrophosphate

(5)

The two isomers, which contain the carbon skeleton of isoprene (1), unite in an enzymic reaction in which the pyrophosphate ion is eliminated; a carbonium ion (6) is shown as an intermediate: this is purely hypothetical. One of the carbon atoms is rendered electron-deficient by the departing group (the pyrophosphate anion), and this electron-deficient carbon atom reacts with the nucleophilic C=C of the other partner. The reaction of an electron-deficient carbon atom (carbonium ion type) with a carbon-carbon double bond was described in § 1 b. This reaction may be contrasted with the aldol reaction, where the intermediates have the character of carbanions. The carbonium ion type of reaction described here constitutes the only exception to the generalization that C—C bonds are formed *in vivo* by additions to carbonyl groups.

† Lynen, Agranoff, Eggerer, Henning, and Möslein, *Angew. Chem.* 1959, **71**, 657; Agranoff, Eggerer, Henning, and Lynen, *J. Biol. Chem.* 1960, **235**, 326; Rilling and Bloch, ibid. 1959, **234**, 1424.

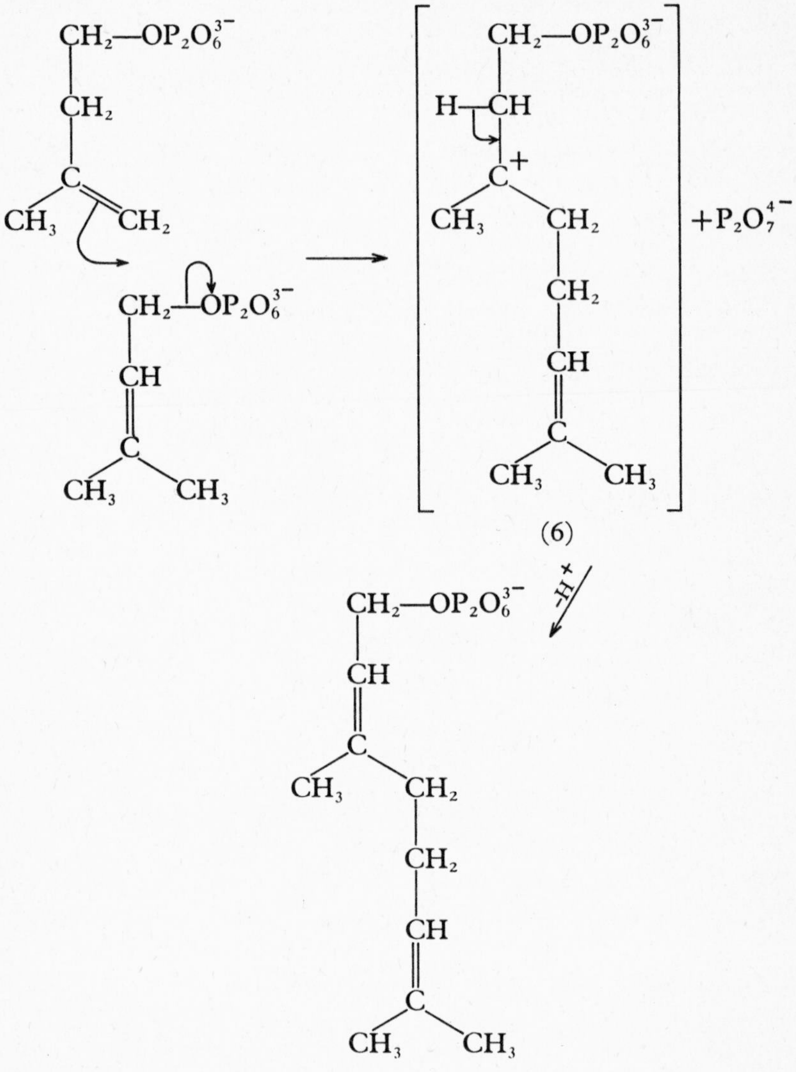

$$CH_2-OP_2O_6^{3-}$$

$$CH_2$$

$$C$$

$$CH_3 \qquad CH_2$$

$$CH_2-OP_2O_6^{3-}$$

$$CH$$

$$C$$

$$CH_3 \qquad CH_3$$

$$\longrightarrow$$

$$\left[\begin{array}{c} CH_2-OP_2O_6^{3-} \\ H-CH \\ C^+ \\ CH_3 \qquad CH_2 \\ CH_2 \\ CH \\ C \\ CH_3 \qquad CH_3 \end{array} \right] + P_2O_7^{4-}$$

(6)

$$CH_2-OP_2O_6^{3-} \qquad \overset{+}{\underset{-H}{\diagup}}$$

$$CH$$

$$C$$

$$CH_3 \qquad CH_2$$

$$CH_2$$

$$CH$$

$$C$$

$$CH_3 \qquad CH_3$$

geranyl pyrophosphate

2. Polymerization of amino acid N-carboxyanhydrides

(*a*) *Condensation polymerization.* The polymerizations of vinyl compounds that have been described in the previous section belong to the class of addition polymerizations: the propagation step is an addition reaction. Condensation polymerizations form the other main class: here a small molecule, such as water, or carbon dioxide, is split off during the reaction. An example of a condensation polymerization is the formation of nylon from hexamethylene diamine (1) and adipic acid (2):

$$H_2N[CH_2]_6NH_2 + HOOC[CH_2]_4COOH \longrightarrow H_2N[CH_2]_6NH \cdot CO[CH_2]_4COOH + H_2O$$

(1)   (2)   dimer

The dimer, a bifunctional molecule, can react with another molecule of either the amine (1) or the acid (2); thus, the general step is

$$H\{HN[CH_2]_6NH \cdot CO[CH_2]_4CO\}_n OH + H\{HN[CH_2]_6NH \cdot CO[CH_2]_4CO\}_m OH$$

$$\downarrow$$

$$H\{HN[CH_2]_6NH \cdot CO[CH_2]_4CO\}_{n+m} OH + H_2O$$

Here there is no division into initiation, propagation, and termination, but there is just one kind of reaction. In such typical condensation polymerizations the polymers can react with each other, whereas in vinyl polymerizations the growing polymers only react with the mono-mer. One of the most important experimental results obtained from studies of condensation polymerizations is that the reactivity of each functional group of the same kind does not decrease in large molecules.†

(*b*) *General features of the polymerization of amino acid* N-*carboxy-anhydrides*. The polymerizations of these N-carboxyanhydrides possess some features of both classes of polymerization. The propagation step in, for example, the polymerization of alanine N-carboxyanhydride (1) is

$$
\begin{array}{c}
\text{Me} \\
\text{CH—CO} \\
\diagup \qquad \diagdown \\
\text{NH} \qquad \text{O} \\
\diagdown \diagup \\
\text{CO}
\end{array}
+ H[HN \cdot CHMe \cdot CO]_n X \longrightarrow H[HN \cdot CHMe \cdot CO]_{n+1} X + CO_2 \quad \text{(i)}
$$

(1)   (2)

Since carbon dioxide is evolved, the reaction must be classified as a condensation polymerization, but here the polymers only react with the monomer and not with each other. The monomer (1) is a cyclic mixed anhydride, and the product (2) is a polypeptide; the nature of the terminal group X depends on the mode of initiation. If, in reaction (i), $n = 1$ and $X = OH$, the amino compound that initiates the reaction is the amino acid, alanine, and the product (2) the dipeptide; it, too, has

† See Flory, *Principles of Polymer Chemistry*, Cornell University Press, 1953, chap. 3, for discussion of this point.

an amino group, and so can react further with another molecule of monomer (1) to give the tripeptide (and carbon dioxide). The process can obviously be continued, so that the final product is a polymer. In each step, one amino group is consumed, but a fresh amino group is formed, so that the concentration of amino groups is not altered by these propagation steps. Formally, the amino groups may be compared with the free radicals at the ends of the growing chains in vinyl polymerizations. The polypeptides formed by polymerization of N-carboxyanhydrides, because they have high molecular weights but simple structures, have proved useful as model substances for the physical investigations of proteins.†

(c) *Polymerization of N-carboxyanhydrides in aqueous solution.* The products of the reaction of N-carboxyanhydrides in aqueous solution depends markedly on the pH. In acid solution, the products are the amino acid and carbon dioxide: e.g.

$$\begin{array}{c} \text{Me} \\ \text{CH—CO} \\ \text{NH} \quad \text{O} \\ \text{CO} \end{array} + H_3O^+ \longrightarrow H_3\overset{+}{N}\cdot CHMe\cdot COOH + CO_2$$

The product in cold alkaline solution is the carbamate (1), which loses carbon dioxide rapidly at room temperature in neutral solution, to give the amino acid

$$\begin{array}{c} \text{Me} \\ \text{CH—CO} \\ \text{NH} \quad \text{O} \\ \text{CO} \end{array} + 2OH^- \longrightarrow \begin{array}{c} Me\cdot CH\cdot COO^- \\ | \\ NH\cdot COO^- \end{array} + H_2O$$

(1)

Except in strongly acid or alkaline solution, polymers are formed. The amino group of the amino acid or peptide competes with the water for the N-carboxyanhydride; this reaction is catalysed by bases (e.g. by the acetate ion). In strongly alkaline solution, the reactive hydroxide ion is present at a high concentration, and so this is the main species reacting with the anhydride, and polymer formation cannot occur. In strongly acid solution the amino group of the amino acid is present exclusively

† Katchalski, *Adv. Protein Chem.* 1951, **6**, 123; Katchalski and Sela, ibid. 1958, **13**, 243; Bamford, Elliott, and Hanby, *Synthetic Polypeptides*, Academic Press, 1956.

in the unreactive protonated form, and so the anhydride is only decomposed by water. Even at pH 5, where only a small fraction of the amino acid is present as $H_2N.CHMe.COO^-$ (it is nearly all present as

$$\overset{+}{H_3N}.CHMe.COO^-),$$

it seems to be the unprotonated amine which reacts with the anhydride.[†] The rate constants are in the range $10^2–10^3$ l. mol^{-1} sec^{-1}, and are thus of the same order as the rate constants for the propagation step in vinyl polymerizations.

(d) *Polymerization of* N-*carboxyanhydrides initiated by amines.* The polymerizations of N-carboxyanhydrides in aqueous solution, or initiated by water in organic solvents, necessarily comprise two stages, proceeding at different rates: one stage is the reaction of the anhydride with water, the other its reaction with the amino group at the end of the growing chain. The situation should be simplified if pre-formed polymer is used as an initiator, as in the polymerization of sarcosine N-carboxyanhydride (1) by polysarcosine dimethylamide (2):[‡]

$$\underset{(1)}{\begin{array}{c}CH_2{-}CO\\ MeN\diagup\quad\diagdown O\\ CO\end{array}} + \underset{(2)}{H[NMe{\cdot}CH_2{\cdot}CO]_n NMe_2} \longrightarrow H[NMe{\cdot}CH_2{\cdot}CO]_{n+1} NMe_2 + CO_2$$

This example was chosen because the polymerization can be conducted in homogeneous solution. If the reactivity of the terminal amino group is independent of the chain length, then the successive bimolecular steps will have the same rate constant. The reaction is first-order, as the concentration of amino groups remains constant. One unexpected feature was that the reaction proceeded more slowly at higher temperatures, i.e. the rate has a negative temperature coefficient. This suggests that an intermediate is formed reversibly, and exothermically, so that the extent of formation of the intermediate is less at higher temperatures. The intermediate may be formulated as (3), which is similar to the intermediate postulated in the reaction of esters with amines (Chapter VII, § 1 a), and more generally, of carbonyl compounds with nucleophilic reagents.

[†] Bartlett and Jones, *J. Amer. Chem. Soc.* 1957, **79**, 2153; Bartlett and Dittmer, ibid., p. 2159.

[‡] Waley and Watson, *Proc. Roy. Soc.* A, 1949, **199**, 499; Ballard and Bamford, ibid. 1954, **223**, 495.

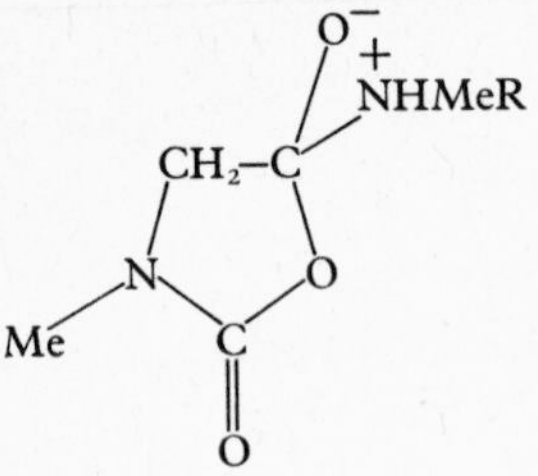

(3) 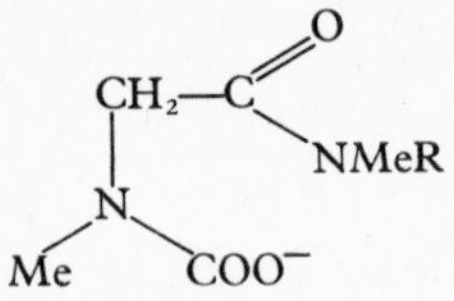   (4) 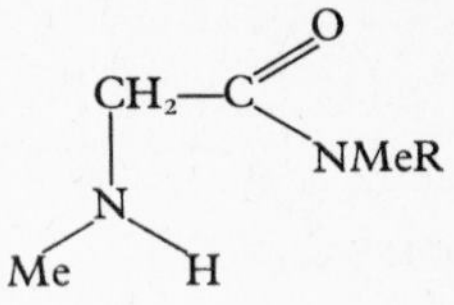   (5)

Although there is no direct evidence for such an intermediate in the polymerizations of other N-carboxyanhydrides, it seems possible that this is a general reaction. The decomposition of the intermediate (3) is base-catalysed (the rate is proportional to the square of the concentration of amino groups), and leads to the carbamate (4), which then rapidly loses carbon dioxide to give the peptide (5). Another feature of this particular polymerization is that it is catalysed by carbon dioxide; the reaction of an amino group with an ester group has also been observed to be catalysed by carbon dioxide, and seems to be due to the formation of carbamates.† The representation of (3) as a dipolar ion and (4) as an anion is somewhat arbitrary, as the timing of the rapid proton transfers to oxygen atoms cannot readily be established.

In the polymerization of an N-carboxyanhydride initiated by an amine, if there is no termination reaction and the ring opens exclusively in the way shown, then the reaction proceeds until all the monomer is consumed, and the degree of polymerization is given by the ratio of the initial concentration of the monomer to that of the amine. Moreover, the molecular weight distribution should be particularly sharp, so that the polypeptide formed will appear homogeneous by most tests. On the whole, these predictions have been verified.‡

Certain unexpected features were first detected in the polymerization of the N-carboxyanhydride (6) of benzyl glutamate, and have since been

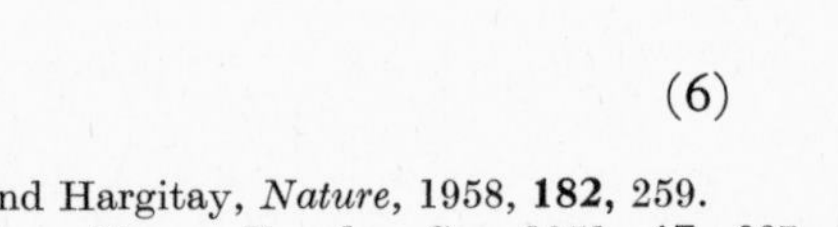

(6)

† Hubert, Buijle, and Hargitay, *Nature*, 1958, **182**, 259.
‡ Fessler and Ogston, *Trans. Faraday Soc.* 1951, **47**, 667; Pope, Weakley, and Williams, *J. Chem. Soc.* 1959, p. 3442.

observed in other instances. If the amount of initiator was such that
the expected degree of polymerization at the end of the reaction was
twenty, the rate constant was found to increase by a factor of about
five roughly half-way through the reaction. This observation was interpreted in terms of the conformation of the growing polymer. When the
polypeptide chain is sufficiently long it exists in a helical form, which
was supposed to be more reactive.[†] The helical form is stabilized by
hydrogen-bonding of the C=O to NH groups in the polypeptide chain.
However, polysarcosine (with a repeating unit, —$NMeCH_2CO$—), which
lacks an NH group and so cannot form a hydrogen-bonded helix, can
also show the phenomenon of an accelerated rate during reaction. In a
number of instances, the increase in rate coincided with the stage when
the growing polymer precipitated from solution. These polypeptides
usually separate as highly swollen gels, and so it seems likely that the
increased rate is due to the reaction taking place more rapidly in the
swollen gel than it does in free solution.[‡]

(e) *'Chain effect' in the polymerization of* N-*carboxyanhydrides*. When
the polymerization of the N-carboxyanhydride of phenylalanine (1) is
initiated by polysarcosine dimethylamide (2) in nitrobenzene, the initial
rate of polymerization is unexpectedly high, and depends on the molecular weight of the initiator.

PhCH₂·CH—CO

HN   O

CO

(1)

H[NMe·CH₂·CO]ₙNMe₂

(2)

H[NH·CH·CO]ₘ[NMe·CH₂·CO]ₙNMe₂

CH₂Ph

(3)

The initial rate increases with the value of n in the initiator (2) up to
about $n = 20$; the products are 'block' copolymers (3) containing a
string of phenylalanine residues and a string of sarcosine residues. The
high initial rate has been observed for several different N-carboxyanhydrides, but seems to be restricted to the one initiator, polysarcosine
dimethylamide. The polypeptide chains of the initiator cannot form
hydrogen bonds with each other, but the N-carboxyanhydride can form
hydrogen bonds with the C=O bond of the initiator. The enhanced
rate is then interpreted as being due to the N-carboxyanhydride forming
a hydrogen-bonded complex with the initiator, at some position along
the initiator chain. As the initiator chain is reasonably flexible this

---

† Doty and Lundberg, *J. Amer. Chem. Soc.* 1956, **78**, 4810; Weingarten, ibid. 1958,
80, 352.

‡ Ballard and Bamford, *J. Chem. Soc.* 1959, p. 1039.

complex should be able to attain a conformation such that the reactive (amino) end of the initiator approaches the anhydride. One possible arrangement is shown below:

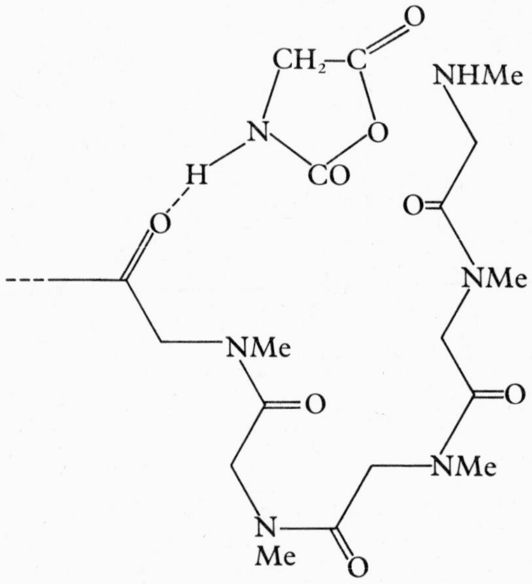

The main effect of this adsorption is to increase the probability of collision between the anhydride and the terminal group of the growing chain, and the situation has been compared with the action of enzymes.†

It is interesting to try to gauge the magnitude of this effect, i.e. to see how much greater is the probability of reaction if two species are held close together. If the two compounds which are to react are both present at a concentration of 0·1 molar, which corresponds to $0.1 \times 6.10^{23} \times 10^{-3}$ molecules per c.c., then the probability of both being simultaneously present in a volume of 100 Å^3 is about 10^{-5}. If we assume that when both molecules are bound to the enzyme the probability of their both being in this volume (and so at a distance suitable for reaction) is unity, then we may speak of the rate enhancement due to proximity as being around 10^5. As the rate enhancement by enzymes may be greater than 10^{10}, it does not seem likely that the effectiveness of enzymes is due mainly to the effect we have considered. Similar conclusions have been reached by a more realistic method.‡

---

† Ballard and Bamford, *Proc. Roy. Soc.* A, 1956, **236**, 384.
‡ Koshland, *J. Cell. Comp. Physiol.* 1956, **47**, suppl. No. 1, p. 217.

3. Enzymic polymerization and depolymerization

There are too many kinds of macromolecules in organisms, and too little is known about the detailed mechanisms of the polymerizations which form them, to do more than note a few common features here. Enzymic polymerizations are condensation polymerizations: the macromolecules are formed from the units with the loss of the elements of water, or phosphoric acid, or of some more complicated species (e.g. uridine diphosphate). A common type of reaction starts from the monomer in the form of a derivative (e.g. glucose-1-phosphate) and preformed polymer (called a primer, e.g. glycogen). The type of reaction is thus formally similar to the polymerization of an N-carboxyanhydride of an amino acid, initiated by preformed polymer. Thus, the reaction catalysed by phosphorylase may be represented as:

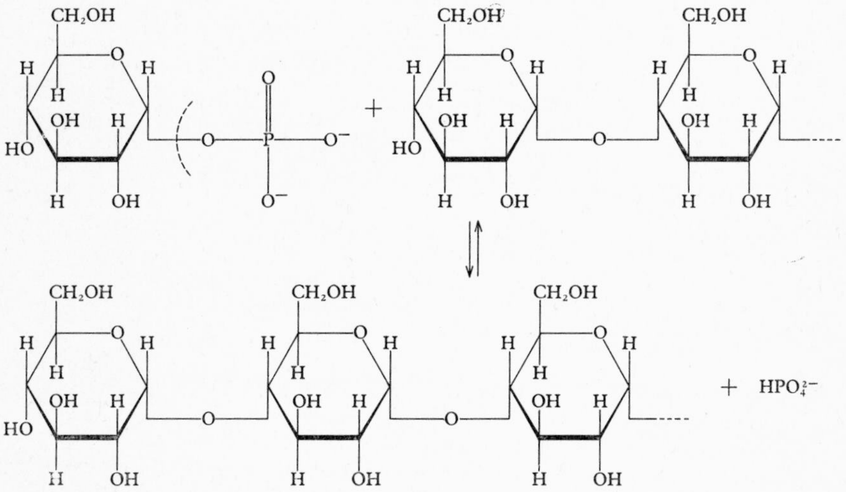

There are, however, many subtleties in this reaction, connected with both the nature of the enzyme (e.g. the presence of pyridoxal phosphate) and the branched nature of the polymer (presence of both 1,4 and 1,6 links).

The action of the amylases on the straight-chain component of starch seems rather simpler. The products obtained by the action of α-amylase are the di- and tri-saccharides, in about the proportions expected if all non-terminal bonds are attacked equally readily. On the other hand, β-amylase gives only the disaccharide, maltose. Alternate bonds (from the non-reducing end) are cleaved by β-amylase, and in this reaction the configuration of the carbon linked to two oxygen atoms is inverted.

Inversion of configuration is a common consequence of (non-enzymic) nucleophilic displacement on an asymmetric carbon atom (Chapter III). However, α-amylase catalyses a hydrolysis in which the configuration is retained, although here, too, the bond broken is the one between the asymmetric carbon atom and the oxygen atom. This result can be explained if there are two steps in the reaction catalysed by α-amylase; if the configuration is inverted in both steps, then the overall result is retention of configuration. Since there is independent evidence (in some cases) for intermediates in which the enzyme is bonded to a moiety of the substrate (see, for example, p. 248), it is natural to suppose that the two steps here correspond to formation, and hydrolysis, of such an intermediate. Retention of configuration is a common consequence of enzymic reactions,† and so this double displacement mechanism may be quite widely applicable. The inversion of configuration with β-amylase suggests a single displacement mechanism, in which the attack by the water molecule causes inversion. The enzyme may facilitate the reaction by providing an electrophilic group which interacts with the oxygen atom linking the glucose units.

† Koshland, *Biol. Rev.* 1953, **28**, 416.

MAIN INDEX

Acetaldehyde, aldol reaction, 175; enzymic reaction with pyruvic acid, 189; enzymic reduction, 205; hydration, 158; reaction with formaldehyde, 192.

Acetals, hydrolysis of, 164.

Acetamide, mesomerism, 24; formation, 250; hydrolysis, 253.

Acetate ion, *see* Acetic acid.

Acetic acid, mesomerism, 24; acidity, 25, 49, 50; conversion into acetyl adenylate, 78, 112; enzymic reaction with oxaloacetic acid, 184.

Acetic anhydride, hydrolysis of, 274.

Acetic chloroacetic anhydride, 275.

Acetic thiokinase, 78, 112.

Acetoacetic acid, decarboxylation of, 256.

Acetoin (acetylmethyl carbinol), enzymic and non-enzymic formation of, 189.

Acetone, anion of, 23; bromination of, 60; dissociation constant, 272; enol and keto forms, 37; formation from acetylacetone, 271; hydration of, 158, 160; in aldol reaction, 176; iodination of, 170.

Acetone dicarboxylic acid, 197, 268.

Acetophenone, mesomerism, 31; reaction with benzaldehyde, 178.

Acetylacetone, alkaline cleavage, 271; ionization, 272.

Acetyl adenylate, 78, 79.

Acetylcholine, 239.

Acetylcholine esterases, 239.

S-Acetyl-coenzyme A, *see* Coenzyme A, S-acetyl.

Acetylene, 17, 18.

Acetyl phosphate, 192.

N-Acetyltyrosine, amide, 237; ethyl ester, 237.

Acid anhydrides, 273.

Acid-base catalysis, general, in enolization, 172, 173; in hydration of acetaldehyde, 159; in formation of oximes, 168; in mutarotation, 162.

Acid-base catalysis, proton-transfer stage, 50, 58.

Acid-base equilibria, 47 ff.; and classification of reagents, 74, 75.

Acid chlorides, 275.

Aconitase, 147.

cis-Aconitic acid, 147, 148, 151.

Acrylic acid, 134.

'Active aldehyde', nature of, 191.

Acylation, by carboxylic esters, 217, 250, 251.

Acyl enzymes, 239.

Acylium ion, 225.

Acyloins (α-hydroxyketones), formation by benzoin reaction, 185; rearrangement of, 286.

Acyl-oxygen fission, in hydrolysis of carboxylic esters, 217 ff.

Addition, 74; *trans* addition, 132, 146.

Adenosine triphosphate (ATP), formation from phosphoenolpyruvic acid, 114; hydrolysis of, 247; modes of cleavage, 112; reaction with acetate ion, 78; reactions with creatine, and with glucose, 109, 113; reaction with mevalonic acid pyrophosphate, 129; reaction with formate ion and tetrahydrofolic acid, 199; structure, *facing* 1.

S-Adenosylmethionine, 107.

Adipic acid, 347.

L-Alanine, in transamination, 212.

Alanine N-carboxyanhydride, 347.

Alcohol dehydrogenase, 205 ff.

Alcohols, addition to aldehydes, 160; dehydration of, 137.

Aldehyde-ketone rearrangement, 285.

Aldehydes, enzymic reduction of, 204 ff.

Aldolase, 180 ff.

Aldol reaction, 175 ff.; comparison with benzoin reaction, 185.

Alkyl bromides, formation of olefines from, 116 ff.; preparation of, 82; reaction with alkali, 86; reaction with iodide ions, 83.

Alkyl groups, *ortho-para* directing nature of, 315.

Alkyl halides, reaction with tertiary amines, 86.

Alkyl-oxygen fission, in hydrolysis of carboxylic esters, 217, 226.

Alkyl radicals, stability of, 135.

Allyl carbonium ion, 23; allyl radical, 35.

Allyl chloride, reactivity of, 85.

Alternating effect, 339, 340.

Aluminium alkoxides, reduction by, 202.

Amides, hydrolysis of, 251 ff.; rearrangement of, 292.

Amines, as catalysts in the aldol reaction, 177, 178; as catalysts in decarboxylations, 258; reaction with alkyl halides, 86; reaction with esters, 250.

Amino acids, enzymic reactions of, 212 ff., 263; N-carboxyanhydrides, polymerization of, 346 ff.

Amino compounds, addition to aldehydes and ketones, 167.

2-Aminopyridine, formation of, 305.

Ammonia, reaction with esters, 250.

Ammonium salts, inhibition of acetylcholine esterase by, 240.

α-Amylase, and β-amylase, 353.

'*p-π*' Analogy, 102, 316.

Aniline, basicity, 25, 26; mesomeric dipole moment, 31; as catalyst for decarboxyla-

Olefines, additions to, 131; formation of, 116 ff.; hydration of, 137; reactions of, 303; yield in formation of, 125.

One-electron addition, in reduction of carbonyl compounds, 201.

'Onium' compounds, 108.

Optimum pH, in formation of oximes, 168; in hydrolysis of phosphates, 242.

Orbitals, definition, 11, 15; hybrid, 15; in aromatic systems, 304–7, 313; overlap of, 13–15, 20, 21; shapes, 11, 12.

Orbits, of the electron in the hydrogen atom, 2; of electrons in other atoms, 4 ff.; subdivision of, 8.

Orientation, and dipole moments, 31; in aromatic nitration, 313 ff.; in hydroxylations, 332; in nucleophilic substitution, 106.

Overlap of orbitals, 13–15, 20, 21.

Oxaloacetic acid, enzymic decarboxylation, 264; enzymic hydrolysis, 273; enzymic reaction with acetic acid, 184; non-enzymic decarboxylation, 257.

Oxalosuccinic acid, 266.

Oxidizing agents, 75.

Oximes, formation of, 167, 168; rearrangement to amides, 297.

2-Oxoglutaric acid, 212.

Oxygen, as inhibitor of vinyl polymerizations, 334; hydroxylations with, 336.

Paired electrons, 9, 15.

Papain, 238.

Pauli Exclusion Principle, 9.

Pauly test, 329.

Pentane, and neopentane, heats of formation, 37.

Pentose phosphate cycle, 188.

Peptide bond, 26.

Peptides, hydrolysis of, 254.

Perfluoro compounds, 294, 296, 298.

Peroxide effect, 135.

Phenol (and phenols), acidity, 25; mesomeric dipole moment, 31; nitration, 310, 313, 314; halogenation, 322–4; diazo coupling, 324–9; formation, 102, 331–3.

Phenyl s-butyl ketone, bromination of, 170, 171.

Phenylglyoxal, 194.

Phosphatases, 247.

Phosphate ion, structure, 22, 23.

Phosphate transfer, 109.

Phosphates, 'high energy', 113.

Phosphates, hydrolysis, 241.

Phosphoenolpyruvic acid, reaction with adenosine diphosphate, 38, 114; carboxylation of, 264.

Phosphoglucomutase, 234.

Phosphoglucose isomerase, 178, 179.

3-Phosphoglyceric acid, 267.

Phosphoketolase, 191, 192.

Phosphomannose isomerase, 179.

Phosphoramidic acid, 110.

Phosphoric acid, esters of, 240.

Phosphorus, nucleophilic displacement on, 78.

Phosphorylases, 247, 353.

Photochemical reactions, 46, 56, 152.

Photosynthesis, 267.

Phthalamic acid, hydrolysis of, 253.

Pinacolic deamination, 286.

Pinacol-pinacone rearrangement, 281 ff.

Piperazine-2,5-dione, 254.

Plane of symmetry, 150.

Polarity of the medium, effect on rate, 68.

Polymerization, 335; enzymic, 353.

Polymethyl methacrylate, 344.

Polypeptides, 348.

Polysarcosine dimethylamide, 351.

Polystyrene, 337 ff.; structure, and properties, 343.

Propagation, in polymerizations, 337.

Propene (propylene), structure, 28; formation, 96, 125; addition to, 133.

n-Propyl bromide, reaction with alkali, 86; reaction with iodide ions, 83.

Proteins, shape, 26, 249; hydrogen bonding, 39; hydrolysis, 255; and polypeptides, 348.

Proton, 1; proton transfers, 47 ff.; in acid catalysis, 50; rapidity of, 58; in enzymic reactions, 58, 236.

Purine, 307.

Pyridine, 305.

Pyridoxal (and phosphate), 212 ff., 263.

Pyridylacetic acid, substituted, decarboxylation of, 191, 260.

Pyrophosphate ion, 112, 241.

Pyrrole, 304.

Pyruvic acid, enzymic reaction with acetaldehyde, 189 ff.; enzymic reduction to lactic acid, 207; in transaminations, 212; reaction with hydroxylamine, 167.

Quantum number, 4, 8; quantum theory, 1.

Quinaldinic acid, decarboxylation of, 261.

Quinones, in Diels–Alder reaction, 142; stability of, 319.

Racemization, during bromination of ketones, 170; in nucleophilic substitution, 93; in tautomerism of imines, 210; of alcohols, 226.

Radiation, absorption and emission of, 2.

Radii, covalent, 33 ff.

Rate, variation with acidity, 68; with polarity of the medium, 68; with structure, 68; with temperature, 65.

Rate constant, 46.

Rate-enhancement, by aldolase, 183; in catalysis, 57; proximity and, 352.

Rates and equilibria, 57; see also Kinetic and thermodynamic control.

Reaction mechanisms, definition of, 55; methods of investigating, 58.

Reactions, classification of, 74.

Reactivity of radicals, 340.

Reagents, classification of, 74, 75.

INDEX OF ENZYMES

THE names of the enzymes given in the Main Index are those used in the book. The systematic names, recommended in the *Report of the Commission on Enzymes* (Oxford: Pergamon Press, 1961), were not available when the text was written, but are given here, together with the code numbers. There are gaps in the first column where no systematic name has been put forward, and in the third column where an enzymic reaction has been discussed in the text without the enzyme having been cited by name.

Systematic name	Code no.	Name used in text	Page
Acetate:CoA ligase (AMP)	6.2.1.1		78, 112
Acetylcholine acetyl-hydrolase	3.1.1.7	*Acetylcholine esterase*	239
Acetyl-CoA:acetyl-CoA acetyl transferase	2.3.1.9	*Thiolase*	269
S-adenosylmethionine:guanidinoacetate methyltransferase	2.1.1.2		109
L-alanine:2-oxoglutarate aminotransferase	2.6.1.2		212
Alcohol:NAD oxidoreductase	1.1.1.1	*Alcohol dehydrogenase*	205
L-aspartate ammonia-lyase	4.3.1.1	*Aspartase*	147
L-aspartate:2-oxoglutarate amino-transferase	2.6.1.1	*'Glutamic aspartic' transaminase*	215
ATP:creatine phosphotransferase	2.7.3.2		109, 113
ATP:D-hexose 6-phosphotransferase	2.7.1.1		109, 111, 112
ATP phosphohydrolase	3.6.1.4		247
ATP:5-pyrophosphomevalonate carboxy-lase (dehydrating)	4.1.1.33		129
ATP:pyruvate phosphotransferase	2.7.1.40		114
Betaine:L-homocysteine methyltransferase	2.1.1.5		108
	3.4.4.5	*Chymotrypsin*	233
Citrate (isocitrate) hydro-lyase	4.2.1.3	*Aconitase*	147
Citrate oxaloacetate-lyase	4.1.3.6	*Citrase*	184
Citrate oxaloacetate-lyase (CoA-acetylating)	4.1.3.7	*'Condensing enzyme'*	184
Dimethylallylpyrophosphate:isopentenyl-pyrophosphate dimethylallyltransferase	2.5.1.1		345, 346
S-dimethyl-β-propiothetin dimethyl-sulphide-lyase	4.4.1.3	*Dimethylpropiothetin dethiomethylase*	129
Dimethylthetin:L-homocysteine methyltransferase	2.1.1.3		108
D-2,3-diphosphoglycerate:D-2-phospho-glycerate phosphotransferase	2.7.5.3	*Phosphoroglyceromutase*	234
Disaccharide glucosyltransferase (non-specific)	2.4.1.7	*Sucrose transglucosylase*	247
	3.4.4.12	*Ficin*	237
Formate:tetrahydrofolate ligase (ADP)	6.3.4.3		199
10-formyltetrahydrofolate amido-hydrolase	3.5.1.10	*'Cyclohydrolase'*	199
β-D-fructofuranoside fructohydrolase	3.2.1.26	*Invertase*	165
4-fumarylacetoacetate fumarylhydrolase	3.7.1.2		273
α-1,4-glucan 4-glucanohydrolase	3.2.1.1	*α-Amylase*	353
α-1,4-glucan maltohydrolase	3.2.1.2	*β-Amylase*	353
α-1,4-glucan orthophosphate glucosyl-transferase	2.4.1.1	*Phosphorylase*	353
D-glucose-1,6-diphosphate:D-glucose-1-phosphate phosphotransferase	2.7.5.1	*Phosphoglucomutase*	234
β-D-glucose:NAD(P) oxidoreductase	1.1.1.47	*Glucose dehydrogenase*	206
D-glucose-6-phosphate ketol-isomerase	5.3.1.9	*Phosphoglucose isomerase*	179
α-D-glucoside glucohydrolase	3.2.1.20	*Maltase*	165
D-glyceraldehyde-3-phosphate ketol-isomerase	5.3.1.1	*Triosephosphate isomerase*	182

PRINTED IN GREAT BRITAIN
AT THE UNIVERSITY PRESS, OXFORD
BY VIVIAN RIDLER
PRINTER TO THE UNIVERSITY